W9-DJN-979

MATHEMATICAL METHODS FOR PHYSICISTS

MATHEMATICAL METHODS

510.02453 Ar35m

FOR PHYSICISTS

GEORGE ARFKEN
DEPARTMENT OF PHYSICS
MIAMI UNIVERSITY
OXFORD, OHIO

ACADEMIC PRESS   New York and London

Copyright © 1966, by Academic Press Inc.
ALL RIGHTS RESERVED.
NO PART OF THIS BOOK MAY BE REPRODUCED IN ANY FORM,
BY PHOTOSTAT, MICROFILM, OR ANY OTHER MEANS, WITHOUT
WRITTEN PERMISSION FROM THE PUBLISHERS.

ACADEMIC PRESS INC.
111 Fifth Avenue, New York, New York 10003

United Kingdom Edition published by
ACADEMIC PRESS INC. (LONDON) LTD.
Berkeley Square House, London W.1

LIBRARY OF CONGRESS CATALOG CARD NUMBER: 65-27740

PRINTED IN THE UNITED STATES OF AMERICA

To Carolyn

PREFACE

Mathematical Methods for Physicists is based upon two courses in mathematics for physicists given by the author over the past fourteen years, one at the junior level and one at the beginning graduate level. This book is intended to provide the student with the mathematics he needs for advanced undergraduate and beginning graduate study in physical science and to develop a strong background for those who will continue into the mathematics of advanced theoretical physics. A mastery of calculus and a willingness to build on this mathematical foundation are assumed.

This text has been organized with two basic principles in view. First, it has been written in a form that it is hoped will encourage independent study. There are frequent cross references but no fixed, rigid page-by-page or chapter-by-chapter sequence is demanded.

The reader will see that mathematics as a language is beautiful and elegant. Unfortunately, elegance all too often means elegance for the expert and obscurity for the beginner. While still attempting to point out the intrinsic beauty of mathematics, elegance has occasionally been reluctantly but deliberately sacrificed in the hope of achieving greater flexibility and greater clarity *for the student*.

Mathematical rigor has been treated in a similar spirit. It is not stressed to the point of becoming a mental block to the use of mathematics. Limitations are explained, however, and warnings given against blind, uncomprehending application of mathematical relations.

The second basic principle has been to emphasize and re-emphasize physical examples in the text and in the exercises to help motivate the student, to illustrate the relevance of mathematics to his science and engineering.

This principle has also played a decisive role in the selection and development of material. The subject of differential equations, for example, is no longer a series of trick solutions of abstract, relatively meaningless puzzles but the solutions and general properties of the differential equations the student will most frequently encounter in a description of our real physical world.

Any work of this sort represents necessarily the influence and help of many people. I acknowledge gratefully my debt to the professors who taught me physics and mathematics and who instilled in me a love of these disciplines. I thank my colleagues for their assistance and helpful criticism. A special note of thanks is due my students over the past fourteen years for their criticisms and reactions which have played a major part in shaping this book. A special acknowledgment is owed to Mrs. Juanita Killough for so patiently and conscientiously typing this manuscript.

Oxford, Ohio

G. A.

INTRODUCTION

Many of the physical examples used to illustrate the applications of mathematics are taken from the fields of electromagnetic theory and quantum mechanics. For convenience the main equations are listed below and the symbols identified. References in these fields are also given.

Electromagnetic theory

Maxwell's Equations (mks units — vacuum)

$$\nabla \cdot \mathbf{D} = \rho \qquad\qquad \nabla \times \mathbf{E} = -\frac{\partial \mathbf{B}}{\partial t}$$

$$\nabla \cdot \mathbf{B} = 0$$

$$\nabla \times \mathbf{H} = \frac{\partial \mathbf{D}}{\partial t} + \mathbf{j}$$

Here $\mathbf{E}$ is the electric field defined in terms of force on a static charge and $\mathbf{B}$ the magnetic inductance defined in terms of force on a moving charge. The related fields $\mathbf{D}$ and $\mathbf{H}$ are given (in vacuum) by

$$\mathbf{D} = \varepsilon_0 \mathbf{E} \qquad \text{and} \qquad \mathbf{B} = \mu_0 \mathbf{H}$$

The quantity ρ represents free charge density while $\mathbf{j}$ is the corresponding current. For additional details see: J. M. Marion, *Classical Electromagnetic Radiation,* New York: Academic Press (1965); W. K. H. Panofsky and M. Phillips, *Classical Electricity and Magnetism,* Reading, Mass.: Addison-Wesley (1955); J. D. Jackson, *Classical Electrodynamics,* New York: Wiley.

Note that Marion and Jackson prefer Gaussian units. A glance at the last two texts and the great demands they make upon the student's mathematical competence should provide considerable motivation for the study of this book.

Quantum Mechanics

Schrödinger Wave Equation (time independent)

$$-\frac{\hbar^2}{2m} \nabla^2 \psi + V\psi = \lambda\psi$$

ψ is the (unknown) wave function. The potential energy, often a function of position, is denoted by V while E is the total energy of the system. The mass of the particle being described by ψ is m. $\hbar$ is Planck's constant h divided by 2π. Among the extremely large number of beginning or intermediate texts we might note: A. Messiah, *Quantum Mechanics* (2 vols), New York; Wiley (1961): R. H. Dicke and J. P. Wittke, *Introduction to Quantum Mechanics,* Reading, Mass.: Addison-Wesley (1960); F. A. Kaempffer, *Concepts in Quantum Mechanics,* New York: Academic Press (1965).

Of particular importance for problems involving one or two electrons we have H. A. Bethe and E. S. Salpeter, *Quantum Mechanics of One- and Two-Electron Atoms,* New York: Academic Press (1957) (reprinted from Encyclopedia of Physics, Vol. XXXV).

CONTENTS

Chapter 3.   Tensor Analysis

Chapter 4.   Matrices and Determinants

Chapter 5.   Infinite Series

Chapter 6.   Functions of a Complex Variable I. Analytic Properties, Conformal Mapping

Chapter 7.   Functions of a Complex Variable II. Calculus of Residues

Chapter 8.   Second-Order Differential Equations

Chapter 9.   Sturm-Liouville Theory—Orthogonal Functions

Chapter 10.   The Gamma Function (Factorial Function)

Chapter 11.   Bessel Functions

Chapter 12.   Legendre Functions

Chapter 13.   Special Functions

Chapter 14. Fourier Series

Chapter 15. Integral Transforms

Chapter 16. Integral Equations

Chapter 17. Calculus of Variations

MATHEMATICAL METHODS FOR PHYSICISTS

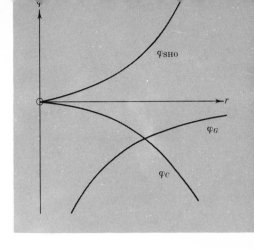

CHAPTER 1

VECTOR ANALYSIS

1.1 Definitions, Elementary Approach

In science and engineering we frequently encounter quantities which have magnitude and magnitude only: mass, time, and temperature. These we label scalar quantities. In contrast, many interesting physical quantities have magnitude and, in addition, an associated direction. This second group includes displacement, velocity, acceleration, force, momentum, and angular momentum. Quantities with magnitude and direction are labeled vector quantities. Usually, in elementary treatments, a vector is defined as a quantity having magnitude and direction. To distinguish vectors from scalars we identify vector quantities with boldface type, that is, **V**.

As an historical sidelight, it is interesting to note that the vector quantities listed are all taken from mechanics but that vector analysis was not used in the development of mechanics and, indeed, had not been created. The need for vector analysis became apparent only with the development of Maxwell's electromagnetic theory and in appreciation of the inherent vector nature of quantities such as electric field and magnetic field.

Our vector may be conveniently represented by an arrow with length proportional to the magnitude. The direction of the arrow gives the direction of the vector, the positive sense of direction being indicated by the point. In this representation vector addition

$$\mathbf{C} = \mathbf{A} + \mathbf{B} \tag{1.1}$$

consists in placing the rear end of vector **B** at the point of vector **A**. Vector **C** is then represented by an arrow drawn from the rear of **A** to the point of **B**. This procedure the triangle law of addition, assigns meaning to Eq. 1.1 and is illustrated in Fig. 1.1.

1

By completing the parallelogram we see that

$$\mathbf{C} = \mathbf{A} + \mathbf{B} = \mathbf{B} + \mathbf{A},\tag{1.2}$$

as shown in Fig. 1.2.

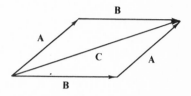

FIG. 1.1   Triangle law of vector addition

FIG. 1.2   Parallelogram law of vector addition

A direct physical example of this parallelogram addition law is provided by a weight suspended by two cords. If the junction point (O in Fig. 1.3) is in equilibrium, the vector sum of the two forces $\mathbf{F}_1$ and $\mathbf{F}_2$ must just cancel the downward

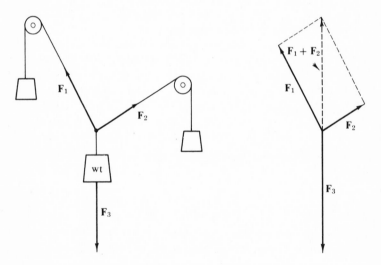

FIG. 1.3   Equilibrium of forces. $\mathbf{F}_1 + \mathbf{F}_2 = -\mathbf{F}_3$

force of gravity, $\mathbf{F}_3$. Here the parallelogram addition law is subject to immediate experimental verification.[1]

Note that the vectors are treated as geometrical objects which are independent of any coordinate system. Indeed, we have not yet introduced a coordinate system. This concept of independence is developed in considerable detail in the next section.

The representation of vector $\mathbf{A}$ by an arrow suggests a second possiblity. Arrow

---

[1] Strictly speaking the parallelogram addition was introduced as a definition. Experiment show that if we assume that the forces are vector quantities and we combine them by parallelogram addition the equilibrium condition of zero resultant force is satisfied.

A (Fig. 1.4), starting from the origin,[1] terminates at the point (x_1, y_1, z_1). Thus, if we agree that the vector is to start at the origin, the positive end may be specified by giving the cartesian coordinates (x_1, y_1, z_1) of the arrow head.

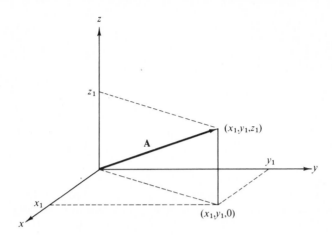

FIG. 1.4   Cartesian components

Although **A** could have represented any vector quantity (momentum, electric field, etc.,), one particularly important vector quantity, the displacement from the origin to the point (x_1, y_1, z_1), is denoted by the special symbol **r**. We then have a choice of referring to the displacement either as the vector **r** or as the collection (x_1, y_1, z_1), the coordinates of its end point.

$$\mathbf{r} = (x_1, y_1, z_1). \qquad (1.3)$$

Using r for the magnitude of vector **r**, Fig. 1.5 shows that the end-point coordinates

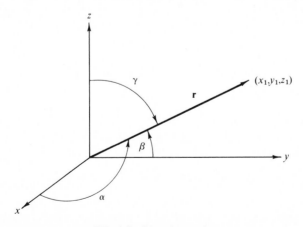

FIG. 1.5   Direction cosines

[1] The reader will see that we could start from any point in our cartesian reference frame, We choose the origin for simplicity.

and the magnitude are related by

$$x_1 = r \cos \alpha,$$

$$y_1 = r \cos \beta, \qquad (1.4)$$

$$z_1 = r \cos \gamma.$$

Cos α, cos β, and cos γ are called the direction cosines, α being the angle between the given vector and the positive x-axis, and so on. One further bit of vocabulary: the quantities x_1, y_1, and z_1 are known as the (cartesian) components of $\mathbf{r}$ or the projections of $\mathbf{r}$.

If we proceed in the same manner, any vector $\mathbf{A}$ may be resolved into its components (or projected onto the coordinate axes) to yield

$$A_x = A \cos \alpha, \qquad (1.5)$$

in which α is the angle between $\mathbf{A}$ and the positive x-axis. Again we may choose to refer to the vector as a single quantity $\mathbf{A}$ or to its components (A_x, A_y, A_z).

At this stage it is convenient to introduce unit vectors along each of the coordinate axes. Let $\mathbf{i}$ be a vector of unit magnitude pointing in the positive x-direction, $\mathbf{j}$, a vector of unit magnitude in the positive y-direction, and $\mathbf{k}$, a vector of unit magnitude in the positive z-direction. Then $\mathbf{i}A_x$ is a vector with magnitude equal to A_x and in the positive x-direction. By vector addition

$$\mathbf{A} = \mathbf{i}A_x + \mathbf{j}A_y + \mathbf{k}A_z, \qquad (1.6)$$

which states that a vector equals the vector sum of its components. Note that if $\mathbf{A}$ vanishes all of its components must vanish individually; that is, if

$$\mathbf{A} = 0,$$

then

$$A_x = A_y = A_z = 0.$$

Finally, by the Pythagorean theorem, the magnitude of vector $\mathbf{A}$ is

$$A = (A_x^2 + A_y^2 + A_z^2)^{1/2}. \qquad (1.7a)$$

This resolution of a vector into its components can be carried out in a variety of coordinate systems, as shown in Chapter 2. Here we shall restrict ourselves to cartesian coordinates.

As a replacement of the graphical technique, addition and subtraction of vectors may now be carried out in terms of their components. For $\mathbf{A} = \mathbf{i}A_x + \mathbf{j}A_y + \mathbf{k}A_z$ and $\mathbf{B} = \mathbf{i}B_x + \mathbf{j}B_y + \mathbf{k}B_z$,

$$\mathbf{A} \pm \mathbf{B} = \mathbf{i}(A_x \pm B_x) + \mathbf{j}(A_y \pm B_y) + \mathbf{k}(A_z \pm B_z). \qquad (1.7b)$$

EXAMPLE 1.1.1

Let

$$\mathbf{A} = 6\mathbf{i} + 4\mathbf{j} + 3\mathbf{k}$$

$$\mathbf{B} = 2\mathbf{i} - 3\mathbf{j} - 3\mathbf{k}.$$

Then by Eq. 1.7*b*

$$\mathbf{A} + \mathbf{B} = 8\mathbf{i} + \mathbf{j}$$

and

$$\mathbf{A} - \mathbf{B} = 4\mathbf{i} + 7\mathbf{j} + 6\mathbf{k}.$$

EXERCISES

1.1.1 Show how to find **A** and **B**, given $\mathbf{A} + \mathbf{B}$ and $\mathbf{A} - \mathbf{B}$.

1.1.2 The vector **A** whose magnitude is 10 units makes equal angles with the coordinate axes. Find A_x, A_y, and A_z.

1.1.3 Calculate the components of a unit vector which lies in the xy-plane and makes equal angles with the positive directions of the x- and y-axes.

1.1.4 Three vectors, **A**, **B**, and **C**, all lie in a horizontal plane. Their magnitudes are 2 miles, 3 miles, and 4 miles and their directions are west, north, and northeast, respectively.
(a) By graphical construction and measurement of magnitude and direction show that

$$(\mathbf{A} + \mathbf{B}) + \mathbf{C} = (\mathbf{B} + \mathbf{C}) + \mathbf{A} = (\mathbf{C} + \mathbf{A}) + \mathbf{B}.$$

(b) Show analytically that

$$\mathbf{A} + \mathbf{B} + \mathbf{C} = (2\sqrt{2} - 2)\mathbf{i} + (2\sqrt{2} + 3)\mathbf{j},$$

where **i** points east and **j** points north and

$$|\mathbf{A} + \mathbf{B} + \mathbf{C}| \simeq 5.89 \text{ miles}.$$

1.1.5 Referring to Exercise 1.1.4, express each of the three given vectors as a linear combination of the other two; that is, find the coefficients α_{ab}, α_{ac} in

$$\mathbf{A} = \alpha_{ab}\mathbf{B} + \alpha_{ac}\mathbf{C}$$

and similarly for **B** and **C**. Use components (analytically, not graphically) and make a precise determination.

Hint. If two vectors are equal, the projection of one on any axis must equal the projection of the other along that same axis.

1.2 Rotation of Coordinates

The definition of vector as a quantity with magnitude and direction breaks down in advanced work. On the one hand, we encounter quantities, such as elastic constants and index of refraction in anisotropic crystals, which have magnitude and direction *but* which are not vectors. On the other hand, our naïve approach is awkward to generalize, to extend to more complex quantities. We seek a new definition of vector, using our displacement vector **r** as a prototype.

There is an important physical basis for our development of a new definition. We describe our physical world by mathematics, but it and any physical predictions we may make must be *independent* of our mathematical analysis. Some writers like to compare the physical system to a building and the mathematical analysis to the scaffolding used to construct the building. In the end the scaffolding is stripped off and the building stands.

In our specific case we shall assume that space is isotropic; that is, there is no preferred direction or all directions are equivalent. Then the physical system being analyzed or the physical law being enunciated cannot and must not depend on our choice or *orientation* of our coordinate system.

Now we return to the concept of vector **r** as a geometric object independent of the coordinate system. Let us look at **r** in two different systems, one rotated in relation to the other.

For simplicity we consider first the two-dimensional case. If the coordinates (x, y) are rotated counterclockwise through an angle φ, *keeping* **r** *fixed*, we get the following relations between the components resolved in the original system (unprimed) and those resolved in the new rotated system (primed):

$$x' = x \cos \varphi + y \sin \varphi,$$
$$y' = - x \sin \varphi + y \cos \varphi \tag{1.8}$$

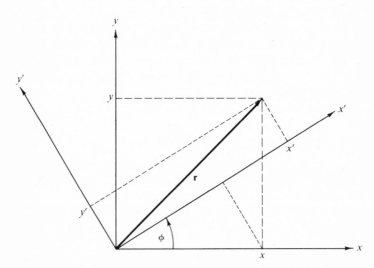

FIG. 1.6   Rotation of cartesian coordinates

We saw in Section 1.1 that a vector could be represented by the coordinates of a point; that is, the coordinates were proportional to the vector components. Hence the components of a vector must transform under rotation as coordinates of a point (such as **r**). Therefore, whenever any pair of quantities (A_x, A_y) in the xy-coordinate system is transformed into (A'_x, A'_y) by this rotation of the coordinate system with

$$A'_x = A_x \cos \varphi + A_y \sin \varphi$$
$$A'_y = - A_x \sin \varphi + A_y \cos \varphi, \tag{1.9}$$

we *define* A_x and A_y as the components of a vector **A**. Our vector now is defined in terms of the transformation of its components under rotation of the coordinate system. If A_x and A_y transform in the same way as x and y, the components of the two-dimensional displacement vector, they are the components of a vector **A**. If A_x and A_y do not show this behavior when the coordinates are rotated, they do not form a vector.

To complete the definition we must assign meaning to A'_x and A'_y in Eq. 1.9. Let us suppose that the components of a vector **A** are functions of the coordinates and perhaps of some other constant vector **c**.

$$A_x = A_x(x, y, c_x, c_y),$$
$$A_y = A_y(x, y, c_x, c_y). \tag{1.9a}$$

In the primed coordinate system **A** has components A'_x and A'_y, which are also functions of position (in the primed system) and **c**.

$$A'_x = A'_x(x', y', c'_x, c'_y)$$
$$A'_y = A'_y(x', y', c'_x, c'_y). \tag{1·9b}$$

If we use Eq. 1.8, the primed quantities x', y', c'_x, c'_y in Eq. 1.9b can be replaced by unprimed quantities *and* the angle of rotation φ. In general, there will be some dependence on the angle of rotation. Such dependence on orientation is unacceptable. It implies the possibility of singling out a preferred reference frame contrary to our initial hypothesis. So we limit ourselves to functions that are independent of the orientation.

Now, for the special case $\varphi = 0$, clearly

$$A_x = A'_x,$$
$$A_y = A'_y.$$

Hence A'_x is the same function of x', y', c'_x, and c'_y as A_x is of the corresponding unprimed quantities and similarly for A'_y and A_y.

EXAMPLE 1.2.1

Given a pair of quantities $(-y, x)$, show that they are the components of a two-dimensional vector.

Since the question of whether or not these are the components of a vector depends, by definition, on their transformation properties, we investigate how they do transform. Let

$$V'_x = -y \cos \varphi + x \sin \varphi,$$
$$V'_y = y \sin \varphi + x \cos \varphi, \tag{1.10}$$

using $V_x = -y$, $V_y = x$. By Eq. 1.10

$$V'_x = -y',$$
$$V'_y = x', \tag{1.11}$$

and using Eq. 1.8 for the coordinate transformation we see that Eq. 1.9, the defining equation of a two-dimensional vector, is satisfied. Therefore $(-y, x)$ are the components of a vector.

EXAMPLE 1.2.2

As an example of quantity that, by our definition, is *not* a vector, consider $\mathbf{V} = \mathbf{i}x - \mathbf{j}y = (x, -y)$. Testing the transformation properties, we have, by Eq. 1.9,

$$V'_x = x' = x \cos \varphi + y \sin \varphi,$$

$$V'_y = -y' = +x \sin \varphi - y \cos \varphi.$$

Using $V_x = x$, $V_y = -y$, we obtain

$$V'_x = V_x \cos \varphi - V_y \sin \varphi,$$

$$V'_y = V_x \sin \varphi + V_y \cos \varphi,$$

which is not our definition of a vector. Hence $(x, -y)$ are *not* the components of a vector.

Many writers prefer to label the functions A_x and A_y satisfying Eq. 1.9 the components of a (two-dimensional) *vector field*. Distinguished from vector fields are *constant vectors* such as $\mathbf{i}$ and $\mathbf{j}$, which do not transform so that $\mathbf{i}'$ is the same function of x' and y' that it is of x and y. Indeed $\mathbf{i}$ is *not* a function of x and y at all; it is a constant. For a further note on constant vectors see Problem 1.2.1.

To go on to three and, later, four dimensions, it becomes convenient to use a more compact notation. Let

$$x \to x_1$$

$$y \to x_2$$

$$a_{11} = \cos \varphi, \qquad a_{12} = \sin \varphi,$$

$$a_{21} = -\sin \varphi, \qquad a_{22} = \cos \varphi. \tag{1.12}$$

Then Eq. 1.9 becomes

$$x'_1 = a_{11}x_1 + a_{12}x_2,$$

$$x'_2 = a_{21}x_1 + a_{22}x_2. \tag{1.13}$$

The coefficient a_{ij} may be interpreted as a direction cosine, the cosine of the angle between x'_i and x_j; that is,

$$a_{12} = \cos(x'_1, x_2) = \sin \varphi,$$

$$a_{21} = \cos(x'_2, x_1) = \cos\left(\varphi + \frac{\pi}{2}\right) = -\sin \varphi.$$

The advantage of the new notation[1] is that it permits us to use the summation

---

[1] The reader may wonder at the replacement of one parameter φ by four parameters a_{ij}. Clearly, the a_{ij} do not constitute a minimum set of parameters. For two dimensions the four a_{ij} are subject to the three constraints given in Eq. 1.18. The justification for the redundant set of direction cosines is the convenience it provides. Hopefully, this convenience will become more apparent in Chapters 3 and 4.

symbol $\sum$ and to rewrite Eqs. 1.13 as

$$x_i' = \sum_{j=1}^{2} a_{ij}x_j, \qquad i = 1, 2. \tag{1.14}$$

Note that i remains as a parameter which gives rise to one equation when it is set equal to 1 and to a second equation when it is set equal to 2. The index j, of course, is a summation index, a dummy index, and just as with a variable of integration j may be replaced by any other convenient symbol.

The generalization to three, four, or N dimensions is very simple. The set of N quantities, V_j, is said to be the components of an N-dimensional vector, $\mathbf{V}$, if and only if the values in a rotated coordinate system are given by

$$V_i' = \sum_{j=1}^{N} a_{ij}V_j, \qquad i = 1, 2, ..., N. \tag{1.15}$$

As before, a_{ij} is the cosine of the angle between x_i' and x_j. Often the upper limit N and the corresponding range of i will not be indicated. It is taken for granted that the reader knows how many dimensions his space has.

From the definition of a_{ij} as the cosine of the angle between the positive x_i' direction and the positive x_j direction we may write (cartesian coordinates)[1]

$$a_{ij} = \frac{\partial x_i'}{\partial x_j} = \frac{\partial x_j}{\partial x_i'}. \tag{1.16}$$

Note carefully that these are *partial derivatives*. By use of Eq. 1.16, Eq. 1.15 becomes

$$V_i' = \sum_{j=1}^{N} \frac{\partial x_i'}{\partial x_j} V_j = \sum_{j=1}^{N} \frac{\partial x_j}{\partial x_i'} V_j. \tag{1.17}$$

The direction cosines a_{ij} satisfy an *orthogonality condition*

$$\sum_{i} a_{ij}a_{ik} = \delta_{jk} \tag{1.18}$$

or, equivalently,

$$\sum_{i} a_{ji}a_{ki} = \delta_{jk}. \tag{1.19}$$

The symbol δ_{jk} is the Kronecker delta defined by

$$\delta_{jk} = 1 \quad \text{for} \quad j = k,$$
$$\delta_{jk} = 0 \quad \text{for} \quad j \neq k. \tag{1.20}$$

The reader may easily verify that Eqs. 1.18 and 1.19 hold in the two-dimensional case by substituting in the specific a_{ij} from Eq. 1.12. The result is the well-known identity $\sin^2 \varphi + \cos^2 \varphi = 1$ for the nonvanishing case. To verify Eq. 1.18 in general form we may use the partial derivative forms of Eqs. 1.16 to obtain

$$\sum_{i} \frac{\partial x_j}{\partial x_i'} \frac{\partial x_k}{\partial x_i'} = \sum_{i} \frac{\partial x_j}{\partial x_i'} \frac{\partial x_i'}{\partial x_k} = \frac{\partial x_j}{\partial x_k}. \tag{1.21}$$

[1] Differentiate $x_i' = \sum a_{ik}x_k$ with respect to x_j. See the discussion following Eq. 1.21.

The last step follows by the standard rules for partial differentiation, assuming that x_j is a function of x_1', x_2', x_3', etc. The final result, $\partial x_j / \partial x_k$, is equal to δ_{jk}, since x_j and x_k ($j \neq k$) are assumed to be perpendicular (two or three dimensions) or orthogonal (for any number of dimensions). If $j = k$, the partial derivative is clearly equal to 1.

In redefining a vector in terms of how its components transform under a rotation of the coordinate system, two points deserve special emphasis:

1. This definition is dveloped because it is useful and appropriate in describing our physical world.

2. This definition is subject to a generalization that will open up the branch of mathematics known as tensor analysis (Chapter 3).

EXERCISES

1.2.1 Given a *constant* vector $\mathbf{V}$ with components $V_x = 1$ and $V_y = 0$, show that the components of V in a rotated system are

$$V_x' = \cos \varphi,$$
$$V_y' = -\sin \varphi,$$

according to the vector transformation law. Clearly a φ dependence has entered and could be expected. We have singled out a preferred direction in space by introducing the constant vector. $\mathbf{V}$ is a vector according to the sense of Section 1.1, and we continue to accept it as a vector because of its usefulness.

1.2.2 Determine whether the following satisfy the vector transformation rule (Eq. 1.15).
(a) $(x - y, x + y, 0)$, for rotations about the z-axis.
(b) $(0, 2z + y, z - 2y)$, for rotations about the x-axis.
(c) $(y^2 + z^2, -xy, -xz)$, for rotations about each of the three coordinate axes.

1.2.3 (a) Show that $(xyc_x + y^2 c_y, -x^2 c_x - xyc_y)$ forms a vector. The quantities c_x and c_y are components of a constant vector $\mathbf{c}$.
(b) Repeat for $(xyc_x - x^2 c_y, y^2 c_x - xyc_y)$.

1.2.4 By considering rotation about any one of the coordinate axes show whether the three functions

$$V_x = a_1(x^2 + y^2 + z^2), \qquad V_y = a_2(x^2 + y^2 + z^2), \quad \text{and} \quad V_z = a_3(x^2 + y^2 + z^2)$$

form the components of a vector. The a_i are constants.

1.2.5 A two-dimensional vector $\mathbf{V}$ has the form $(ax + by, cx + dy)$ with a, b, c, and d constants. Show that $\mathbf{V}$ is a linear combination of the radial vector $\mathbf{r} = \mathbf{i}x + \mathbf{j}y$ and the tangential vector $\mathbf{t} = \mathbf{i}y - \mathbf{j}x$.

$$\mathbf{V} = a\mathbf{r} + b\mathbf{t}.$$

Hint. The vector transformation law must hold (a) for all angles and (b) for all points, (x, y).

1.3 Scalar or Dot Product

Having defined vectors, we now proceed to combine them. The laws for combining vectors must be mathematically consistent. From the possibilities that are consistent we select two that are both mathematically and physically interesting. A third possibility is introduced in Chapter 3, in which we form tensors.

The combination of $AB \cos \theta$, in which A and B are the magnitudes of two

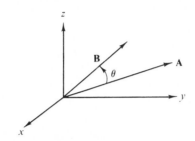

FIG. 1.7 Scalar product $\mathbf{A} \cdot \mathbf{B} = AB \cos \theta$

vectors and θ, the angle between them, occurs frequently in physics. For instance,

$$\text{work} = \text{force} \times \text{displacement} \times \cos \theta$$

is usually interpreted as displacement times the projection of the force along the displacement.

With such applications in mind, we define

$$\mathbf{A} \cdot \mathbf{B} = A_x B_x + A_y B_y + A_z B_z = \sum_i A_i B_i \tag{1.22}$$

as the scalar or dot product of $\mathbf{A}$ and $\mathbf{B}$. We note that from this definition $\mathbf{A} \cdot \mathbf{B} = \mathbf{B} \cdot \mathbf{A}$. Our unit vectors $\mathbf{i}$, $\mathbf{j}$, and $\mathbf{k}$ satisfy the relations

$$\mathbf{i} \cdot \mathbf{i} = \mathbf{j} \cdot \mathbf{j} = \mathbf{k} \cdot \mathbf{k} = 1, \tag{1.22a}$$

whereas

$$\mathbf{i} \cdot \mathbf{j} = \mathbf{i} \cdot \mathbf{k} = \mathbf{j} \cdot \mathbf{k} = 0,$$
$$\mathbf{j} \cdot \mathbf{i} = \mathbf{k} \cdot \mathbf{i} = \mathbf{k} \cdot \mathbf{j} = 0. \tag{1.22b}$$

If we reorient our axes and let $\mathbf{A}$ define a new x-axis,[1] then

$$A_x = A, \qquad A_y = 0, \qquad A_z = 0$$

and

$$B_x = B \cos \theta.$$

Then by Eq. 1.22

$$\mathbf{A} \cdot \mathbf{B} = AB \cos \theta, \tag{1.23}$$

which may be taken as a second definition of scalar product. This shows that work is the scalar product of force and displacement.

[1] The invariance of $\mathbf{A} \cdot \mathbf{B}$ under rotation of the coordinates is proved later in this section.

EXAMPLE 1.3.1

For the two vectors **A** and **B** of Example 1.1.1, $\mathbf{A} = 6\mathbf{i} + 4\mathbf{j} + 3\mathbf{k}$, $\mathbf{B} = 2\mathbf{i} - 3\mathbf{j} - 3\mathbf{k}$,

$$\mathbf{A} \cdot \mathbf{B} = (12 - 12 - 9) = -9$$

by Eq. 1.22. In this case the projection of **A** on **B** (or **B** on **A**) is negative. Actually

$$|\mathbf{A}| = (36 + 16 + 9)^{1/2} = (61)^{1/2} = 7.82,$$
$$|\mathbf{B}| = (\ 4 + \ 9 + 9)^{1/2} = (22)^{1/2} = 4.70,$$

and $\cos \theta = 0.408$, $\theta = 114.1°$.

If $\mathbf{A} \cdot \mathbf{B} = 0$ and we know that $\mathbf{A} \neq 0$ and $\mathbf{B} \neq 0$, then from Eq. 1.23 $\cos \theta = 0$ or $\theta = 90°$, $270°$, etc. The vectors **A** and **B** must be perpendicular. Alternately we may say **A** and **B** are orthogonal. The unit vectors **i**, **j**, and **k** are mutually orthogonal.

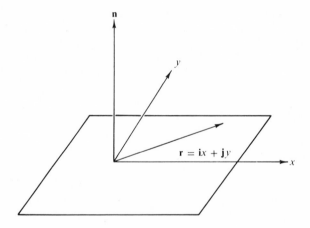

FIG. 1.8   A normal vector

To develop this notion of orthogonality one more step, suppose that **n** is a unit vector and **r** is a nonzero vector in the xy-plane; that is, $\mathbf{r} = \mathbf{i}x + \mathbf{j}y$. If

$$\mathbf{n} \cdot \mathbf{r} = 0$$

for *all* choices of **r**, then **n** must be perpendicular (orthogonal) to the xy-plane.

We have not yet shown that the word scalar is justified or that the scalar product is indeed a scalar quantity. To do this we investigate the behavior of $\mathbf{A} \cdot \mathbf{B}$ under a rotation of the coordinate system. By use of Eq. 1.15

$$A'_x B'_x + A'_y B'_y + A'_z B'_z = \sum_i a_{xi} A_i \sum_j a_{xj} B_j$$
$$+ \sum_i a_{yi} A_i \sum_j a_{yj} B_j$$
$$+ \sum_i a_{zi} A_i \sum_j a_{zj} B_j. \qquad (1.24)$$

Using the indices k and l to sum over x, y, and z, we obtain

$$\sum_k A'_k B'_k = \sum_l \sum_i \sum_j a_{li} A_i a_{lj} B_j, \tag{1.25}$$

and, by rearranging the terms on the right-hand side,

$$\sum_k A'_k B'_k = \sum_i \sum_j \sum_l (a_{lj} a_{lj}) A_i B_j$$

$$= \sum_i \sum_j \delta_{ij} A_i B_j$$

$$= \sum_i A_i B_i. \tag{1.26}$$

The last two steps follow by using Eq. 1.19, the orthogonality condition of the direction cosines, and Eq. 1.20, which defines the Kronecker delta. The effect of the Kronecker delta is to cancel all terms in a summation over either index except the term for which the indices are equal. In Eq. 1.26 its effect is to set $j = i$ and to eliminate the summation over j. Of course, we could equally well set $i = j$ and eliminate the summation over i. Equation 1.26 gives us

$$\sum_k A'_k B'_k = \sum_i A_i B_i, \tag{1.27}$$

which is just our definition of a scalar quantity, one that remains *invariant* under the rotation of the coordinate system.

In a similar approach which exploits this concept of invariance we take $\mathbf{C} = \mathbf{A} + \mathbf{B}$ and dot it into itself.

$$\mathbf{C} \cdot \mathbf{C} = (\mathbf{A} + \mathbf{B}) \cdot (\mathbf{A} + \mathbf{B})$$

$$= \mathbf{A} \cdot \mathbf{A} + \mathbf{B} \cdot \mathbf{B} + 2\mathbf{A} \cdot \mathbf{B}. \tag{1.28}$$

Since

$$\mathbf{C} \cdot \mathbf{C} = C^2, \tag{1.29}$$

the square of the magnitude of vector $\mathbf{C}$ and thus an invariant quantity, we see that

$$\mathbf{A} \cdot \mathbf{B} = \tfrac{1}{2}(C^2 - A^2 - B^2), \qquad \text{invariant.} \tag{1.30}$$

Since the right-hand side of Eq. 1.30 is invariant—that is, a scalar quantity—the left-hand side, $\mathbf{A} \cdot \mathbf{B}$, must also be invariant under rotation of the coordinate system. Hence $\mathbf{A} \cdot \mathbf{B}$ is a scalar.

Equation 1.28 is really another form of the law of cosines which is

$$C^2 = A^2 + B^2 + 2AB \cos \theta. \tag{1.31}$$

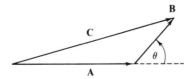

FIG. 1.9 The law of cosines

Comparing Eqs. 1.28 and 1.31, we have another verification of Eq. 1.23, or, if preferred, a vector derivation of the law of cosines.

An interesting illustration of the geometric interpretation of the scalar product is provided by an example from a branch of general relativity. Consider a four-dimensional sphere

$$x^2 + y^2 + z^2 + w^2 = 1$$

in x, y, z, w space. The surface of this four-dimensional sphere may be described by the vector $\mathbf{r} = (x, y, z, w)$ with the restriction that $|\mathbf{r}| = 1$. It is possible to construct a unit vector $\mathbf{t}$ that is tangential to this four-dimensional sphere over its entire surface. As one possible example,

$$\mathbf{t} = (y, -x, w, -z).$$

The reader may verify that

$$\mathbf{t} \cdot \mathbf{t} = 1,$$

therefore unit magnitude, and

$$\mathbf{t} \cdot \mathbf{r} = 0,$$

therefore tangential, over the entire sphere.

The two-dimensional analog exists (cf. Example 1.1.1), but there is no three-dimensional analog. Hair growing out of a sphere cannot be combed down all over. There will be a cowlick.

EXERCISES

1.3.1 By expansion of the scalar product show that if two vectors have direction cosines α_1, β_1, γ_1 and α_2, β_2, γ_2, respectively,

$$\text{cosine } \theta = \alpha_1 \alpha_2 + \beta_1 \beta_2 + \gamma_1 \gamma_2$$

where θ is the angle between the two vectors.

1.3.2 What is the cosine of the angle between the vectors

$$\mathbf{A} = 3\mathbf{i} + 4\mathbf{j} + \mathbf{k}$$

and

$$\mathbf{B} = \mathbf{i} - \mathbf{j} + \mathbf{k}$$

$$Ans. \cos \theta = 0, \qquad \theta = \frac{\pi}{2}.$$

1.3.3 Two unit magnitude vectors $\mathbf{a}_i$ and $\mathbf{a}_j$ are required to be either parallel or perpendicular to each other. Show that $\mathbf{a}_i \cdot \mathbf{a}_j$ provides an interpretation of Eq. 1.18, the direction cosine orthogonality relation.

1.3.4 Find the components of the vector $\mathbf{A} = 3\mathbf{i} - 3\mathbf{j} + 4\mathbf{k}$ in the directions of the two vectors whose direction angles are 80, 40, and θ°.

1.3.5 The vector **r**, starting at the origin, terminates at and specifies the point in space (x, y, z).
Find the surface swept out by **r** if
(a) $(\mathbf{r} - \mathbf{a}) \cdot \mathbf{a} = 0$,
(b) $(\mathbf{r} - \mathbf{a}) \cdot \mathbf{r} = 0$.
The vector **a** is a constant (constant in magnitude and direction).

1.4 Vector or Cross Product

A second form of vector multiplication employs the sine of the included angle instead of the cosine. For instance, the angular momentum of a body is defined as

$$\text{angular momentum} = \text{radius arm} \times \text{linear momentum}$$

$$= \text{distance} \times \text{linear momentum} \times \sin\theta.$$

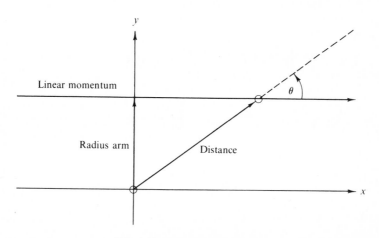

FIG. 1.10   Angular momentum

For convenience in treating problems relating to quantities such as angular momentum, torque, and angular velocity we define the vector or cross product as

$$\mathbf{C} = \mathbf{A} \times \mathbf{B},$$

with

$$C = AB \sin\theta. \tag{1.32}$$

Unlike the preceding case of the scalar product, **C** is now a vector, and we assign it a direction perpendicular to the plane of **A** and **B** such that **A**, **B**, and **C** form a right-handed system. With this choice of direction we have

$$\mathbf{A} \times \mathbf{B} = -\mathbf{B} \times \mathbf{A}, \qquad \text{anticommutation.} \tag{1.32a}$$

From this definition of cross product we have

whereas

$$\mathbf{i} \times \mathbf{i} = \mathbf{j} \times \mathbf{j} = \mathbf{k} \times \mathbf{k} = 0, \tag{1.32b}$$

$$\mathbf{i} \times \mathbf{j} = \mathbf{k}, \qquad \mathbf{j} \times \mathbf{k} = \mathbf{i}, \qquad \mathbf{k} \times \mathbf{i} = \mathbf{j}$$

and

$$\mathbf{j} \times \mathbf{i} = -\mathbf{k}, \qquad \mathbf{k} \times \mathbf{j} = -\mathbf{i}, \qquad \mathbf{i} \times \mathbf{k} = -\mathbf{j}. \tag{1.32c}$$

The familiar magnetic field **B** is usually defined by the vector product force equation[1]

$$\mathbf{F}_M = q\mathbf{v} \times \mathbf{B}.$$

Here **v** is the velocity of the electric charge q and $\mathbf{F}_M$ is the resulting force on the moving charge.

The cross product has an important geometrical interpretation which we shall use in subsequent sections. In the parallelogram defined by **A** and **B** (Fig. 1.11)

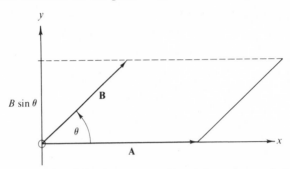

FIG. 1.11   Parallelogram representation of the vector product

$B \sin \theta$ is the height if A is taken as the length of the base. Then $|\mathbf{A} \times \mathbf{B}| = AB \sin \theta$ is the *area* of the parallelogram. As a vector, $\mathbf{A} \times \mathbf{B}$ is the area of the parallelogram defined by **A** and **B**, with the area vector normal to the plane of the parallelogram.

Parenthetically it might be noted that Eq. 1.32c and a modified Eq. 1.32b form the starting point for the development of *quaternions*. Equation 1.32b is replaced by $\mathbf{i} \times \mathbf{i} = \mathbf{j} \times \mathbf{j} = \mathbf{k} \times \mathbf{k} = -1$.

An alternate definition of the vector product $\mathbf{C} = \mathbf{A} \times \mathbf{B}$ consists in specifying the components of **C**:

$$C_x = A_y B_z - A_z B_y,$$
$$C_y = A_z B_y - A_x B_z, \qquad (1.33)$$
$$C_z = A_x B_y - A_y B_x,$$

or

$$C_i = A_j B_k - A_k B_j, \qquad i, j, k \text{ all different}, \qquad (1.34)$$

and with cyclic permutation of the indices $i, j,$ and k. The vector product **C** may be conveniently represented by a determinant[2]

$$\mathbf{C} = \begin{vmatrix} \mathbf{i} & \mathbf{j} & \mathbf{k} \\ A_x & A_y & A_z \\ B_x & B_y & B_z \end{vmatrix}. \qquad (1.35)$$

Expansion of the determinant across the top row reproduces the three components of **C** listed in Eq. 1.33.

[1] The electric field **E** is assumed here to be zero.
[2] Cf. Section 4.1 for a summary of determinants.

EXAMPLE 1.4.1

With **A** and **B** given in Example 1.1.1,

$$\mathbf{A} = 6\mathbf{i} + 4\mathbf{j} + 3\mathbf{k},$$

$$\mathbf{B} = 2\mathbf{i} - 3\mathbf{j} - 3\mathbf{k},$$

$$\mathbf{A} \times \mathbf{B} = \begin{vmatrix} \mathbf{i} & \mathbf{j} & \mathbf{k} \\ 6 & 4 & 3 \\ 2 & -3 & -3 \end{vmatrix}$$

$$= \mathbf{i}(-12 + 9) - \mathbf{j}(-18 - 6) + \mathbf{k}(-18 - 8)$$

$$= -3\mathbf{i} + 24\mathbf{j} - 26\mathbf{k}.$$

To show the equivalence of Eq. 1.32 and the component definition, Eq. 1.33, let us form $\mathbf{A} \cdot \mathbf{C}$ and $\mathbf{B} \cdot \mathbf{C}$, using Eq. 1.33. We have

$$\mathbf{A} \cdot \mathbf{C} = \mathbf{A} \cdot (\mathbf{A} \times \mathbf{B}) = A_x(A_y B_z - A_z B_y)$$

$$+ A_y(A_z B_x - A_x B_z) \tag{1.36}$$

$$+ A_z(A_x B_y - A_y B_x) = 0.$$

Similarly,

$$\mathbf{B} \cdot \mathbf{C} = \mathbf{B} \cdot (\mathbf{A} \times \mathbf{B}) = 0. \tag{1.37}$$

Equations 1.36 and 1.37 show that **C** is perpendicular to both **A** and **B** ($\cos \theta = 0$, $\theta = \pm 90°$) and therefore perpendicular to the plane they determine. The positive direction is determined by considering special cases such as the unit vectors $\mathbf{i} \times \mathbf{j} = \mathbf{k}$ ($C_z = +A_x B_y$).

The magnitude is obtained from

$$(\mathbf{A} \times \mathbf{B}) \cdot (\mathbf{A} \times \mathbf{B}) = A^2 B^2 - (A \cdot B)^2$$

$$= A^2 B^2 - A^2 B^2 \cos^2 \theta \tag{1.38}$$

$$= A^2 B^2 \sin^2 \theta.$$

Hence

$$C = AB \sin \theta. \tag{1.39}$$

The big first step in Eq. 1.38 may be verified by expanding out in component form using Eq. 1.33 for $\mathbf{A} \times \mathbf{B}$ and Eq. 1.22 for the dot product. From Eqs. 1.36, 1.37, and 1.39 we see the equivalence of Eqs. 1.32 and 1.33, the two definitions of vector product.

There still remains the problem of verifying that $\mathbf{C} = \mathbf{A} \times \mathbf{B}$ is indeed a vector, that is, that it obeys Eq. 1.15, the vector transformation law. Starting in a rotated (primed system)

$$C_i' = A_j' B_k' - A_k' B_j', \qquad i, j, \text{ and } k \text{ in cyclic order,}$$

$$= \sum_l a_{jl} A_l \sum_m a_{km} B_m - \sum_l a_{kl} A_l \sum_m a_{jm} B_m \tag{1.40}$$

$$= \sum_{l,m} (a_{jl} a_{km} - a_{kl} a_{jm}) A_l B_m.$$

The combination of direction cosines in parentheses vanishes for $m = l$. We therefore have j and k taking on fixed values, dependent on the choice of i, and six combinations of l and m. If $i = 3$, then $j = 1$, $k = 2$ (cyclic order), and we have the following direction cosine combinations

$$a_{11}a_{22} - a_{21}a_{12} = a_{33},$$

$$a_{13}a_{21} - a_{13}a_{11} = a_{32}, \tag{1.41}$$

$$a_{12}a_{23} - a_{22}a_{13} = a_{31}$$

and their negatives. Equations 1.41 are identities satisfied by the direction cosines. Substituting back into Eq. 1.40,

$$\begin{aligned} C_3' &= a_{33}A_1B_2 + a_{32}A_3B_1 + a_{31}A_2B_3 \\ &\quad - a_{33}A_2B_1 - a_{32}A_1B_3 - a_{31}A_3B_2 \\ &= a_{31}C_1 + a_{32}C_2 + a_{33}C_3 \\ &= \sum_n a_{3n}C_n. \end{aligned} \tag{1.42}$$

By permuting indices to pick up C_1' and C_2', we see that Eq. 1.15 is satisfied and **C** is indeed a vector. It should be mentioned here that this vector nature of the cross product is an accident associated with the three-dimensional nature of ordinary space.[1] It will be seen in Chapter 3 that the cross product may also be treated as a second-rank antisymmetric tensor!

EXERCISES

1.4.1 Two vectors **A** and **B** are given by
$$\mathbf{A} = 2\mathbf{i} + 4\mathbf{j} + 6\mathbf{k},$$
$$\mathbf{B} = 3\mathbf{i} - 3\mathbf{j} - 5\mathbf{k}.$$

Compute the scalar and vector products $\mathbf{A} \cdot \mathbf{B}$ and $\mathbf{A} \times \mathbf{B}$.

1.4.2 Show that
(a) $(\mathbf{A} - \mathbf{B}) \cdot (\mathbf{A} + \mathbf{B}) = A^2 - B^2$,
(b) $(\mathbf{A} - \mathbf{B}) \times (\mathbf{A} + \mathbf{B}) = 2\mathbf{A} \times \mathbf{B}$.
The associative laws needed here,

$$\mathbf{A} \cdot (\mathbf{B} + \mathbf{C}) = \mathbf{A} \cdot \mathbf{B} + \mathbf{A} \cdot \mathbf{C}$$

and

$$\mathbf{A} \times (\mathbf{B} + \mathbf{C}) = \mathbf{A} \times \mathbf{B} + \mathbf{A} \times \mathbf{C},$$

may easily be verified (if desired) by expansion in cartesian components.

1.4.3 The coordinates of the three vertices of a triangle are (2, 1, 5), (5, 2, 8), and (4, 8, 2). Compute its area by vector methods.

[1] Specifically Eq. 1.41 holds only for three-dimensional space.

1.4.4 Given the three vectors,
$$\mathbf{P} = 3\mathbf{i} + 2\mathbf{j} - \mathbf{k},$$
$$\mathbf{Q} = -6\mathbf{i} - 4\mathbf{j} + 2\mathbf{k},$$
$$\mathbf{R} = \mathbf{i} - 2\mathbf{j} - \mathbf{k},$$
find two that are perpendicular and two that are parallel or antiparallel.

1.4.5 Using the vectors
$$\mathbf{P} = \mathbf{i}\cos\theta + \mathbf{j}\sin\theta,$$
$$\mathbf{Q} = \mathbf{i}\cos\varphi - \mathbf{j}\sin\varphi,$$
$$\mathbf{R} = \mathbf{i}\cos\varphi + \mathbf{j}\sin\varphi,$$
prove the familiar trigonometric identities
$$\sin(\theta + \varphi) = \sin\theta\cos\varphi + \cos\theta\sin\varphi,$$
$$\cos(\theta + \varphi) = \cos\theta\cos\varphi - \sin\theta\sin\varphi.$$

1.4.6 (a) Find a vector $\mathbf{A}$ that is perpendicular to
$$\mathbf{U} = 2\mathbf{i} + \mathbf{j} - \mathbf{k}$$
$$\mathbf{V} = \mathbf{i} - \mathbf{j} + \mathbf{k}.$$

(b) What is $\mathbf{A}$ if, in addition to this requirement, we also demand that it have unit magnitude?

1.4.7 If four vectors $\mathbf{a}$, $\mathbf{b}$, $\mathbf{c}$, and $\mathbf{d}$ all lie in the same plane, show that
$$(\mathbf{a} \times \mathbf{b}) \times (\mathbf{c} \times \mathbf{d}) = 0.$$

Hint. Consider the directions of the cross-product vectors.

1.4.8 Find the sides and angles of the spherical triangle ABC defined by the three vectors
$$\mathbf{A} = (1, 0, 0),$$
and
$$\mathbf{B} = \left(\frac{1}{\sqrt{2}}, 0, \frac{1}{\sqrt{2}}\right),$$
$$\mathbf{C} = \left(0, \frac{1}{\sqrt{2}}, \frac{1}{\sqrt{2}}\right).$$
Each vector starts from the origin.

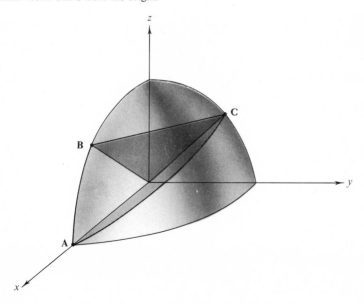

FIG. 1.12 Spherical triangle

1.4.9 The magnetic inductance **B** is *defined* by the Lorentz force equation

$$\mathbf{F} = q(\mathbf{v} \times \mathbf{B}).$$

Carrying out three experiments, we find that if

$$\mathbf{v} = \mathbf{i}, \qquad \frac{\mathbf{F}}{q} = 2\mathbf{k} - 4\mathbf{j},$$

$$\mathbf{v} = \mathbf{j}, \qquad \frac{\mathbf{F}}{q} = 4\mathbf{i} - \mathbf{k},$$

and

$$\mathbf{v} = \mathbf{k}, \qquad \frac{\mathbf{F}}{q} = \mathbf{j} - 2\mathbf{i}.$$

From the results of these three separate experiments calculate the magnetic inductance **B**.

Ans. $\mathbf{B} = \mathbf{i} + 2\mathbf{j} + 4\mathbf{k}.$

1.4.10 The origin and the three vectors **A**, **B**, and **C** (all of which start at the origin) define a tetrahedron. Taking the *outward* direction as positive, calculate the total vector area of the four tetrahedral surfaces.

1.5 Triple Scalar Product, Triple Vector Product

Sections 1.3 and 1.4 cover the two types of multiplication of interest here. However, there are combinations of three vectors, $\mathbf{A} \cdot (\mathbf{B} \times \mathbf{C})$ and $\mathbf{A} \times (\mathbf{B} \times \mathbf{C})$, which occur with sufficient frequency to deserve further attention. The combination

$$\mathbf{A} \cdot (\mathbf{B} \times \mathbf{C})$$

is known as the triple scalar product. $\mathbf{B} \times \mathbf{C}$ yields a vector which, dotted into **A**, gives a scalar. We note that $(\mathbf{A} \cdot \mathbf{B}) \times \mathbf{C}$ represents a scalar crossed into a vector, an operation that is not defined. Hence, if we agree to exclude this undefined interpretation, the parentheses may be omitted and the triple scalar product written $\mathbf{A} \cdot \mathbf{B} \times \mathbf{C}$.

Using Eq. 1.33 for the cross product and Eq. 1.22 for the dot product,

$$\mathbf{A} \cdot \mathbf{B} \times \mathbf{C} = A_x(B_y C_z - B_z C_y)$$

$$+ A_y(B_z C_x - B_x C_z)$$

$$+ A_z(B_x C_y - B_y C_x)$$

$$= \mathbf{B} \cdot \mathbf{C} \times \mathbf{A} = \mathbf{C} \cdot \mathbf{A} \times \mathbf{B}$$

$$= -\mathbf{A} \cdot \mathbf{C} \times \mathbf{B} = -\mathbf{C} \cdot \mathbf{B} \times \mathbf{A} = -\mathbf{B} \cdot \mathbf{A} \times \mathbf{C}, \qquad \text{etc.} \qquad (1.43)$$

The high degree of symmetry present in the component expansion should be noted. Every term contains the factors A_i, B_j, and C_k. If i, j, and k are in cyclic order (x, y, z), the sign is positive. If the order is anticyclic, the sign is negative. Further, the dot and the cross may be interchanged,

$$\mathbf{A} \cdot \mathbf{B} \times \mathbf{C} = \mathbf{A} \times \mathbf{B} \cdot \mathbf{C} \qquad (1.44)$$

A convenient representation of the component expansion of Eq. 1.43 is provided by the determinant

$$\mathbf{A} \cdot \mathbf{B} \times \mathbf{C} = \begin{vmatrix} A_x & A_y & A_z \\ B_x & B_y & B_z \\ C_x & C_y & C_z \end{vmatrix} \qquad (1.45)$$

The rules for interchanging rows and columns of a determinant[1] provide an immediate verification of the permutations listed in Eq. 1.43, whereas the symmetry of $\mathbf{A}$, $\mathbf{B}$, and $\mathbf{C}$ in the determinant form suggests the relation given in Eq. 1.44.

The triple products encountered in Section 1.5, which show that $\mathbf{A} \times \mathbf{B}$ was perpendicular to both $\mathbf{A}$ and $\mathbf{B}$, were special cases of the general result (Eq. 1.43).

The triple scalar product has a direct geometrical interpretation. The three vectors $\mathbf{A}$, $\mathbf{B}$, and $\mathbf{C}$ may be interpreted as defining a parallelepiped (Fig. 1.13).

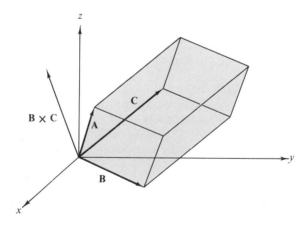

FIG. 1.13   Parallelepiped representation of triple scalar product

$$|\mathbf{B} \times \mathbf{C}| = BC \sin \theta$$
$$= \text{area of parallelogram base.} \qquad (1.46)$$

The direction, of course, is normal to the base. Dotting $\mathbf{A}$ into this means multiplying the base area by the projection of $\mathbf{A}$ onto the normal, or base times height. Therefore

$\mathbf{A} \cdot \mathbf{B} \times \mathbf{C} = $ volume of parallelepiped defined by $\mathbf{A}$, $\mathbf{B}$, and $\mathbf{C}$.

[1] Cf. Section 4.1 for a summary of the properties of determinants.

EXAMPLE 1.5.1

For

$$\mathbf{A} = \mathbf{i} + 2\mathbf{j} - \mathbf{k},$$
$$\mathbf{B} = \mathbf{j} + \mathbf{k},$$
$$\mathbf{C} = \mathbf{i} - \mathbf{j},$$

$$\mathbf{A} \cdot \mathbf{B} \times \mathbf{C} = \begin{vmatrix} 1 & 2 & -1 \\ 0 & 1 & 1 \\ 1 & -1 & 0 \end{vmatrix}. \tag{1.47}$$

By expansion by minors across the top row the determinant equals

$$1(0 + 1) - 2(0 - 1) - 1(0 - 1) = 4.$$

This is the volume of the parallelepiped defined by $\mathbf{A}$, $\mathbf{B}$, and $\mathbf{C}$. The reader should note that $\mathbf{A} \cdot \mathbf{B} \times \mathbf{C}$ may sometimes turn out to be negative! This problem and its interpretation are considered in Chapter 3.

The second triple product of interest is $\mathbf{A} \times (\mathbf{B} \times \mathbf{C})$. Here the parentheses must be retained, as may be seen by considering the special case

$$\mathbf{i} \times (\mathbf{i} \times \mathbf{j}) = \mathbf{i} \times \mathbf{k} = -\mathbf{j} \tag{1.48}$$

but

$$(\mathbf{i} \times \mathbf{i}) \times \mathbf{j} = 0.$$

That the triple vector product is a vector follows from our discussion of vector product. Also, we see that the direction of the resulting vector is perpendicular to $\mathbf{A}$ and to $\mathbf{B} \times \mathbf{C}$. The plane defined by $\mathbf{B}$ and $\mathbf{C}$ is perpendicular to $\mathbf{B} \times \mathbf{C}$ and so $\mathbf{A} \times (\mathbf{B} \times \mathbf{C})$ lies in this plane. This means that $\mathbf{A} \times (\mathbf{B} \times \mathbf{C})$ will be a linear combination of $\mathbf{B}$ and $\mathbf{C}$. We find that

$$\mathbf{A} \times (\mathbf{B} \times \mathbf{C}) = \mathbf{B}(\mathbf{A} \cdot \mathbf{C}) - \mathbf{C}(\mathbf{A} \cdot \mathbf{B}), \tag{1.49}$$

a relation sometimes known as the *BAC-CAB* rule. This result may be verified by the direct though not very elegant method of expanding into cartesian components (cf. Problem 1.5.1).

It might be noted here that as vectors are independent of the coordinates so a vector equation is independent of the particular coordinate system. The coordinate system only determines the components. If the vector equation can be established in cartesian coordinates, it is established and valid in any of the coordinate systems to be introduced in Chapter 2.

EXAMPLE 1.5.2

By using the three vectors given in Example 1.5.1 we obtain

$$\mathbf{A} \times (\mathbf{B} \times \mathbf{C}) = (\mathbf{j} + \mathbf{k})(1 - 2) - (\mathbf{i} - \mathbf{j})(2 - 1)$$
$$= -\mathbf{i} - \mathbf{k}$$

by Eq. 1.49. In detail,

$$\mathbf{B} \times \mathbf{C} = \begin{vmatrix} \mathbf{i} & \mathbf{j} & \mathbf{k} \\ 0 & 1 & 1 \\ 1 & -1 & 0 \end{vmatrix} = \mathbf{i} + \mathbf{j} - \mathbf{k}$$

and

$$\mathbf{A} \times (\mathbf{B} \times \mathbf{C}) = \begin{vmatrix} \mathbf{i} & \mathbf{j} & \mathbf{k} \\ 1 & 2 & -1 \\ 1 & 1 & -1 \end{vmatrix} = -\mathbf{i} - \mathbf{k}.$$

Other, more complicated, products may be simplified by using these forms of the triple scalar and triple vector products.

The triple scalar product finds an interesting and important application in the construction of a reciprocal crystal lattice. Let $\mathbf{a}$, $\mathbf{b}$, and $\mathbf{c}$ (not necessarily mutually perpendicular) represent the vectors that define a crystal lattice. The distance from one lattice point to another may then be written

$$\mathbf{r} = n_a \mathbf{a} + n_b \mathbf{b} + n_c \mathbf{c}, \tag{1.50}$$

with n_a, n_b, and n_c taking on integral values. With these vectors we may form

$$\mathbf{a}' = \frac{\mathbf{b} \times \mathbf{c}}{\mathbf{a} \cdot \mathbf{b} \times \mathbf{c}}, \qquad \mathbf{b}' = \frac{\mathbf{c} \times \mathbf{a}}{\mathbf{a} \cdot \mathbf{b} \times \mathbf{c}}, \qquad \mathbf{c}' = \frac{\mathbf{a} \times \mathbf{b}}{\mathbf{a} \cdot \mathbf{b} \times \mathbf{c}}. \tag{1.50a}$$

We see that $\mathbf{a}'$ is perpendicular to the plane containing $\mathbf{b}$ and $\mathbf{c}$ and has a magnitude proportional to a^{-1}. In fact, we can readily show that

$$\mathbf{a}' \cdot \mathbf{a} = \mathbf{b}' \cdot \mathbf{b} = \mathbf{c}' \cdot \mathbf{c} = 1, \tag{1.50b}$$

whereas

$$\mathbf{a}' \cdot \mathbf{b} = \mathbf{a}' \cdot \mathbf{c} = \mathbf{b}' \cdot \mathbf{a} = \mathbf{b}' \cdot \mathbf{c} = \mathbf{c}' \cdot \mathbf{a} = \mathbf{c}' \cdot \mathbf{b} = 0. \tag{1.50c}$$

It is from Eqs. 1.50b and 1.50c that the name reciprocal lattice is derived. This reciprocal lattice is useful in problems relating to the scattering of waves from the various planes in a crystal. Further details may be found in R. B. Leighton's *Principles of Modern Physics*, pp. 440–448. New York: McGraw-Hill (1959).

EXERCISES

1.5.1 Verify the expansion of the triple vector product
$$\mathbf{A} \times (\mathbf{B} \times \mathbf{C}) = \mathbf{B}(\mathbf{A} \cdot \mathbf{C}) - \mathbf{C}(\mathbf{A} \cdot \mathbf{B})$$
by direct expansion in cartesian coordinates.

1.5.2 Show that
$$\mathbf{a} \times (\mathbf{b} \times \mathbf{c}) + \mathbf{b} \times (\mathbf{c} \times \mathbf{a}) + \mathbf{c} \times (\mathbf{a} \times \mathbf{b}) = 0.$$

1.5.3 A vector $\mathbf{A}$ is decomposed into a radial vector $\mathbf{A}_r$ and a tangential vector $\mathbf{A}_t$. If $\mathbf{r}_0$ is a unit vector in the radial direction, show that

(a) $\mathbf{A}_r = \mathbf{r}_0(\mathbf{A} \cdot \mathbf{r}_0)$

and

(b) $\mathbf{A}_t = -\mathbf{r}_0 \times (\mathbf{r}_0 \times \mathbf{A})$.

1.5.4 Prove that a necessary and sufficient condition for the three (nonvanishing) vectors $\mathbf{A}$, $\mathbf{B}$, and $\mathbf{C}$ to be coplanar is the vanishing of the triple scalar product

$$\mathbf{A} \cdot \mathbf{B} \times \mathbf{C} = 0.$$

1.5.5 Three vectors $\mathbf{A}$, $\mathbf{B}$, and $\mathbf{C}$ are given by

$$\mathbf{A} = 3\mathbf{i} - 2\mathbf{j} + 2\mathbf{k},$$
$$\mathbf{B} = 6\mathbf{i} + 4\mathbf{j} - 2\mathbf{k},$$
$$\mathbf{C} = -3\mathbf{i} - 2\mathbf{j} - 4\mathbf{k}.$$

Compute the values of $\mathbf{A} \cdot \mathbf{B} \times \mathbf{C}$ and $\mathbf{A} \times (\mathbf{B} \times \mathbf{C})$, $\mathbf{C} \times (\mathbf{A} \times \mathbf{B})$ and $\mathbf{B} \times (\mathbf{C} \times \mathbf{A})$.

1.5.6 A force $\mathbf{F}$ acts on a body at a distance $\mathbf{r}$ from a chosen origin. Show that the resulting torque L about any axis through the origin is $L = \mathbf{r} \times \mathbf{F} \cdot \mathbf{a}$. Here $\mathbf{a}$ is the unit vector along the axis.

1.5.7 Given

$$\mathbf{a}' = \frac{\mathbf{b} \times \mathbf{c}}{\mathbf{a} \cdot \mathbf{b} \times \mathbf{c}}, \qquad \mathbf{b}' = \frac{\mathbf{c} \times \mathbf{a}}{\mathbf{a} \cdot \mathbf{b} \times \mathbf{c}}, \qquad \mathbf{c}' = \frac{\mathbf{a} \times \mathbf{b}}{\mathbf{a} \cdot \mathbf{b} \times \mathbf{c}} \quad \text{and} \quad \mathbf{a} \cdot \mathbf{b} \times \mathbf{c} \neq 0,$$

show that

(a) $\mathbf{x}' \cdot \mathbf{y} = \delta_{xy}$, $(\mathbf{x}, \mathbf{y} = \mathbf{a}, \mathbf{b}, \mathbf{c})$,

(b) $\mathbf{a}' \cdot \mathbf{b}' \times \mathbf{c}' = (\mathbf{a} \cdot \mathbf{b} \times \mathbf{c})^{-1}$,

(c) $\mathbf{a} = \dfrac{\mathbf{b}' \times \mathbf{c}'}{\mathbf{a} \cdot \mathbf{b} \times \mathbf{c}}$.

1.5.8 If $\mathbf{x}' \cdot \mathbf{y} = \delta_{xy}$, $(\mathbf{x}, \mathbf{y} = \mathbf{a}, \mathbf{b}, \mathbf{c})$, prove that

$$\mathbf{a}' = \frac{\mathbf{b} \times \mathbf{c}}{\mathbf{a} \cdot \mathbf{b} \times \mathbf{c}}.$$

(This is the converse of Problem 1.5.7.)

1.5.9 Show that any vector $\mathbf{V}$ may be expressed in terms of the reciprocal vectors $\mathbf{a}'$, $\mathbf{b}'$, $\mathbf{c}'$ by

$$\mathbf{V} = (\mathbf{V} \cdot \mathbf{a})\mathbf{a}' + (\mathbf{V} \cdot \mathbf{b})\mathbf{b}' + (\mathbf{V} \cdot \mathbf{c})\mathbf{c}'.$$

1.5.10 Show that the first step in Eq. 1.38, which is

$$(\mathbf{A} \times \mathbf{B}) \cdot (\mathbf{A} \times \mathbf{B}) = A^2 B^2 - (\mathbf{A} \cdot \mathbf{B})^2,$$

is consistent with the *BAC-CAB* rule for a triple vector product.

1.5.11 Analyze and criticize the following alternate derivation of the *BAC-CAB* rule:

(a) $\mathbf{B} \times \mathbf{C}$ is perpendicular to both $\mathbf{B}$ and $\mathbf{C}$.

(b) The triple product $\mathbf{A} \times (\mathbf{B} \times \mathbf{C})$ is perpendicular to $\mathbf{B} \times \mathbf{C}$ and therefore lies in the plane defined by $\mathbf{B}$ and $\mathbf{C}$. In mathematical form

$$\mathbf{A} \times (\mathbf{B} \times \mathbf{C}) = b\mathbf{B} + c\mathbf{C},$$

in which b and c are scalar coefficients.

(c) The triple vector product is proportional to the magnitude of $\mathbf{A}$, to the magnitude of $\mathbf{B}$, and the magnitude of $\mathbf{C}$. We incorporate this proportionality by letting

$$b = b_1 \mathbf{A} \cdot \mathbf{C} \quad \text{and} \quad c = c_1 \mathbf{A} \cdot \mathbf{B}.$$

Now b_1 and c_1 are constants that are independent of the magnitudes of $\mathbf{A}$, $\mathbf{B}$, and $\mathbf{C}$.

(d) Evaluation of the constants b_1 and c_1 is carried out by considering special cases:

$$\mathbf{A} = \mathbf{j}, \mathbf{B} = \mathbf{i}, \quad \text{and} \quad \mathbf{C} = \mathbf{j} \quad \text{leads to } b_1 = 1;$$
$$\mathbf{A} = \mathbf{i}, \mathbf{B} = \mathbf{i}, \quad \text{and} \quad \mathbf{C} = \mathbf{j} \quad \text{leads to } c_1 = -1.$$

Substituting back, we have the *BAC-CAB* rule,

$$\mathbf{A} \times (\mathbf{B} \times \mathbf{C}) = \mathbf{B}(\mathbf{A} \cdot \mathbf{C}) - \mathbf{C}(\mathbf{A} \cdot \mathbf{B}).$$

1.5.12 Given the three vectors **A**, **B**, and **C**,

$$\mathbf{A} = \mathbf{i} + \mathbf{j},$$
$$\mathbf{B} = \mathbf{j} + \mathbf{k},$$
$$\mathbf{C} = \mathbf{i} - \mathbf{k}.$$

(a) Compute the triple scalar product, $\mathbf{A} \cdot \mathbf{B} \times \mathbf{C}$. Noting that $\mathbf{A} = \mathbf{B} + \mathbf{C}$, give a geometric interpretation of your result for the triple scalar product.

(b) Compute $\mathbf{A} \times (\mathbf{B} \times \mathbf{C})$.

1.6 Gradient, **V**

Suppose that $\varphi(x, y, z)$ is a scalar point function, that is, a function whose value depends on the values of the coordinates (x, y, z). As a scalar, it must have the same value at a given fixed point in space, independent of the rotatation of our coordinate system, or

$$\varphi'(x_1', x_2', x_3') = \varphi(x_1, x_2, x_3). \tag{1.51}$$

By differentiating with respect to x_i' we obtain

$$\frac{\partial \varphi'(x_1', x_2', x_3')}{\partial x_i'} = \frac{\partial \varphi(x_1, x_2, x_3)}{\partial x_i'}$$

$$= \sum_j \frac{\partial \varphi}{\partial x_j} \frac{\partial x_j}{\partial x_i'} = \sum_j a_{ij} \frac{\partial \varphi}{\partial x_j} \tag{1.52}$$

by the rules of partial differentiation and Eq. 1.16. But comparison with Eq. 1.17, the vector transformation law, now shows that we have *constructed* a vector with components $\partial \varphi / \partial x_j$. This vector we label the gradient of φ.

A convenient symbolism is

$$\nabla \varphi = \mathbf{i} \frac{\partial \varphi}{\partial x} + \mathbf{j} \frac{\partial \varphi}{\partial y} + \mathbf{k} \frac{\partial \varphi}{\partial z} \tag{1.53}$$

or

$$\nabla = \mathbf{i} \frac{\partial}{\partial x} + \mathbf{j} \frac{\partial}{\partial y} + \mathbf{k} \frac{\partial}{\partial z}. \tag{1.54}$$

$\nabla \varphi$ (or del φ) is our gradient of the scalar φ, whereas ∇ (del) itself is a vector differential operator (available to operate on or to differentiate a scalar φ). It should be emphasized that this operator is a hybrid creature that must satisfy both the laws for handling vectors and the laws of partial differentiation.

EXAMPLE 1.6.1

Calculate the gradient of $f(r) = f(\sqrt{x^2 + y^2 + z^2})$.

$$\mathbf{V}f(r) = \mathbf{i}\frac{\partial f(r)}{\partial x} + \mathbf{j}\frac{\partial f(r)}{\partial y} + \mathbf{k}\frac{\partial f(r)}{\partial z}.$$

Now $f(r)$ depends on x through the dependence of r on x. Therefore

$$\frac{\partial f(r)}{\partial x} = \frac{df(r)}{dr}\cdot\frac{\partial r}{\partial x} = \frac{df}{dr}\cdot\frac{x}{r}.$$

Substituting into the equation for $\mathbf{V}f(r)$,

$$f(r) = (\mathbf{i}x + \mathbf{j}y + \mathbf{k}z)\frac{1}{r}\frac{df}{dr}$$

$$= \frac{\mathbf{r}}{r}\frac{df}{dr}$$

$$= \mathbf{r}_0\frac{df}{dr}.$$

Here $\mathbf{r}_0$ is a unit vector in the *positive* radial direction.

One immediate application of $\mathbf{V}\varphi$ is to dot it into an increment of length

$$d\mathbf{r} = \mathbf{i}\,dx + \mathbf{j}\,dy + \mathbf{k}\,dz. \tag{1.55}$$

Thus we obtain

$$(\mathbf{V}\varphi)\cdot d\mathbf{r} = \frac{\partial\varphi}{\partial x}\,dx + \frac{\partial\varphi}{\partial y}\,dy + \frac{\partial\varphi}{\partial z}\,dz \tag{1.56}$$

$$= d\varphi,$$

the change in the scalar function φ corresponding to a change in position $d\mathbf{r}$. Now consider P and Q to be two points on a surface $\varphi(x, y, z) = C$, a constant. These points are chosen so that Q is a distance $d\mathbf{r}$ from P. Then, moving from P to Q, the change in $\varphi(x, y, z) = C$ is given by

$$d\varphi = (\mathbf{V}\varphi)\cdot d\mathbf{r}$$

$$= 0, \tag{1.57}$$

since we stay on the surface $\varphi(x, y, z) = C$. This shows that $\mathbf{V}\varphi$ is perpendicular to $d\mathbf{r}$. Since $d\mathbf{r}$ may have any direction from P as long as it stays in the surface φ, point Q being restricted to the surface, but having arbitrary direction, $\mathbf{V}\varphi$ is seen to be normal to the surface $\varphi = $ constant.

If we now permit $d\mathbf{r}$ to take us from one surface $\varphi = C_1$ to an adjacent surface $\varphi = C_2$,

$$d\varphi = C_2 - C_1 = \Delta C$$

$$= (\mathbf{V}\varphi)\cdot d\mathbf{r}. \tag{1.58}$$

For a given $d\varphi$, $|d\mathbf{r}|$ is a minimum when it is chosen parallel to $\mathbf{V}\varphi$ ($\cos\theta = 1$); or, for a given $|d\mathbf{r}|$, the change in the scalar function φ is maximized by choosing $d\mathbf{r}$

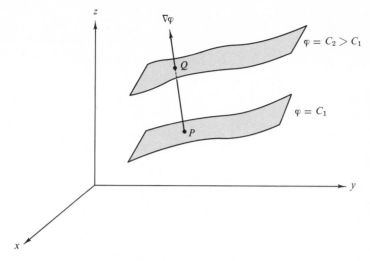

FIG. 1.14 Gradient

parallel to $\nabla\varphi$. *This identifies $\nabla\varphi$ as a vector having the direction of the maximum space rate of change of φ,* an identification that will be useful in Chapter 2 when we consider noncartesian coordinate systems.

The gradient of a scalar is of extreme importance in physics in expressing the relation between a force field and a potential field.

$$\text{Force} = -\nabla \text{ (potential).} \tag{1.59}$$

This is illustrated by both gravitational and electrostatic fields, among others. The reader should satisfy himself that the minus sign in Eq. 1.59 results in water flowing downhill rather than uphill!

EXERCISES

1.6.1 Show that $\nabla(uv) = v\nabla u + u\nabla v$, where u and v are differentiable scalar functions of x, y, and z.

1.6.2 If $S(x, y, z) = (x^2 + y^2 + z^2)^{-3/2}$, find
(a) ∇S at the point $(1, 2, 3)$;
(b) the magnitude of the gradient of S, $|S_\Delta|$ at $(1, 2, 3)$;
and
(c) the direction cosines of ∇S at $(1, 2, 3)$.

1.6.3 Given a vector $\mathbf{r}_{12} = \mathbf{i}(x_1 - x_2) + \mathbf{j}(y_1 - y_2) + \mathbf{k}(z_1 - z_2)$, show that $\nabla_1 r_{12}$ (gradient with respect to x_1, y_1, and z_1 of the magnitude of r_{12}) is a unit vector in the direction of $\mathbf{r}_{12}$.

1.6.4 (a) Show that a necessary and sufficient condition that $u(x, y, z)$ and $v(x, y, z)$ are related by some function $f(u, v) = 0$ is that $(\nabla u) \times (\nabla v) = 0$.

(b) If $u = u(x, y)$ and $v = v(x, y)$, show that the condition $(\nabla u) \times (\nabla v) = 0$ leads to the two-dimensional Jacobian

$$J\left(\frac{u, v}{x, y}\right) = \begin{vmatrix} \dfrac{\partial u}{\partial x} & \dfrac{\partial u}{\partial y} \\[2ex] \dfrac{\partial v}{\partial x} & \dfrac{\partial v}{\partial y} \end{vmatrix} = 0.$$

The functions u and v are assumed differentiable.

1.6.5 (a) Show that a necessary and sufficient condition that three functions $u(x, y, z)$, $v(x, y, z)$ and $w(x, y, z)$ are related by some function $F(u, v, w) = 0$ is that $(\nabla u) \cdot (\nabla v) \times (\nabla w) = 0$.

   (b) Show that this triple scalar product of gradients is equivalent to the three-dimensional Jacobian

$$J\left(\frac{u, v, w}{x, y, z}\right) = \begin{vmatrix} \dfrac{\partial u}{\partial x} & \dfrac{\partial u}{\partial y} & \dfrac{\partial u}{\partial z} \\[2ex] \dfrac{\partial v}{\partial x} & \dfrac{\partial v}{\partial y} & \dfrac{\partial v}{\partial z} \\[2ex] \dfrac{\partial w}{\partial x} & \dfrac{\partial w}{\partial y} & \dfrac{\partial w}{\partial z} \end{vmatrix} = 0.$$

Assume that the needed derivatives exist.

1.6.6 If a vector function $\mathbf{F}$ depends on both space coordinates (x, y, z) and time t, show that

$$d\mathbf{F} = (d\mathbf{r} \cdot \nabla) \mathbf{F} + \frac{\partial \mathbf{F}}{\partial t} \, dt.$$

1.7 Divergence, $\nabla \cdot$

Differentiating a vector function is a simple extension of differentiating scalar quantities. Suppose $\mathbf{r}(t)$ describes the position of a satellite at some time t. Then, for differentiation with respect to time,

$$\frac{d\mathbf{r}(t)}{dt} = \lim_{\Delta t \to 0} \frac{\mathbf{r}(t + \Delta t) - \mathbf{r}(t)}{\Delta t}$$

$$= \mathbf{v}, \qquad \text{linear velocity.}$$

Graphically, we again have the slope of a curve, orbit, or trajectory, as shown in Fig. 1.15.

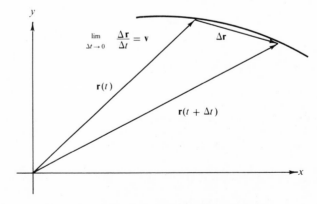

FIG. 1.15   Differentiation of a vector

If we resolve $\mathbf{r}(t)$ into its cartesian components, $d\mathbf{r}/dt$ always reduces directly to a vector sum of not more than three (for three-dimensional space) scalar derivatives. In other coordinate systems (Chapter 2) the situation is a little more complicated, for the unit vectors are no longer constant in direction. Differentiation with respect to the space coordinates is handled in the same way as differentiation with respect to time, as will be seen in the following paragraphs.

In Section 1.6 ∇ was defined as a vector operator. Now, paying careful attention to both its vector and its differential properties, we let it operate on a vector. First, as a vector we dot it into a second vector to obtain

$$\nabla \cdot \mathbf{V} = \frac{\partial V_x}{\partial x} + \frac{\partial V_y}{\partial y} + \frac{\partial V_z}{\partial z}, \tag{1.60}$$

known as the divergence of $\mathbf{V}$. This is a scalar, as discussed in Section 1.3.

EXAMPLE 1.7.1

Calculate $\nabla \cdot \mathbf{r}$.

$$\nabla \cdot \mathbf{r} = \left(\mathbf{i} \frac{\partial}{\partial x} + \mathbf{j} \frac{\partial}{\partial y} + \mathbf{k} \frac{\partial}{\partial z} \right) \cdot (\mathbf{i}x + \mathbf{j}y + \mathbf{k}z)$$

$$= \frac{\partial x}{\partial x} + \frac{\partial y}{\partial y} + \frac{\partial z}{\partial z},$$

or

$$\nabla \cdot \mathbf{r} = 3.$$

EXAMPLE 1.7.2

Generalizing Example 1.7.1,

$$\nabla \cdot \mathbf{r} \, f(r) = \frac{\partial}{\partial x} [x \, f(r)] + \frac{\partial}{\partial y} [y \, f(r)] + \frac{\partial}{\partial z} [z \, f(r)]$$

$$= 3f(r) + r \frac{df}{dr}.$$

In particular, if $f(r) = r^{n-1}$,

$$\nabla \cdot \mathbf{r} r^{n-1} = \nabla \cdot \mathbf{r}_0 r^n$$

$$= 3r^{n-1} + (n-1)r^{n-1}$$

$$= (n+2)r^{n-1}.$$

This divergence vanishes for $n = -2$, an important fact in Section 1.14.

To develop a feeling for the physical significance of the divergence, consider $\nabla \cdot (\rho \mathbf{v})$ with $\mathbf{v}(x, y, z)$, the velocity of a compressible fluid and $\rho(x, y, z)$, its density at point (x, y, z). If we consider a small volume $dx \, dy \, dz$ (Fig. 1.16), the fluid flowing into this volume per unit time (positive x-direction) through the face $EFGH$

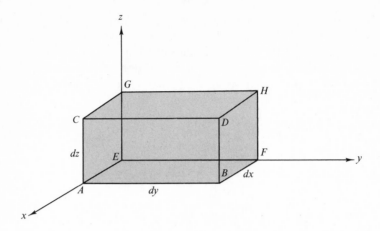

FIG. 1.16   Differential rectangular parallelepiped (in first or positive octant)

is (rate of flow in) $_{EFGH} = \rho v_x \, dy \, dz$. The rate of flow out (still positive x-direction) through face $ABCD$ is

$$(\text{rate of flow out})_{ABCD} = \left[\rho v_x + \frac{\partial}{\partial x}(\rho v_x)\, dx\right] dy \, dz,$$

the derivative[1] allowing for the possibility of nonuniform density or velocity or both.[2] The net rate of flow *out*, for these two faces, is simply the difference between these two flows, or

$$\text{net rate of flow out}\Bigg|_x = \frac{\partial}{\partial x}(\rho v_x)\, dx \, dy \, dz.$$

Adding the net rate of flow out for the other four faces of our volume element,

$$\begin{aligned}\text{net flow out}\\ (\text{per unit time})\end{aligned} = \left[\frac{\partial}{\partial x}(\rho v_x) + \frac{\partial}{\partial y}(\rho v_y) + \frac{\partial}{\partial z}(\rho v_z)\right] dx \, dy \, dz$$

$$= \mathbf{\nabla} \cdot (\rho \mathbf{v})\, dx \, dy \, dz. \qquad (1.61)$$

Therefore the net flow of our compressible fluid out of the volume element $dx \, dy \, dz$ per unit volume per unit time is $\mathbf{\nabla} \cdot (\rho \mathbf{v})$. Hence the name *divergence*. A direct

---

[1] This expression gives the start of a Maclaurin expansion,

$$f(h) = f(0) + \frac{df}{dx}\, h + \frac{d^2 f}{dx^2}\frac{h^2}{2!} + \cdots$$

(Section 5.6), in which $h = dx$. Each derivative is evaluated at the initial point $x = 0$.

[2] Strictly speaking, ρv_x is averaged over face $EFGH$ and the expression $\rho v_x + (\partial/\partial x)(\rho v_x)\, dx$ is similarly averaged over face $ABCD$. Using an arbitrarily small differential volume, the averages reduce to the values used here.

application is in the continuity equation

$$\frac{\partial \rho}{\partial t} + \mathbf{V} \cdot (\rho \mathbf{v}) = 0, \tag{1.62}$$

which simply states that a net flow out of the volume results in a decreased density inside the volume.

The combination $\mathbf{V} \cdot (f\mathbf{V})$, in which f is a scalar function and $\mathbf{V}$ a vector, may be written

$$\mathbf{V} \cdot (f\mathbf{V}) = \frac{\partial}{\partial x}(fV_x) + \frac{\partial}{\partial y}(fV_y) + \frac{\partial}{\partial z}(fV_z)$$

$$= \frac{\partial f}{\partial x}V_x + f\frac{\partial V_x}{\partial x} + \frac{\partial f}{\partial y}V_y + f\frac{\partial V_y}{\partial y}$$

$$+ \frac{\partial f}{\partial z}V_z + f\frac{\partial V_z}{\partial z}$$

$$= (\nabla f) \cdot \mathbf{V} + f\mathbf{V} \cdot V, \tag{1.62a}$$

which is just what we would expect for the derivative of a product.

If we have the special case of the divergence of a vector vanishing,

$$\mathbf{V} \cdot \mathbf{B} = 0, \tag{1.63}$$

the vector $\mathbf{B}$ is said to be solenoidal, the term coming from the example in which $\mathbf{B}$ is the magnetic inductance and Eq. 1.63 appears as one of Maxwell's equations.

EXERCISES

1.7.1 Prove $\mathbf{V} \cdot (\mathbf{a} \times \mathbf{b}) = \mathbf{b} \cdot \mathbf{V} \times \mathbf{a} - \mathbf{a} \cdot \mathbf{V} \times \mathbf{b}$.

Hint. Treat as a triple scalar product.

1.7.2 Show, by rotating the coordinates, that $\mathbf{V}' \cdot \mathbf{V}' = \mathbf{V} \cdot \mathbf{V}$ and that therefore, by definition, the divergence of a vector is a scalar quantity. (Two-dimensional rotation will suffice.)

1.7.3 A rigid body is rotating with constant angular velocity $\boldsymbol{\omega}$. Show that the linear velocity $\mathbf{v}$ is solenoidal.

1.7.4 The electrostatic field of a point q is

$$\mathbf{E} = \frac{q}{4\pi\varepsilon_0} \cdot \frac{\mathbf{r}_0}{r^2}.$$

Calculate the divergence of $\mathbf{E}$.

1.8   Curl, $\nabla \times$

Another possible operation with the vector operator ∇ is to cross it into a vector. We obtain

$$\nabla \times \mathbf{V} = \mathbf{i}\left(\frac{\partial}{\partial y} V_z - \frac{\partial}{\partial z} V_y\right) + \mathbf{j}\left(\frac{\partial}{\partial z} V_x - \frac{\partial}{\partial x} V_z\right) + \mathbf{k}\left(\frac{\partial}{\partial x} V_y - \frac{\partial}{\partial y} V_x\right)$$

$$= \begin{vmatrix} \mathbf{i} & \mathbf{j} & \mathbf{k} \\ \dfrac{\partial}{\partial x} & \dfrac{\partial}{\partial y} & \dfrac{\partial}{\partial z} \\ V_x & V_y & V_z \end{vmatrix}, \quad (1.64)$$

which is called the curl of $\mathbf{V}$. In expanding this determinant form or in any operation with ∇, the derivative nature of ∇ must be considered. Specifically, $\mathbf{V} \times \mathbf{V}$ is defined only as an operator, another vector differential operator. It is certainly not equal, in general, to $-\mathbf{V} \times \mathbf{V}$.[1] If ∇ is crossed into the product of a scalar and a vector, we can show

$$\nabla \times (f\mathbf{V})\bigg|_x = \mathbf{i}\left[\frac{\partial}{\partial y}(fV_z) - \frac{\partial}{\partial z}(fV_y)\right]$$

$$= \mathbf{i}\left(f\frac{\partial V_z}{\partial y} + \frac{\partial f}{\partial y}V_z - f\frac{\partial V_y}{\partial z} - \frac{\partial f}{\partial z}V_z\right)$$

$$= f\nabla \times \mathbf{V}|_x + (\nabla f) \times \mathbf{V}|_x. \quad (1.65)$$

If we permute the coordinates $x \to y$, $y \to z$, $z \to x$ to pick up the y-component and then permute them a second time to pick up the z-component,

$$\nabla \times (f\mathbf{V}) = f\nabla \times \mathbf{V} + (\nabla f) \times \mathbf{V}, \quad (1.66)$$

which is the vector product analog of Eq. (1.62a).

EXAMPLE 1.8.1

Calculate $\nabla \times \mathbf{r} f(r)$
By Eq. 1.66

$$\nabla \times \mathbf{r} f(r) = f(r)\nabla \times \mathbf{r} + [\nabla f(r)] \times \mathbf{r}.$$

First,

$$\nabla \times \mathbf{r} = \begin{vmatrix} \mathbf{i} & \mathbf{j} & \mathbf{k} \\ \dfrac{\partial}{\partial x} & \dfrac{\partial}{\partial y} & \dfrac{\partial}{\partial z} \\ x & y & z \end{vmatrix} = 0.$$

---

[1] In this same spirit, if $\mathbf{A}$ is a differential operator, it is not necessarily true that $\mathbf{A} \times \mathbf{A} = 0$. Specifically, for the quantum mechanical angular momentum *operator*, $\mathbf{L} = i\hbar(\mathbf{r} \times \nabla)$, we find that $\mathbf{L} \times \mathbf{L} = i\hbar\mathbf{L}$.

Second, using $\nabla f(r) = \mathbf{r}_0 (df/dr)$ (Example 1.6.1),

$$\nabla \times \mathbf{r} f(r) = \frac{df}{dr} \mathbf{r}_0 \times \mathbf{r} = 0.$$

The vector product vanishes, since $\mathbf{r} = \mathbf{r}_0 r$ and $\mathbf{r}_0 \times \mathbf{r}_0 = 0$.

The name curl has developed because in a sense $\nabla \times \mathbf{V}$ describes the rotation of the vector field $\mathbf{V}$ at the point at which the curl of $\mathbf{V}$ is evaluated. Suppose we have a rigid body in the xy-plane rotating about the z-axis with angular velocity $\boldsymbol{\omega}$. The linear velocity $\mathbf{v}$ at a given point described by $\mathbf{r}$ is given by

$$\mathbf{v} = \boldsymbol{\omega} \times \mathbf{r}. \tag{1.67}$$

Let us calculate $\nabla \times \mathbf{v}$. We find

$$\nabla \times \mathbf{v} = \nabla \times (\boldsymbol{\omega} \times \mathbf{r}). \tag{1.68}$$

By rearranging terms in Eq. 1.50 to respect the operator nature of ∇,

$$\nabla \times (\boldsymbol{\omega} \times \mathbf{r}) = \nabla \cdot \mathbf{r} \boldsymbol{\omega} - \nabla \cdot \boldsymbol{\omega} \mathbf{r}. \tag{1.69}$$

Here ∇ is dotted into the first vector, but as a differential operator it operates on *both* vectors. Expanding,

$$\nabla \times (\boldsymbol{\omega} \times \mathbf{r}) = \boldsymbol{\omega} \nabla \cdot \mathbf{r} + \mathbf{r} \cdot \nabla \boldsymbol{\omega}$$
$$- \mathbf{r} \nabla \cdot \boldsymbol{\omega} - \boldsymbol{\omega} \cdot \nabla \mathbf{r}. \tag{1.70}$$

If $\boldsymbol{\omega}$ is constant, the second and third terms on the right side of Eq. 1.70 vanish. Further, we have

$$\nabla \cdot \mathbf{r} = 3 \tag{1.71}$$

from Example 1.7.1 and

$$\boldsymbol{\omega} \cdot \nabla \mathbf{r} = \omega_x \frac{\partial}{\partial x} (\mathbf{i}x + \mathbf{j}y + \mathbf{k}z)$$

$$+ \omega_y \frac{\partial}{\partial y} (\mathbf{i}x + \mathbf{j}y + \mathbf{k}z)$$

$$+ \omega_z \frac{\partial}{\partial z} (\mathbf{i}x + \mathbf{j}y + \mathbf{k}z) \tag{1.72}$$

$$= \mathbf{i}\omega_x + \mathbf{j}\omega_y + \mathbf{k}\omega_z$$

$$= \boldsymbol{\omega}.$$

By substituting Eqs. 1.71 and 1.72 into 1.70,

$$\nabla \times \mathbf{v} = \nabla \times (\boldsymbol{\omega} \times \mathbf{r}) = 2\boldsymbol{\omega}, \tag{1.73}$$

or the curl of the linear velocity of our rigid body is twice the angular velocity. In Section 1.12 an interpretation of $\nabla \times \mathbf{V}$ as a circulation measurable in terms of tiny paddlewheels will be developed.

Whenever the curl of a vector $\mathbf{V}$ vanishes,

$$\nabla \times \mathbf{V} = 0, \tag{1.74}$$

V is labeled irrotational. The most important physical examples of irrotational vectors are the gravitational and electrostatic forces. In each case

$$\mathbf{V} = C\,\frac{\mathbf{r}_0}{r^2} = C\,\frac{\mathbf{r}}{r^3}, \tag{1.75}$$

where C is a constant and $\mathbf{r}_0$ is the unit vector in the outward radial direction. For the gravitational case we have $C = -Gm_1m_2$, given by Newton's law of universal gravitation. If $C = q_1q_2/4\pi\varepsilon_0$, we have Coulomb's law of electrostatics (mks units). The force **V** given in Eq. 1.75 may be shown to be irrotational by direct expansion into cartesian components as we did in Example 1.8.1. Another approach is developed in Chapter 2, in which we express $\mathbf{V} \times$, the curl, in terms of spherical polar coordinates.

EXERCISES

1.8.1   Show that $\mathbf{u} \times \mathbf{v}$ is solenoidal if $\mathbf{u}$ and $\mathbf{v}$ are each irrotational.

1.8.2   If **A** is irrotational, show that $\mathbf{A} \times \mathbf{r}$ is solenoidal.

1.8.3   Show, by rotating the coordinates, that the components of the curl of a vector transform as a vector.
Hint. The direction cosine identities of Eq. 1.41 are available as needed.

1.8.4   If (a) $\mathbf{V} = \mathbf{i}V_x(x, y) + \mathbf{j}V_y(x, y)$ and (b) $\nabla \times \mathbf{V} \neq 0$, prove that $\nabla \times \mathbf{V}$ is perpendicular to **V**.

1.8.5   The quantum mechanical angular momentum operators are

$$L_x = -i\hbar\left(y\,\frac{\partial}{\partial z} - z\,\frac{\partial}{\partial y}\right),$$

$$L_y = -i\hbar\left(z\,\frac{\partial}{\partial x} - x\,\frac{\partial}{\partial z}\right),$$

$$L_z = -i\hbar\left(x\,\frac{\partial}{\partial y} - y\,\frac{\partial}{\partial x}\right).$$

Show that
$$L_xL_y - L_yL_x = i\hbar L_z,$$
hence
$$\mathbf{L} \times \mathbf{L} = i\hbar\mathbf{L}.$$

1.8.6   Verify the vector identity
$$\nabla(\mathbf{A} \cdot \mathbf{B}) = (\mathbf{B} \cdot \nabla)\mathbf{A} + (\mathbf{A} \cdot \nabla)\mathbf{B} + \mathbf{B} \times (\nabla \times \mathbf{A}) + \mathbf{A} \times (\nabla \times \mathbf{B}).$$

1.8.7   Verify the vector identity
$$\nabla \times (\mathbf{A} \times \mathbf{B}) = (\mathbf{B} \cdot \nabla)\mathbf{A} - (\mathbf{A} \cdot \nabla)\mathbf{B} - \mathbf{B}(\nabla \cdot \mathbf{A}) + \mathbf{A}(\nabla \cdot \mathbf{B}).$$

1.9 Successive Application of ∇

We have now defined gradient, divergence, and curl to obtain vector, scalar, and vector quantities, respectively. Letting ∇ operate on each of these quantities, we obtain

(a) $\nabla \cdot \nabla \varphi$

(b) $\nabla \times \nabla \varphi$

(c) $\nabla \nabla \cdot \mathbf{V}$

(d) $\nabla \cdot \nabla \times \mathbf{V}$

(e) $\nabla \times (\nabla \times \mathbf{V})$,

all five expressions involving second derivatives and all five appearing in the second-order differential equations of mathematical physics, particularly in electromagnetic theory.

The first expression, $\nabla \cdot \nabla \varphi$, the divergence of the gradient, is named the Laplacian of φ. We have

$$\nabla \cdot \nabla \varphi = \left(\mathbf{i} \frac{\partial}{\partial x} + \mathbf{j} \frac{\partial}{\partial y} + \mathbf{k} \frac{\partial}{\partial z} \right) \cdot \left(\mathbf{i} \frac{\partial \varphi}{\partial x} + \mathbf{j} \frac{\partial \varphi}{\partial y} + \mathbf{k} \frac{\partial \varphi}{\partial z} \right)$$

$$= \frac{\partial^2 \varphi}{\partial x^2} + \frac{\partial^2 \varphi}{\partial y^2} + \frac{\partial^2 \varphi}{\partial z^2}.$$

When φ is the electrostatic potential, we have

$$\nabla \cdot \nabla \varphi = 0.$$

which is Laplace's equation of electrostatics. Often the combination $\nabla \cdot \nabla$ is written ∇^2.

EXAMPLE 1.9.1

Calculate $\nabla \cdot \nabla g(r)$.
Referring to Examples 1.6.1 and 1.7.1,

$$\nabla \cdot \nabla \, g(r) = \nabla \cdot \mathbf{r}_0 \frac{dg}{dr}$$

$$= \frac{2}{r} \frac{dg}{dr} + \frac{d^2 g}{dr^2},$$

replacing $f(r)$ in Example 1.7.2 by $1/r \cdot dg/dr$. If $g(r) = r^n$, this reduces to

$$\nabla \cdot \nabla r^n = n(n+1) r^{n-2}.$$

This will vanish for $n = 0$ [$g(r) = $ constant] and for $n = -1$, that is, $g(r) = 1/r$ is a solution of Laplace's equation, $\nabla^2 g(r) = 0$.

Expression (b) may be written

$$\mathbf{V} \times \mathbf{V}\varphi = \begin{vmatrix} \mathbf{i} & \mathbf{j} & \mathbf{k} \\ \dfrac{\partial}{\partial x} & \dfrac{\partial}{\partial y} & \dfrac{\partial}{\partial z} \\ \dfrac{\partial \varphi}{\partial x} & \dfrac{\partial \varphi}{\partial y} & \dfrac{\partial \varphi}{\partial z} \end{vmatrix}. \tag{1.76}$$

By expanding the determinant,

$$\mathbf{V} \times \mathbf{V}\varphi = \mathbf{i}\left(\frac{\partial^2 \varphi}{\partial y\, \partial z} - \frac{\partial^2 \varphi}{\partial z\, \partial y} \right) + \mathbf{j}\left(\frac{\partial^2 \varphi}{\partial z\, \partial x} - \frac{\partial^2 \varphi}{\partial x\, \partial z} \right)$$

$$+ \mathbf{k}\left(\frac{\partial^2 \varphi}{\partial x\, \partial y} - \frac{\partial^2 \varphi}{\partial y\, \partial x} \right) \tag{1.77}$$

$$= 0,$$

assuming that the order of partial differentiation may be interchanged. This will be true as long as the first partial derivatives of φ are continuous functions. Then, from Eq. 1.77, the curl of a gradient is identically zero. All gradients, then, are irrotational.

Expression (d) is a triple scalar product which may be written

$$\mathbf{V} \cdot \mathbf{V} \times \mathbf{V} = \begin{vmatrix} \dfrac{\partial}{\partial x} & \dfrac{\partial}{\partial y} & \dfrac{\partial}{\partial z} \\ \dfrac{\partial}{\partial_x} & \dfrac{\partial}{\partial y} & \dfrac{\partial}{\partial z} \\ V_x & V_y & V_z \end{vmatrix}. \tag{1.78}$$

Again, assuming continuity so that the order of differentiation is immaterial, we obtain

$$\mathbf{V} \cdot \mathbf{V} \times \mathbf{V} = 0. \tag{1.79}$$

The divergence of a curl vanishes or all curls are solenoidal. In Section 1.15 we shall see that vectors may be resolved into solenoidal and irrotational parts by Helmholtz' theorem.

Two of the remaining expressions satisfy a relation

$$\mathbf{V} \times (\mathbf{V} \times \mathbf{V}) = \mathbf{V}\mathbf{V} \cdot \mathbf{V} - \mathbf{V} \cdot \mathbf{V}\mathbf{V}. \tag{1.80}$$

This follows immediately from Eq. 1.49, the *BAC-CAB* rule, which we rewrite so that **C** appears at the extreme right of each term. The term $\mathbf{V} \cdot \mathbf{V}\mathbf{V}$ was not included in our list, but it may be *defined* by Eq. 1.80. If **V** is expanded in cartesian coordinates, so that the unit vectors are constant in direction as well as in magnitude, $\mathbf{V} \cdot \mathbf{V}\mathbf{V}$, a vector Laplacian, reduces to

$$\mathbf{V} \cdot \mathbf{V}\mathbf{V} = \mathbf{i}\mathbf{V} \cdot \mathbf{V} V_x + \mathbf{j}\mathbf{V} \cdot \mathbf{V} V_y + \mathbf{k}\mathbf{V} \cdot \mathbf{V} V_z,$$

a vector sum of ordinary scalar Laplacians. By expanding in cartesian coordinates, we may verify Eq. 1.80 as a vector identity.

One important application of this vector relation (Eq. 1.80), is in the derivation of the electromagnetic wave equation. In vacuum Maxwell's equations become

$$\mathbf{V} \cdot \mathbf{B} = 0, \tag{1.81a}$$

$$\mathbf{V} \cdot \mathbf{E} = 0, \tag{1.81b}$$

$$\mathbf{V} \times \mathbf{B} = \varepsilon_0 \mu_0 \frac{\partial \mathbf{E}}{\partial t}, \tag{1.81c}$$

$$\mathbf{V} \times \mathbf{E} = -\frac{\partial \mathbf{B}}{\partial t}. \tag{1.81d}$$

Here $\mathbf{E}$ is the electric field, $\mathbf{B}$, the magnetic inductance, and ε_0 and μ_0, the electric and magnetic permitivities (mks units). Suppose we eliminate $\mathbf{B}$ from Eqs. 1.81c and 1.81d. We may do this by taking the curl of both sides of Eq. 1.81d and the time derivative of both sides of Eq. 1.81c. Since the space and time derivatives commute,

$$\frac{\partial}{\partial t} \mathbf{V} \times \mathbf{B} = \mathbf{V} \times \frac{\partial \mathbf{B}}{\partial t}, \tag{1.82}$$

and we obtain

$$\mathbf{V} \times (\mathbf{V} \times \mathbf{E}) = -\varepsilon_0 \mu_0 \frac{\partial^2 \mathbf{E}}{\partial t^2}. \tag{1.83}$$

Application of Eqs. 1.80 and of 1.81b yields

$$\mathbf{V} \cdot \mathbf{V} \mathbf{E} = \varepsilon_0 \mu_0 \frac{\partial^2 \mathbf{E}}{\partial t^2}, \tag{1.84}$$

the electromagnetic vector wave equation. Again, if $\mathbf{E}$ is expressed in cartesian coordinates, Eq. 1.84 separates into three scalar wave equations, each involving a scalar Laplacian.

EXERCISES

1.9.1 Prove that $\mathbf{V} \times (\varphi \, \mathbf{V} \, \varphi) = 0$.

1.9.2 Prove that $(\nabla u) \times (\nabla v)$ is solenoidal where u and v are differentiable scalar functions.

1.9.3 φ is a scalar satisfying Laplace's equation, $\nabla^2 \varphi = 0$. Show that $\nabla \varphi$ is *both* solenoidal and irrotational.

1.9.4 Show that
$$\mathbf{C}_1 = \mathbf{V}\psi, \qquad \mathbf{C}_2 = \mathbf{V} \times \mathbf{a}\psi, \quad \text{and} \quad \mathbf{C}_3 = \mathbf{V} \times (\mathbf{V} \times \mathbf{a}\psi)$$
are solutions of the vector wave equation
$$\nabla^2 \mathbf{C} + k^2 \mathbf{C} = \mathbf{V}\mathbf{V} \cdot \mathbf{C} - \mathbf{V} \times \mathbf{V} \times \mathbf{C} + k^2 \mathbf{C} = 0,$$

where ψ satisfies the scalar wave equation

$$\nabla^2\psi + k^2\psi = 0$$

and $\mathbf{a}$ is a constant vector.

(b) Show that $\mathbf{C}_1$ and $\mathbf{C}_2$ are orthogonal, that $\mathbf{C}_1$ is irrotational, and that $\mathbf{C}_2$ and $\mathbf{C}_3$ are solenoidal.

1.9.5 Show that the identity

$$\nabla \times (\nabla \times \mathbf{V}) = \nabla\nabla \cdot \mathbf{V} - \nabla \cdot \nabla\mathbf{V}$$

follows from the BAC-CAB rule for a triple vector product. Justify any alteration of the order of factors in the BAC and CAB terms.

1.9.6 Show that any solution of the equation

$$\nabla \times \nabla \times \mathbf{A} - k^2\mathbf{A} = 0$$

automatically satisfies the vector Helmholtz equation

$$\nabla^2\mathbf{A} + k^2\mathbf{A} = 0$$

and the solenoidal condition

$$\nabla \cdot \mathbf{A} = 0.$$

1.9.7 A scalar potential u_{LM}, $u_{LM} = j_L(ka)\,Y_{LM}(\theta, \varphi)$ satisfies the scalar Helmholtz equation

$$\nabla^2 u_{LM} + k^2 u_{LM} = 0.$$

By using the angular momentum operator,

$$\mathbf{L} = -i(\mathbf{r} \times \nabla),$$

we may construct vector potentials by

$$\mathbf{A}_{LM}^E = -\frac{1}{k}\nabla \times \mathbf{L}u_{LM}$$

and

$$\mathbf{A}_{LM}^M = i\mathbf{L}u_{LM} .$$

Show that A_{LM}^M and A_{LM}^E satisfy

$$\nabla \times \nabla \times \mathbf{A} - k^2\mathbf{A} = 0.$$

1.9.8 The time-dependent Schrödinger wave equation is

$$[-\frac{\hbar^2}{2m}\nabla \cdot \nabla + V(\mathbf{r})]\psi(\mathbf{r}, t) = i\hbar\,\frac{\partial\psi}{\partial t} .$$

Let

$$\psi(\mathbf{r}, t) = A(\mathbf{r}, t)\,e^{\,iS(\mathbf{r},t)/\hbar}.$$

(a) Show that this leads to the two equations (separating real and imaginary parts)

$$\frac{\partial S}{\partial t} + \frac{(\nabla S)^2}{2m} + V = \frac{\hbar^2}{2m}\frac{\nabla^2 A}{A}$$

and

$$m\,\frac{\partial A}{\partial t} + (\nabla A) \cdot (\nabla S) + \frac{A}{2}\nabla^2 S = 0.$$

(b) In quantum mechanics the particle (probability) density ρ is identified with A^2 and the particle current $\mathbf{J}$ with $A^2\nabla S/m$. Show that the last equation of part (a) above is equivalent to the continuity equation

$$\nabla \cdot \mathbf{J} + \frac{\partial\rho}{\partial t} = 0.$$

1.9.9 With ψ a scalar function show that

$$(\mathbf{r} \times \nabla) \cdot (\mathbf{r} \times \nabla)\psi = r^2\,\nabla^2\psi - r^2\,\frac{\partial^2\psi}{\partial r^2} - 2r\,\frac{\partial\psi}{\partial r} .$$

1.10 Vector Integration

The next step after differentiating vectors is to integrate them. Let us start with line integrals and then proceed to surface and volume integrals. In each case the method of attack will be to reduce the vector integral to scalar integrals with which the reader is assumed familiar. Using an increment of length $d\mathbf{r}$, we may encounter the line integrals

$$\int_c \varphi \, d\mathbf{r}, \tag{1.85a}$$

$$\int_c \mathbf{V} \cdot d\mathbf{r}, \tag{1.85b}$$

$$\int_c \mathbf{V} \times d\mathbf{r}, \tag{1.85c}$$

in each of which the integral is over some contour C that may be open or closed. With φ, a scalar, the first integral reduces immediately to

$$\int_c \varphi \, d\mathbf{r} = \mathbf{i} \int_c \varphi(x, y, z) \, dx + \mathbf{j} \int_c \varphi(x, y, z) \, dy$$

$$+ \mathbf{k} \int_c \varphi(x, y, z) \, dz. \tag{1.86}$$

This separation has employed the relation

$$\int \mathbf{i}\varphi \, dx = \mathbf{i} \int \varphi \, dx, \tag{1.87}$$

which is permissible because the cartesian unit vectors $\mathbf{i}$, $\mathbf{j}$, and $\mathbf{k}$ are constant in both magnitude and direction. Perhaps this is obvious here, but it will not be true in the noncartesian systems encountered in Chapter 2.

The three integrals on the right side of Eq. 1.86 are ordinary scalar integrals and, to avoid complications, we shall assume that they are Riemann integrals. Note, however, that the integral with respect to x cannot be evaluated unless y and z are known in terms of x and similarly for the integrals with respect to y and z. This simply means that the path of integration C must be specified. Unless the integrand has special properties that lead the integral to depend only on the value of the end points, the value will depend on the particular choice of contour C. For instance, if we choose the very special case $\varphi = 1$, Eq. 1.85a is just the vector distance from the start of contour C to the end point, in this case independent of the choice of path connecting fixed end points. With $d\mathbf{r} = \mathbf{i} \, dx + \mathbf{j} \, dy + \mathbf{k} \, dz$, the second and third forms also reduce to scalar integrals and, like Eq. 1.85a, are dependent, in general, on the choice of path. The form (Eq. 1.85b) is exactly the same as that encountered when we calculate the work done with a force that varies along the path,

$$W = -\int \mathbf{F} \cdot d\mathbf{r}. \tag{1.88}$$

In this expression $\mathbf{F}$ is the force exerted on a particle or on an object to overcome the pre-existing force field, electrostatic, gravitational, and so on.

EXAMPLE 1.10.1

Integrate the scalar function $r^2 = x^2 + y^2$ from the origin to the point $(1, 1)$ using a directed length increment $d\mathbf{r}$; that is, evaluate

$$\int_{0,0}^{1,1} (x^2 + y^2)\, d\mathbf{r}$$

If we expand $d\mathbf{r}$, the integral becomes

$$\int_{0,0}^{1,1} (x^2 + y^2)(\mathbf{i}\, dx + \mathbf{j}\, dy) = \mathbf{i} \int_{0,0}^{1,1} (x^2 + y^2)\, dx + \mathbf{j} \int_{0,0}^{1,1} (x^2 + y^2)\, dy.$$

Let us choose the path shown in Fig. 1.17. This means that $y = 0$ in the first integral

FIG. 1.17

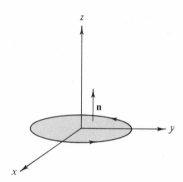

FIG. 1.18   Right-hand rule for the positive normal

and $x = 1$ in the second. By substituting into the integrals we get

$$\int_{0,0}^{1,1} (x^2 + y^2)\, d\mathbf{r} = \mathbf{i} \int_{0,y=0}^{1} (x^2 + y^2)\, dx + \mathbf{j} \int_{0,x=1}^{1} (x^2 + y^2)\, dy = \mathbf{i}\tfrac{1}{3} + \mathbf{j}\tfrac{4}{3}.$$

The reader may show that the path $(0, 0) \to (0, 1) \to (1, 1)$ yields $\mathbf{i}\tfrac{4}{3} + \mathbf{j}\tfrac{1}{3}$, whereas the path $x = y$ gives $\mathbf{i}\tfrac{2}{3} + \mathbf{j}\tfrac{2}{3}$. The value of the integral depends on the path chosen.

Surface integrals appear in the same forms as line integrals, the element of area also being a vector, $d\boldsymbol{\sigma}$.[1] Often this area element is written $\mathbf{n}\, dA$ in which $\mathbf{n}$ is a unit (normal) vector to indicate the positive direction. There are two conventions for choosing the positive direction. First, if the surface is a closed surface, we agree to take the outward normal as positive. Second, if the surface is an open surface, the positive normal depends on the direction in which the perimeter of the open surface is traversed. If the right-hand fingers are placed in the direction of travel around the perimeter, the positive normal is indicated by the thumb of the right hand. As an illustration, a circle in the xy-plane (Fig. 1.18) mapped out from x to y to $-x$ to $-y$ and back to x will have its positive normal parallel to the positive z-axis (for our right-handed coordinate system). If the reader ever encounters one-sided surfaces,

---

[1] Recall that in Section 1.4 the area (of a parallelogram) represented a cross-product *vector*.

such as Moebius strips, it is suggested that he either cut them and form reasonable, well-behaved surfaces or label them pathological and send them to the nearest mathematics department.

The surface integral $\int \mathbf{v} \cdot d\boldsymbol{\sigma}$ may be interpreted as a flow or flux through the given surface. This is really what we did in Section 1.7 to obtain the significance of the term divergence. This identification reappears in Section 1.11 as Gauss's theorem.

Volume integrals are somewhat simpler, for the volume element $d\tau$ is a scalar quantity. We have

$$\int_V \mathbf{V} \, d\tau = \mathbf{i} \int_V V_x \, d\tau + \mathbf{j} \int_V V_y \, d\tau + \mathbf{k} \int_V V_z \, d\tau, \qquad (1.89)$$

again reducing the vector integral to a vector sum of scalar integrals.

One interesting and significant application of our surface and volume integrals is their use in developing alternate definitions of our differential relations. We find

$$\nabla\varphi = \lim_{\int d\tau \to 0} \frac{\int \varphi \, d\boldsymbol{\sigma}}{\int d\tau}, \qquad (1.90)$$

$$\nabla \cdot \mathbf{V} = \lim_{\int d\tau \to 0} \frac{\int \mathbf{V} \cdot d\boldsymbol{\sigma}}{\int d\tau}, \qquad (1.91)$$

$$\nabla \times \mathbf{V} = \lim_{\int d\tau \to 0} \frac{\int d\boldsymbol{\sigma} \times \mathbf{V}}{\int d\tau}. \qquad (1.92)$$

In these three equations $\int d\tau$ is the volume of a small region of space and $d\boldsymbol{\sigma}$ is the vector area element of this volume. The identification of Eq. 1.91 as the divergence of V was carried out in Section 1.7. Here we show that Eq. 1.90 is consistent with our earlier definition of $\nabla\varphi$ (Eq. 1.53). For simplicity we choose $\int d\tau$ to be the differential volume $dx \, dy \, dz$ (Fig. 1.13). This time we place the origin at the geometric center of our volume element. The area integral leads to six integrals, one

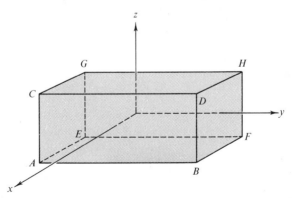

FIG. 1.19 Differential rectangular parallelepiped (origin at center)

for each of the six faces. Remembering that $d\boldsymbol{\sigma}$ is outward, $d\boldsymbol{\sigma} \cdot \mathbf{i} = -|d\boldsymbol{\sigma}|$ for surface $EFGH$, and $+|d\boldsymbol{\sigma}|$ for surface $ABCD$, we have

$$\int \varphi \, d\boldsymbol{\sigma} = -\mathbf{i} \int_{EFHG} \left(\varphi - \frac{\partial \varphi}{\partial x} \frac{dx}{2}\right) dy \, dz + \mathbf{i} \int_{ABDC} \left(\varphi + \frac{\partial \varphi}{\partial x} \frac{dx}{2}\right) dy \, dz$$

$$-\mathbf{j} \int_{AEGC} \left(\varphi - \frac{\partial \varphi}{\partial y} \frac{dy}{2}\right) dx \, dz + \mathbf{j} \int_{BFHD} \left(\varphi + \frac{\partial \varphi}{\partial y} \frac{dy}{2}\right) dx \, dz$$

$$-\mathbf{k} \int_{ABFE} \left(\varphi - \frac{\partial \varphi}{\partial z} \frac{dz}{2}\right) dx \, dy + \mathbf{k} \int_{CDHG} \left(\varphi + \frac{\partial \varphi}{\partial z} \frac{dz}{2}\right) dx \, dy.$$

Each integrand is evaluated at the origin with a correction included to correct for the displacement of the center of the face from the origin. Having chosen the total volume to be of differential size ($\int d\tau = dx \, dy \, dz$), we drop the integral signs on the right and obtain

$$\int \varphi \, d\boldsymbol{\sigma} = \left(\mathbf{i} \frac{\partial \varphi}{\partial x} + \mathbf{j} \frac{\partial \varphi}{\partial y} + \mathbf{k} \frac{\partial \varphi}{\partial z}\right) dx \, dy \, dz. \qquad (1.93)$$

Dividing by

$$\int d\tau = dx \, dy \, dz,$$

Eq. 1.90 is verified.

This verification has been oversimplified in ignoring other correction terms beyond the first derivatives. These additional terms, which are introduced in Section 5.6 when the Taylor expansion is developed, vanish in the limit

$$\int d\tau \to 0 \; (dx \to 0, \, dy \to 0, \, dz \to 0).$$

This, of course, is the reason for specifying in Eqs. 1.90, 1.91, and 1.92 that this limit be taken.

Verification of Eq. 1.92 follows these same lines exactly, using a differential volume $dx \, dy \, dz$.

EXERCISES

1.10.1   The force field acting on a two-dimensional linear oscillator may be described by

$$\mathbf{F} = -\mathbf{i}kx - \mathbf{j}ky.$$

Compare the work done moving against this force field when going from (1, 1) to (4, 4) by the following straight-line paths:
(a) $(1, 1) \to (4, 1) \to (4, 4)$
(b) $(1, 1) \to (1, 4) \to (4, 4)$
(c) $(1, 1) \to (4, 4)$ along $x = y$.
This means evaluating

$$-\int_{(1,1)}^{(4,4)} \mathbf{F} \cdot d\mathbf{r}$$

along each path.

1.10.2 Find the work done going around a unit circle in the xy-plane:
(a) counterclockwise from 0 to π,
(b) clockwise from 0 to $-\pi$,
doing work *against* a force field given by

$$\mathbf{F} = \frac{-\mathbf{i}y}{x^2 + y^2} + \frac{\mathbf{j}x}{x^2 + y^2}.$$

Note that the work done depends on the path.

1.10.3 Evaluate

$$\frac{1}{3} \int_s \mathbf{r} \cdot d\boldsymbol{\sigma}$$

over the unit cube defined by the point $(0, 0)$ and the unit intercepts on the positive x-, y-, and z-axes. Note that (a) $\mathbf{r} \cdot d\boldsymbol{\sigma}$ is zero for three of the surfaces and (b) each of the three remaining surfaces contributes the same amount to the integral.

1.10.4 Show, by expansion of the surface integral, that

$$\lim_{\int d\tau \to 0} \frac{\int_s d\boldsymbol{\sigma} \times \mathbf{V}}{\int d\tau} = \boldsymbol{\nabla} \times \mathbf{V}.$$

Hint. Choose the volume to be a differential volume, $dx\, dy\, dz$.

1.10.5 Calculate the work you do in going from point $(1, 1)$ to point $(3, 3)$. The force *you exert* is given by
$$\mathbf{F} = \mathbf{i}(x - y) + \mathbf{j}(x + y).$$

Specify clearly the path you choose. Note that this force field is nonconservative.

1.11 Gauss's Theorem

Here we verify a useful relation between a surface integral of a vector and the volume integral of a derivative of the vector. Let us assume that the vector $\mathbf{V}$ and $\boldsymbol{\nabla} \cdot \mathbf{V}$ are continuous over the region of interest. Then Gauss's theorem states that

$$\int_S \mathbf{V} \cdot d\boldsymbol{\sigma} = \int_V \boldsymbol{\nabla} \cdot \mathbf{V}\, d\tau. \tag{1.94}$$

We have seen (Eq. 1.61) that $\boldsymbol{\nabla} \cdot \mathbf{V}$ may be interpreted as a net outflow of fluid per unit volume. Hence the right-hand side of Eq. 1.94 is the total rate of flow of fluid out of the volume over which we are integrating. Recognizing that the left side is also just a description of the flow out through the surface enclosing our volume, Gauss's theorem is proved.

For a detailed, rigorous proof along mathematical rather than physical lines the reader should consult Kellogg's *Foundations of Potential Theory* or some of the other references listed.

A frequently useful corollary of Gauss's theorem is a relation known as Green's theorem. If u and v are two scalar functions, we have the identities

$$\boldsymbol{\nabla} \cdot (u \, \boldsymbol{\nabla} v) = u \, \boldsymbol{\nabla} \cdot \boldsymbol{\nabla} v + (\boldsymbol{\nabla} u) \cdot (\boldsymbol{\nabla} v), \tag{1.95}$$

$$\boldsymbol{\nabla} \cdot (v \, \boldsymbol{\nabla} u) = v \, \boldsymbol{\nabla} \cdot \boldsymbol{\nabla} u + (\boldsymbol{\nabla} v) \cdot (\boldsymbol{\nabla} u). \tag{1.96}$$

Subtracting Eq. 1.96 from Eq. 1.95, integrating over a volume (u, v, and their derivatives, assumed continuous), and applying Eq. 1.94 (Gauss's theorem), we obtain

$$\int_V (u\, \mathbf{V} \cdot \mathbf{V}v - v\, \mathbf{V} \cdot \mathbf{V}u)\, d\tau = \int_S (u\, \mathbf{V}v - v\, \mathbf{V}u) \cdot d\boldsymbol{\sigma}. \qquad (1.97)$$

This is Green's theorem. We use it in Section 1.15 and in later chapters. An alternate form derived from Eq. 1.95 alone is

$$\int_S u\, \mathbf{V}v \cdot d\boldsymbol{\sigma} = \int_V u\, \mathbf{V} \cdot \mathbf{V}v\, d\tau + \int_V \mathbf{V}u \cdot \mathbf{V}v\, d\tau. \qquad (1.98)$$

Although Eq. 1.94 involving the divergence is by far the most important form of Gauss's theorem, volume integrals involving the gradient and the curl may also appear. Suppose

$$\mathbf{V}(x, y, z) = V(x, y, z)\mathbf{a}, \qquad (1.99)$$

in which $\mathbf{a}$ is a vector with constant magnitude and constant but arbitrary direction. (You pick the direction, but once you have chosen it, hold it fixed.)

Equation 1.94 becomes

$$\mathbf{a} \cdot \int_S V\, d\boldsymbol{\sigma} = \int_V \mathbf{V} \cdot \mathbf{a}V\, d\tau$$

$$= \mathbf{a} \cdot \int_V \mathbf{V}V\, d\tau \qquad (1.100)$$

by Eq. 1.62a. This may be rewritten

$$\mathbf{a} \cdot \left[\int_S V\, d\boldsymbol{\sigma} - \int_V \mathbf{V}V\, d\tau \right] = 0. \qquad (1.101)$$

Since $|\mathbf{a}| \neq 0$ and its direction is arbitrary, meaning that the cosine of the included angle cannot *always* vanish, the term in brackets must be zero. The result is

$$\int_S V\, d\boldsymbol{\sigma} = \int_V \mathbf{V}V\, d\tau. \qquad (1.102)$$

In a similar manner, using $\mathbf{V} = \mathbf{a} \times \mathbf{P}$ in which $\mathbf{a}$ is a constant vector, we may show

$$\int_S d\boldsymbol{\sigma} \times \mathbf{P} = \int_V \mathbf{V} \times \mathbf{P}\, d\tau. \qquad (1.103)$$

EXERCISES

1.11.1 Prove Gauss's theorem in the form

$$\int_S d\boldsymbol{\sigma} \times \mathbf{P} = \int_V \mathbf{V} \times \mathbf{P}\, d\tau.$$

1.11.2 Prove that

$$\int_S d\boldsymbol{\sigma} = 0,$$

if S is a closed surface.

1.11.3 Show that

$$\frac{1}{3} \int_S \mathbf{r} \cdot d\boldsymbol{\sigma} = V,$$

where V is the volume enclosed by the closed surface S.

1.11.4 If $\mathbf{B} = \nabla \times \mathbf{A}$, show that

$$\int_S \mathbf{B} \cdot d\boldsymbol{\sigma} = 0$$

for any closed surface S.

1.12 Stokes's Theorem

Gauss's theorem relates the volume integral of a derivative of a function to an integral of the function over the closed surface bounding the volume. Here we consider an analogous relation between the surface integral of a derivative of a function and the line integral of the function, the path of integration being the perimeter bounding the surface. Let us start with a surface integral of a curl and transform it.

$$\int_S \nabla \times \mathbf{V} \cdot d\boldsymbol{\sigma} = \int_S \left(\frac{\partial V_x}{\partial z} \, d\sigma_y - \frac{\partial V_x}{\partial y} \, d\sigma_z \right.$$

$$+ \frac{\partial V_y}{\partial x} \, d\sigma_z - \frac{\partial V_y}{\partial z} \, d\sigma_x \qquad (1.104)$$

$$\left. + \frac{\partial V_z}{\partial y} \, d\sigma_x - \frac{\partial V_z}{\partial x} \, d\sigma_y \right),$$

expanding the integrand as a triple scalar product. The integration is over some given surface. Let us orient our cartesian coordinate axes so that this surface intersects the plane $x = c$, a constant, along the line AB as shown in Fig. 1.20.

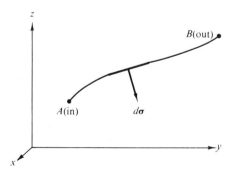

FIG. 1.20 Intersection of surface S with plane $x = c$

With the perimeter of the surface described by a line going through the $x = c$-plane in the negative direction at A and in the positive direction at B, $d\boldsymbol{\sigma}$ will be down as shown.

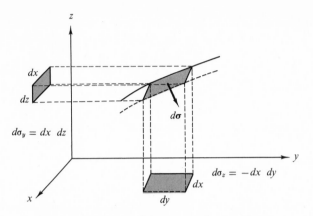

FIG. 1.21   Projection of $d\boldsymbol{\sigma}$ on xy and on xz planes

In particular,

$$d\sigma_y = dx\, dz,$$
$$d\sigma_z = -dx\, dy. \tag{1.105}$$

The increment dx enters when we consider the strip of surface intercepted between the planes $x = c$ and $x = c + dx$. Integrating the derivatives of V_x over this strip, we obtain

$$\int_S \left(\frac{\partial V_x}{\partial z}\, d\sigma_y - \frac{\partial V_x}{\partial y}\, d\sigma_z \right) = \int_S \left(\frac{\partial V_x}{\partial y}\, dy + \frac{\partial V_x}{\partial z}\, dz \right) dx. \tag{1.106}$$

Since x is held constant in the integration from A to B,

$$\frac{\partial V_x}{\partial y}\, dy + \frac{\partial V_x}{\partial z}\, dz = dV_x \tag{1.107}$$

and our surface integral becomes

$$\int dx \int_A^B dV_x = \int V_x(x, y_B, z_B)\, dx - \int V_x(x, y_A, z_A)\, dx. \tag{1.107a}$$

Our choice of direction in describing the perimeter leads to

$$dx = d\lambda_x \quad \text{at } B, \qquad \text{right side of perimeter,}$$
$$dx = -d\lambda_x \quad \text{at } A, \qquad \text{left side of parameter,}$$

where $d\boldsymbol{\lambda}$ is a vector differential length along the perimeter. Finally, letting x range far enough to cover the entire surface,

$$\int_S \left(\frac{\partial V_x}{\partial z}\, d\sigma_y - \frac{\partial V_x}{\partial y}\, d\sigma_z \right) = \oint V_x\, d\lambda_x. \tag{1.108}$$

The symbol $\oint$ indicates an integral around a closed path, in this case, the periphery of the surface. Either by cyclic permutation of the coordinates or by repeating the integration (derivatives of V_y and a plane $y = c$, etc.) we obtain similar results for the derivatives of V_y and of V_z. Adding

$$\int \mathbf{\nabla} \times \mathbf{V} \cdot d\mathbf{\sigma} = \oint (V_x \, d\lambda_x + V_y \, d\lambda_y + V_z \, d\lambda_z)$$

$$= \oint \mathbf{V} \cdot d\mathbf{\lambda}. \tag{1.109}$$

This is Stokes's theorem. Again, the reader who desires greater mathematical rigor is referred to Kellogg's *Foundations of Potential Theory*.

As with Gauss's theorem, other relations between surface and line integrals are possible. We find

$$\int_S d\mathbf{\sigma} \times \mathbf{\nabla}\varphi = \oint \varphi \, d\mathbf{\lambda} \tag{1.110}$$

and

$$\int_S (d\mathbf{\sigma} \times \mathbf{\nabla}) \times \mathbf{P} = \oint d\mathbf{\lambda} \times \mathbf{P}. \tag{1.111}$$

Equation 1.110 may readily be verified by the substitution $\mathbf{V} = \mathbf{a}\varphi$ in which $\mathbf{a}$ is a vector of constant magnitude and of constant direction, as in Section 1.11. Substituting into Stokes's theorem, Eq. 1.109,

$$\int_S (\mathbf{\nabla} \times \mathbf{a}\varphi) \cdot d\mathbf{\sigma} = - \int_S \mathbf{a} \times \mathbf{\nabla}\varphi \cdot d\mathbf{\sigma}$$

$$= -\mathbf{a} \cdot \int_S \mathbf{\nabla}\varphi \times d\mathbf{\sigma}. \tag{1.112}$$

For the line integral

$$\oint \mathbf{a}\varphi \cdot d\mathbf{\lambda} = \mathbf{a} \cdot \oint \varphi \, d\mathbf{\lambda}, \tag{1.113}$$

and we obtain

$$\mathbf{a} \cdot \left(\oint \varphi \, d\mathbf{\lambda} + \int_S \mathbf{\nabla}\varphi \times d\mathbf{\sigma} \right) = 0. \tag{1.114}$$

Since the choice of direction of $\mathbf{a}$ is arbitrary, the expression in parentheses must vanish, thus verifying Eq. 1.110. Equation 1.111 may be derived in a similar manner by using $\mathbf{V} = \mathbf{a} \times \mathbf{P}$, in which $\mathbf{a}$ is again a constant vector.

Returning to Eq. 1.109, $\oint \mathbf{V} \cdot d\mathbf{\lambda}$ may be interpreted as a flow of fluid, a circulation around a loop. If we take our surface to be a circle of area $\mathbf{k} \, d\sigma$,

$$|\mathbf{\nabla} \times \mathbf{V}| \, d\sigma = \text{circulation around } d\sigma \text{ in } xy\text{-plane}.$$

This is the basis for measuring the curl of $\mathbf{V}$ by the rotation of a tiny paddlewheel. If the little paddlewheel does not rotate, the circulation is zero and $\mathbf{V}$, by Stokes's theorem, is irrotational. This circulation concept is the basis for the usual proof of Stokes's theorem. The original surface is divided into differential surface elements. Circulation currents along interior lines cancel and we are left with a circulation around the perimeter of the original surface.

The main application of Stokes's theorem is in potential theory, the subject of the next section.

EXERCISES

1.12.1   Prove Stokes's theorem in the form

$$\int_S (d\boldsymbol{\sigma} \times \nabla) \times \mathbf{P} = \oint d\boldsymbol{\lambda} \times \mathbf{P}.$$

1.12.2   A vector $\mathbf{t} = -\mathbf{i}y + \mathbf{j}x$. With the help of Stokes's theorem, show that the integral around a continuous closed curve in the xy-plane

$$\tfrac{1}{2} \oint \mathbf{t} \cdot d\boldsymbol{\lambda} = \tfrac{1}{2} \oint (x \, dy - y \, dx) = A,$$

the area enclosed by the curve.

1.12.3   Integrating around the perimeter of a surface in the xy-plane, show that the scalar magnitude of

$$\oint \mathbf{r} \times d\mathbf{r}$$

is twice the area of the surface.

1.12.4   Prove that

$$\int_S \nabla \times \mathbf{V} \cdot d\boldsymbol{\sigma} = 0,$$

if S is a closed surface.

1.12.5   Prove that

$$\oint u \, \nabla v \cdot d\boldsymbol{\lambda} = - \oint v \, \nabla u \cdot d\boldsymbol{\lambda}.$$

1.12.6   Prove that

$$\oint u \, \nabla v \cdot d\boldsymbol{\lambda} = \int_S (\nabla u) \times (\nabla v) \cdot d\boldsymbol{\sigma}.$$

1.12.7   Find the fallacy in the following derivation.[1]

$$\nabla \cdot \mathbf{B} = 0. \tag{1}$$

Maxwell's equation.

$$\int \nabla \cdot \mathbf{B} \, d\tau = \int \mathbf{B} \cdot d\boldsymbol{\sigma} = 0. \tag{2}$$

Gauss's theorem and Eq. 1.

$$\mathbf{B} = \nabla \times \mathbf{A}. \tag{3}$$

A solenoidal vector (**B**) may be expressed as the curl of some vector (vector potential).

$$\int \mathbf{B} \cdot d\boldsymbol{\sigma} = \int \nabla \times \mathbf{A} \cdot d\boldsymbol{\sigma} = 0. \tag{4}$$

Substitution of Eq. 3 into Eq. 2,

$$\int \nabla \times \mathbf{A} \cdot d\boldsymbol{\sigma} = \oint \mathbf{A} \cdot d\boldsymbol{\lambda}. \tag{5}$$

Stokes's theorem.

$$\mathbf{A} = \nabla \varphi. \tag{6}$$

Equations 5 and 6 are equivalent conditions for a conservative field.

$$\mathbf{B} = \nabla \times \mathbf{A} = \nabla \times \nabla \varphi = 0.$$

The curl of a gradient vanishes. Therefore all magnetic fields (**B**) vanish. (Magnetic fields are not real.)

[1] *Am. J. Phys.* **27**, 526 (1959).

1.13 Potential Theory

Scalar potential. If a force over a given region of space S can be expressed as the negative gradient of a scalar function φ,

$$F = -\nabla\varphi, \tag{1.115}$$

we will call φ a scalar potential. The force $\mathbf{F}$ appearing as the negative gradient of a single-valued scalar potential is labeled a *conservative* force. We want to know when a scalar potential function exists. To answer this question, we establish two other relations as equivalent to Eq. 1.115. These are

$$\nabla \times \mathbf{F} = 0 \tag{1.116}$$

and

$$\oint \mathbf{F} \cdot d\mathbf{r} = 0, \tag{1.117}$$

for every closed path in our region S. We proceed to show that each of these three equations implies the other two.

Let us start with

$$\mathbf{F} = -\nabla\varphi. \tag{1.118}$$

Then

$$\nabla \times \mathbf{F} = -\nabla \times \nabla\varphi = 0$$

by Eq. 1.77 or Eq. 1.115 implies Eq. 1.116. Turning to the line integral,

$$\oint \mathbf{F} \cdot d\mathbf{r} = -\oint \nabla\varphi \cdot d\mathbf{r}$$

$$= -\oint d\varphi, \tag{1.119}$$

using Eq. 1.56. Now $d\varphi$ integrates to give φ. Since we have specified a closed loop, the end points coincide and we get zero for every closed path in our region S for which Eq. 1.116 holds. It is important to note the restriction here that the potential be single-valued and that Eq. 1.115 hold for *all* points in S. This problem may arise in using a scalar magnetic potential, a perfectly valid procedure as long as no net current is encircled. As soon as we choose a path in space that encircles a net current, the scalar magnetic potential ceases to be single-valued and our analysis no longer applies.

Continuing this demonstration of equivalence, let us assume that Eq. 1.117 holds. If $\oint \mathbf{F} \cdot d\mathbf{r} = 0$ for all paths in S, we see that the value of the integral joining two distinct points A and B is independent of the path. Our premise is that

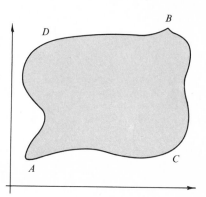

FIG. 1.22 Possible paths for doing work

$$\oint_{ACBDA} \mathbf{F} \cdot d\mathbf{r} = 0.$$

Therefore

$$\int_{ACB} \mathbf{F} \cdot d\mathbf{r} = -\int_{BDA} \mathbf{F} \cdot d\mathbf{r} = \int_{ADB} \mathbf{F} \cdot d\mathbf{r}, \qquad (1.120)$$

reversing the sign by reversing the direction of integration. Physically, this means that the work done in going from A to B is independent of the path and that the work done in going around a closed path is zero. This is the reason for labeling such a force conservative: energy is conserved.

With the result shown in Eq. 1.20, we have the work done dependent only on the end points, A and B. That is

$$\int_A^B \mathbf{F} \cdot d\mathbf{r} = \varphi(A) - \varphi(B). \qquad (1.121)$$

The choice of sign on the right-hand side is arbitrary. The choice here is made to achieve agreement with Eq. 1.115 and to ensure that water will run downhill rather than uphill. For points A and B separated by a length $d\mathbf{r}$, Eq. 1.121 becomes

$$\mathbf{F} \cdot d\mathbf{r} = -d\varphi$$
$$= -\nabla\varphi \cdot d\mathbf{r} \qquad (1.122)$$

This may be rewritten

$$(\mathbf{F} + \nabla\varphi) \cdot d\mathbf{r} = 0, \qquad (1.123)$$

and since $d\mathbf{r}$ is arbitrary, Eq. 1.115 must follow. If

$$\oint \mathbf{F} \cdot d\mathbf{r} = 0,$$

we may obtain Eq. 1.116 by using Stokes's theorem (Eq. 1.109).

$$\oint \mathbf{F} \cdot d\mathbf{r} = \int \nabla \times \mathbf{F} \cdot d\boldsymbol{\sigma}. \qquad (1.124)$$

If we take the path of integration to be the perimeter of a differential area $d\boldsymbol{\sigma}$, the integrand in the surface integral must vanish. Hence Eq. 1.117 implies Eq. 1.116.

Finally, if $\nabla \times \mathbf{F} = 0$, we need only reverse our statement of Stokes's theorem (Eq. 1.124) to derive Eq. 1.117. Then, by Eqs. 1.121 to 1.123 our initial statement $\mathbf{F} = -\nabla\varphi$ is derived. The equivalence is demonstrated.

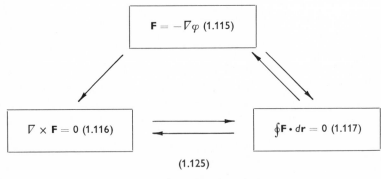

(1.125)

FIG. 1.23 Equivalent formulations

To summarize, a single-valued scalar potential function φ exists if and only if $\mathbf{F}$ is irrotational or the work done around every closed loop is zero. The gravitational and electrostatic force fields given by Eq. 1.75 are irrotational and therefore conservative. Gravitational and electrostatic scalar potentials exist.

EXAMPLE 1.13.1

Find the scalar potential for the gravitational force on a unit mass m_1,

$$\mathbf{F}_G = -\frac{Gm_1m_2\mathbf{r}_0}{r^2} = -\frac{k\mathbf{r}_0}{r^2}, \qquad \text{radially } inward.$$

By integrating Eq. 1.115 from infinity into position $\mathbf{r}$ we obtain

$$\varphi_G(r) - \varphi_G(\infty) = -\int_\infty^r \mathbf{F}_G \cdot d\mathbf{r} = +\int_r^\infty \mathbf{F}_G \cdot d\mathbf{r}. \qquad (1.125)$$

By use of $\mathbf{F}_G = -\mathbf{F}_{\text{applied}}$, a comparison with Eq. 1.88 shows that the potential is the work done in bringing our unit mass in from infinity. (We can define only potential difference. Here we arbitrarily assign infinity to be a zero of potential.) The integral on the right-hand side of Eq. 1.125 is negative, meaning that $\varphi_G(r)$ is negative. Since $\mathbf{F}_G$ is radial, we obtain a contribution to φ only when $d\mathbf{r}$ is radial or

$$\varphi_G(r) = \int_r^\infty -\frac{k\,dr}{r^2} = -\frac{k}{r}$$

$$= -\frac{Gm_1m_2}{r}.$$

The final negative sign is a consequence of the attractive force of gravity.

EXAMPLE 1.13.2

Calculate the scalar potential for the *centrifugal* force per unit mass, $\mathbf{F}_C = \omega^2 r\mathbf{r}_0$, radially *outward*. Physically, this might be you on a large horizontal spinning disk at an amusement park. Proceeding as in Example 1.13.1, but integrating from the origin outward and taking $\varphi_C(0) = 0$,

$$\varphi_C(r) = -\int_0^r \mathbf{F}_C \cdot d\mathbf{r} = -\frac{\omega^2 r^2}{2}.$$

If we reverse signs, taking $\mathbf{F}_{\text{SHO}} = -k\mathbf{r}$, we obtain $\varphi_{\text{SHO}} = \frac{1}{2}kr^2$, the simple harmonic oscillator potential.

The gravitational, centrifugal, and simple harmonic oscillator potentials are shown in Fig. 1.24. Clearly the simple harmonic oscillator yields stability and describes a restoring force. The centrifugal potential describes an unstable situation.

In thermodynamics, which is sometimes called a search for exact differentials, we encounter equations of the form

$$df = P(x, y)\,dx + Q(x, y)\,dy. \qquad (1.126)$$

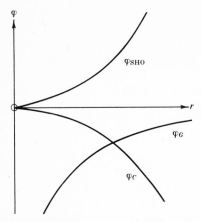

FIG. 1.24   Potential energy versus distance (gravitational, centrifugal, and simple harmonic oscillator)

The usual problem is to determine whether $\int (P(x, y)\, dx + Q(x, y)\, dy)$ depends only on the end points, that is, whether df is indeed an exact differential. The necessary and sufficient condition is that

$$df = \frac{\partial f}{\partial x}\, dx + \frac{\partial f}{\partial y}\, dy \qquad (1.126a)$$

or that

$$P(x, y) = \frac{\partial f}{\partial x},$$

$$Q(x, y) = \frac{\partial f}{\partial y}. \qquad (1.126b)$$

Equations 1.126b depend on the relation

$$\frac{\partial P(x, y)}{\partial y} = \frac{\partial Q(x, y)}{\partial x} \qquad (1.126c)$$

being satisfied. This, however, is exactly analogous to Eq. 1.116, the requirement that **F** be irrotational. Indeed the z-component of Eq. 1.116 yields

$$\frac{\partial F_x}{\partial y} = \frac{\partial F_y}{\partial x}, \qquad (1.126d)$$

Vector potential.   In some branches of physics, especially electromagnetic theory, it is convenient to introduce a vector potential **A**, such that a (force) field **B** is given by

$$\mathbf{B} = \mathbf{V} \times \mathbf{A}. \qquad (1.127)$$

Clearly, if Eq. 1.127 holds, $\mathbf{V} \cdot \mathbf{B} = 0$ by Eq. 1.79 and **B** is solenoidal. Here we want to develop a converse, to show that when **B** is solenoidal a vector potential **A** exists. We demonstrate the existence of **A** by actually calculating it. Suppose $\mathbf{B} = \mathbf{i}b_1 + \mathbf{j}b_2 + \mathbf{k}b_3$ and our unknown $\mathbf{A} = \mathbf{i}a_1 + \mathbf{j}a_2 + \mathbf{k}a_3$. By Eq. 1.127

$$\frac{\partial a_3}{\partial y} - \frac{\partial a_2}{\partial z} = b_1, \qquad (1.128a)$$

$$\frac{\partial a_1}{\partial z} - \frac{\partial a_3}{\partial x} = b_2,$$ (1.128b)

$$\frac{\partial a_2}{\partial x} - \frac{\partial a_1}{\partial y} = b_3.$$ (1.128c)

Let us assume that the coordinates have been chosen so that $\mathbf{A}$ is parallel to the yz-plane, that is, $a_1 = 0$. Then

$$b_2 = -\frac{\partial a_3}{\partial z}$$

$$b_3 = \frac{\partial a_2}{\partial x}.$$ (1.129)

Integrating,

$$a_2 = \int_{x_0}^{x} b_3 \, dx + f_2(y, \, z),$$

$$a_3 = -\int_{x_0}^{x} b_2 \, dx + f_3(y, z),$$ (1.130)

where f_2 and f_3 are arbitrary functions of y and z but are *not* functions of x. Equation 1.128a becomes

$$\frac{\partial a_3}{\partial y} - \frac{\partial a_2}{\partial z} = -\int_{x_0}^{x} \left(\frac{\partial b_2}{\partial y} + \frac{\partial b_3}{\partial z} \right) dx + \frac{\partial f_3}{\partial y} - \frac{\partial f_2}{\partial z}$$

$$= \int_{x_0}^{x} \frac{\partial b_1}{\partial x} \, dx + \frac{\partial f_3}{\partial y} - \frac{\partial f_2}{\partial z},$$ (1.131)

using $\mathbf{V} \cdot \mathbf{B} = 0$. Integrating with respect to x, we obtain

$$\frac{\partial a_3}{\partial y} - \frac{\partial a_2}{\partial z} = b_1(x, y, z) - b_1(x_0, y, z) + \frac{\partial f_3}{\partial y} - \frac{\partial f_2}{\partial z}.$$ (1.132)

Remembering that f_3 and f_2 are arbitrary functions of y and z, we choose

$$f_2 = 0,$$

$$f_3 = \int_{y_0}^{y} b_1(x_0, y, z) \, dy,$$ (1.133)

so that the right-hand side of Eq. 1.132 reduces to $b_1(x, y, z)$ in agreement with Equation 1.128a. With f_2 and f_3 given by Eq. 1.133, we can construct $\mathbf{A}$.

$$\mathbf{A} = \mathbf{j} \int_{x_0}^{x} b_3(x, y, z) \, dx$$

$$+ \mathbf{k} \left[\int_{y_0}^{y} b_1(x_0, y, z) \, dy - \int_{x_0}^{x} b_2(x, y, z) \, dx \right].$$ (1.134)

This is not quite complete. We may add any constant, since $\mathbf{B}$ is a derivative of $\mathbf{A}$. What is much more important, we may add any gradient of a scalar function $\mathbf{V}\varphi$

without affecting **B** at all. Finally, the functions f_2 and f_3 are not unique. Other choices could have been made. It will be seen in Section 1.15 that we may still specify $\mathbf{V} \cdot \mathbf{A}$.

EXAMPLE 1.13.3

   To illustrate the construction of a magnetic vector potential, we take the special but still important case of a constant magnetic inductance

$$\mathbf{B} = \mathbf{k}B_z, \qquad (1.135)$$

in which B_z is a constant. Equation 1.128 becomes

$$\frac{\partial a_3}{\partial y} - \frac{\partial a_2}{\partial z} = 0,$$

$$\frac{\partial a_1}{\partial z} - \frac{\partial a_3}{\partial x} = 0, \qquad (1.136)$$

$$\frac{\partial a_2}{\partial x} - \frac{\partial a_1}{\partial y} = B_z.$$

If we assume that $a_1 = 0$, as before, then by Eq. 1.134

$$\mathbf{A} = \mathbf{j} \int^x B_z \, dx$$

$$= \mathbf{j} x B_z, \qquad (1.137)$$

setting a constant of integration equal to zero. It can readily be seen that this **A** satisfies Eq. 1.127.

   To show that the choice $a_1 = 0$ was not sacred or at least not required, let us try setting $a_3 = 0$. From Eq. 1.136

$$\frac{\partial a_2}{\partial z} = 0, \qquad (1.138a)$$

$$\frac{\partial a_1}{\partial z} = 0, \qquad (1.138b)$$

$$\frac{\partial a_2}{\partial x} - \frac{\partial a_1}{\partial y} = B_z. \qquad (1.138c)$$

We see a_1 and a_2 are independent of z or

$$a_1 = a_1(x, y), \qquad a_2 = a_2(x, y). \qquad (1.139)$$

Equation 1.138c is satisfied if we take

$$a_2 = p \int^x B_2 \, dx = pxB_z \qquad (1.140)$$

and

$$a_1 = (p - 1) \int^y B_z \, dy = (p - 1)yB_z, \qquad (1.141)$$

with p any constant. Then

$$\mathbf{A} = \mathbf{i}(p-1)yB_z + \mathbf{j}pxB_z. \tag{1.142}$$

Again, Eqs. 1.127, 1.135, and 1.142 are seen to be consistent. Comparison of Eqs. 1.137 and 1.142 shows immediately that $\mathbf{A}$ is not unique. The difference between Eqs. 1.137 and 1.142 and the appearance of the parameter p in Eq. 1.142 may be accounted for by rewriting Eq. 1.142 as

$$\mathbf{A} = \tfrac{1}{2}(\mathbf{i}y - \mathbf{j}x)B_z$$

$$+ (p - \tfrac{1}{2})(\mathbf{i}y + \mathbf{j}x)B_z \tag{1.143}$$

with[1]

$$= -\tfrac{1}{2}(\mathbf{i}y - \mathbf{j}x)B_z + (p - \tfrac{1}{2})B_z\,\nabla\varphi$$

$$\varphi = xy. \tag{1.144}$$

The first term in $\mathbf{A}$ corresponds to the usual form

$$\mathbf{A} = \tfrac{1}{2}(\mathbf{B} \times \mathbf{r}) \tag{1.145}$$

for $\mathbf{B}$, a constant.

In many problems the magnetic vector potential $\mathbf{A}$ will be obtained from the current distribution that produces the magnetic inductance $\mathbf{B}$. This means solving Poisson's (vector) equation (cf. Exercise 1.14.1).

EXERCISES

1.13.1 Determine which of the following forces are derived from potentials and describe the physical nature of the force fields. Set up the potential in cases in which this can be done. *Caution.* Watch the behavior of $\mathbf{F}$ at the origin.

(a) $\mathbf{F} = \mathbf{i}\dfrac{-y}{x^2 + y^2} + \mathbf{j}\dfrac{x}{x^2 + y^2}$.

(b) $\mathbf{F} = \mathbf{i}\dfrac{y}{r} - \mathbf{j}\dfrac{x}{r}$.

(c) $\mathbf{F} = \mathbf{i}x\,f(r) + \mathbf{j}y\,f(r) + \mathbf{k}z\,f(r)$.

(d) $\mathbf{F} = \mathbf{i}\,f_1(x) + \mathbf{j}f_2(y) + \mathbf{k}\,f_3(z)$ $\qquad f(r), f_1(x), f_2(y), f_3(z)$ all arbitrary.

1.13.2 If

$$\mathbf{B} = \frac{\mathbf{r_0}}{r^2} = \left(\frac{x}{r^3}, \frac{y}{r^3}, \frac{z}{r^3}\right),$$

find a vector $\mathbf{A}$ such that $\nabla \times \mathbf{A} = \mathbf{B}$. One possible solution is

$$\mathbf{A} = \frac{\mathbf{i}yz}{r(x^2 + y^2)} - \frac{\mathbf{j}xz}{r(x^2 + y^2)}.$$

[1] $\varphi(x, y) = xy$ is clearly not a scalar function in the sense that the term was used in Section 1.3; that is, xy is not invariant to rotations about the z-axis. If such invariance is demanded, the parameter p must be set equal to $\tfrac{1}{2}$.

1.13.3 A sphere of radius a is uniformly charged (throughout its volume). Construct the electrostatic potential $\varphi(r)$ for $0 \leqslant r < \infty$. *Hint.* In Section 1.14 it is shown that the Coulomb force on a test charge at $r = r_0$ depends only on the charge at distances less than r_0 and is independent of the charge at distances greater than r_0. Note that this applies to a *spherically symmetric* charge distribution.

1.13.4 Show that the pair of equations
$$A = \tfrac{1}{2}(B \times r),$$
$$B = \nabla \times A,$$
is satisfied by any constant vector B (any orientation).

1.14 Gauss's Law, Poisson's Equation

Gauss's Law.   Consider a point electric charge q at the origin of our coordinate system. This produces an electric field E given by

$$E = \frac{q r_0}{4\pi\varepsilon_0 r^2}. \tag{1.146}$$

We now derive Gauss's law which states that the surface integral

$$\int_S E \cdot d\sigma = \begin{cases} \dfrac{q}{\varepsilon_0}, \\ 0 \end{cases} \tag{1.147}$$

q/ε_0 if the closed surface S includes the origin (where q is located) and zero if the surface does not include the origin.

Using Gauss's theorem, Eq. 1.95 (and neglecting the $q/4\pi\varepsilon_0$),

$$\int_S \frac{r_0 \cdot d\sigma}{r^2} = \int_V \nabla \cdot \left(\frac{r_0}{r^2}\right) d\tau = 0. \tag{1.148}$$

by Example 1.7.1, provided the surface S does not include the origin, where the integrands are not defined. This proves the second part of Gauss's law.

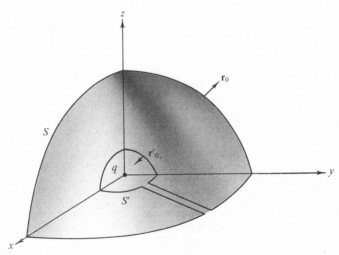

FIG. 1.25 Exclusion of the origin

The first part, in which the surface S must include the origin, may be handled by surrounding the origin with a small sphere S' of radius δ. So that there will be no question what is inside and what is outside, imagine the volume outside the outer surface S and the volume inside surface $S'(r < \delta)$ connected by a small hole. This joins surfaces S and S', combining them into one single simply connected closed surface. Because the radius of the imaginary hole may be made vanishingly small, there is no additional contribution to the surface integral. Gauss's theorem now applies to the volume between S and S' without any difficulty. We have

$$\int_S \frac{\mathbf{r}_0 \cdot d\boldsymbol{\sigma}}{r^2} + \int_S \frac{\mathbf{r}_0 \cdot d\boldsymbol{\sigma}'}{\delta^2} = 0. \tag{1.149}$$

We may evaluate the second integral, for $d\boldsymbol{\sigma}' = -\mathbf{r}_0\delta^2\, d\Omega$, in which $d\Omega$ is an element of solid angle. The minus sign appears because we agreed in Section 1.10 to have the positive normal $\mathbf{r}_0'$ *outward* from the volume. In this case our outward $\mathbf{r}_0'$ is in the negative radial direction, $\mathbf{r}_0' = -\mathbf{r}_0$. By integrating over all angles

$$\int_{S'} \frac{\mathbf{r}_0 \cdot d\boldsymbol{\sigma}'}{\delta^2} = -\int_{S'} \frac{\mathbf{r}_0 \cdot \mathbf{r}_0\delta^2\, d\Omega}{\delta^2} = -4\pi. \tag{1.150}$$

With the constants from Eq. 1.146, this results in

$$\int_S \mathbf{E} \cdot d\boldsymbol{\sigma} = \frac{q}{4\pi\varepsilon_0}\, 4\pi = \frac{q}{\varepsilon_0}, \tag{1.151}$$

completing the proof of Gauss's law. Notice carefully that although the surface S may be spherical it *need not* be spherical.

Going just a bit further, we consider a distributed charge so that

$$q = \int_V \rho\, d\tau. \tag{1.152}$$

Equation 1.151 still applies, with q now interpreted as the total distributed charge enclosed by surface S.

$$\int_S \mathbf{E} \cdot d\boldsymbol{\sigma} = \int_V \frac{\rho}{\varepsilon_0}\, d\tau. \tag{1.153}$$

Using Gauss's theorem, we have

$$\int_V \mathbf{\nabla} \cdot \mathbf{E}\, d\tau = \int_V \frac{\rho}{\varepsilon_0}\, d\tau. \tag{1.154}$$

Since our volume is completely arbitrary, the integrands must be equal or

$$\mathbf{\nabla} \cdot \mathbf{E} = \frac{\rho}{\varepsilon_0}, \tag{1.155}$$

one of Maxwell's equations. If we reverse the argument, Gauss's law follows immediately from Maxwell's equation.

Poisson's equation. Replacing $\mathbf{E}$ by $-\mathbf{\nabla}\varphi$, Eq. 1.155 becomes

$$\mathbf{\nabla} \cdot \mathbf{\nabla}\varphi = -\frac{\rho}{\varepsilon_0}, \tag{1.156}$$

which is Poisson's equation. For the condition $\rho = 0$ this reduces to an even more famous equation,

$$\mathbf{V} \cdot \mathbf{V}\varphi = 0, \tag{1.157}$$

Laplace's equation. We shall encounter Laplace's equation frequently in discussing various coordinate systems (Chapter 2) and in discussing the special functions of mathematical physics which appear as its solutions. Poisson's equation will be invaluable in developing the theory of Green's functions (Sections 8.6 and 16.5).

EXERCISES

1.14.1 Using Maxwell's equations, show that for a static system (steady current) the magnetic vector potential $\mathbf{A}$ satisfies a vector Poisson equation,

$$\mathbf{V}^2\mathbf{A} = -\mu\mathbf{j},$$

provided we require $\mathbf{V} \cdot \mathbf{A} = 0$.

1.14.2 Develop Gauss's Law for the two-dimensional case in which

$$\varphi = -q \frac{\ln r}{2\pi\varepsilon_0}, \qquad \mathbf{E} = -\mathbf{V}\varphi = q \frac{\mathbf{r}_0}{2\pi\varepsilon_0 r}.$$

Here q is the charge at the origin or the line charge per unit length if our two-dimensional system is a unit thickness slice of a three-dimensional (circular cylindrical) system. The variable r is measured radially outward from the line charge.

1.14.3 (a) Show that Gauss's law follows from Maxwell's equation

$$\mathbf{V} \cdot \mathbf{E} = \frac{\rho}{\varepsilon_0}$$

(b) Assuming that the electric field of a point charge q is spherically symmetric, show that Gauss's law implies the Coulomb inverse square expression

$$\mathbf{E} = \frac{q\mathbf{r}_0}{4\pi\varepsilon_0 r^2}.$$

1.15 Helmholtz' Theorem

In Section 1.13 it was emphasized that the choice of a magnetic vector potential $\mathbf{A}$ was not unique. The divergence of $\mathbf{A}$ was still undetermined. In this section two theorems about the divergence and curl of a vector are developed. The first theorem is as follows.

A vector is uniquely specified by giving its divergence and its curl within a region and its normal component over the boundary. Let us take

$$\mathbf{V} \cdot \mathbf{V}_1 = s,$$

$$\mathbf{V} \times \mathbf{V}_1 = \mathbf{c}, \tag{1.158}$$

where s may be interpreted as a source (charge) density and $\mathbf{c}$, as a circulation (current) density. Assuming also that the normal component V_n on the boundary is given, we want to show that $\mathbf{V}_1$ is unique. We do this by assuming the existance of a second vector $\mathbf{V}_2$, which satisfies Eq. 1.158 and has the same normal component over the boundary, and then showing that $\mathbf{V}_1 - \mathbf{V}_2 = 0$. Let

$$\mathbf{W} = \mathbf{V}_1 - \mathbf{V}_2.$$

Then

$$\mathbf{V} \cdot \mathbf{W} = 0 \tag{1.159}$$

and

$$\mathbf{V} \times \mathbf{W} = 0. \tag{1.160}$$

From Section 1.13 we may put

$$\mathbf{W} = -\nabla\varphi. \tag{1.161}$$

Substituting this into Eq. 1.159, we obtain

$$\mathbf{V} \cdot \mathbf{V}\varphi = 0, \tag{1.162}$$

Laplace's equation.

Now we draw upon Green's theorem in the form given in Eq. 1.98, letting u and v each equal φ. Since

$$W_n = V_{1n} - V_{2n} = 0 \tag{1.163}$$

on the boundary, Green's theorem reduces to

$$\int_V (\mathbf{V}\varphi) \cdot (\mathbf{V}\varphi) \, d\tau = \int_V \mathbf{W} \cdot \mathbf{W} \, d\tau = 0, \tag{1.164}$$

The quantity $\mathbf{W} \cdot \mathbf{W} = W^2$ is non-negative and so we must have

$$\mathbf{W} = \mathbf{V}_1 - \mathbf{V}_2 = 0 \tag{1.165}$$

everywhere. Thus $\mathbf{V}_1$ is unique, proving the theorem.

The second theorem we shall prove is Helmholtz' theorem. A vector $\mathbf{V}$ satisfying Eq. 1.158 with both source and circulation densities vanishing at infinity may be written as the sum of two parts, one of which is irrotational, the other solenoidal.

We seek to show that a given vector $\mathbf{V}$ may be written

$$\mathbf{V} = -\nabla\varphi + \mathbf{V} \times \mathbf{A}, \tag{1.166}$$

$-\nabla\varphi$ being irrotational and $\mathbf{V} \times \mathbf{A}$ being solenoidal. In particular, φ, corresponding to a scalar potential is given by

$$\varphi(\mathbf{r}_1) = \frac{1}{4\pi} \int \frac{s(\mathbf{r}_2)}{r_{12}} \, d\tau_2 \tag{1.167}$$

and $\mathbf{A}$ corresponding to a vector potential is given by

$$\mathbf{A}(\mathbf{r}_1) = \frac{1}{4\pi} \int \frac{\mathbf{c}(\mathbf{r}_2)}{r_{12}} \, d\tau_2. \tag{1.168}$$

Here the argument $\mathbf{r}_1$ indicates (x_1, y_1, z_1), the field point; $\mathbf{r}_2$, the coordinates of the source point (x_2, y_2, z_2), whereas

$$r_{12} = [(x_1 - x_2)^2 + (y_1 - y_2)^2 + (z_1 - z_2)^2]^{1/2}. \tag{1.169}$$

When a direction is associated with r_{12}, the positive direction is taken to be away from the source toward the field point. Vectorially, $\mathbf{r}_{12} = \mathbf{r}_1 - \mathbf{r}_2$, as shown in

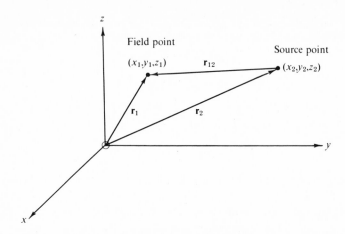

FIG. 1.26   Source and field points

Fig. 1.26. Of course, s and $\mathbf{c}$ must vanish sufficiently rapidly at large distances so that the integrals exist.

Equation 1.166 expresses $\mathbf{V}$ in the desired form, resolved into irrotational and solenoidal parts. With the scalar potential φ given by Eq. 1.167 and the vector potential $\mathbf{A}$ by Eq. 1.168, we seek to show that $\mathbf{V}$ (Eq. 1.166) satisfies the conditions of Eqs. 1.158, that is, that

$$\mathbf{V} \cdot \mathbf{V} = s,$$

$$\mathbf{V} \times \mathbf{V} = c.$$

Then, by the preceding theorem, $\mathbf{V}$ is uniquely specified. The validity of Eq. 1.166 is established. Helmholtz' theorem is proved.

First the divergence of $\mathbf{V}$ is given by

$$\mathbf{V} \cdot \mathbf{V} = -\mathbf{V} \cdot \mathbf{V}\varphi$$
$$= -\frac{1}{4\pi} \mathbf{V} \cdot \mathbf{V} \int \frac{s(\mathbf{r}_2)}{r_{12}}\, d\tau_2, \tag{1.170}$$

the divergence of the curl vanishing. The Laplacian operator, $\mathbf{V} \cdot \mathbf{V}$ or $\mathbf{V}^2$, operates on the field coordinates (x_1, y_1, z_1) and so commutes with the integration with respect to (x_2, y_2, z_2). We have

$$\mathbf{V} \cdot \mathbf{V} = -\frac{1}{4\pi} \int s(\mathbf{r}_2)\mathbf{V}_1^2\left(\frac{1}{r_{12}}\right) d\tau_2. \tag{1.171}$$

In Section 1.14 we showed in the development of Gauss's law that

$$\int \mathbf{V} \cdot \left(\frac{\mathbf{r}_0}{r^2}\right) d\tau = \int \mathbf{V}^2\left(\frac{1}{r}\right) d\tau = \begin{cases} -4\pi \\ 0 \end{cases}. \tag{1.172}$$

depending on whether the integration included the origin $r = 0$. This result may be conveniently expressed by introducing the Dirac delta function, $\delta(r)$,

$$\mathbf{V}^2\left(\frac{1}{r}\right) = -4\pi\,\delta(r). \tag{1.173}$$

This Dirac delta function is *defined* by its assigned properties

$$\delta(r) = 0, \qquad r \neq 0, \tag{1.174a}$$

$$\int f(r)\,\delta(r)\,d\tau = f(0), \tag{1.174b}$$

where $f(r)$ is any well-behaved function and the volume of integration includes the origin. As a special case of Eq. 1.174b,

$$\int \delta(r)\,d\tau = 1. \tag{1.175}$$

The quantity $\delta(r)$ is really not a function at all, since it is undefined (infinite) at $r = 0$. For this reason it has sometimes been disparaged by conservative mathematicians. Gradually it is being accepted as a notation for a limit. We shall use it here in terms of its defining properties (Eqs. 1.174). It is discussed at some length in Section 8.6.

We must make two minor modifications in Eq. 1.173 before applying it. First, our source is at r_2, not at the origin. This means that the 4π in Gauss's law appears if and only if the surface includes the point $\mathbf{r} = \mathbf{r}_2$. To show this, Eq. 1.173 is rewritten:

$$\mathbf{V}^2\left(\frac{1}{r_{12}}\right) = -4\pi\,\delta(\mathbf{r}_1 - \mathbf{r}_2). \tag{1.176}$$

This shift of the source to $\mathbf{r}_2$ may be incorporated in the defining equations (1.174) as

$$\delta(\mathbf{r}_1 - \mathbf{r}_2) = 0, \qquad \mathbf{r}_1 \neq \mathbf{r}_2, \tag{1.177a}$$

$$\int f(\mathbf{r}_1)\,\delta(\mathbf{r}_1 - \mathbf{r}_2)\,d\mathbf{r}_1 = f(\mathbf{r}_2). \tag{1.177b}$$

Second, noting that differentiating r_{12}^{-1} twice with respect to x_2, y_2, z_2 is the same as differentiating *twice* with respect to x_1, y_1, z_1:

$$\mathbf{V}_1^2\left(\frac{1}{r_{12}}\right) = \mathbf{V}_2^2\left(\frac{1}{r_{12}}\right) = -4\pi\,\delta(\mathbf{r}_1 - \mathbf{r}_2)$$

$$= -4\pi\,\delta(\mathbf{r}_2 - \mathbf{r}_1). \tag{1.178}$$

We could equally well have noted that from its defining properties

$$\delta(\mathbf{r}_1 - \mathbf{r}_2) = \delta(\mathbf{r}_2 - \mathbf{r}_1). \tag{1.179}$$

Rewriting Eq. 1.171 and using the Dirac delta function, Eq. 1.178, we may integrate to obtain

$$\mathbf{V} \cdot \mathbf{V} = -\frac{1}{4\pi}\int s(\mathbf{r}_2)\mathbf{V}_2^2\left(\frac{1}{r_{12}}\right)d\mathbf{r}_2$$

$$= -\frac{1}{4\pi}\int s(\mathbf{r}_2)(-4\pi)\,\delta(\mathbf{r}_2 - \mathbf{r}_1)\,d\mathbf{r}_2$$

$$= s(\mathbf{r}_1). \tag{1.180}$$

The final step follows from Eq. 1.177*a* with the subscripts 1 and 2 exchanged. Our result, Eq. 1.180 shows that the assumed form of **V** and of the scalar potential φ are in agreement with the given divergence (Eq. 1.158).

To complete the proof of Helmholtz' theorem we need to show that our assumptions are consistent with the second part of Eq. 1.158, that is, that the curl of **V** is equal to $\mathbf{c}(r_1)$. From Eq. 1.166

$$\nabla \times \mathbf{V} = \nabla \times \nabla \times \mathbf{A}$$

$$= \nabla\nabla \cdot \mathbf{A} - \nabla^2\mathbf{A}. \tag{1.181}$$

The first term, $\nabla\nabla \cdot \mathbf{A}$ leads to

$$\nabla\nabla \cdot \mathbf{A} = \int \mathbf{c}(\mathbf{r}_2) \cdot \nabla_1\nabla_1\left(\frac{1}{r_{12}}\right) d\tau_2 \tag{1.182}$$

by Eq. 1.168. Again replacing the second derivatives with respect to x_1, y_1, z_1 by second derivatives with respect to x_2, y_2, z_2, we integrate each component of Eq. 1.182 by parts:

$$\nabla\nabla \cdot \mathbf{A}\bigg|_x = \int \mathbf{c}(\mathbf{r}_2) \cdot \nabla_2 \frac{\partial}{\partial x_2}\left(\frac{1}{r_{12}}\right) d\tau_2$$

$$= \int \nabla_2 \cdot \left[\mathbf{c}(\mathbf{r}_2) \frac{\partial}{\partial x_2}\left(\frac{1}{r_{12}}\right)\right] d\tau_2 - \int \left[\nabla_2 \cdot \mathbf{c}(\mathbf{r}_2)\right]\frac{\partial}{\partial x_2}\left(\frac{1}{r_{12}}\right) d\tau_2 \tag{1.183}$$

The second integral vanishes because the circulation density **c** is solenoidal. The first integral may be transformed to a surface integral by Gauss's theorem. If **c** is bounded in space or vanishes faster than $1/r$ for large r, so that the integral in Eq. 1.168 exists, then by choosing a sufficiently large surface the first integral on the right-hand side of Eq. 1.183 also vanishes.

With $\nabla \cdot \mathbf{A} = 0$, Eq. 1.181 now reduces to

$$\nabla \times \mathbf{V} = -\nabla^2\mathbf{A}$$

$$= -\frac{1}{4\pi} \int c(\mathbf{r}_2)\nabla_1^2\left(\frac{1}{r_{12}}\right) d\mathbf{r}_2 . \tag{1.184}$$

This is exactly like Eq. 1.171 except that the scalar $s(\mathbf{r}_2)$ is replaced by the vector circulation density $\mathbf{c}(\mathbf{r}_2)$. Introducing the Dirac delta function, as before, as a convenient way of carrying out the integration, it is seen that Eq. 1.184 reduces to Eq. 1.158. We see that our assumed form of **V**, given by Eq. 1.166, and of the vector potential **A**, given by Eq. 1.168, are in agreement with Eq. 1.158 specifying the curl of **V**.

This completes the proof of Helmholtz' theorem, showing that a vector may be resolved into irrotational and solenoidal parts. Applied to the electromagnetic field, we have resolved our field vector **V** into an irrotational electric field **E**, derived from a scalar potential φ, and a solenoidal magnetic field **B**, derived from a vector potential **A**. The source density $s(\mathbf{r})$ may be interpreted as an electric charge density (divided by electric permutivity ε), whereas the circulation density $\mathbf{c}(\mathbf{r})$ becomes electric current density (times magnetic permutivity μ).

EXERCISES

1.15.1 (a) Assuming that $\mathbf{P}$ is a solution of the vector Poisson equation, $\nabla_1^2 \mathbf{P}(\mathbf{r}_1) = -\mathbf{V}(\mathbf{r}_1)$,

$$\mathbf{P}(\mathbf{r}_1) = \frac{1}{4\pi} \int_V \frac{\mathbf{V}(\mathbf{r}_2)}{r_{12}} d\tau_2,$$

develop an alternate proof of Helmholtz' theorem, showing that $\mathbf{V}$ may be written as

$$\mathbf{V} = \nabla \varphi + \nabla \times \mathbf{A},$$

where

$$\mathbf{A} = \nabla \times \mathbf{P},$$

and

$$\varphi = \nabla \cdot \mathbf{P}.$$

(b) Solving the vector Poisson equation, we find

$$\mathbf{P}(\mathbf{r}_1) = \frac{1}{4\pi} \int_V \frac{\mathbf{V}(\mathbf{r}_2)}{r_{12}} d\tau_2.$$

Show that this solution substituted into φ and $\mathbf{A}$ of part (a) leads to the expressions given for φ and $\mathbf{A}$ in Section 1.15.

REFERENCES

KELLOGG, O. D., *Foundations of Potential Theory*. New York: Dover (1953). Originally published 1929.

   The classic text on potential theory.

LASS, H., *Vector and Tensor Analysis*. New York: McGraw-Hill (1950).

   One of the clearest presentations of vector analysis. Written to be read and understood.

SCHWARTZ, M., S. GREEN, W. A. RUTLEDGE, *Vector Analysis with Applications to Geometry and Physics*. New York: Harper and Row (1960).

   Excellent account of the elements of vector analysis with a wealth of applications in electromagnetism.

WREDE, R. C., *Introduction to Vector and Tensor Analysis*. New York: Wiley (1963).

   Fine historical introduction. Excellent discussion of differentiation of vectors and applications to mechanics.

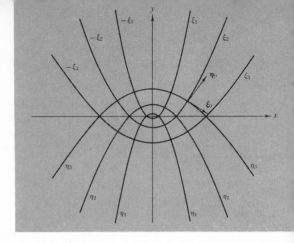

CHAPTER 2

COORDINATE SYSTEMS

In Chapter 1 we restricted ourselves almost completely to cartesian coordinate systems. A cartesian coordinate system offers the unique advantage that all three unit vectors, $\mathbf{i}$, $\mathbf{j}$, and $\mathbf{k}$, are constant. We did introduce the radial distance $\mathbf{r}$ but even this was treated as a function of x, y, and z. Unfortunately, not all physical problems are well adapted to solution in cartesian coordinates. For instance, if we have a central force problem, $\mathbf{F} = \mathbf{r}_0\, F(r)$, such as gravitational or electrostatic force, cartesian coordinates may be unusually inappropriate. Such a problem literally screams for the use of a coordinate system in which the radial distance is taken to be one of the coordinates, that is, spherical polar coordinates.

The point is that the coordinate system should be chosen to fit the problem, to exploit any constraint or symmetry present in it. Then, hopefully, it will be more readily soluble than if we had forced it into a cartesian framework. Quite often "more readily soluble" will mean that we have a partial differential equation that can be split into separate ordinary differential equations, often in "standard form" in the new coordinate system. This technique, the separation of variables, is discussed in Section 2.5.

We are primarily interested in coordinates in which the equation

$$\mathbf{V}^2\psi + k^2\psi = 0 \tag{2.1}$$

is separable. Equation 2.1 is much more general than it may appear. If

$k^2 = 0$	Eq. 2.1 → Laplace's equation,
$k^2 = (+)$ constant	Helmholtz' equation,
$k^2 = (-)$ constant	Diffusion equation (space part),
$k^2 = $ constant $\times$ kinetic energy	Schrödinger wave equation.

It has been shown (L. P. Eisenhart, *Phys. Rev.* **45**, 427 (1934)) that there are eleven coordinate systems in which Eq. 2.1 is separable, all of which can be considered particular cases of the confocal ellipsoidal system. In addition, we shall touch briefly on three other systems that are useful in solving Laplace's equation.

Naturally there is a price that must be paid for the use of a noncartesian co-ordinate system. We have not yet written expressions for gradient, divergence, or curl in any of the noncartesian coordinate systems. Such expressions are developed in very general form in Section 2.2. First we must develop a system of curvilinear coordinates, a general system that may be specialized to any of the fourteen particular systems of interest.

2.1 Curvilinear Coordinates

In cartesian coordinates we deal with three mutually perpendicular families of planes: $x = $ constant, $y = $ constant, and $z = $ constant. Imagine that we super-impose on this system three other families of surfaces. The surfaces of any one family need not be parallel to each other and they need not be planes. The three new families of surfaces need not be mutually perpendicular, but for simplicity we shall quickly impose this condition (Eq. 2.7). We may describe any point (x, y, z) as the intersection of three planes in cartesian coordinates or as the intersection of the three surfaces which form our new, curvilinear coordinates. Describing the curvi-linear coordinate surfaces by $q_1 = $ constant, $q_2 = $ constant, $q_3 = $ constant, we may identify our point by (q_1, q_2, q_3) as well as by (x, y, z). This means that in principle we may write

$$x = x(q_1, q_2, q_3),$$
$$y = y(q_1, q_2, q_3), \qquad (2.2)$$
$$z = z(q_1, q_2, q_3),$$

specifying x, y, z in terms of the q's and the inverse relations,

$$q_1 = q_1(x, y, z),$$
$$q_2 = q_2(x, y, z), \qquad (2.3)$$
$$q_3 = q_3(x, y, z).$$

With each family of surface $q_i = $ constant, we can associate a unit vector $\mathbf{a}_i$ normal to the surface $q_i = $ constant and in the direction of increasing q_i.

The square of the distance between two neighboring points is given by

$$ds^2 = dx^2 + dy^2 + dz^2 = \sum_{ij} h_{ij}^2 \, dq_i \, dq_j. \qquad (2.4)$$

The coefficients h_{ij}^2, which we now proceed to investigate, may be viewed as speci-fying the nature of the coordinate system (q_1, q_2, q_3). Collectively, these coefficients are referred to as the *metric*.

The first step in the determination of h_{ij}^2 is the partial differentiation of Eq. 2.2 which yields

$$dx = \frac{\partial x}{\partial q_1} \, dq_1 + \frac{\partial x}{\partial q_2} \, dq_2 + \frac{\partial x}{\partial q_3} \, dq_3, \qquad (2.5)$$

and similarly for dy and dz. Squaring and substituting into Eq. 2.4, we have

$$h_{ij}^2 = \frac{\partial x}{\partial q_i}\frac{\partial x}{\partial q_j} + \frac{\partial y}{\partial q_i}\frac{\partial y}{\partial q_j} + \frac{\partial z}{\partial q_i}\frac{\partial z}{\partial q_j}. \tag{2.6}$$

At this point we limit ourselves to orthogonal (mutually perpendicular surfaces) coordinate systems which means (cf. Exercise 2.1.1)

$$h_{ij} = 0, \qquad i \neq j. \tag{2.7}$$

Now, to simplify the notation, we write $h_{ii} = h_i$ so that

$$ds^2 = (h_1\, dq_1)^2 + (h_2\, dq^2)^2 + (h_3\, dq_3)^2. \tag{2.8}$$

Our specific coordinate systems are described in subsequent sections by specifying these scale factors h_1, h_2, and h_3. Conversely, the scale factors may be conveniently identified by the relation

$$ds_i = h_i\, dq_i \tag{2.9}$$

for any given dq_i, holding the other q's constant. Note that the three curvilinear coordinates q_1, q_2, q_3 need not be lengths. The scale factors h_i may depend on the q's and they may have dimensions. The *product* $h_i\, dq_i$ must have dimensions of length.

From Eq. 2.9 we may immediately develop the area and volume elements

$$d\sigma_{ij} = ds_i\, ds_j = h_i h_j\, dq_i\, dq_j \tag{2.10}$$

and

$$d\tau = ds_1\, ds_2\, ds_3 = h_1 h_2 h_3\, dq_1\, dq_2\, dq_3. \tag{2.11}$$

The expressions in Eqs. 2.10 and 2.11 agree, of course, with the results of using the transformation equations, Eq. 2.2, and Jacobians.

EXERCISES

2.1.1 Show that limiting our attention to orthogonal coordinate systems implies that $h_{ij} = 0$ for $i \neq j$ (Eq. 2.7).

2.1.2 Show that the Jacobian

$$J\left(\frac{x, y, z}{q_1, q_2, q_3}\right) = h_1 h_2 h_3$$

and thus that the volume element given by

$$J\left(\frac{x, y, z}{q_1, q_2, q_3}\right) dq_1\, dq_2\, dq_3$$

is $h_1 h_2 h_3\, dq_1\, dq_2\, dq_3$ in agreement with Eq. 2.11.

2.1.3 With q_1, q_2, q_3 curvilinear coordinates, show that

$$\frac{\partial \mathbf{r}}{\partial q_1}, \quad \frac{\partial \mathbf{r}}{\partial q_2}, \quad \frac{\partial \mathbf{r}}{\partial q_3}$$

and

$$\nabla q_1, \nabla q_2, \nabla q_3,$$

are reciprocal sets of vectors. *Hint.* Note that

(a)
$$\frac{\partial x}{\partial q_i} = h_i \frac{\partial x}{\partial s_i},$$

(b)
$$\frac{\partial q_i}{\partial x} = \frac{1}{h_i} \frac{\partial x}{\partial s_i} = \frac{1}{h_i} \frac{\partial s_i}{\partial x}.$$

2.1.4 The u-, v-, z-coordinate system frequently used in electrostatics and in hydrodynamics is defined by

$$xy = u,$$
$$x^2 - y^2 = v,$$
$$z = z.$$

This u-, v-, z-system is orthogonal.
(a) In words, describe briefly the nature of each of the three families of coordinate surfaces.
(b) Sketch the system in the xy-plane showing the intersections of surfaces of constant u and surfaces of constant v with the xy-plane.
(c) Indicate the directions of the unit vector u_0 and v_0 in all four quadrants.
(d) Finally, is this u-, v-, z-system right-handed or left-handed?

2.2 Differential Vector Operations

The starting point for developing the gradient, divergence, and curl operators in curvilinear coordinates is our interpretation of the gradient as the vector having the magnitude and direction of the maximum space rate of change (cf. Section 1.6). From this interpretation the component of $\nabla \psi(q_1, q_2, q_3)$ in the direction normal to the family of surfaces $q_1 = $ constant is given by[1]

$$\nabla \psi \mid_1 = \frac{\partial \psi}{\partial s_1} = \frac{\partial \psi}{h_1 \partial q_1}, \tag{2.12}$$

since this is the rate of change of ψ for varying q_1, holding q_2 and q_3 fixed. The quantity ds_1 is a differential length in the direction of increasing q_1 (cf. Eq. 2.9). In Section 2.1 we introduced a unit vector $\mathbf{a}_1$ to indicate this direction. By repeating Eq. 2.12 for q_2 and again for q_3 and adding vectorially the gradient becomes

$$\nabla \psi(q_1, q_2, q_3) = \mathbf{a}_1 \frac{\partial \psi}{\partial s_1} + \mathbf{a}_2 \frac{\partial \psi}{\partial s_2} + \mathbf{a}_3 \frac{\partial \psi}{\partial s_3}$$

$$= \mathbf{a}_1 \frac{\partial \psi}{h_1 \partial q_1} + \mathbf{a}_2 \frac{\partial \psi}{h_2 \partial q_2} + \mathbf{a}_3 \frac{\partial \psi}{h_3 \partial q_3} \tag{2.13}$$

The divergence operator may be obtained from the second definition (Eq. 1.91) of Chapter 1 or equivalently from Gauss's theorem, Section 1.11. Let us use

---

[1] Here the use of φ to label a function is avoided because it is conventional to use this symbol to denote an azimuthal coordinate.

Eq. 1.91:

$$\mathbf{\nabla} \cdot \mathbf{V}(q_1, q_2, q_3) = \lim_{\int d\tau \to 0} \frac{\int \mathbf{V} \cdot d\mathbf{\sigma}}{\int d\tau} \tag{2.14}$$

with a differential volume $h_1 h_2 h_3 \, dq_1 \, dq_2 \, dq_3$. Note that the positive directions have

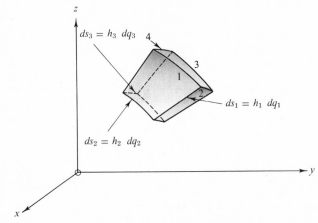

FIG. 2.1 Curvilinear volume element

been chosen so that (q_1, q_2, q_3) or $(\mathbf{a}_1, \mathbf{a}_2, \mathbf{a}_3)$ form a right-handed set.

The area integral for the two faces $q_1 = $ constant is given by

$$\left[V_1 h_2 h_3 + \frac{\partial}{\partial q_1} (V_1 h_2 h_3) \, dq_1 \right] dq_2 \, dq_3 - V_1 h_2 h_3 \, dq_2 \, dq_3$$

$$= \frac{\partial}{\partial q_1} (V_1 h_2 h_3) \, dq_1 \, dq_2 \, dq_3 \tag{2.15}$$

exactly as in Sections 1.7 and 1.10.[1] Adding in the similar results for the other two pairs of surfaces, we obtain

$$\int \mathbf{V}(q_1, q_2, q_3) \cdot d\mathbf{\sigma}$$

$$= \left[\frac{\partial}{\partial q_1} (V_1 h_2 h_2) + \frac{\partial}{\partial q_2} (V_2 h_3 h_1) + \frac{\partial}{\partial q_3} (V_3 h_1 h_2) \right] dq_1 \, dq_2 \, dq_3. \tag{2.16}$$

Division by our differential volume (Eq. 2.14) yields

$$\mathbf{\nabla} \cdot \mathbf{V}(q_1, q_2, q_3) = \frac{1}{h_1 h_2 h_3} \left[\frac{\partial}{\partial q_1} (V_1 h_2 h_3) + \frac{\partial}{\partial q_2} (V_2 h_3 h_1) + \frac{\partial}{\partial q_3} (V_3 h_1 h_2) \right]. \tag{2.17}$$

In Eq. 2.17 V_i is the component of $\mathbf{V}$ in the $\mathbf{a}_i$-direction, increasing q_i, that is, $V_i = \mathbf{a}_i \cdot \mathbf{V}$.

We may obtain the Laplacian by combining Eqs. 2.13 and 2.17, using $\mathbf{V} = $

[1] Since we take the limit $dq_1, dq_2, dq_3 \to 0$, the second and higher order derivatives will drop out.

$\nabla\psi(q_1, q_2, q_3)$. This leads to

$\nabla \cdot \nabla\psi(q_1, q_2, q_3)$

$$= \frac{1}{h_1 h_2 h_3}\left[\frac{\partial}{\partial q_1}\left(\frac{h_2 h_3}{h_1}\frac{\partial\psi}{\partial q_1}\right) + \frac{\partial}{\partial q_2}\left(\frac{h_3 h_1}{h_2}\frac{\partial\psi}{\partial q_2}\right) + \frac{\partial}{\partial q_3}\left(\frac{h_1 h_2}{h_3}\frac{\partial\psi}{\partial q_3}\right)\right]. \quad (2.18a)$$

Finally, to develop $\nabla \times \mathbf{V}$, let us apply Stokes's theorem (Section 1.12) and, as with the divergence, take the limit as the surface area becomes vanishingly small. Working on one component at a time, we consider a differential surface element in the curvilinear surface $q_1 = $ constant. From

$$\int_s \nabla \times \mathbf{V} \cdot d\boldsymbol{\sigma} = \nabla \times \mathbf{V}\,|_1\, h_2 h_3\, dq_2\, dq_3 \quad (2.18b)$$

Stokes's theorem yields

$$\nabla \times \mathbf{V}\,|_1\, h_2 h_3\, dq_2\, dq_3 = \oint \mathbf{V} \cdot d\boldsymbol{\lambda}, \quad (2.19)$$

with the line integral lying in the surface $q_1 = $ constant. Following the loop

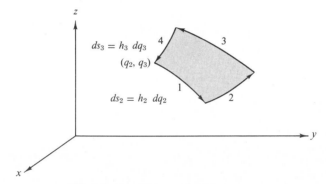

FIG. 2.2 Curvilinear surface element

(1, 2, 3, 4) of Fig. 2.2,

$$\oint \mathbf{V}(q_1, q_2, q_3) \cdot d\boldsymbol{\lambda} = V_2 h_2\, dq_2 + \left[V_3 h_3 + \frac{\partial}{\partial q_2}(V_3 h_3)\, dq_2\right] dq_3$$

$$- \left[V_2 h_2 + \frac{\partial}{\partial q_3}(V_2 h_2)\, dq_3\right] dq_2 - V_3 h_3\, dq_3$$

$$= \left[\frac{\partial}{\partial q_2}(h_3 V_3) - \frac{\partial}{\partial q_3}(h_2 V_2)\right] dq_2\, dq_3. \quad (2.20)$$

We pick up a positive sign when going in the positive direction on parts 1 and 2 and a negative sign on parts 3 and 4 because here we are going in the negative direction. From Eq. 2.19

$$\nabla \times \mathbf{V}\,|_1 = \frac{1}{h_2 h_3}\left[\frac{\partial}{\partial q_2}(h_3 V_3) - \frac{\partial}{\partial q_3}(h_2 V_2)\right]. \quad (2.21)$$

The remaining two components of $\mathbf{V} \times \mathbf{V}$ may be picked up by cyclic permutation of the indices. As in Chapter 1, it is often convenient to write the curl in determinant form:

$$\mathbf{V} \times \mathbf{V} = \frac{1}{h_1 h_2 h_3} \begin{vmatrix} \mathbf{a}_1 h_1 & \mathbf{a}_2 h_2 & \mathbf{a}_3 h_3 \\ \dfrac{\partial}{\partial q_1} & \dfrac{\partial}{\partial q_2} & \dfrac{\partial}{\partial q_3} \\ h_1 V_1 & h_2 V_2 & h_3 V_3 \end{vmatrix}. \tag{2.22}$$

This completes the determination of $\mathbf{V}$, $\mathbf{V} \cdot$, $\mathbf{V} \times$, and the Laplacian $\mathbf{V}^2$ in curvilinear coordinates. Armed with these general expressions, we proceed to study the eleven systems in which Eq. 2.1 is separable (cf. Section 2.5) for $k^2 \neq 0$ and three special coordinate systems (bipolar, toroidal, and bispherical coordinates).

EXERCISES

2.2.1 With $\mathbf{a}_1$ a unit vector in the direction of increasing q_1, show that

(a) $\mathbf{V} \cdot \mathbf{a}_1 = \dfrac{1}{h_1 h_2 h_3} \dfrac{\partial (h_2 h_3)}{\partial q_1}$

(b) $\mathbf{V} \times \mathbf{a}_1 = \dfrac{1}{h_1} \left[\mathbf{a}_2 \dfrac{\partial h_1}{h_3 \, \partial q_3} - \mathbf{a}_3 \dfrac{\partial h_1}{h_2 \, \partial q_2} \right]$

2.2.2 Show that the orthogonal unit vectors $\mathbf{a}_i$ may be defined by

$$\mathbf{a}_i = \frac{1}{h_i} \frac{\partial \mathbf{r}}{\partial q_i} \tag{a}$$

In particular show that $\mathbf{a}_i \cdot \mathbf{a}_i = 1$ leads to an expression for h_i in agreement with Eq. 2.6. Eq. (a) above may be taken as a starting point for deriving

$$\frac{\partial \mathbf{a}_i}{\partial q_j} = \mathbf{a}_j \frac{\partial h_j}{h_i \, \partial q_i}, \qquad i \neq j$$

and

$$\frac{\partial \mathbf{a}_i}{\partial q_i} = - \sum_{j \neq i} \mathbf{a}_j \frac{\partial h_i}{h_j \, \partial q_j}.$$

2.2.3 Develop arguments to show that ordinary dot and cross products (not involving $\mathbf{V}$) in orthogonal curvilinear coordinates proceed as in cartesian coordinates *with no involvement of scale factors*.

2.1.4 Using curvilinear coordinates and the vector identity

$$\mathbf{V} \cdot \mathbf{V} \mathbf{V} = \mathbf{V} \mathbf{V} \cdot \mathbf{V} - \mathbf{V} \times (\mathbf{V} \times \mathbf{V})$$

obtain the curvilinear form of the vector Laplacian, $\mathbf{V} \cdot \mathbf{V} \mathbf{V}$.

2.3 Special Coordinate Systems—Rectangular Cartesian Coordinates

It has been emphasized that the choice of coordinate system may depend on constraints or symmetry conditions in the problem to be solved. It is perhaps convenient to list our fourteen systems, classifying them according to whether or not they have an axis of translation (perpendicular to a family of parallel plane surfaces) or an axis of rotational symmetry.

TABLE 2.1

Axis of Translation	Axis of Rotation	Neither
Cartesian (3 axes)		Confocal ellipsoidal
Circular cylindrical	Circular cylindrical	
	Spherical polar (3 axes)	
Elliptic cylindrical	Prolate spheroidal	
	Oblate spheroidal	
Parabolic cylindrical	Parabolic	
Bipolar	Toroidal	
	Bispherical	
		Conical
		Confocal paraboloidal

Table 2.1 contains fifteen entries—circular cylindrical coordinates with an axis of translation which is also an axis of rotational symmetry. The spacing in the table has been chosen to indicate relations between various coordinate systems. If we consider the two-dimensional version ($z = 0$) of a system with an axis of translation (left column) and rotate it about an axis of reflection symmetry, we generate the corresponding coordinate systems listed to the right in the center column. For instance, rotating the ($z = 0$)-plane of the elliptic cylindrical system about the major axis generates the prolate spheroidal system; rotating about the minor axis yields the oblate spheroidal system.

We do consider three systems with neither an axis of translation nor an axis of rotation. It might be noted that in this asymmetric group the confocal ellipsoidal system is sometimes taken as the most general system and almost all the others[1] are derived from it.

Rectangular cartesian coordinates.   These are the cartesian coordinates on which Chapter 1 is based. In this simplest of all systems

$$h_1 = h_x = 1,$$
$$h_2 = h_y = 1,$$ (2.23)
$$h_3 = h_z = 1.$$

[1] Excluding the bipolar system and its two rotational forms, toroidal and bispherical.

The families of coordinate surfaces are three sets of parallel planes: $x = $ constant, $y = $ constant, and $z = $ constant. The cartesian coordinate system is unique in that all its h_i's are constant. This will be a significant advantage in treating tensors in Chapter 3. Note also that the unit vectors, $\mathbf{a}_1$, $\mathbf{a}_2$, $\mathbf{a}_3$ or $\mathbf{i}$, $\mathbf{j}$, $\mathbf{k}$, have *fixed* directions.

From Eqs. 2.13, 2.17, 2.18, and 2.22 we reproduce the results of Chapter 1,

$$\boldsymbol{\nabla}\psi = \mathbf{i}\,\frac{\partial\psi}{\partial x} + \mathbf{j}\,\frac{\partial\psi}{\partial y} + \mathbf{k}\,\frac{\partial\psi}{\partial z}, \tag{2.24}$$

$$\boldsymbol{\nabla}\cdot\mathbf{V} = \frac{\partial V_x}{\partial x} + \frac{\partial V_y}{\partial y} + \frac{\partial V_z}{\partial z}, \tag{2.25}$$

$$\boldsymbol{\nabla}\cdot\boldsymbol{\nabla}\psi = \frac{\partial^2\psi}{\partial x^2} + \frac{\partial^2\psi}{\partial y^2} + \frac{\partial^2\psi}{\partial z^2}, \tag{2.26}$$

$$\boldsymbol{\nabla}\times\mathbf{V} = \begin{vmatrix} \mathbf{i} & \mathbf{j} & \mathbf{k} \\ \dfrac{\partial}{\partial x} & \dfrac{\partial}{\partial y} & \dfrac{\partial}{\partial z} \\ V_x & V_y & V_z \end{vmatrix}. \tag{2.27}$$

2.4 Spherical Polar Coordinates (r, θ, φ)

Relabeling (q_1, q_2, q_3) as (r, θ, φ), the spherical polar coordinate system consists of the following:

1. Concentric spheres centered at the origin,

$$r = (x^2 + y^2 + z^2)^{1/2} = \text{constant}.$$

2. Right circular cones centered on the z-(polar) axis, vertices at the origin,

$$\theta = \text{arc cos}\,\frac{z}{(x^2 + y^2 + z^2)^{1/2}} = \text{constant}.$$

3. Half planes through the z-(polar) axis,

$$\varphi = \text{arc tan}\,\frac{y}{x} = \text{constant}.$$

By our arbitrary choice of definitions of θ, the polar angle, and φ, the azimuth angle, the z-axis is singled out for special treatment. The transformation equations corresponding to Eq. 2.2 are

$$x = r \sin\theta \cos\varphi,$$

$$y = r \sin\theta \cos\varphi, \tag{2.28}$$

$$z = r \cos\theta,$$

measuring θ from the positive z-axis and φ in the xy-plane from the positive x-axis.

The ranges of values are $0 \leq r < \infty$, $0 \leq \theta \leq \pi$, and $0 \leq \varphi \leq 2\pi$. From Eq. 2.6

$$
\begin{aligned}
h_1 &= h_r = 1, \\
h_2 &= h_\theta = r, \\
h_3 &= h_\varphi = r \sin \theta.
\end{aligned}
\tag{2.29}
$$

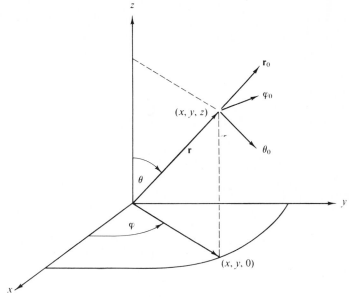

FIG. 2.3 Spherical polar coordinates

It must be emphasized that the unit vectors $\mathbf{r}_0$, $\boldsymbol{\theta}_0$, and $\boldsymbol{\varphi}_0$ vary in direction as the angles θ and φ vary. In terms of the fixed direction cartesian unit vectors $\mathbf{i}$, $\mathbf{j}$, and $\mathbf{k}$,

$$
\begin{aligned}
\mathbf{r}_0 &= \mathbf{i} \sin \theta \cos \varphi + \mathbf{j} \sin \theta \sin \varphi + \mathbf{k} \cos \theta, \\
\boldsymbol{\theta}_0 &= \mathbf{i} \cos \theta \cos \varphi + \mathbf{j} \cos \theta \sin \varphi - \mathbf{k} \sin \theta, \\
\boldsymbol{\varphi}_0 &= -\mathbf{i} \sin \varphi + \mathbf{j} \cos \varphi.
\end{aligned}
$$

From Section 2.2, relabeling the curvilinear coordinate unit vectors $\mathbf{a}_1$, $\mathbf{a}_2$, $\mathbf{a}_3$ as $\mathbf{r}_0$, $\boldsymbol{\theta}_0$, and $\boldsymbol{\varphi}_0$,

$$
\psi = \mathbf{r}_0 \frac{\partial \psi}{\partial r} + \boldsymbol{\theta}_0 \frac{1}{r} \frac{\partial \psi}{\partial \theta} + \boldsymbol{\varphi}_0 \frac{1}{r \sin \theta} \frac{\partial \psi}{\partial \varphi},
\tag{2.30}
$$

$$
\nabla \cdot \mathbf{V} = \frac{1}{r^2 \sin \theta} \left[\sin \theta \frac{\partial}{\partial r} \left(r^2 V_r \right) + r \frac{\partial}{\partial \theta} (\sin \theta \, V_\theta) + r \frac{\partial V_\varphi}{\partial \varphi} \right],
\tag{2.31}
$$

$$
\nabla \cdot \nabla \psi = \frac{1}{r^2 \sin \theta} \left[\sin \theta \frac{\partial}{\partial r} \left(r^2 \frac{\partial \psi}{\partial r} \right) + \frac{\partial}{\partial \theta} \left(\sin \theta \frac{\partial \psi}{\partial \theta} \right) + \frac{1}{\sin \theta} \frac{\partial^2 \psi}{\partial \varphi^2} \right],
\tag{2.32}
$$

$$
\nabla \times \mathbf{V} = \frac{1}{r^2 \sin \theta}
\begin{vmatrix}
\mathbf{r}_0 & r\boldsymbol{\theta}_0 & r \sin \theta \, \boldsymbol{\varphi}_0 \\
\dfrac{\partial}{\partial r} & \dfrac{\partial}{\partial \theta} & \dfrac{\partial}{\partial \varphi} \\
V_r & rV_\theta & r \sin \theta \, V_\varphi
\end{vmatrix}
\tag{2.33}
$$

Occasionally the vector Laplacian $\mathbf{V}^2\mathbf{V}$ is needed in spherical polar coordinates. It is best obtained by using the vector identity (Eq. 1.80) of Chapter 1. For future reference

$$\mathbf{V}^2\mathbf{V}|_r = \left(-\frac{2}{r^2} + \frac{2}{r}\frac{\partial}{\partial r} + \frac{\partial^2}{\partial r^2} + \frac{\cos\theta}{r^2\sin\theta}\frac{\partial}{\partial\theta} + \frac{1}{r^2}\frac{\partial^2}{\partial\theta^2} + \frac{1}{r^2\sin^2\theta}\frac{\partial^2}{\partial\varphi^2}\right)V_r$$

$$+ \left(-\frac{2}{r^2}\frac{\partial}{\partial\theta} - \frac{2\cos\theta}{r^2\sin\theta}\right)V_\theta + \left(-\frac{2}{r^2\sin\theta}\frac{\partial}{\partial\varphi}\right)V_\varphi$$

$$= \mathbf{V}^2 V_r - \frac{2}{r^2}V_r - \frac{2}{r^2}\frac{\partial V_\theta}{\partial\theta} - \frac{2\cos\theta}{r^2\sin\theta}V_\theta - \frac{2}{r^2\sin\theta}\frac{\partial V_\varphi}{\partial\varphi}, \tag{2.34}$$

$$\mathbf{V}^2\mathbf{V}|_\theta = \mathbf{V}^2 V_\theta - \frac{1}{r^2\sin^2\theta}V_\theta + \frac{2}{r^2}\frac{\partial V_r}{\partial\theta} - \frac{2\cos\theta}{r^2\sin^2\theta}\frac{\partial V_\varphi}{\partial\varphi}, \tag{2.35}$$

$$\mathbf{V}^2\mathbf{V}|_\varphi = \mathbf{V}^2 V_\varphi - \frac{1}{r^2\sin^2\theta}V_\varphi + \frac{2}{r^2\sin\theta}\frac{\partial V_r}{\partial\varphi} + \frac{2\cos\theta}{r^2\sin^2\theta}\frac{\partial V_\theta}{\partial\varphi}. \tag{2.36}$$

These expressions for the components of $\mathbf{V}^2\mathbf{V}$ are undeniably messy, but sometimes they are needed. There is no guarantee that nature will always be simple.

EXAMPLE 2.4.1

Using Eqs. 2.30–2.33, we can reproduce by inspection some of the results derived in Chapter 1 by laborious application of cartesian coordinates.
From Eq. 2.30

$$\mathbf{V}f(r) = \mathbf{r}_0\frac{df}{dr}, \tag{2.37}$$

$$\mathbf{V}r^n = \mathbf{r}_0 nr^{n-1}.$$

From Eq. 2.31

$$\mathbf{V}\cdot\mathbf{r}_0 f(r) = \frac{2}{r}f(r) + \frac{df}{dr},$$

$$\mathbf{V}\cdot\mathbf{r}_0 r^n = (n+2)r^{n-1}. \tag{2.38}$$

From Eq. 2.32

$$\mathbf{V}^2 f(r) = \frac{2}{r}\frac{df}{dr} + \frac{d^2 f}{dr^2}, \tag{2.39}$$

$$\mathbf{V}^2 r^n = n(n+1)r^{n-2}. \tag{2.40}$$

Finally, from Eq. 2.33

$$\mathbf{V}\times\mathbf{r}_0 f(r) = 0. \tag{2.41}$$

EXAMPLE 2.4.2

The computation of the magnetic vector potential of a single current loop in the xy plane involves the evaluation of

$$\mathbf{V} = \mathbf{V}\times[\mathbf{V}\times\boldsymbol{\varphi}_0 A_\varphi(r,\theta)]. \tag{2.41a}$$

In spherical polar coordinates this reduces as follows:

$$\mathbf{V} = \nabla \times \frac{1}{r^2 \sin \theta} \begin{vmatrix} \mathbf{r}_0 & r\mathbf{\theta}_0 & r\sin\theta\mathbf{\varphi}_0 \\ \dfrac{\partial}{\partial r} & \dfrac{\partial}{\partial \theta} & \dfrac{\partial}{\partial \varphi} \\ 0 & 0 & r\sin\theta A_\varphi(r,\theta) \end{vmatrix}$$

$$= \nabla \times \frac{1}{r^2 \sin\theta} \left[\mathbf{r}_0 \frac{\partial}{\partial\theta}(r\sin\theta A_\varphi) - r\mathbf{\theta}_0 \frac{\partial}{\partial r}(r\sin\theta A_\varphi) \right]. \tag{2.41b}$$

Taking the curl a second time,

$$\mathbf{V} = \frac{1}{r^2 \sin\theta} \begin{vmatrix} \mathbf{r}_0 & r\mathbf{\theta}_0 & r\sin\theta\mathbf{\varphi}_0 \\ \dfrac{\partial}{\partial r} & \dfrac{\partial}{\partial\theta} & \dfrac{\partial}{\partial\varphi} \\ \dfrac{1}{r^2\sin\theta}\dfrac{\partial}{\partial\theta}(r\sin\theta A_\varphi) & -\dfrac{1}{\sin\theta}\dfrac{\partial}{\partial r}(r\sin\theta A_\varphi) & 0 \end{vmatrix}. \tag{2.41c}$$

By expanding the determinant

$$\mathbf{V} = -\mathbf{\varphi}_0 \left\{ \frac{1}{r}\frac{\partial^2}{\partial r^2}(rA_\varphi) + \frac{1}{r^2}\frac{\partial}{\partial\theta}\left[\frac{1}{\sin\theta}\frac{\partial}{\partial\theta}(\sin\theta A_\varphi) \right] \right\}$$

$$= -\mathbf{\varphi}_0 \left[\nabla^2 A_\varphi(r,\theta) - \frac{1}{r^2\sin^2\theta}A_\varphi(r,\theta) \right].$$

In Chapter 12 we shall see that **V** leads to the associated Legendre equation and that A_φ may be given by a series of associated Legendre polynomials.

EXERCISES

2.4.1 Resolve the spherical polar unit vectors into their cartesian components.

$$\mathbf{r}_0 = \mathbf{i}\sin\theta\cos\varphi + \mathbf{j}\sin\theta\sin\varphi + \mathbf{k}\cos\theta,$$
$$\mathbf{\theta}_0 = \mathbf{i}\cos\theta\cos\varphi + \mathbf{j}\cos\theta\sin\varphi - \mathbf{k}\sin\theta,$$
$$\mathbf{\varphi}_0 = -\mathbf{i}\sin\varphi + \mathbf{j}\cos\varphi.$$

2.4.2 Resolve the cartesian unit vectors into their spherical polar components.

$$\mathbf{i} = \mathbf{r}_0\sin\theta\cos\varphi + \mathbf{\theta}_0\cos\theta\cos\varphi - \mathbf{\varphi}_0\sin\varphi,$$
$$\mathbf{j} = \mathbf{r}_0\sin\theta\sin\varphi + \mathbf{\theta}_0\cos\theta\sin\varphi + \mathbf{\varphi}_0\cos\varphi,$$
$$\mathbf{k} = \mathbf{r}_0\cos\theta - \mathbf{\theta}_0\sin\theta.$$

2.4.3 A particle is moving through space. Find the spherical coordinate components of its velocity and acceleration:

$$v_r = \dot{r},$$

$$v_\theta = r\dot{\theta},$$

$$v_\varphi = r\sin\theta\,\dot{\varphi},$$

$$a_r = \ddot{r} - r\dot{\theta}^2 - r\sin\theta\,\dot{\varphi}^2,$$

$$a_\theta = r\ddot{\theta} + 2\dot{r}\dot{\theta} - r\sin\theta\cos\theta\,\dot{\varphi}^2,$$

$$a_\varphi = r\sin\theta\,\ddot{\varphi} + 2\dot{r}\sin\theta\,\dot{\varphi} + 2r\cos\theta\,\dot{\theta}\dot{\varphi}.$$

2.4.4 A particle m moves in response to a central force according to Newton's second law

$$m\ddot{\mathbf{r}} = \mathbf{r}_0\,f(r).$$

Show that $\mathbf{r} \times \dot{\mathbf{r}} = \mathbf{c}$, a constant and that the geometric interpretation of this leads to Kepler's second law.

2.4.5 Express $\partial/\partial x$, $\partial/\partial y$, $\partial/\partial z$ in spherical polar coordinates.

$$\frac{\partial}{\partial x} = \sin\theta\cos\varphi\frac{\partial}{\partial r} + \cos\theta\cos\varphi\frac{1}{r}\frac{\partial}{\partial\theta} - \frac{\sin\varphi}{r\sin\theta}\frac{\partial}{\partial\varphi},$$

$$\frac{\partial}{\partial y} = \sin\theta\sin\varphi\frac{\partial}{\partial r} + \cos\theta\sin\varphi\frac{1}{r}\frac{\partial}{\partial\theta} + \frac{\cos\varphi}{r\sin\theta}\frac{\partial}{\partial\varphi},$$

$$\frac{\partial}{\partial z} = \cos\theta\frac{\partial}{\partial r} - \sin\theta\frac{1}{r}\frac{\partial}{\partial\theta}.$$

2.4.6 From Exercise 2.4.5 show that

$$-i\left(x\frac{\partial}{dy} - y\frac{\partial}{dx}\right) = -i\frac{\partial}{\partial\varphi}.$$

This is the quantum mechanical operator corresponding to the z-component of angular momentum.

2.4.7 Show that the following three forms (spherical coordinates) of $\nabla^2\,\psi(r)$ are equivalent.

(a) $\dfrac{1}{r^2}\dfrac{d}{dr}\left[r^2\dfrac{d\psi(r)}{dr}\right]$,

(b) $\dfrac{1}{r}\dfrac{d^2}{dr^2}\left[r\psi(r)\right]$,

(c) $\dfrac{d^2\psi(r)}{dr^2} + \dfrac{2}{r}\dfrac{d\psi(r)}{dr}$.

The second form is particularly convenient in establishing a correspondence between spherical polar and cartesian descriptions of a problem.

2.4.8 If $\nabla^2\psi = 0$, show that $\nabla^2\,\nabla^2(r^2\psi) = 0$.

2.4.9 One model of the solar corona assumes that the steady-state equation of heat flow

$$\nabla\cdot(k\,\nabla T) = 0$$

is satisfied. Here, k, the thermal conductivity, is proportional to $T^{5/2}$. Assuming that the temperature T is proportional to r^n, show that the heat flow equation is satisfied by $T = T_0(r_0/r)^{2/7}$.

2.4.10 Verify the following vector operator equations:

(a) $\nabla = \mathbf{r}_0(\mathbf{r}_0\cdot\nabla) - \mathbf{r}_0\times(\mathbf{r}_0\times\nabla)$,

(b) $\nabla\times(\mathbf{r}\times\nabla) = \mathbf{r}\nabla^2 - \nabla\left(1 + r\dfrac{\partial}{\partial r}\right)$.

2.4.11 A certain force field is given by

$$\mathbf{F} = \mathbf{r}_0 \frac{2P\cos\theta}{r^3} + \mathbf{\theta}_0 \frac{P}{r^3}\sin\theta, \qquad r \ge P/2,$$

(in spherical polar coordinates).
(a) Examine $\nabla \times \mathbf{F}$ to see if a potential exists.
(b) Calculate $\oint \mathbf{F} \cdot d\lambda$ for a unit circle in the plane $\theta = \pi/2$.
    What does this indicate about the force being conservative or nonconservative?
(c) If you believe that $\mathbf{F}$ may be described by $\mathbf{F} = -\nabla\varphi$, find φ. Otherwise simply state
    that no acceptable potential exists.

2.4.12 (a) Show that $\mathbf{A} = -\mathbf{\varphi}_0 (\cot\theta/r)$ is a solution of $\nabla \times \mathbf{A} = \mathbf{r}_0/r^2$.
(b) Show that this spherical polar coordinate solution agrees with the solution given for
    Exercise 1.13.2:

$$\mathbf{A} = \mathbf{i}\frac{yz}{r(x^2 + y^2)} - \mathbf{j}\frac{xz}{r(x^2 + y^2)}.$$

Note that the solution diverges for $\theta = 0, \pi$ corresponding to $x, y = 0$.
(c) Finally, show that $\mathbf{A} = -\mathbf{\theta}_0 \varphi(\sin\theta/r)$ is a solution. Note that although this solution
    does not diverge $(r \ne 0)$ it is no longer single-valued for all possible azimuth angles.

2.4.13 Show that in spherical polar coordinates Maxwell's equations become

$$\frac{1}{r\sin\theta}\left[\frac{\partial}{\partial\theta}(\sin\theta E_\varphi) - \frac{\partial E_\theta}{\partial\varphi}\right] + \mu_0\frac{\partial E_r}{\partial t} = 0,$$

$$\frac{1}{r\sin\theta}\frac{\partial E_r}{\partial\varphi} - \frac{1}{r}\frac{\partial(rE_\varphi)}{\partial r} + \mu_0\frac{\partial H_\theta}{\partial t} = 0,$$

$$\frac{1}{r}\frac{\partial(rE_\theta)}{\partial r} - \frac{1}{r}\frac{\partial E_r}{\partial\theta} + \mu_0\frac{\partial H_\varphi}{\partial t} = 0,$$

$$\frac{1}{r^2}\frac{\partial}{\partial r}(r^2 H_r) + \frac{1}{r\sin\theta}\frac{\partial}{\partial\theta}(\sin\theta H_\theta) + \frac{1}{r\sin\theta}\frac{\partial H_\varphi}{\partial\varphi} = 0,$$

and four additional equations corresponding to them but with $\mathbf{E} \to \mathbf{H}$ and $\mu_0\mathbf{H} \to -\varepsilon_0\mathbf{E}$.

2.4.14 Modern physics lays great stress on the property of parity—whether a quantity remains
invariant or changes sign under an inversion of the coordinate system.
(a) Show that the inversion (reflection through the origin) of a point (r, θ, φ) relative to
    fixed x-, y-, z-axes consists of the transformation

$$r \to r,$$
$$\theta \to \pi - \theta,$$
$$\varphi \to \pi + \varphi.$$

(b) Show that $\mathbf{r}_0$ and $\mathbf{\varphi}_0$ have odd parity (reversal of direction) and that $\mathbf{\theta}_0$ has even parity.

2.4.15 A vector $\mathbf{V}$ is tangential to the surface of a sphere. The curl of $\mathbf{V}$ is radial. What does this
imply about the radial dependence of the spherical polar components of $\mathbf{V}$?

2.4.16 With the quantum mechanical angular momentum operator defined as $\mathbf{L} = -i(\mathbf{r} \times \nabla)$,
show that

(a) $L_x + iL_y = e^{i\varphi}\left(\dfrac{\partial}{\partial\theta} + i\cot\theta\dfrac{\partial}{\partial\varphi}\right)$,

(b) $L_x - iL_y = -e^{-i\varphi}\left(\dfrac{\partial}{\partial\theta} - i\cot\theta\dfrac{\partial}{\partial\varphi}\right)$.

2.4.17 (a) From the results of Exercise 2.4.1 calculate the partial derivatives of $\mathbf{r}_0, \mathbf{\theta}_0$, and $\mathbf{\varphi}_0$
    with respect to r, θ, and φ.

(b) With ∇ given by

$$\mathbf{r}_0 \frac{\partial}{\partial r} + \boldsymbol{\theta}_0 \frac{1}{r} \frac{\partial}{\partial \theta} + \boldsymbol{\varphi}_0 \frac{1}{r \sin \theta} \frac{\partial}{\partial \varphi}$$

(greatest space rate of change), use the results of part (a) to calculate $\nabla \cdot \nabla \psi$. Here is an alternate derivation of the Laplacian.

2.5   Separation of Variables

In cartesian coordinates the Helmholtz equation (Eq. 2.1) becomes

$$\frac{\partial^2 \psi}{\partial x^2} + \frac{\partial^2 \psi}{\partial y^2} + \frac{\partial^2 \psi}{\partial z^2} + k^2 \psi = 0, \tag{2.42}$$

using Eq. 2.26 for the Laplacian. For the present let k^2 be a constant. Perhaps the simplest way of treating a partial differential equation such as 2.42 is to split it up into a set of ordinary differential equations. This may be done as follows: Let

$$\psi(x, y, z) = X(x)\, Y(y)\, Z(z) \tag{2.43}$$

and substitute back into Eq. 2.42. How do we know Eq. 2.43 is valid? The answer is very simple. We do not know it is valid! Rather we are proceeding in the spirit of let's try it and see if it works. If our attempt succeeds, then Eq. 2.43 will be justified. If it does not succeed, we shall find out soon enough and then we shall have to try another attack such as Green's functions, integral transforms, or brute force numerical analysis. With ψ assumed given by Eq. 2.43, Eq. 2.42 becomes

$$YZ \frac{d^2 X}{dx^2} + XZ \frac{d^2 Y}{dy^2} + XY \frac{d^2 Z}{dz^2} + k^2 XYZ = 0. \tag{2.44}$$

Dividing by $\psi = XYZ$ and rearranging terms, we obtain

$$\frac{1}{X} \frac{d^2 X}{dx^2} = -k^2 - \frac{1}{Y} \frac{d^2 Y}{dy^2} - \frac{1}{Z} \frac{d^2 Z}{dz^2}. \tag{2.45}$$

Equation 2.45 exhibits one separation of variables. The left-hand side is a function of x alone, whereas the right-hand side depends only on y and z. So Eq. 2.45 is a sort of paradox. A function of x is equated to a function of y and z, but x, y, and z are all independent coordinates. This independence means that the behavior of x as an independent variable is not determined by y and z. The paradox is resolved by setting each side equal to a constant, a constant of separation. We choose[1]

$$\frac{1}{X} \frac{d^2 X}{dx^2} = -l^2, \tag{2.46}$$

$$-k^2 - \frac{1}{Y} \frac{d^2 Y}{dy^2} - \frac{1}{Z} \frac{d^2 Z}{dz^2} = -l^2. \tag{2.47}$$

Now, turning our attention to Eq. 2.47,

$$\frac{1}{Y} \frac{d^2 Y}{dy^2} = -k^2 + l^2 - \frac{1}{Z} \frac{d^2 Z}{dz^2}, \tag{2.48}$$

---

[1] The choice of sign, completely arbitrary here, will be fixed in specific problems by the need to satisfy specific boundary conditions.

and a second separation has been achieved. Here we have a function of y equated to a function of z and the same paradox appears. We resolve it as before by equating each side to another constant of separation, $-m^2$,

$$\frac{1}{Y}\frac{d^2Y}{dy^2} = -m^2, \tag{2.49}$$

$$\frac{1}{Z}\frac{d^2Z}{dz^2} = -k^2 + l^2 + m^2 = -n^2, \tag{2.50}$$

introducing a constant n^2 by $k^2 = l^2 + m^2 + n^2$ to produce a symmetric set of equations. Now we have three ordinary differential equations (2.46, 2.49, and 2.50) to replace Eq. 2.42. Our assumption (Eq. 2.43) has succeeded and is thereby justified.

Our solution should be labeled according to the choice of our constants l, m, and n, that is,

$$\psi_{lmn}(x, y, z) = X_l(x)\, Y_m(y)\, Z_n(z). \tag{2.50a}$$

Subject to the conditions of the problem being solved and to the condition $k^2 = l^2 + m^2 + n^2$, we may choose l, m, and n as we like, and Eq. 2.50a will still be a solution of Eq. 2.1, provided $X_l(x)$ is a solution of Eq. 2.46, etc. We may develop the most general solution of Eq. 2.1 by taking a linear combination of solutions ψ_{lmn}.

$$\Psi = \sum_{l,m,n} a_{lmn}\psi_{lmn}. \tag{2.50b}$$

The constant coefficients a_{lmn} are finally chosen to permit Ψ to satisfy the boundary conditions of the problem.

How is this possible? What is the justification for writing Eq. 2.50b? The justification is found in noting that $\nabla^2 + k^2$ is a linear (differential) operator. A linear operator $\mathscr{L}$ is defined as an operator with the following two properties:

$$\mathscr{L}(a\psi) = a\mathscr{L}\psi,$$

where a is a constant and

$$\mathscr{L}(\psi_1 + \psi_2) = \mathscr{L}\psi_1 + \mathscr{L}\psi_2.$$

As a consequence of these properties, any linear combination of solutions of a linear differential equation is also a solution. From its explicit form $\nabla^2 + k^2$ is seen to have these two properties (and is therefore a linear operator). Equation 2.50b then follows as a direct application of these two defining properties.

A further generalization may be noted. The separation process just described would go through just as well for

$$k^2 = f(x) + g(y) + h(z) + k'^2, \tag{2.50c}$$

with k'^2 a new constant.

We would simply have

$$\frac{1}{X}\frac{d^2X}{dx^2} + f(x) = -l^2 \tag{2.50d}$$

replacing Eq. 2.46. The solutions X, Y, and Z would be different, but the technique of splitting the partial differential equation and of taking a linear combination of solutions would be the same.

In case the reader wonders what is going on here, this technique of separation of variables of a partial differential equation has been introduced to illustrate the usefulness of these coordinate systems. The solutions of the resultant ordinary differential equations are developed in Chapters 8 through 13.

Let us try to separate Eq. 2.1, again with k^2 constant, in spherical polar coordinates. Using Eq. 2.32, we obtain

$$\frac{1}{r^2 \sin \theta} \left[\sin \theta \frac{\partial}{\partial r} \left(r^2 \frac{\partial \psi}{\partial r} \right) + \frac{\partial}{\partial \theta} \left(\sin \theta \frac{\partial \psi}{\partial \theta} \right) + \frac{1}{\sin \theta} \frac{\partial^2 \psi}{\partial \varphi^2} \right] = -k^2 \psi. \tag{2.51}$$

Now, in analogy with Eq. 2.43 we try

$$\psi(r, \theta, \varphi) = R(r)\, \Theta(\theta)\, \Phi(\varphi). \tag{2.52}$$

By substituting back into Eq. 2.51 and dividing by $R\Theta\Phi$, we have

$$\frac{1}{Rr^2} \frac{d}{dr} \left(r^2 \frac{dR}{dr} \right) + \frac{1}{\Theta r^2 \sin \theta} \frac{d}{d\theta} \left(\sin \theta \frac{d\Theta}{d\theta} \right) + \frac{1}{\Phi r^2 \sin^2 \theta} \frac{d^2 \Phi}{d\varphi^2} = -k^2. \tag{2.53}$$

Note that all derivatives are now ordinary derivatives rather than partials. By multiplying by $r^2 \sin^2 \theta$ we can isolate $(1/\Phi)(d^2\Phi/d\varphi^2)$ to obtain

$$\frac{1}{\Phi} \frac{d^2 \Phi}{d\varphi^2} = r^2 \sin^2 \theta \left[-k^2 - \frac{1}{r^2 R} \frac{d}{dr} \left(r^2 \frac{dR}{dr} \right) - \frac{1}{r^2 \sin \theta \, \Theta} \frac{d}{d\theta} \left(\sin \theta \frac{d\Theta}{d\theta} \right) \right]. \tag{2.54}$$

Equation 2.54 relates a function of φ alone to a function of r and θ alone. Since r, θ, and φ are independent variables, we equate each side of Eq. 2.54 to a constant. Here a little consideration can simplify the later analysis. In almost all physical problems φ will appear as an azimuth angle. This suggests a periodic solution rather than an exponential. With this in mind, let us use $-m^2$ as the separation constant. Any constant will do, but this one will make life a little easier. Then

$$\frac{1}{\Phi} \frac{d^2 \Phi(\varphi)}{d\varphi^2} = -m^2 \tag{2.55}$$

and

$$\frac{1}{r^2 R} \frac{d}{dr} \left(r^2 \frac{dR}{dr} \right) + \frac{1}{r^2 \sin \theta \, \Theta} \frac{d}{d\theta} \left(\sin \theta \frac{d\Theta}{d\theta} \right) - \frac{m^2}{r^2 \sin^2 \theta} = -k^2. \tag{2.56}$$

Multiplying Eq. 2.56 by r^2 and rearranging terms, we obtain

$$\frac{1}{R} \frac{d}{dr} \left(r^2 \frac{dR}{dr} \right) + r^2 k^2 = -\frac{1}{\sin \theta \, \Theta} \frac{d}{d\theta} \left(\sin \theta \frac{d\Theta}{d\theta} \right) + \frac{m^2}{\sin^2 \theta}. \tag{2.57}$$

Again the variables are separated. We equate each side to a constant Q and finally obtain

$$\frac{1}{\sin \theta} \frac{d}{d\theta} \left(\sin \theta \frac{d\Theta}{d\theta} \right) - \frac{m^2}{\sin^2 \theta} \Theta + Q\Theta = 0, \tag{2.58}$$

$$\frac{1}{r^2} \frac{d}{dr} \left(r^2 \frac{dR}{dr} \right) + k^2 R - \frac{QR}{r^2} = 0. \tag{2.59}$$

Once more we have replaced a partial differential equation of three variables by three ordinary differential equations. The solutions of these ordinary differential equations are disucssed in Chapters 11 and 12. In Chapter 12, for example, Eq. 2.58 is identified as the associated Legendre equation in which the constant Q becomes $l(l + 1)$; l is an integer.

Again, our most general solution may be written

$$\psi_{Qm}(r, \theta, \varphi) = \sum_{Q,m} R_Q(r)\, \Theta_{Qm}(\theta)\, \Phi_m(\varphi). \tag{2.60a}$$

The restriction that k^2 be a constant is unnecessarily severe. The separation process will still be possible for k^2 as general as

$$k^2 = f(r) + \frac{1}{r^2}\, g(\theta) + \frac{1}{r^2 \sin^2\theta}\, h(\varphi) + k'^2. \tag{2.60b}$$

In the hydrogen atom problem, one of the most important examples of the Schrödinger wave equation with a closed form solution we have $k^2 = f(r)$. Equation 2.59 for the hydrogen atom becomes the associated Laguerre equation. Separation of variables and an investigation of the resulting ordinary differential equations are taken up again in Section 8.3. Now we return to an investigation of the remaining special coordinate systems.

EXERCISES

2.5.1 By letting the operator $\nabla^2 + k^2$ act on the general form $a_1 \psi_1(x, y, z) + a_2 \psi_2(x, y, z)$, show that it is linear, that is, that $(\nabla^2 + k^2)(a_1\psi_1 + a_2\psi_2) = a_1(\nabla^2 + k^2)\psi_1 + a_2(\nabla^2 + k^2)\psi_2$.

2.5.2 Verify that

$$\nabla^2 \psi(r, \theta, \varphi) + \left[k^2 + f(r) + \frac{1}{r^2}\, g(\theta) + \frac{1}{r^2 \sin^2\theta}\, h(\varphi) \right] \psi(r, \theta, \varphi) = 0$$

is separable (in spherical polar coordinates). The functions f, g, and h are functions only of the variables indicated; k^2 is a constant.

2.5.3 An atomic (quantum mechanical) particle is confined inside a rectangular box of sides a, b, and c. The particle is described by a wave function ψ which satisfies the Schrödinger wave equation

$$-\frac{\hbar^2}{2m}\, \nabla^2 \psi = E\psi.$$

The wave function is required to vanish at each surface of the box (but not to be identically zero). This condition imposes constraints on the separation constants and therefore on the energy E. What is the smallest value of E for which such a solution can be obtained?

$$Ans.\ E = \frac{\pi^2 \hbar^2}{2m} \left(\frac{1}{a^2} + \frac{1}{b^2} + \frac{1}{c^2} \right).$$

2.6 Circular Cylindrical Coordinates (ρ, φ, z)

From Fig. 2.4 we obtain the transformation relations

$$x = \rho \cos \varphi.$$

$$y = \rho \sin \varphi, \tag{2.61}$$

$$z = z,$$

using ρ for the perpendicular distance from the z-axis and saving r for the distance from the origin. According to these equations or from the length elements the scale factors are

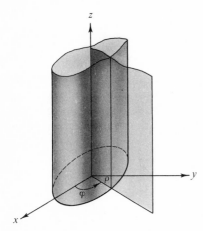

FIG. 2.4 Circular cylinder co-ordinates

$$h_1 = h_\rho = 1,$$

$$h_2 = h_\varphi = \rho, \tag{2.62}$$

$$h_3 = h_z = 1.$$

The families of coordinate surfaces shown in Fig. 2.4 are

1. Right circular cylinders having the z-axis as a common axis,

$$\rho = (x^2 + y^2)^{1/2} = \text{constant}.$$

2. Half planes through the z-axis,

$$\varphi = \tan^{-1}\left(\frac{y}{x}\right) = \text{constant}.$$

3. Planes parallel to the xy-plane, as in the cartesian system,

$$z = \text{constant}.$$

The limits on ρ, φ and z are

$$0 \leqslant \rho < \infty, \qquad 0 \leqslant \varphi \leqslant 2\pi, \quad \text{and} \quad -\infty < z < \infty.$$

From Eqs. 2.13, 2.17, 2.18, and 2.22,

$$\nabla\psi(\rho, \varphi, z) = \boldsymbol{\rho}_0 \frac{\partial\psi}{\partial\rho} + \boldsymbol{\varphi}_0 \frac{1}{\rho}\frac{\partial\psi}{\partial\varphi} + \mathbf{k}\frac{\partial\psi}{\partial z}, \tag{2.63}$$

$$\mathbf{V}\cdot\mathbf{V} = \frac{1}{\rho}\frac{\partial}{\partial\rho}(\rho V_\rho) + \frac{1}{\rho}\frac{\partial V_\varphi}{\partial\varphi} + \frac{\partial V_z}{\partial z}, \tag{2.64}$$

$$\nabla^2\psi = \frac{1}{\rho}\frac{\partial}{\partial\rho}\left(\rho\frac{\partial\psi}{\partial\rho}\right) + \frac{1}{\rho^2}\frac{\partial^2\psi}{\partial\varphi^2} + \frac{\partial^2\psi}{\partial z^2}, \tag{2.65}$$

$$\mathbf{V} \times \mathbf{V} = \frac{1}{\rho} \begin{vmatrix} \boldsymbol{\rho_0} & \rho\boldsymbol{\varphi_0} & \mathbf{k} \\ \dfrac{\partial}{\partial\rho} & \dfrac{\partial}{\partial\varphi} & \dfrac{\partial}{\partial z} \\ V_\rho & \rho V_\varphi & V_z \end{vmatrix}. \tag{2.66}$$

Finally, for problems such as circular wave guides or cylindrical cavity resonators the vector Laplacian $\mathbf{V}^2\mathbf{V}$ resolved in circular cylindrical coordinates is

$$\mathbf{V}^2\mathbf{V}|_\rho = \nabla^2 V_\rho - \frac{1}{\rho^2} V_\rho - \frac{2}{\rho^2} \frac{\partial V_\varphi}{\partial\varphi},$$

$$\mathbf{V}^2\mathbf{V}|_\varphi = \nabla^2 V_\varphi - \frac{1}{\rho^2} V_\varphi + \frac{2}{\rho^2} \frac{\partial V_\rho}{\partial\varphi}, \tag{2.67}$$

$$\mathbf{V}^2\mathbf{V}|_z = \nabla^2 V_z.$$

The basic reason for the form of the z-component is that the z-axis is a cartesian axis, that is,

$$\mathbf{V}^2(\boldsymbol{\rho_0} V_\rho + \boldsymbol{\varphi_0} V_\varphi + \mathbf{k} V_z) = \mathbf{V}^2(\boldsymbol{\rho_0} V_\rho + \boldsymbol{\varphi_0} V_\varphi) + \mathbf{k}\, \mathbf{V}^2 V_z$$

$$= \boldsymbol{\rho_0} f(V_\rho, V_\varphi) + \boldsymbol{\varphi_0} g(V_\rho, V_\varphi) + \mathbf{k}\, \mathbf{V}^2 V_z.$$

The operator $\mathbf{V}^2$ operating on the $\boldsymbol{\rho_0}$, $\boldsymbol{\varphi_0}$ unit vectors stays in the $\boldsymbol{\rho_0}\,\boldsymbol{\varphi_0}$-plane. This behavior holds in all such cylindrical systems.

EXAMPLE 2.6.1

The wave equation for the space-dependent amplitude of an electromagnetic wave in a cylindrical wave guide is

$$\mathbf{V}^2\psi + k^2\psi = 0.$$

For a wave guide with perfectly conducting walls there is no attentuation and therefore no·z-dependence. (Here the central axis of the cylindrical wave guide is taken to be the z-axis). Then, using Eq. 2.65, we have

$$\frac{1}{\rho}\frac{\partial}{\partial\rho}\left(\rho\frac{\partial\psi}{\partial\rho}\right) + \frac{1}{\rho^2}\frac{\partial^2\psi}{\partial\varphi^2} + k^2\psi = 0. \tag{2.68}$$

We try

$$\psi(\rho, \varphi) = P(\rho)\,\Phi(\varphi) \tag{2.69}$$

to obtain

$$\frac{1}{P\rho}\frac{d}{d\rho}\left(\rho\frac{dP}{d\rho}\right) + \frac{1}{\Phi\rho^2}\frac{d^2\Phi}{d\varphi^2} + k^2 = 0. \tag{2.70}$$

Mutliplying by ρ^2 to isolate the φ-dependence, we set

$$\frac{1}{\Phi}\frac{d^2\Phi}{d\varphi^2} = -m^2, \tag{2.71}$$

again choosing $-m^2$ since φ is an azimuth angle and again expecting solutions of the form $\sin m\varphi$, $\cos m\varphi$ rather than real exponentials. The radial equation becomes

$$\frac{1}{\rho}\frac{d}{d\rho}\left(\rho\,\frac{dP}{d\rho}\right) + \left(k^2 - \frac{m^2}{\rho^2}\right)P = 0. \tag{2.72}$$

This is Bessel's equation. The solutions are developed in Chapter 11.

EXERCISES

2.6.1 Resolve the circular cylindrical unit vectors into their cartesian components.

$$\boldsymbol{\rho}_0 = \mathbf{i}\cos\varphi + \mathbf{j}\sin\varphi,$$
$$\boldsymbol{\varphi}_0 = -\mathbf{i}\sin\varphi + \mathbf{j}\cos\varphi,$$
$$\mathbf{k}_0 = \mathbf{k}.$$

2.6.2 Resolve the cartesian unit vectors into their circular cylindrical components.

$$\mathbf{i} = \boldsymbol{\rho}_0\cos\varphi - \boldsymbol{\varphi}_0\sin\varphi,$$
$$\mathbf{j} = \boldsymbol{\rho}_0\sin\varphi + \boldsymbol{\varphi}_0\cos\varphi,$$
$$\mathbf{k} = \mathbf{k}_0.$$

2.6.3 A particle is moving through space. Find the circular cylindrical components of its velocity and acceleration.

$$v_\rho = \dot{\rho}, \qquad a_\rho = \ddot{\rho} - \rho\dot{\varphi}^2,$$
$$v_\varphi = \rho\dot{\varphi}, \qquad a_\varphi = \rho\ddot{\varphi} + 2\dot{\rho}\dot{\varphi},$$
$$v_z = \ddot{z}, \qquad a_z = \dot{z}.$$

2.6.4 A conducting wire along the z-axis carries a current I. The resulting magnetic vector potential is given by

$$\mathbf{A} = \mathbf{k}\,\frac{\mu I}{2\pi}\ln\left(\frac{1}{\rho}\right).$$

Show that the magnetic inductance $\mathbf{B}$ is given by

$$\mathbf{B} = \boldsymbol{\varphi}_0\,\frac{\mu I}{2\pi\rho}.$$

2.6.5 Solve Laplace's equation $\nabla^2\psi = 0$, in cylindrical coordinates for $\psi = \psi(\rho)$.

$$Ans.\ \psi = k\,\ln\frac{\rho}{\rho_0}$$

2.6.6 In right circular cylindrical coordinates a particular vector function is given by

$$\mathbf{V}(\rho, \varphi) = \mathbf{\rho}_0 V_\rho(\rho, \varphi) + \mathbf{\varphi}_0 V_\varphi(\rho, \varphi).$$

Show that $\nabla \times \mathbf{V}$ has only a z-component. Note that this result will hold for any vector confined to a surface $q_3 = $ constant as long as the products $h_1 V_1$ and $h_2 V_2$ are each independent of q_3.

2.6.7 A force is described by

$$\mathbf{F} = -\mathbf{i}\,\frac{y}{x^2 + y^2} + \mathbf{j}\,\frac{x}{x^2 + y^2}\,.$$

(a) Express $\mathbf{F}$ in circular cylindrical coordinates.

Operating entirely in circular cylindrical coordinates for (b) and (c),

(b) calculate the curl of $\mathbf{F}$ and

(c) calculate the work done by $\mathbf{F}$ in encircling the unit circle once counterclockwise.

(d) How do you reconcile the results of (b) and (c)?

2.6.8 Show that the Helmholtz equation

$$\nabla^2 \psi + k^2 \psi = 0$$

is still separable in circular cylindrical coordinates if k^2 is generalized to $k^2 + f(\rho) + (1/\rho^2)g(\varphi) + h(z)$.

2.7 Elliptic Cylindrical Coordinates (u, v, z)

One reasonable way of classifying the separable coordinate systems is to start with the confocal ellipsoidal system (Section 2.15) and derive the other systems as degenerate cases. Details of this procedure will be found in Morse and Feshbach's *Methods of Mathematical Physics*, Chapter 5. Here, to emphasize the application rather than a derivation, we take the coordinate systems in order of symmetry properties, proceeding with those that have an axis of translation. All of those with an axis of translation are essentially two-dimensional systems with a third dimension (the z-axis) tacked on.

For the elliptic cylindrical system we have

$$x = a \cosh u \cos v,$$

$$y = a \sinh u \sin v, \tag{2.73}$$

$$z = z.$$

The families of coordinate surfaces are the following:

1. Elliptic cylinders, $u = $ constant, $0 \leqslant u < \infty$.

2. Hyperbolic cylinders, $v = $ constant, $0 \leqslant v \leqslant 2\pi$.

3. Planes parallel to the xy-plane, $z = $ constant, $-\infty < z < \infty$.

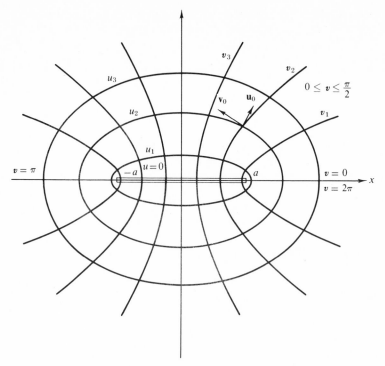

FIG. 2.5 Elliptic cylindrical coordinates

This may be seen by inverting Eq. 2.73. Squaring each side,

$$x^2 = a^2 \cosh^2 u \cos^2 v, \tag{2.74}$$

$$y^2 = a^2 \sinh^2 u \sin^2 v, \tag{2.75}$$

from which

$$\frac{x^2}{a^2 \cosh^2 u} + \frac{y^2}{a^2 \sinh^2 u} = 1, \tag{2.76}$$

$$\frac{x^2}{a^2 \cos^2 v} - \frac{y^2}{a^2 \sin^2 v} = 1. \tag{2.77}$$

Holding u constant, Eq. 2.76 yields a family of ellipses with the x-axis the major one. For $v =$ constant, Eq. 2.77 gives hyperbolas with focal points on the x-axis.

The scale factors are

$$h_1 = h_u = a(\sinh^2 u + \sin^2 v)^{1/2},$$
$$h_2 = h_v = a(\sinh^2 u + \sin^2 v)^{1/2}, \tag{2.78}$$
$$h_3 = h_z = 1.$$

We shall meet this system again as a two-dimensional system in Chapter 6 when we take up conformal mapping.

EXERCISES

2.7.1 Let $\cosh u = q_1$, $\cos v = q_2$, $z = q_3$. Find the new scale factors h_{q_1} and h_{q_2}.

$$h_{q_1} = a \left(\frac{q_1^2 - q_2^2}{q_1^2 - 1} \right)^{1/2},$$

$$h_{q_2} = a \left(\frac{q_1^2 - q_2^2}{1 - q_2^2} \right)^{1/2}.$$

2.8 Parabolic Cylindrical Coordinates (ξ, η, z)

The transformation equations,

$$x = \xi\eta,$$
$$y = \tfrac{1}{2}(\eta^2 - \xi^2), \qquad\qquad (2.79)$$
$$z = z,$$

generate two sets of orthogonal parabolic cylinders (Fig. 2.6). By solving Eq. 2.79 for ξ and η we obtain the following:

1. Parabolic cylinders, $\xi = $ constant,[1] $-\infty < \xi < \infty$.

2. Parabolic cylinders, $\eta = $ constant, $0 \leqslant \eta < \infty$.

3. Planes parallel to the xy-plane, $z = $ constant, $-\infty < z < \infty$.

From Eq. 2.6 the scale factors are

$$h_1 = h_\xi = (\xi^2 + \eta^2)^{1/2},$$
$$h_2 = h_\eta = (\xi^2 + \eta^2)^{1/2}, \qquad\qquad (2.80)$$
$$h_3 = h_z = 1.$$

2.9 Bipolar Coordinates (ξ, η, z)

This is an oddball coordinate system. It is not a degenerate case of the confocal ellipsoidal coordinates. Equation 2.1 is not completely separable in this system even for $k^2 = 0$ (cf. Exercise 2.9.2). It is included here as an example of how an unusual coordinate system may be chosen to fit a problem.

---

[1] The parabolic cylinder $\xi = $ constant is invariant to the sign of ξ. We must let ξ (or η) go negative to cover negative values of x.

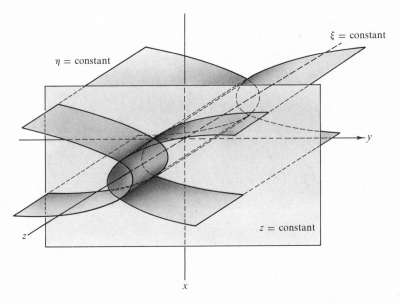

FIG. 2.6 Parabolic cylindrical coordinates. (*Top*) Cross section

The transformation equations are

$$x = \frac{a \sinh \eta}{\cosh \eta - \cos \xi}, \qquad (2.81a)$$

$$y = \frac{a \sin \xi}{\cosh \eta - \cos \xi}, \qquad (2.81b)$$

$$z = z. \qquad (2.81c)$$

Dividing Eq. 2.81a by 2.81b, we obtain

$$\frac{x}{y} = \frac{\sinh \eta}{\sin \xi}. \qquad (2.82)$$

Using Eq. 2.82 to eliminate ξ from Eq. 2.81a, we have

$$(x - a \coth \eta)^2 + y^2 = a^2 \operatorname{csch}^2 \eta. \qquad (2.83)$$

Using Eq. 2.82 to eliminate η from Eq. 2.81b, we have

$$x^2 + (y - a \cot \xi)^2 = a^2 \csc^2 \xi. \qquad (2.84)$$

From Eqs. 2.83 and 2.84 we may identify the coordinate surfaces as follows:

1. Circular cylinders, center at $y = a \cot \xi$,

$$\xi = \text{constant}, \qquad 0 \leqslant \xi \leqslant 2\pi.$$

2. Circular cylinders, center at $x = a \coth \eta$,

$$\eta = \text{constant}, \qquad -\infty < \eta < \infty.$$

3. Planes parallel to xy-plane,

$$z = \text{constant}, \qquad -\infty < z < \infty.$$

When $\eta \to \infty$, $\coth \eta \to 1$ and $\operatorname{csch} \eta \to 0$. Equation 2.83 has a solution $x = a$, $y = 0$. Similarly, when $\eta \to -\infty$, a solution is $x = -a$, $y = 0$, the circle degenerating to a point, the cylinder to a line. The family of circles (in the xy-plane) described by Eq. 2.84 passes through both of these points. This follows from noting that $x = \pm a$, $y = 0$ are solutions of Eq. 2.84 for any value of ξ.

The scale factors for the bipolar system are

$$h_1 = h_\xi = \frac{a}{\cosh \eta - \cos \xi},$$

$$h_2 = h_\eta = \frac{a}{\cosh \eta - \cos \xi}, \qquad (2.85)$$

$$h_3 = h_z = 1.$$

To see how the bipolar system may be useful let us start with the three points $(a, 0)$, $(-a, 0)$, and (x, y) and the two distance vectors ρ_1 and ρ_2 at angles of θ_1

FIG. 2.7 Bipolar coordinates

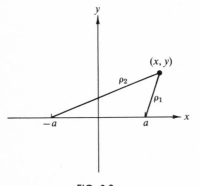

FIG. 2.8

and θ_2 from the positive x-axis. From Fig. 2.8

$$\rho_1^2 = (x - a)^2 + y^2,$$
$$\rho_2^2 = (x + a)^2 + y^2, \tag{2.86}$$

and

$$\tan \theta_1 = \frac{y}{x - a},$$
$$\tan \theta_2 = \frac{y}{x + a}. \tag{2.87}$$

We define[1]

$$\eta_{12} = \ln \frac{\rho_2}{\rho_1}, \tag{2.88a}$$

$$\xi_{12} = \theta_1 - \theta_2. \tag{2.88b}$$

By taking $\tan \xi_{12}$ and Eq. 2.87

$$\tan \xi_{12} = \frac{\tan \theta_1 - \tan \theta_2}{1 + \tan \theta_1 \tan \theta_2}$$

$$= \frac{y/(x - a) - y/(x + a)}{1 + y^2/(x - a)(x + a)}. \tag{2.89}$$

[1] The notation ln is used to indicate $\log_e$.

From Eq. 2.89, Eq. 2.84 follows directly. This identifies ξ as $\xi_{12} = \theta_1 - \theta_2$. Solving Eq. 2.88$a$ for ρ_2/ρ_1 and combining this with Eq. 2.86, we get

$$e^{2\eta_{12}} = \frac{\rho_2^2}{\rho_1^2} = \frac{(x+a)^2 + y^2}{(x-a)^2 + y^2} \tag{2.90}$$

Multiplication by $e^{-\eta_{12}}$ and use of the definitions of hyperbolic sine and cosine produces Eq. 2.83, which identifies η as $\eta_{12} = \ln(\rho_2/\rho_1)$. The following example exploits this identification.

EXAMPLE 2.9.1

An infinitely long straight wire carries a current I in the negative z-direction. A second wire, parallel to the first, carries a current I in the positive z-direction. Using

$$d\mathbf{A} = \frac{\mu_0}{4\pi} I \frac{d\lambda}{r}, \tag{2.91}$$

find $\mathbf{A}$, the magnetic vector potential, and $\mathbf{B}$, the magnetic inductance.

From Eq. 2.91 $\mathbf{A}$ has only a z-component. Integrating over each wire from 0 to P and taking the limit as $P \to \infty$, we obtain

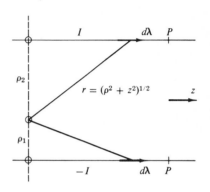

FIG. 2.9 Antiparallel electric currents

$$A_z = \frac{\mu_0 I}{4\pi} \lim_{P \to \infty} \left(2 \int_0^P \frac{dz}{\sqrt{\rho_2^2 + z^2}} - 2 \int_0^P \frac{dz}{\sqrt{\rho_1^2 + z^2}} \right), \tag{2.92}$$

$$A_z = \frac{\mu_0 I}{4\pi} \lim_{P \to \infty} 2[\ln(z + \sqrt{\rho_2^2 + z^2})|_0^P - \ln(z + \sqrt{\rho_1^2 + z^2})|_0^P],$$

$$= \frac{\mu_0 I}{4\pi} \left(\lim_{P \to \infty} 2 \ln \frac{P + \sqrt{\rho_2^2 + P^2}}{P + \sqrt{\rho_1^2 + P^2}} - 2 \ln \frac{\rho_2}{\rho_1} \right). \tag{2.93}$$

This reduces to

$$A_z = -\frac{\mu_0 I}{2\pi} \ln \frac{\rho_2}{\rho_1} = -\frac{\mu_0 I}{2\pi} \eta. \tag{2.94}$$

So far there has been no need for bipolar coordinates. Now, however, let us calculate the magnetic inductance $\mathbf{B}$ from $\mathbf{B} = \mathbf{V} \times \mathbf{A}$. From Eqs. 2.22 and 2.85

$$\mathbf{B} = \frac{(\cosh\eta - \cos\xi)^2}{a^2} \begin{vmatrix} h_\xi\xi_0 & h_\eta\eta_0 & \mathbf{k} \\ \dfrac{\partial}{\partial\xi} & \dfrac{\partial}{\partial\eta} & \dfrac{\partial}{\partial z} \\ 0 & 0 & \dfrac{-\mu_0 I}{2\pi}\eta \end{vmatrix},$$

$$= -\xi_0 \frac{(\cosh\eta - \cos\xi)}{a} \cdot \frac{\mu_0 I}{2\pi}. \tag{2.95}$$

The magnetic field has only a ξ_0-component. The reader is urged to try to compute **B** in some other coordinate system.

We shall return to bipolar coordinates in Sections 2.13 and 2.14 to derive the toroidal and bispherical coordinate systems.

EXERCISES

2.9.1 Verify that the surfaces $\xi = b_i$ and $\eta = c_j$ are orthogonal by the following methods:
(a) Show that the slope of one surface (the intersection with a ($z =$ constant)-plane) is the negative reciprocal of the slope of the other surface.
(b) Calculate $h_{\xi\eta}^2$.

2.9.2 (a) Show that Laplace's equation, $\nabla^2 \psi(\xi, \eta, z,) = 0$ is *not* completely separable in bipolar coordinates.
(b) Show that a complete separation is possible if we require that $\psi = \psi(\xi, \eta)$, that is, if we restrict ourselves to a two-dimensional system.

2.9.3 Find the capacitance per unit length of two conducting cylinders of radii b and c and of infinite length, with axes parallel and a distance d apart.

$$C = \frac{2\pi\varepsilon_0}{\eta_1 - \eta_2}.$$

2.9.4 As a limiting case of Exercise 2.9.3, find the capacitance per unit length between a conducting cylinder and a conducting infinite plane parallel to the axis of the cylinder.

$$C = \frac{2\pi\varepsilon_0}{\eta_1}.$$

2.10 Prolate Spheroidal Coordinates (u, v, φ)

Let us start with the elliptic coordinates of Section 2.7 as a two-dimensional system. We can generate a three-dimensional system by rotating about the major or minor elliptic axes and introducing φ as an azimuth angle (Fig. 2.10). Rotating first about the major axis gives us prolate spheroidal coordinates with the following coordinate surfaces:

1. Prolate spheroids,

$$u = \text{constant}, \quad 0 \leqslant u < \infty.$$

2. Hyperboloids of two sheets,

$$v = \text{constant}, \quad 0 \leqslant v \leqslant \pi,$$

3. Half planes through the z-axis,

$$\varphi = \text{constant}, \quad 0 \leqslant \varphi \leqslant 2\pi.$$

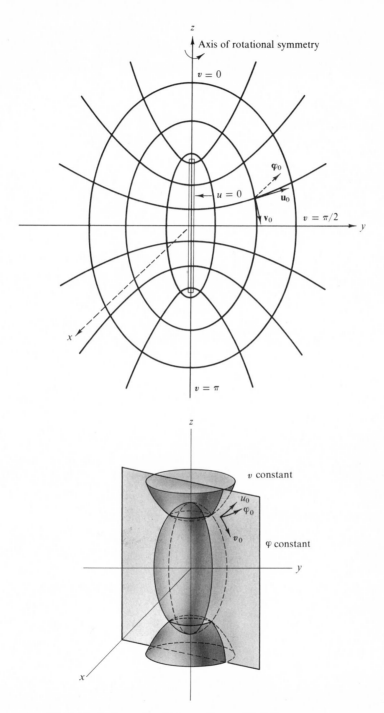

FIG. 2.10 Prolate spheroidal coordinates. (*Top*) Cross section

The transformation equations are

$$x = a \sinh u \sin v \cos \varphi,$$

$$y = a \sinh u \sin v \sin \varphi, \qquad (2.96)$$

$$z = a \cosh u \cos v.$$

Note that we have permuted our cartesian axes to make the axis of rotational symmetry the z-axis. The scale factors for this system are

$$h_1 = h_u = a(\sinh^2 u + \sin^2 v)^{1/2}.$$

$$= a(\cosh^2 u - \cos^2 v)^{1/2},$$

$$\qquad (2.97)$$

$$h_2 = h_v = a(\sinh^2 u + \sin^2 v)^{1/2},$$

$$h_3 = h_\varphi = a \sinh u \sin v.$$

The prolate spheroidal coordinates are rather important in physics, primarily because of their usefulness in treating "two-center" problems. The two centers will correspond to the two focal points, $(0, 0, a)$ and $(0, 0, -a)$, of the ellipsoids and hyperboloids of revolution. As shown in Fig. 2.11, we label the distance from the left focal point to the point (z, x), r_1, and the corresponding distance from the right focal point r_2.

$$r_1 + r_2 = \text{constant}, \qquad \text{for fixed } u.$$

FIG. 2.11

The point (z, x) is described in terms of u and v by Eqs. 2.96. The azimuth is irrelevant here. From the properties of the ellipse and hyperbola we know

$$r_1 + r_2 = \text{constant}, \qquad \text{for fixed } u,$$

$$r_1 - r_2 = \text{constant}, \qquad \text{for fixed } v.$$

$$\qquad (2.98)$$

Using

$$r_1 = [(a + z)^2 + x^2]^{1/2},$$

$$r_2 = [(a - z)^2 + x^2]^{1/2},$$

$$\qquad (2.99)$$

and Eq. 2.96, we find

$$r_1 = a(\cosh u + \cos v),$$

$$r_2 = a(\cosh u - \cos v),$$

$$\qquad (2.100)$$

or

$$\frac{r_1 + r_2}{2a} = \cosh u$$

$$\qquad (2.101)$$

$$\frac{r_1 - r_2}{2a} = \cos v$$

This means u is a function of the sum of the distances from the two centers, whereas v is a function of the difference of the distances from the two centers.

To facilitate this application of the coordinate system we change the variable by introducing

$$\xi_1 = \cosh u, \qquad 1 \leqslant \xi_1 < \infty,$$

$$\xi_2 = \cos v, \qquad -1 \leqslant \xi_2 \leqslant 1, \qquad (2.102)$$

$$\xi_3 = \varphi, \qquad 0 \leqslant \xi_3 \leqslant 2\pi.$$

Note carefully that

$$h_{\xi_1} = h_{\cosh u} \neq h_u. \qquad (2.103)$$

New variables involve new scale factors.

EXAMPLE 2.10.1

The hydrogen molecule ion is a system composed of two protons which we take to be fixed at the focal points and one electron. The Schrödinger wave equation for this system is

$$\frac{h^2}{2M} \nabla^2 \psi - \frac{e^2}{r_1} \psi - \frac{e^2}{r_2} \psi + \frac{e^2}{r_{12}} \psi = E\psi. \qquad (2.104)$$

The variables r_1 and r_2 are defined in Fig. 2.11, and r_{12}, the proton-proton distance, is just $2a$. The problem is to separate the variables in Eq. 2.104.

In choosing the prolate spheroidal coordinates, ξ_1, ξ_2, ξ_3, our first step is to calculate the scale factors. From Eqs. 2.96 and 2.102

$$h_{\xi_1} = a\left(\frac{\xi_1^2 - \xi_2^2}{\xi_1^2 - 1}\right)^{1/2},$$

$$h_{\xi_2} = a\left(\frac{\xi_1^2 - \xi_2^2}{1 - \xi_2^2}\right)^{1/2}, \qquad (2.105)$$

$$h_{\xi_3} = a(\xi_1^2 - 1)^{1/2}(1 - \xi_2^2)^{1/2}.$$

Using these scale factors and Eq. 2.18, we find

$$\nabla^2 \psi = \frac{1}{a^2}\left\{ \frac{1}{(\xi_1^2 - \xi_2^2)} \frac{\partial}{\partial \xi_1}\left[(\xi_1^2 - 1)\frac{\partial \psi}{\partial \xi_1}\right] + \frac{1}{(\xi_1^2 - \xi_2^2)} \frac{\partial}{\partial \xi_2}\left[(1 - \xi_2^2)\frac{\partial \psi}{\partial \xi_2}\right] \right.$$

$$\left. + \frac{1}{(\xi_1^2 - 1)(1 - \xi_2^2)} \frac{\partial^2 \psi}{\partial \xi_3^2}\right\}. \qquad (2.106)$$

From Eq. 2.100

$$\frac{e^2}{r_1} + \frac{e^2}{r_2} = \frac{e^2 2a\xi_1}{a^2(\xi_1^2 - \xi_2^2)}. \qquad (2.107)$$

By substituting Eqs. 2.106 and 2.107 into Eq. 2.104 and using the now standard procedure,

$$\psi(\xi_1, \xi_2, \xi_3) = f_1(\xi_1)\, f_2(\xi_2)\, f_3(\xi_3), \qquad (2.108)$$

we can quickly isolate the azimuthal (ξ_3) dependence to obtain

$$-\frac{\hbar^2}{2Ma^2}\left\{\frac{1}{(\xi_1^2-\xi_2^2)}\frac{1}{f_1}\frac{d}{d\xi_1}\left[(\xi_1^2-1)\frac{df_1}{d\xi_1}\right]\right.$$

$$\left.+\frac{1}{(\xi_1^2-\xi_2^2)f_2}\frac{d}{d\xi_2}\left[(1-\xi_2^2)\frac{df_2}{d\xi_2}\right]\right\}-\frac{2e^2}{a}\frac{\xi_1}{(\xi_1^2-\xi_2^2)}-E'$$

$$=\frac{\hbar^2}{2Ma^2}\frac{1}{(\xi_1^2-1)(1-\xi_2^2)f_3}\frac{d^2f_3}{d\xi_2^2}.\qquad(2.109)$$

Here we have used $E' = E - e^2/r_{12}$, a constant. As in Sections 2.5 and 2.6, we set

$$\frac{1}{f_3}\frac{d^2f_3}{d\xi_3^2}=-m^2.\qquad(2.110)$$

Equation 2.109 may be simplified to yield

$$\frac{1}{f_1}\frac{d}{d\xi_1}\left[(\xi_1^2-1)\frac{df_1}{d\xi_1}\right]+\frac{1}{f_2}\frac{d}{d\xi_2}\left[(1+\xi_2^2)\frac{df_2}{d\xi_2}\right]+\frac{4Mae^2}{\hbar^2}+\frac{2Ma^2E'}{\hbar^2}(\xi_1^2-\xi_2^2)$$

$$=m^2\left[\frac{1}{\xi_1^2-1}+\frac{1}{1-\xi_2^2}\right].\qquad(2.111)$$

The variables ξ_1 and ξ_2 separate by inspection, and we have one second-order differential equation for $f_1(\xi_1)$ and another for $f_2(\xi_2)$.

EXERCISES

2.10.1 Calculate h_ξ^2, h_η^2, and h_φ^2 (ξ, η, φ) for $\xi = \cosh u$ and $\eta = \cos v$.

2.10.2 Show that $h_{uv}^2 = 0$ (prolate spheroidal coordinates).

2.10.3 In the quantum mechanical analysis of the hydrogen molecule by the Heitler-London method we encounter the integral

$$I_{\mathrm{HL}}=\frac{1}{\pi a_0^3}\int e^{-(r_1+r_2)/a_0}\,d\tau,$$

in which the volume integral is over all space. Introduce prolate spheroidal coordinates and evaluate the integral.   *Ans.* $I_{\mathrm{HL}}=\left(1+\dfrac{2a}{a_0}+\dfrac{4a^2}{3a_0^2}\right)e^{-2a/a_0}$.

2.10.4 Using $\xi = \cosh u$, $\eta = \cos v$, show that the volume element in prolate spheroidal coordinates obtained by direct transformation of

$$d\tau = a^3\,(\sinh^2 u + \sin^2 v)\sinh u \sin v\,du\,dv\,d\varphi$$

is

$$d\tau = -a^3(\xi^2 - \eta^2)\,d\xi\,d\eta\,d\varphi.$$

(The minus sign will be taken out by reversing the limits of integration over η.)

2.10.5   Using prolate spheroidal coordinates, set up the volume integral representing the volume of a given prolate ellipsoid using (a) u, v, φ and (b) ξ, η, φ. Evaluate the integrals and show that your results are equivalent to the usual result given in terms of the semi axes,

$$V = \frac{4}{3}\pi a_0^2 b_0,$$

where a_0 is the semi-minor axis and b_0, the semimajor axis.

2.11   Oblate Spheroidal Coordinates (u, v, φ)

When the elliptic coordinates of Section 2.7 (taken as a two-dimensional set) are rotated about the minor elliptic axis, we generate another three-dimensional spheroidal system, the oblate spheroidal coordinate system. Again φ is the azimuthal angle. The coordinate surfaces are the following:

1. Oblate spheroids,
$$u = \text{constant}, \qquad 0 \leqslant u < \infty.$$

2. Hyperboloids of one sheet,
$$v = \text{constant},[1] \qquad -\frac{\pi}{2} \leqslant v \leqslant \frac{\pi}{2}.$$

3. Half planes through the z-axis,
$$\varphi = \text{constant}, \qquad 0 \leqslant \varphi \leqslant 2\pi.$$

The transformation equations relating to cartesian coordinates may be written

$$x = a \cosh u \cos v \cos \varphi$$

$$y = a \cosh u \cos v \sin \varphi$$

$$z = \sinh u \sin v.$$

The scale factors become

$$h_1 = h_u = a\,(\sinh^2 u + \sin^2 v)^{1/2}$$
$$= a(\cosh^2 u - \cos^2 v)^{1/2},$$
$$h_2 = h_v = a(\sinh^2 u + \sin^2 v)^{1/2},$$
$$h_3 = h_\varphi = a \cosh u \cos v.$$

(2.112)

Since holding u constant results in an oblate spheroid which is a good approximation to a planetary surface, this coordinate system has been useful in describing the earth's gravitational field. (J. P. Vinti, *Phys. Rev. Letters* **3**, 8 (1959)). Both prolate and oblate spheroidal coordinates are used in Section 12.10 to illustrate Legendre functions of the second kind.

Note carefully that if we require φ to advance from x to y as usual and if we insist on the order (u, v, φ), this system is left-handed! This will introduce an over-all

---

[1] Note that v has a range of only π in contrast to the range of 2π for elliptic cylindrical coordinates (Section 2.7). The negative values of v generate negative values of z.

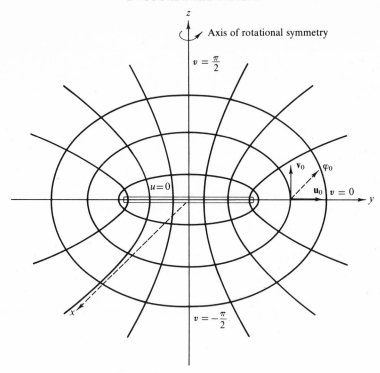

FIG. 2.12   Oblate spheroidal coordinates. Cross section

(-1) in the expression for the curl. To get back to a right-handed system it is necessary to use only (v, u, φ),

$$\mathbf{v}_0 \times \mathbf{u}_0 = +\boldsymbol{\varphi}_0$$

or let $v \to (\pi/2) - v$ in the transformation equations.

EXERCISES

2.11.1 Separate Laplace's equation in oblate spheroidal coordinates. Solve the φ-dependent differential equation.

2.11.2 A thin conducting metal disk of radius a carries a total electric charge Q. Find the capacitance of the disk and the distribution of charge over the surface of the disk.

$$C = 8a\varepsilon_0 \, ,$$

$$\sigma = \frac{\varphi}{4\pi a\sqrt{a^2 - r^2}} \qquad \text{(on each side)}.$$

2.12 Parabolic Coordinates (ξ, η, φ)

In Section 2.8 two sets of orthogonal confocal parabolas were described. Imagine that we have taken the system shown in the xy-plane (Fig. 2.6) and have rotated about the y-axis the axis of symmetry for each set of parabolas. This generates two sets of orthogonal confocal paraboloids. By permuting the coordinates (cyclically) so that the axis of rotation is the z-axis we have the following:

1. Paraboloids about the positive z axis,

$$\xi = \text{constant}, \qquad 0 \leqslant \xi < \infty.$$

2. Paraboloids about the negative z-axis,

$$\eta = \text{constant}, \qquad 0 \leqslant \eta < \infty.$$

3. Half planes through the z-axis,

$$\varphi = \text{constant}, \qquad 0 \leqslant \varphi \leqslant 2\pi.$$

Measuring the azimuth from the x-axis in the xy-plane, as usual, we obtain

$$
\begin{aligned}
x &= \xi \eta \cos \varphi, \\
y &= \xi \eta \sin \varphi, \\
z &= \tfrac{1}{2}(\eta^2 - \xi^2).
\end{aligned}
\tag{2.113}
$$

From Eq. 2.113 we find the scale factors

$$
\begin{aligned}
h_1 &= h_\xi = (\xi^2 + \eta)^{1/2}, \\
h_2 &= h_\eta = (\xi^2 + \eta^2)^{1/2}, \\
h_3 &= h_\varphi = \xi \eta.
\end{aligned}
\tag{2.114}
$$

From Fig. 2.13 it is seen that

$$\xi_0 \times \eta_0 = -\varphi_0,$$

that is, the parabolic system (ξ, η, φ) given here is a left-handed system. Equations 2.113 imply that ξ and η each have dimensions of $(\text{length})^{1/2}$. For this reason some writers prefer to use $\xi^{1/2}$ in place of our ξ and $\eta^{1/2}$ in place of our η. Others have interchanged ξ and η.

The parabolic coordinates have found an application in the analysis of the Stark effect,[1] the shift of energy levels which results when an atom is placed in an *electric* field.

---

[1] H. A. Bethe and E. S. Salpeter. *Quantum Mechanics of One- and Two-Electron Atoms.* New York: Academic Press (1957).

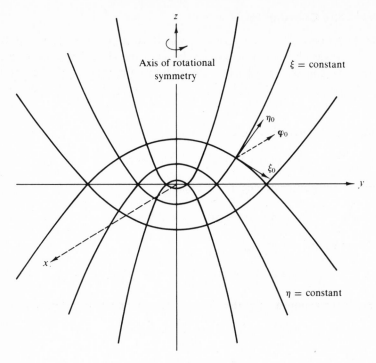

FIG. 2.13   Parabolic coordinates

EXAMPLE 2.12.1   THE STARK EFFECT

The presence of the external electric field E_0, along the positive z-axis, adds a potential energy term $-eE_0 z$ to the Schrödinger wave equation. For hydrogen we have

$$-\frac{\hbar^2}{2M}\nabla^2\psi - \frac{e^2}{r}\psi - eE_0 z\psi = E\psi. \tag{2.115}$$

Once more the problem is to separate the variables.

Using Eqs. 2.18 and 2.114, we obtain

$$\nabla^2\psi = \frac{1}{\xi\eta(\xi^2+\eta^2)}\left\{\frac{\partial}{\partial\xi}\left[\xi\eta\,\frac{\partial\psi}{\partial\xi}\right] + \frac{\partial}{\partial\eta}\left[\xi\eta\,\frac{\partial\psi}{\partial\eta}\right]\right\} + \frac{1}{\xi^2\eta^2}\frac{\partial^2\psi}{\partial\varphi^2}. \tag{2.116}$$

We also find

$$r = \frac{\xi^2 + \eta^2}{2}. \tag{2.117}$$

Using Eqs. 2.116, 2.117, and $\psi = f(\xi)\,g(\eta)\,\Phi(\varphi)$, Eq. 2.115 becomes

$$\frac{\hbar^2}{2M} \frac{1}{(\xi^2 + \eta^2)} \left[\frac{1}{\xi f} \frac{d}{d\xi} \left(\xi \frac{d_f}{d\xi} \right) + \frac{1}{\eta g} \frac{d}{d\eta} \left(\eta \frac{dg}{d\eta} \right) \right]$$

$$+ \frac{\hbar^2}{2M} \frac{1}{\xi^2 \eta^2} \frac{1}{\Phi} \frac{d^2 \Phi}{d\varphi^2} + \frac{2e^2}{\xi^2 + \eta^2} + \frac{eE_0}{2} (\eta^2 - \xi^2) + E = 0. \quad (2.118)$$

Setting

$$\frac{1}{\Phi} \frac{d^2 \Phi}{d\varphi^2} = -m^2, \quad (2.119)$$

Eq. 2.118 may readily be split into the two equations:

$$\frac{\hbar^2}{2M} \left[\frac{1}{\xi f} \frac{d}{d\xi} \left(\xi \frac{df}{d\xi} \right) - \frac{m^2}{\xi^2} \right] + E\xi^2 - \frac{eE_0 \xi^4}{2} + A = 0. \quad (2.120)$$

and

$$\frac{\hbar^2}{2M} \left[\frac{1}{\eta g} \frac{d}{d\eta} \left(\eta \frac{dg}{d\eta} \right) - \frac{m^2}{\eta^2} \right] + E\eta^2 + \frac{eE_0 \eta^4}{2} + B = 0. \quad (2.121)$$

The constants A and B are arbitrary except for the constraint $A + B = 2e^2$.

Other applications of parabolic coordinates are included in the problems.

EXERCISES

2.12.1 A concept of particular importance in atomic and nuclear physics is that of parity, the property of a wave function being either even or odd under inversion of the coordinates. In cartesian coordinates this inversion or parity operator P acting on (x, y, z) gives

$$P(x, y, z) = -x, -y, -z.$$

Write out the corresponding operator equations in the following coordinate systems:
(a) Spherical polar (r, θ, φ)
(b) Circular cylindrical (ρ, φ, z)
(c) Prolate spheroidal (u, v, φ)
(d) Prolate spheroidal (ξ, η, φ)
(e) Oblate spheroidal (u, v, φ)
(f) Parabolic (ξ, η, φ)

2.12.2 A heavy particle moves on the inside surface of a paraboloid whose axis is vertical and whose vertex rests on the ground. Set up the problem in the Lagrangian formulation, introducing the constraints by the method of Lagrange multipliers, and show that the pressure of the particle on the surface is proportional to the curvature of the parabola at that point. *Note.* The Lagrangian formulation and the Lagrange multipliers are discussed in Chapter 17.

2.12.3   (a) The wave equation for the hydrogenlike atom is

$$-\frac{\hbar^2}{2m}\,\nabla^2 u + Vu = Eu,$$

where V, the potential energy of the electron is

$$V = -\frac{Ze^2}{r}$$

and E is the total energy, a number. Show that variables can be separated by using parabolic coordinates.

(b) Show that the variables also separate in prolate spheroidal coordinates with the nucleus at one of the foci.

2.12.4   In the wave equation for Coulomb scattering $V = (ZZ'e^2)/r$, in which Ze and $Z'e$ are the charges on the first and second particles, respectively. Using parabolic coordinates, show that

$$u = e^{ikz} f(\xi)$$

gives a solution in which $f(\xi)$ satisfies the confluent hypergeometric equation.

2.12.5   Find h_ξ^2, h_η^2, and h_φ^2 if the parabolic coordinates (ξ, η, φ) are related to the usual cartesian coordinates by

$$x = \sqrt{\xi\eta}\cos\varphi, \qquad y = \sqrt{\xi\eta}\sin\varphi,$$

$$z = \tfrac{1}{2}(\xi - \eta).$$

2.12.6   Investigate the three-dimensional coordinate system that results when the *two*-dimensional (ξ, η) parabolic system of Section 2.8 is rotated about the x-axis .

2.13 Toroidal Coordinates (ξ, η, φ)

This system is formed by rotating the xy-plane of the bipolar system (Section 2.9) about the y-axis of Fig. 2.7. The circles centered on the y-axis ($\xi = $ constant) yield spheres, whereas the circles centered on the x-axis ($\eta = $ constant) form toroids. By relabeling the coordinates so that the axis of rotation is again the z-axis, the transformation equations are

$$x = \frac{a\,\sinh\eta\,\cos\varphi}{\cosh\eta - \cos\xi},$$

$$y = \frac{a\,\sinh\eta\,\sin\varphi}{\cosh\eta - \cos\xi}, \tag{2.122}$$

$$z = \frac{a\,\sin\xi}{\cosh\eta - \cos\xi}.$$

From these equations the scale factors are

$$h_1 = h_\xi = \frac{a}{\cosh \eta - \cos \xi},$$

$$h_2 = h_\eta = \frac{a}{\cosh \eta - \cos \xi}, \tag{2.123}$$

$$h_3 = h_\varphi = \frac{a \sinh \eta}{\cosh \eta - \cos \xi}.$$

The coordinate surfaces formed by the rotation are the following:

1. Spheres centered at $(0, 0, a \cot \xi)$ with radii, $a|\csc \xi|$,

$$\xi = \text{constant}, \qquad 0 \leqslant \xi \leqslant 2\pi.$$

$$2az \cot \xi = x^2 + y^2 + z^2 - a^2, \tag{2.124}$$

2. Toroids,

$$\eta = \text{constant}, \qquad 0 \leqslant \xi \leqslant 2\pi.$$

The cross sections are circles displaced a distance $a \coth \eta$ from the z-axis and of radii $a \operatorname{csch} \eta$,

$$4a^2(x^2 + y^2) \coth^2 \eta = (x^2 + y^2 + z^2 + a^2)^2. \tag{2.125}$$

3. Half planes through the z-axis,

$$\varphi = \text{constant}, \qquad 0 \leqslant \varphi \leqslant 2\pi.$$

Laplace's equation is not completely separable in toroidal coordinates. This coordinate system has some physical applications (such as describing vortex rings) but they are rare and the system is seldom used.

Again, as in the two preceding sections, note that (ξ, η, φ) yields a left-handed set. To transform to a right-handed system perhaps the simplest way is to take the coordinates in the order (η, ξ, φ).

EXERCISES

2.13.1   Show that the surface area of a toroid defined by the adjacent figure is $(2\pi a) \times (2\pi b)$ = $4\pi^2 ab$.

2.14   Bispherical Coordinates (ξ, η, φ)

Returning to the bipolar coordinates of Section 2.9, a rotation of the xy-plane shown in Fig. 2.7, about the x-axis generates two families of orthogonal intersecting

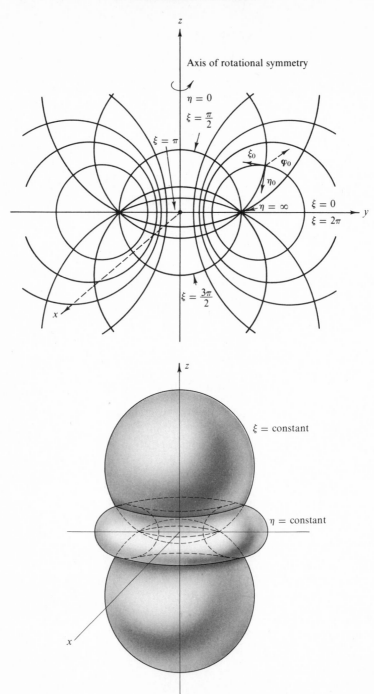

FIG. 2.14   Toroidal coordinates. (*Top*) Cross section

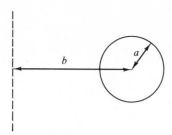

FIG. 2.15

spheres. Adding planes of constant azimuth, this is our bispherical system with transformation equations:

$$x = \frac{a \sin \xi \cos \varphi}{\cosh \eta - \cos \xi},$$

$$y = \frac{a \sin \xi \sin \varphi}{\cosh \eta - \cos \xi},$$

$$z = \frac{a \sinh \eta}{\cosh \eta - \cos \xi}.$$

(2.126)

Once more the axis of rotation has been relabeled the z-axis. The scale factors become

$$h_1 = h_\xi = \frac{a}{\cosh \eta - \cos \xi},$$

$$h_2 = h_\eta = \frac{a}{\cosh \eta - \cos \xi},$$

$$h_3 = h_\varphi = \frac{a \sin \xi}{\cosh \eta - \cos \xi}.$$

(2.127)

The coordinate surfaces are the following:

1. A fourth-order surface of revolution about the z-axis,

$$\xi = \text{constant}, \qquad 0 < \xi < \frac{\pi}{2}, \qquad \text{"dimples" on } z\text{-axis},$$

$$\xi = \frac{\pi}{2}, \qquad \text{sphere},$$

$$\frac{\pi}{2} < \xi < \pi, \qquad \text{cusps on } z\text{-axis}.$$

2. Spheres of radius $a|\text{csch } \eta|$ centered at $(0, 0, a \coth \eta)$,

$$\eta = \text{constant}, \qquad -\infty < \eta < \infty.$$

3. Half planes through the z axis,

$$\varphi = \text{constant}, \qquad 0 \leqslant \varphi \leqslant 2\pi.$$

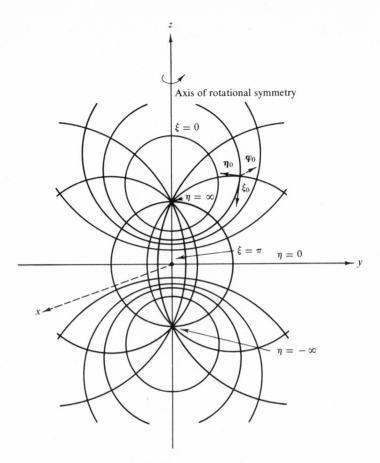

FIG. 2.16 Bispherical coordinates

Laplace's equation is partly separable in this system, though the general equation (2.1), $k^2 \neq 0$, is not separable. The bispherical coordinate system has been found to be useful in specialized electrostatic problems such as the capacitance between a conducting sphere and a nearby conducting plane (cf. Exercise 2.14.1).

EXERCISES

2.14.1 Using bispherical coordinates find the capacitance between a conducting sphere and (nonintersecting) conducting plane.

2.15   Confocal Ellipsoidal Coordinates (ξ_1, ξ_2, ξ_3)

This very general coordinate system has the following three families of co-ordinate surfaces:

1. Ellipsoids (no two axes are equal), $\xi_1 = $ constant,

$$\frac{x^2}{a^2 - \xi_1} + \frac{y^2}{b^2 - \xi_1} + \frac{z^2}{c^2 - \xi_1} = 1. \qquad (2.128)$$

2. Hyperboloids of one sheet, $\xi_2 = $ constant,

$$\frac{x^2}{a^2 - \xi_2} + \frac{y^2}{b^2 - \xi_2} - \frac{z^2}{\xi_2 - c^2} = 1. \qquad (2.129)$$

3. Hyperboloids of two sheets, $\xi_3 = $ constant,

$$\frac{x^2}{a^2 - \xi_3} - \frac{y^2}{\xi_3 - b^2} - \frac{z^2}{\xi_3 - c^2} = 1. \qquad (2.130)$$

The constants a, b, c are parameters which describe the ellipsoids and hyperboloids subject to the constraints

$$a_2 > \xi_3 > b^2 > \xi_2 > c^2 > \xi_1. \qquad (2.131)$$

In Eqs. 2.128, 2.129, and 2.130, the minus signs resulting from these constraints were shown explicitly.

The transformation equations are

$$x^2 = \frac{(a^2 - \xi_1)(a^2 - \xi_2)(a^2 - \xi_3)}{(a^2 - b^2)(a^2 - c^2)},$$

$$y^2 = \frac{(b^2 - \xi_1)(b^2 - \xi_2)(\xi_3 - b^2)}{(a^2 - b^2)(b^2 - c^2)}, \qquad (2.132)$$

$$z^2 = \frac{(c^2 - \xi_1)(\xi_2 - c^2)(\xi_3 - c^2)}{(a^2 - c^2)(b^2 - c^2)}.$$

After an undue amount of algebra, the scale factors are found to be

$$h_1 = h_{\xi_1} = \frac{1}{2}\left[\frac{(\xi_2 - \xi_1)(\xi_3 - \xi_1)}{(a^2 - \xi_1)(b^2 - \xi_1)(c^2 - \xi_1)}\right]^{1/2}$$

$$h_2 = h_{\xi_2} = \frac{1}{2}\left[\frac{(\xi_3 - \xi_2)(\xi_2 - \xi_1)}{(a^2 - \xi_2)(b^2 - \xi_2)(c^2 - \xi_2)}\right]^{1/2} \qquad (2.133)$$

$$h_3 = h_{\xi_3} = \frac{1}{2}\left[\frac{(\xi_3 - \xi_1)(\xi_3 - \xi_2)}{(a^2 - \xi_3)(\xi_3 - b^2)(\xi_3 - c^2)}\right]^{1/2},$$

As with the equations of the coordinate surfaces, the symmetry of this set has been sacrificed by requiring each factor to be positive.

From the transformation equations (2.132) it will be seen that a given point $P(\xi_1, \xi_2, \xi_3)$ corresponds to eight possible points ($\pm x$, $\pm y$, $\pm z$), the cartesian coordinates appearing as squares. This eightfold multiplicity may be resolved by introducing an appropriate sign convention for ξ_1, ξ_2 and ξ_3 or by bringing in elliptic functions or related functions.

Although this coordinate system has been useful in problems of mathematical physics, its very generality makes it cumbersome and awkward to use. Since this text proports to be an introduction, we shall restrict ourselves to ellipsoids with axes of rotational symmetry.

2.16   Conical Coordinates (ξ_1, ξ_2, ξ_3)

This is one of the more unusual (and less useful) degenerate forms of the confocal ellipsoidal coordinate system of the preceding section. The coordinate surfaces are the following:

1. Spheres centered at the origin, radii ξ_1, $\xi_1 = $ constant,

$$x^2 + y^2 + z^2 = \xi_1^2. \tag{2.134}$$

2. Cones of elliptic cross section with apexes at the origin and axes along the z-axis, $\xi_2 = $ constant,

$$\frac{x^2}{\xi_2^2} + \frac{y^2}{\xi_2^2 - b^2} = \frac{z^2}{c^2 - \xi_2^2}. \tag{2.135}$$

3. Elliptic cones, apexes at the origin, axes along the x-axis, $\xi_3 = $ constant,

$$\frac{x^2}{\xi_3^2} = \frac{y^2}{b^2 - \xi_3^2} + \frac{z^2}{c^2 - \xi_3^2}. \tag{2.136}$$

As in Section 2.15, the parameters b and c satisfy constraints

$$c^2 > \xi_2^2 > b^2 > \xi_3^2. \tag{2.137}$$

Inverting the set of equations (2.134), (2.135), and (2.136), the transformation equations

$$x^2 = \left(\frac{\xi_1 \xi_2 \xi_3}{bc}\right)^2,$$

$$y^2 = \frac{\xi_1^2(\xi_2^2 - b^2)(b^2 - \xi_3^2)}{b^2(c^2 - b^2)}, \tag{2.138}$$

$$z^2 = \frac{\xi_1^2(c^2 - \xi_2^2)(c^2 - \xi_3^2)}{c^2(c^2 - b^2)}$$

are obtained. Then by Eq. 2.6 the scale factors are

$$h_1 = h_{\xi_1} = 1,$$

$$h_2 = h_{\xi_2} = \left[\frac{\xi_1^2(\xi_2^2 - \xi_3^2)}{(\xi_2^2 - b^2)(c^2 - \xi_2^2)}\right]^{1/2} \tag{2.139}$$

$$h_3 = h_{\xi_3} = \left[\frac{\xi_1^2(\xi_2^2 - \xi_3^2)}{(b^2 - \xi_3^2)(c^2 - \xi_3^2)}\right]^{1/2}$$

This really oddball coordinate system has been almost completely ignored. Recently, however, it was found useful to describe the angular momentum eigenfunctions of an asymmetric rotor.[1]

2.17 Confocal Paraboloidal Coordinates (ξ_1, ξ_2, ξ_3)

Except for the bipolar, toroidal, and bispherical coordinate systems, all the coordinate systems in this chapter are derivable from the confocal ellipsoidal coordinates (Section 2.15). The last of these degenerate or special systems is the confocal paraboloidal system. Here the coordinate surfaces are the following:

1. Confocal paraboloids of elliptic cross section extending along the negative z-axis, $\xi_1 = $ constant,

$$\frac{x^2}{a^2 - \xi_1} + \frac{y^2}{b^2 - \xi_1} + 2z + \xi_1 = 0. \tag{2.140}$$

2. Hyperbolic paraboloids, $\xi_2 = $ constant,

$$\frac{x^2}{a^2 - \xi_2} - \frac{y^2}{\xi_2 - b^2} + 2z + \xi_2 = 0. \tag{2.141}$$

3. Confocal paraboloids of elliptic cross section extending along the positive z-axis, $\xi_3 = $ constant,

$$\frac{x^2}{\xi_3 - a^2} + \frac{y^2}{\xi_3 - b^2} - 2z - \xi_3 = 0. \tag{2.142}$$

As in Sections 2.15 and 2.16, there are constraints on the parameters and variables

$$\xi_3 > a^2 > \xi_2 > b^2 > \xi_1. \tag{2.143}$$

The transformation equations are

$$x^2 = \frac{(a^2 - \xi_1)(a^2 - \xi_2)(\xi_3 - a^2)}{a^2 - b^2},$$

$$y^2 = \frac{(b^2 - \xi_1)(\xi_2 - b^2)(\xi_3 - b^2)}{a^2 - b^2}, \tag{2.144}$$

$$z = \tfrac{1}{2}(a^2 + b^2 - \xi_1 - \xi_2 - \xi_3)$$

with resulting scale factors

$$h_1 = h_{\xi_1} = \frac{1}{2}\left[\frac{(\xi_2 - \xi_1)(\xi_3 - \xi_1)}{(a^2 - \xi_1)(b^2 - \xi_1)}\right]^{1/2}$$

$$h_2 = h_{\xi_2} = \frac{1}{2}\left[\frac{(\xi_3 - \xi_2)(\xi_2 - \xi_1)}{(a^2 - \xi_2)(\xi_2 - b^2)}\right]^{1/2} \tag{2.145}$$

$$h_3 = h_{\xi_3} = \frac{1}{2}\left[\frac{(\xi_3 - \xi_1)(\xi_3 - \xi_2)}{(\xi_3 - a^2)(\xi_3 - b^2)}\right]^{1/2}.$$

[1] R. D. Spence, *Am. J. Phys.* **27**, 329 (1959).

Applications of this system have been developed in electromagnetic theory[1] but within the scope of this book the system is of little interest.

REFERENCES

MORSE, P. M., and H. FESHBACH. *Methods of Theoretical Physics*. New York: McGraw-Hill (1953). Chapter 5 includes a description of most of the coordinate systems presented here. Note carefully that Morse and Feshbach are not above using left-handed coordinate systems even for cartesian coordinates. Elsewhere in this excellent (and difficult) book are many examples of the use of the various coordinate systems in solving physical problems.

[1] J. C. Maxwell. *A Treatise on Electricity and Magnetism*. Vol. I, 3rd Ed. Oxford: Oxford University Press (1904), Chapter X.

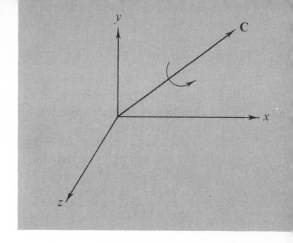

CHAPTER 3

TENSOR ANALYSIS

3.1 Introduction, Definitions

Tensors are important in many areas of physics, including general relativity and electromagnetic theory. One of the more prolific sources of tensor quantities is the anisotropic solid. Here the elastic, optical, electrical, and magnetic properties may well involve tensors. The elastic properties of the anisotropic solid are considered in some detail in Section 3.5. As an introductory illustration, let us consider the flow of electric current. We can write Ohm's law in the usual form

$$\mathbf{j} = \sigma\mathbf{E},\tag{3.1}$$

with current density $\mathbf{j}$ and electric field $\mathbf{E}$, both vector quantities. If we have an isotropic medium, σ, the conductivity, is a scalar, and for the x-component, for example,

$$j_1 = \sigma E_1.\tag{3.2}$$

However, if our medium is anisotropic, as in many crystals, the current density in the x-direction may depend on the electric fields in the y- and z-directions as well as on the field in the x-direction. Assuming a linear relationship, we must replace Eq. 3.2 with

$$j_1 = \sigma_{11}E_1 + \sigma_{12}E_2 + \sigma_{13}E_3\tag{3.3}$$

and, in general,

$$j_i = \sum_k \sigma_{ik}E_k.\tag{3.4}$$

For ordinary three-dimensional space the scalar conductivity σ has given way to a set of nine elements, σ_{ik}.

$$\sigma \rightarrow \begin{pmatrix} \sigma_{11} & \sigma_{12} & \sigma_{13} \\ \sigma_{21} & \sigma_{22} & \sigma_{23} \\ \sigma_{31} & \sigma_{32} & \sigma_{33} \end{pmatrix}.\tag{3.5}$$

This array of nine elements actually forms a tensor, as shown in Section 3.3.

In Chapter 1 a quantity that did not change under rotations of the coordinate system that is, an invariant quantity, was labeled a scalar. A quantity whose components transformed like those of the distance of a point from a chosen origin (Eq. 1.13, Section 1.2) was called a vector. This transformation property was adopted as the defining characteristic of a vector. There is a possible ambiguity in this definition (Eq. 3.6),

$$A_i' = \sum_j a_{ij} A_j, \tag{3.6}$$

in which a_{ij} is the cosine of the angle between the x_i'-axis and the x_j-axis.

If we start with our prototype vector $\mathbf{r}$, then

$$x_i' = \sum_j \frac{\partial x_i'}{\partial x_j} x_j \tag{3.7}$$

by partial differentiation. If we set

$$a_{ij} = \frac{\partial x_i'}{\partial x_j}, \tag{3.8}$$

Eqs. 3.6 and 3.7 are consistent. Any set of quantities A_j transforming according to

$$A_i' = \sum_j \frac{\partial x_i'}{\partial x_j} A_j \tag{3.9}$$

is defined as a contravariant vector.

However, we have already encountered a slightly different type of vector transformation. The gradient of a scalar, $\nabla \varphi$, defined by

$$\nabla \varphi = \mathbf{i} \frac{\partial \varphi}{\partial x_1} + \mathbf{j} \frac{\partial \varphi}{\partial x_2} + \mathbf{k} \frac{\partial \varphi}{\partial x_3} \tag{3.10}$$

(using x_1, x_2, x_3 for x, y, z), transforms as

$$\frac{\partial \varphi'}{\partial x_i'} = \sum_j \frac{\partial \varphi}{\partial x_j} \frac{\partial x_j}{\partial x_i'}, \tag{3.11}$$

using $\varphi = \varphi(x, y, z) = \varphi(x', y', z') = \varphi'$, φ being defined as a scalar quantity. Notice that this differs from Eq. 3.9 in that we have $\partial x_j / \partial x_i'$ instead of $\partial x_i' / \partial x_j$. Equation 3.11 is taken as the definition of a covariant vector with the gradient as the prototype.

In cartesian coordinates

$$\frac{\partial x_j}{\partial x_i'} = \frac{\partial x_i'}{\partial x_j} = a_{ij}, \tag{3.12}$$

and there is no difference between contravariant and covariant transformations. In other systems Eq. 3.12 in general does not apply, and the distinction between contravariant and covariant is real and must be observed. In the remainder of this section the components of a contravariant vector are denoted by a superscript, A^i, whereas a subscript is used for the components of a covariant vector A_i.

To remove some of the fear and mystery from the term tensor, let us rechristen a scalar as a tensor of rank zero and relabel a vector as a tensor of first rank.

Then we proceed to define contravariant, mixed, and covariant tensors of second rank by the following equations

$$A'^{ij} = \sum_{kl} \frac{\partial x_i'}{\partial x_k} \frac{\partial x_j'}{\partial x_l} A^{kl},$$

$$B'^i{}_j = \sum_{kl} \frac{\partial x_i'}{\partial x_k} \frac{\partial x_l}{\partial x_j'} B^k{}_l, \tag{3.13}$$

$$C_{ij}' = \sum_{kl} \frac{\partial x_k}{\partial x_i'} \frac{\partial x_l}{\partial x_j'} C_{kl}.$$

We see that A^{kl} is contravariant with respect to both indices, C_{kl} is covariant with respect to both indices, and $B^k{}_l$ transforms contravariantly with respect to the first index k but covariantly with respect to the second index l. Once again, if we are using cartesian coordinates, all three forms of the tensors of second rank, contravariant, mixed, and covariant are the same.

The second-rank tensor **A** (components A^{kl}) may be conveniently represented by writing out its components in a square array, (3×3 if we are in three-dimensional space)

$$\mathbf{A} = \begin{pmatrix} A^{11} & A^{12} & A^{13} \\ A^{21} & A^{22} & A^{23} \\ A^{31} & A^{32} & A^{33} \end{pmatrix} \tag{3.14}$$

This does not mean that any square array of numbers or functions forms a tensor. The essential condition is that the components transform according to Eq. 3.13.

This transformation requirement may be illustrated by examining in detail the two-dimensional tensor

$$\mathbf{T} = \begin{pmatrix} -xy & -y^2 \\ x^2 & xy \end{pmatrix}$$

In a primed (rotated) coordinate system the $T^{11'}$-component must be $-x'y'$. We check to see if this is consistent with the defining equation (3.13).

$$T^{11'} = -x'y' \overset{?}{=} \sum_{kl} \frac{\partial x_1'}{\partial x_k} \frac{\partial x_1'}{\partial x_l} T^{kl}$$

$$= \sum_{kl} a_{1k} a_{1l} T^{kl},$$

setting i and j equal to 1. Expressing the left-hand side in the unprimed coordinates and substituting in specific values for a_{1k}, a_{1l} and T^{kl}, we obtain

$$-(x \cos \theta + y \sin \theta)(-x \sin \theta + y \cos \theta)$$

$$\overset{?}{=} \cos^2 \theta T^{11} + \cos \theta \sin \theta T^{12} + \sin \theta \cos \theta T^{21} + \sin^2 \theta T^{22}$$

$$= -xy \cos^2 \theta - y^2 \cos \theta \sin \theta + x^2 \sin \theta \cos \theta + xy \sin^2 \theta.$$

We have an identity showing that Eq. 3.13 is satisfied (for $T^{11'}$). Repetition of the other three components verifies that all transform in accordance with Eq. 3.13 and that **T** therefore is a second-rank tensor.

This transformation property is not something to be taken for granted. **For** instance, if one algebraic sign were changed, if T^{22} were $-xy$ instead of $+xy$, then

$$T^{11'} \neq \sum_{kl} a_{1k} a_{1l} T^{kl}$$

and the array

$$\begin{pmatrix} -xy & -y^2 \\ x^2 & -xy \end{pmatrix}$$

is not a tensor. It is not a tensor because it does not contain the required transformation properties.

The addition and subtraction of tensors is defined in terms of the individual elements just as for vectors. To add or subtract two tensors, the corresponding elements are added or subtracted. If

$$\mathbf{A} + \mathbf{B} = \mathbf{C}, \tag{3.15}$$

then

$$A^{ij} + B^{ij} = C^{ij}.$$

Of course, **A** and **B** must be tensors of the same rank and both expressed in a space of the same number of dimensions.

In tensor analysis it is customary to adopt a summation convention to put Eq. 3.13 and subsequent tensor equations in a more compact (and, for the beginning student, a more obscure) form. As long as we are distinguishing between contravariance and covariance, let us agree that when an index appears on one side of an equation, once as a superscript and once as a subscript, we automatically sum over that index. Then we may write the second expression in Eq. 3.13 as

$$B'^i_j = \frac{\partial x'_i}{\partial x_k} \frac{\partial x_l}{\partial x'_j} B^k_l, \tag{3.16}$$

with the summation of the right-hand side over k and l implied. This is the summation convention.

To illustrate the use of the summation convention and some of the techniques of tensor analysis, let us show that the now familiar Kronecker delta, δ_{kl}, is really a mixed tensor of second rank, δ^k_l. The question is, does δ^k_l transform according to Eq. 3.13? This is our criterion for calling it a tensor. We have, using the summation convention,

$$\delta^k_l \frac{\partial x'_i}{\partial x_k} \frac{\partial x_l}{\partial x'_j} = \frac{\partial x'_i}{\partial x_k} \frac{\partial x_k}{\partial x'_j} \tag{3.17}$$

by definition of the Kronecker delta. Now

$$\frac{\partial x'_i}{\partial x_k} \frac{\partial x_k}{\partial x'_j} = \frac{\partial x'_i}{\partial x'_j} \tag{3.18}$$

by direct partial differentiation of the right-hand side. However, x'_i and x'_j are independent coordinates, and therefore the variation of one with respect to the other must be zero if they are different, unity if they coincide; that is,

$$\frac{\partial x_i'}{\partial x_j'} = \delta_j'^i \tag{3.19}$$

Hence

$$\delta_j'^i = \frac{\partial x_i'}{\partial x_k} \frac{\partial x_l}{\partial x_j'} \delta_l^k,$$

showing that the δ_l^k are indeed the components of a mixed second-rank tensor. The Kronecker delta has one further interesting property. It has the same components in all of our rotated coordinate systems and is therefore called isotropic. In Section 3.4 we shall meet a third-rank isotropic tensor.

The order in which the indices appear in our description of a tensor is important. In general A^{mn} is independent of A^{nm}, but there are some cases of special interest. If

$$A^{mn} = A^{nm}, \tag{3.20}$$

we call the tensor symmetric. If, on the other hand,

$$A^{mn} = -A^{nm}, \tag{3.21}$$

the tensor is antisymmetric. Clearly every (second-rank) tensor can be resolved into symmetric and antisymmetric parts by the identity

$$A^{mn} = \tfrac{1}{2}(A^{mn} + A^{nm}) + \tfrac{1}{2}(A^{mn} - A^{nm}), \tag{3.22}$$

the first term on the right being a symmetric tensor, the second, an antisymmetric tensor. This resolution into symmetric and antisymmetric tensors will reappear in the theory of elasticity (Section 3.5). A similar resolution of functions into symmetric and antisymmetric parts is of extreme importance to quantum mechanics.

EXERCISES

3.1.1 (a) Prove that

$$\mathbf{A} = \begin{pmatrix} y^2 & -xy \\ -xy & x^2 \end{pmatrix} \quad \text{and} \quad \mathbf{B} = \begin{pmatrix} -xy & x^2 \\ -y^2 & xy \end{pmatrix}$$

are tensors.

(b) Prove that

$$\mathbf{C} = \begin{pmatrix} y^2 & xy \\ xy & x^2 \end{pmatrix} \quad \text{and} \quad \mathbf{D} = \begin{pmatrix} xy & y^2 \\ x^2 & -xy \end{pmatrix}$$

are *not* tensors.

3.1.2 The four-dimensional fourth-order Riemann-Christoffel curvature tensor of general relativity, R_{iklm}, satisfies the symmetry relations

$$R_{iklm} = -R_{ikml} = -R_{kilm}$$

With the indices running from 1 to 4, show that the number of independent components is reduced from 256 to 36 and that the condition

$$R_{iklm} = R_{lmik}$$

further reduces the number of independent components to 21. Finally, if the components satisfy an identity $R_{iklm} + R_{ilmk} + R_{imkl} = 0$, show that the number of independent components is reduced to 20. *Note.* The final three-term identity furnishes new information only if all four indices are different. Then it reduces the number of independent components by one third.

3.1.3   Separate the tensor

$$\begin{pmatrix} -xy & x^2 \\ -y^2 & xy \end{pmatrix}$$

into symmetric and antisymmetric parts.

3.1.4   Show that if the components of any tensor of any rank vanish in some one particular coordinate system they vanish in all coordinate systems.

3.1.5   The components of tensor **A** are equal to the corresponding components of tensor **B** in one particular coordinate system, i.e.

$$A_{ji}^0 = B_{ij}^0$$

Show that tensor **A** is equal to tensor **B**, $A_{ij} = B_{ij}$, in *all* coordinate systems.

3.1.6 T_{iklm} is antisymmetric with respect to all pairs of indices. How many independent components has it (three-dimensional space)?

3.2   Contraction, Direct Product

When dealing with vectors, we formed a scalar product (Section 1.3) by summing products of corresponding components:

$$\mathbf{A} \cdot \mathbf{B} = A_i B_i \qquad \text{(summation convention)}. \tag{3.23}$$

The generalization of this expression in tensor analysis is a process known as contraction. Two indices, one covariant and the other contravariant, are set equal to each other and then (as implied by the summation convention), we sum over this repeated index. For example, let us contract the second-rank mixed tensor $B'^i{}_j$.

$$B'^i{}_j \rightarrow B'^i{}_i = \frac{\partial x'_i}{\partial x_k} \frac{\partial x_l}{\partial x'_i} B_l^k$$

$$= \frac{\partial x_l}{\partial x_k} B_l^k \tag{3.24}$$

by Eq. 3.18 and then by Eq. 3.19:

$$B'^i{}_i = \delta_k^l B_l^k = B_k^k. \tag{3.25}$$

Our contracted second-rank mixed tensor is invariant and therefore a scalar. This is exactly what we obtained in Section 1.3 for the dot product of two vectors and Section 1.7 for the divergence of a vector. In general, the operation of contraction reduces the rank of a tensor by two.

The components of a covariant vector (first-rank tensor) a_i and those of a contravariant vector (first-rank tensor) b^j may be multiplied component by component to give the general term $a_i b^j$. This, by Eq. 3.13, is actually a second-rank tensor, for

$$a_i' b'^j = \frac{\partial x_k}{\partial x_i'} a_k \frac{\partial x_j'}{\partial x_l} b^l$$

$$= \frac{\partial x_k}{\partial x_i'} \frac{\partial x_j'}{\partial x_l} (a_k b^l). \tag{3.26}$$

Contracting,

$$a_i' b^{i'} = a_k b^k, \tag{3.27}$$

as in Eqs. 3.24 and 3.25 to give the regular scalar product.

The operation of adjoining two vectors a_i and b^j as in the last paragraph is known as forming the direct product. For the case of two vectors, the direct product is a tensor of second rank. In this sense we may attach meaning to **VE**, which was not defined within the framework of vector analysis. In general, the direct product of two tensors is a tensor of rank equal to the sum of the two initial ranks, that is,

$$A_j^i B^{kl} = C_j^{ikl}, \tag{3.28}$$

where C_j^{ikl} is a tensor of fourth rank.

So far the distinction between a covariant transformation and a contravariant transformation has been maintained because it does exist in noncartesian space and because it is of great importance in general relativity. At this point we refer the student interested in general relativity to the many excellent specialized texts in that field and restrict ourselves in the remainder of this chapter to cartesian coordinate systems. As noted in Section 3.1, the distinction between contravariance and covariance disappears and all indices are henceforth shown as subscripts. We restate the summation convention and the operation of contraction.

Summation convention.   When a subscript (letter, not number) appears twice on one side of an equation, summation with respect to that subscript is implied.

Contraction.   Contraction consists of setting two unlike indices (subscripts) equal to each other and then summing as implied by the summation convention.

EXERCISES

3.2.1 If $T_{...i}$ is a tensor of rank n, show that $\partial T_{...i}/\partial x_j$ is a tensor of rank $n+1$ (cartesian coordinates). *Note.* In noncartesian coordinate systems the coefficients a_{ij} are, in general, functions of the coordinates, and the simple derivative of a tensor of rank n is not a tensor except in the special case of $n = 0$. In this case the derivative does yield a covariant vector (tensor of rank 1) by Eq. 3.11.

3.2.2   If $T_{ijk...}$ is a tensor of rank n, show that $\sum \partial T_{ijk...}/\partial x_j$ is a tensor of rank $n - 1$ (cartesian coordinates).

3.2.3   A quantity L is a scalar function of *noncartesian* variables q_i, their time derivatives $\dot{q}_i$, and sometimes also of time t explicitly, that is,

$$L'(q'_i, \dot{q}'_i, t) = L(q_i, \dot{q}_i, t).$$

Show that

$$\frac{d}{dt}\left(\frac{\partial L}{\partial \dot{q}_j}\right) - \frac{\partial L}{\partial q_j}$$

are the components of a vector, the coordinate derivatives of the transformation coefficients, $\partial x_m/\partial x'_n$ cancelling out.

Note. q_j and $\dot{q}_j$ are treated as independent variables in describing L. However,

$$\frac{\partial \dot{q}_j}{\partial \dot{q}'_i} \neq 0.$$

3.2.4   If the scalar function L of the preceding exercise is chosen to be the Lagrangian $L = T - V$, the kinetic energy minus the potential energy of a particle or system of particles, show that the vector

$$\frac{d}{dt}\left(\frac{\partial L}{\partial \dot{q}_j}\right) - \frac{\partial L}{\partial q_j}$$

equals zero in a cartesian coordinate system and therefore in all coordinate systems related to x_j by

$$q_i = a_{ij}x_j.$$

Since the q_i were assumed to be noncartesian coordinates, these transformation coefficients a_{ij} will *not* be direction cosines. This is one way of developing the Lagrangian formulation of classical mechanics. The usual derivation employs the calculus of variations (Chapter 17).

3.3   Quotient Rule

If A_i and B_j are vectors, we have seen in Section 3.2 how we may easily show that $A_i B_j$ is a second-rank tensor. Here we are concerned with a variety of inverse relations. Consider such equations as

$$K_i A_i = B \tag{3.29a}$$

$$K_{ij}A_j = B_i \tag{3.29b}$$

$$K_{ij}A_{jk} = B_{ik} \tag{3.29c}$$

$$K_{ijkl}A_{ij} = B_{kl} \tag{3.29d}$$

$$K_{ij}A_k = B_{ijk} \tag{3.29e}$$

In each of these expressions **A** and **B** are known tensors of rank indicated by the number of indices and **A** is arbitrary. In each case K is an unknown quantity. We wish to establish the transformation properties of K. The quotient rule asserts that if the equation of interest holds in all (rotated) cartesian coordinate systems, K is a tensor of the indicated rank. Consider Eq. 3.29b as an illustration. In our primed coordinate system

$$K'_{ij}A'_j = B'_i = a_{ik}B_k, \tag{3.30}$$

using the vector transformation properties of **B**. Since the equation holds in all rotated cartesian coordinate systems,

$$a_{ik}B_k = a_{ik}(K_{kl}A_l). \tag{3.31}$$

Now transforming **A** back into the primed coordinate system[1] (cf. Eq. 3.9),

$$K'_{ij}A'_j = a_{ik}K_{kl}a_{jl}A'_j \tag{3.32}$$

Rearranging,

$$(K'_{ij} - a_{ik}a_{jl}K_{kl})A'_j = 0. \tag{3.33}$$

This must hold for each value of the index i and for every primed coordinate system. Since the A'_j are arbitrary,[2] we conclude

$$K'_{ij} = a_{ik}a_{jl}K_{kl}, \tag{3.34}$$

which is our definition of a second-rank tensor.

The other equations may be treated the same way, giving rise to other forms of the quotient rule. One minor pitfall should be noted. The quotient rule does not necessarily apply if B is zero. The transformation properties of zero are indeterminate.

EXERCISES

3.3.1 The double summation $\sum_{ij} K_{ij}A_iB_j$ is invariant for any two vectors A_i and B_j. Prove that K_{ij} is a second-rank tensor. *Note.* In the form ds^2 (invariant) $= g_{ij}\,dx_i\,dx_j$, this result shows that g_{ij}, the "metric" is a tensor.

3.3.2 The equation $K_{ij}A_{jk} = B_{ik}$ holds for all orientations of the coordinate system. If **A** and **B** are second-order tensors, show that **K** is a second-order tensor also.

3.4 Pseudotensors, Dual Tensors

So far our coordinate transformations have been restricted to pure rotations. We now consider the effect of reflections or inversions. If we have transformation coefficients $a_{ij} = -\delta_{ij}$, then by Eq. 3.7

$$x_i = -x'_i, \tag{3.35}$$

---

[1] Note carefully the order of the indices of the direction cosine a_{jl} in this *inverse* transformation. We have

$$A_l = \sum_j \frac{\partial x_l}{\partial x_j} A'_j = \sum_j a_{jl}A'_j.$$

[2] We might, for instance, take $A'_1 = 1$ and $A'_m = 0$ for $m \neq 1$. Then the equation $K'_{i1} = a_{ik}a_{1l}K_{kl}$ follows immediately. The rest of Eq. 3.34 comes from other special choices of the arbitrary A'_j.

which is an inversion. Note carefully that this transformation changes our initial right-handed coordinate system into a left-handed coordinate system. Our prototype vector **r** with components (x_1, x_2, x_3) transforms to $\mathbf{r}' = (x_1', x_2', x_3') = (-x_1, -x_2, -x_3)$. This new vector **r**' has negative components, relative to the new transformed set of axes. As shown in Fig. 3.1, the result of reversing signs of

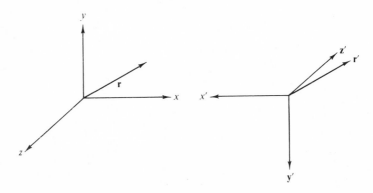

FIG. 3.1   Inversion of cartesian coordinates—polar vector

both axes and components is to leave the vector (an arrow in space) exactly as it was before the transformation was carried out. The distance vector **r** and all other vectors behaving this way under reflection or inversion of the coordinate system are called polar vectors.

A fundamental difference appears when we encounter a vector defined as the cross product of two polar vectors. Let $\mathbf{C} = \mathbf{A} \times \mathbf{B}$, where both **A** and **B** are polar vectors. From Eq. 1.33 of Section 1.4 the components of **C** are given by

$$C_1 = A_2 B_3 - A_3 B_2. \tag{3.36}$$

and so on. Now, when the coordinate system is inverted, $A_i \to -A_i$, $B_j \to -B_j$ but from its definition $C_k \to +C_k$; that is, our cross-product vector, vector **C**, does *not* behave like a polar vector under inversion. To distinguish, we label it a pseudovector or axial vector (see Fig. 3.2). The term axial vector is frequently used

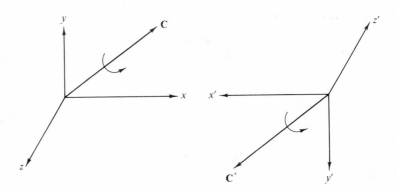

FIG. 3.2   Inversion of cartesian coordinates—axial vector

because these cross products often arise from a description of rotation. Examples are

angular velocity, $\quad\boldsymbol{\omega} = \mathbf{r} \times \mathbf{v},$

angular momentum, $\quad\mathbf{L} = \mathbf{r} \times \mathbf{p},$

torque, $\quad\mathbf{N} = \mathbf{r} \times \mathbf{f},$

magnetic field $\mathbf{B}$, $\quad\dfrac{\partial \mathbf{B}}{\partial t} = -\boldsymbol{\nabla} \times \mathbf{E}.$

Clearly, axial vectors occur frequently in elementary physics, although this fact is usually not pointed out. In a right-handed coordinate system an axial vector $\mathbf{C}$ has a sense of rotation associated with it given by a right-hand rule (cf. Section 1.4). In the inverted, left-handed system the sense of rotation is a left-handed rotation. This is indicated by the curved arrows in Fig. 3.2.

In general, pseudovectors and pseudotensors will transform as

$$C_i' = |a|a_{ij}C_j,$$
$$A_{ij}' = |a|a_{ik}a_{jl}A_{kl},\tag{3.37}$$

where $|a|$ is the determinant of the array of coefficients a_{mn}. In our inversion the determinant is

$$|a| = \begin{vmatrix} -1 & 0 & 0 \\ 0 & -1 & 0 \\ 0 & 0 & -1 \end{vmatrix} = -1.\tag{3.38}$$

For a reflection of one axis, the x-axis,

$$|a| = \begin{vmatrix} -1 & 0 & 0 \\ 0 & 1 & 0 \\ 0 & 0 & 1 \end{vmatrix} = -1,\tag{3.39}$$

and again the determinant $|a| = -1$. On the other hand, for all pure rotations the determinant $|a|$ is always $+1$. This is discussed further in Section 4.3. Often quantities that transform according to Eq. 3.37 are known as tensor densities. They are regular tensors as far as rotations are concerned, differing from tensors only in reflections or inversions of the coordinates, and then the only difference is the appearance of an additional minus sign from the determinant $|a|$.

In Chapter 1 the triple scalar product $S = \mathbf{A} \times \mathbf{B} \cdot \mathbf{C}$ was shown to be a scalar (under rotations). Now by considering the transformation given by Eq. 3.35 we see that $S \to -S$, proving that the triple scalar product is actually a pseudoscalar. This behavior was forshadowed by the geometrical analogy of a volume. If all three parameters of the volume, length, depth, and height, change from positive distances to negative distances, the product of the three will be negative.

The pseudoscalar nature of the volume element has an interesting implication. In Maxwell's equation

$$\mathbf{\nabla} \cdot \mathbf{E} = -\frac{\rho}{\varepsilon_0}$$

let us call $\mathbf{V}$ and $\mathbf{E}$ polar vectors and ε_0, a scalar. Then ρ, the charge per unit volume, must be a scalar quantity; but volume has just been shown to be pseudo-scalar. Hence electric charge is also a pseudoscalar quantity.

For future use it is convenient to introduce the three-dimensional Levi-Civita symbol ε_{ijk} defined by

$$\varepsilon_{123} = \varepsilon_{231} = \varepsilon_{312} = 1,$$

$$\varepsilon_{132} = \varepsilon_{213} = \varepsilon_{321} = -1, \tag{3.40}$$

$$\text{all other } \varepsilon_{ijk} = 0.$$

Suppose, now, that we have a third-rank pseudotensor δ_{ijk}, which in one particular coordinate system is equal to our ε_{ijk}. Then

$$\delta'_{ijk} = |a|a_{ip}a_{jq}a_{kr}\varepsilon_{pqr} \tag{3.41}$$

by definition of pseudotensor. Now

$$a_{1p}a_{2q}a_{3r}\varepsilon_{pqr} = |a| \tag{3.42}$$

by direct expansion of the determinant, showing that $\delta'_{123} = |a|^2 = 1 = \varepsilon_{123}$. Considering the other possibilities one by one, we find

$$\delta'_{ijk} = \varepsilon_{ijk} \tag{3.43}$$

for rotations and reflections. Hence our ε_{ijk} is a pseudotensor. More than that, it is seen to be an isotropic pseudotensor with the same components in all rotated cartesian coordinate systems.

With any *antisymmetric* second-rank tensor C_{ij} (in three-dimensional space) we may associate a dual pseudovector C_i defined by

$$C_i = \tfrac{1}{2}\varepsilon_{ijk}C_{jk}. \tag{3.44}$$

Here the antisymmetric C_{jk} may be written

$$C_{jk} = \begin{pmatrix} 0 & C_{12} & -C_{31} \\ -C_{12} & 0 & C_{23} \\ C_{31} & -C_{23} & 0 \end{pmatrix}. \tag{3.45}$$

We know that C_i must transform as a vector under rotations from the double contraction of the fifth-rank (pseudo) tensor $\varepsilon_{ijk}C_{mn}$ but that it is really a pseudo-vector from the pseudo nature of ε_{ijk}. Specifically, the components of $\mathbf{C}$ are given by

$$(C_1, C_2, C_3) = (C_{23}, C_{31}, C_{12}). \tag{3.46}$$

Notice the cyclic order of the indices that comes from the cyclic order of the components of ε_{ijk}. This duality, given by Eq. 3.46, means that our three-dimensional vector product may literally be taken to be either a pseudovector or an anti-symmetric second-rank tensor, depending on how we chose to write it out.

If we take three (polar) vectors **A**, **B**, and **C**, we may define

$$V_{ijk} = \begin{vmatrix} A_i & B_i & C_i \\ A_j & B_j & C_j \\ A_k & B_k & C_k \end{vmatrix}$$

$$= A_i B_j C_k - A_i B_k C_j + \cdots \qquad (3.47)$$

By an extension of the analysis of Section 3.1 each term $A_p B_q C_r$ is seen to be a third-rank tensor, making V_{ijk} a tensor of third rank. From its definition as a determinant it is totally antisymmetric, reversing sign under the interchange of any two indices, that is, the interchange of any two rows of the determinant. The dual quantity is

$$V = \frac{1}{3!} \varepsilon_{ijk} V_{ijk} \qquad (3.48)$$

clearly a pseudoscalar. By expansion it is seen that

$$V = \begin{vmatrix} A_1 & B_1 & C_1 \\ A_2 & B_2 & C_2 \\ A_3 & B_3 & C_3 \end{vmatrix}, \qquad (3.49)$$

our familiar triple scalar product.

For use in showing the covariance of Maxwell's equations we want to extend this dual vector analysis to four-dimensional space and, in particular, to indicate that the four-dimensional volume element, $dx_1 \, dx_2 \, dx_3 \, dx_4$, is a pseudoscalar.

We introduce the Levi-Civita symbol δ_{ijkl}, the four-dimensional analog of ε_{ijk}. This quantity δ_{ijkl} is defined as totally antisymmetric in all four indices. If $(ijkl)$ is an even permutation of $(1, 2, 3, 4)$, then δ_{ijkl} is defined as $+1$; if it is an odd permutation, then δ_{ijkl} is -1. The Levi-Civita δ_{ijkl} may be proved a pseudotensor of rank 4 by analysis similar to that used for establishing the nature of ε_{ijk}. Introducing a fourth-rank tensor,

$$H_{ijkl} = \begin{vmatrix} A_i & B_i & C_i & D_i \\ A_j & B_j & C_j & D_j \\ A_k & B_k & C_k & D_k \\ A_l & B_l & C_l & D_l \end{vmatrix}, \qquad (3.50)$$

built from the polar vectors **A**, **B**, **C**, and **D**, we may define the dual quantity

$$H = \frac{1}{4!} \delta_{ijkl} H_{ijkl}. \qquad (3.51)$$

We actually have a quadruple summation which reduces the rank to zero. From the pseudo nature of δ_{ijkl}, H is a pseudoscalar. Now we let **A**, **B**, **C**, and **D** be infinitesimal displacements along the four coordinate axes (Minkowski space),

$$\mathbf{A} = (dx_1, 0, 0, 0)$$
$$\mathbf{B} = (0, dx_2, 0, 0), \text{etc.}, \tag{3.52}$$

and

$$H = dx_1 \, dx_2 \, dx_3 \, dx_4, \tag{3.53}$$

the four-dimensional volume element, is now identified as a pseudoscalar. This could have been expected from the results of the special theory of relativity. The Lorentz-Fitzgerald contraction of $dx_1 \, dx_2 \, dx_3$ just balances the time dilation of dx_4.

We slipped into this four dimensional space as a simple mathematical extension of the three-dimensional space and, indeed, we could just as easily have discussed 5-, 6-, or N-dimensional space. This is typical of the power of the component analysis. Physically, this four-dimensional space is usually taken as Minkowski space,

$$(x_1, x_2, x_3, x_4) = (x, y, z, ict), \tag{3.54}$$

where t is time. This is the merger of space and time achieved in special relativity. The transformations that describe the rotations in four-dimensional space are the Lorentz transformations of special relativity.

For some applications, particularly in the quantum theory of angular momentum, our cartesian tensors are not particularly convenient. In mathematical language our general second-rank tensor A_{ij} is reducible, which means that it can be decomposed into parts of lower tensor rank. Actually, we have already done this. From Eq. 3.25

$$A = A_{ii} \tag{3.55}$$

is a scalar quantity, the trace of A_{ij}.[1]

The antisymmetric portion

$$B_{ij} = \tfrac{1}{2}(A_{ij} - A_{ji}) \tag{3.56}$$

has just been shown to be equivalent to a (pseudo) vector, or

$$B_{ij} = C_k \qquad \text{cyclic permutation of } i, j, k. \tag{3.57}$$

By subtracting the scalar A and the vector C_k from our original tensor, we have an irreducible, symmetric, zero-trace second-rank tensor, S_{ij}, in which

$$S_{ij} = \tfrac{1}{2}(A_{ij} + A_{ji}) - \tfrac{1}{3}A\delta_{ij}, \tag{3.58}$$

with five independent components. Then, finally, our original cartesian tensor may be written

$$A_{ij} = \tfrac{1}{3}A\delta_{ij} + C_k + S_{ij}. \tag{3.59}$$

The three quantities A, C_k, and S_{ij} form spherical tensors of rank 0, 1, and 2, respectively, transforming like the spherical harmonics Y_L^M (Chapter 12) for $L = 0$, 1, and 2. Further details of such spherical tensors and their uses will be found in the book by Rose, cited in Chapter 12.

---

[1] An alternate approach, using matrices, is given in Section 4.3. Cf. Exercise 4.3.10.

EXERCISES

3.4.1 An antisymmetric square array is given by

$$\begin{pmatrix} 0 & C_3 & -C_2 \\ -C_3 & 0 & C_1 \\ C_2 & -C_1 & 0 \end{pmatrix} = \begin{pmatrix} 0 & C_{12} & C_{13} \\ -C_{12} & 0 & C_{23} \\ -C_{13} & -C_{23} & 0 \end{pmatrix},$$

where (C_1, C_2, C_3) form a pseudovector. Assuming that the relation

$$C_i = \frac{1}{2!} \varepsilon_{ijk} C_{jk}$$

holds in all coordinate systems, prove that C_{jk} is a tensor. (This is another form of the quotient theorem).

3.4.2 The operator

$$\nabla^2 - \frac{1}{c^2} \frac{\partial^2}{\partial \varepsilon^2}$$

may be written as

$$\sum_{i=1}^{4} \frac{\partial^2}{\partial x_i^2},$$

using $x_4 = ict$. This is the four-dimensional Laplacian, usually called the d'Alembertian and denoted by $\Box^2$. Show that it is a *scalar* operator.

3.4.3 Show that
(a) $\delta_{ii} = 3$,
(b) $\delta_{ij}\varepsilon_{ijk} = 0$,
(c) $\varepsilon_{ipq}\varepsilon_{jpq} = 2\delta_{ij}$,
(d) $\varepsilon_{ijk}\varepsilon_{ijk} = 6$.

3.4.4 Show that

$$\varepsilon_{ijk}\varepsilon_{pqk} = \delta_{ip}\delta_{jq} - \delta_{iq}\delta_{jp}.$$

3.4.5 Verify that each of the following fourth-order tensors is isotropic, that is, that it has the same form independent of any rotation of the coordinate systems.
(a) $\delta_{ij}\delta_{kl}$,
(b) $\delta_{ik}\delta_{jl} + \delta_{il}\delta_{jk}$,
(c) $\delta_{ik}\delta_{jl} - \delta_{il}\delta_{jk}$.

3.4.6 Prove that ε_{ijk}, an isotropic tensor, is actually a pseudotensor by considering an inversion or a reflection that will exhibit its pseudo nature explicitly.

3.5 Dyadics

Occasionally, particularly in the older literature and older textbooks, the reader will see references to dyads or dyadics. The dyadic is a somewhat clumsy device for extending ordinary vector analysis to cover tensors of second rank.

If we adjoin two vectors **i** and **j** to form the combination **ij**, we have a dyad. Multiplication (scalar or vector) from the left involves the left-hand member of the pair and leaves the right-hand member strictly alone:

$$\mathbf{A} \cdot \mathbf{ij} = [(\mathbf{i}A_x + \mathbf{j}A_y + \mathbf{k}A_z) \cdot \mathbf{i}]\mathbf{j}$$
$$= A_x\mathbf{j}. \tag{3.60}$$

Multiplication from the right is just the reverse; that is,

$$\mathbf{ij} \cdot \mathbf{A} = \mathbf{i}[\mathbf{j} \cdot (\mathbf{i}A_x + \mathbf{j}A_y + \mathbf{k}A_z)]$$
$$= \mathbf{i}A_y. \tag{3.61}$$

From this we see that, in general, the operation of multiplication is noncommutative. It must be emphasized strongly that the **i** and **j** of the dyad **ij** are not operating on each other. If they had scalar coefficients, these would be multiplied together, but as far as the unit vectors are concerned there is no dot or cross product involved; they are just sitting there. As just shown, the order is significant **ij** ≠ **ji**. We thus have a composite quantity which depends in part on the ordering. This dependence on ordering will reappear when we study matrices (Chapter 4) and complex quantities (Chapter 6), the complex number being literally an ordered pair of real numbers.

Extending this construction, we adjoin two vectors **A** and **B** to form

$$\mathbf{T} = \mathbf{AB} = (\mathbf{i}A_x + \mathbf{j}A_y + \mathbf{k}A_z)(\mathbf{i}B_x + \mathbf{j}B_y + \mathbf{k}B_z)$$
$$= \mathbf{ii}A_xB_x + \mathbf{ij}A_xB_y + \mathbf{ik}A_xB_z$$
$$+ \mathbf{ji}A_yB_x + \mathbf{jj}A_yB_y + \mathbf{jk}A_yB_z$$
$$+ \mathbf{ki}A_zB_x + \mathbf{kj}A_zB_y + \mathbf{kk}A_zB_z. \tag{3.62}$$

The quantity **T** = **AB** is a dyadic formed as shown from a combination of dyads. We have proved (Section 3.2) that this product of two vectors **AB** is a tensor of second rank. Hence, dyadics are tensors of second rank, written in a form that preserves the vector nature but obscures the tensor transformation properties.

It has already been noted that the multiplication of a vector and a dyadic is not commutative, but there is an important special case in which the operation is commutative. We take the dyadic **AB** and set

$$\mathbf{a} \cdot \mathbf{AB} = \mathbf{AB} \cdot \mathbf{a}, \tag{3.63}$$

where **a** is an arbitrary vector. If **a** = **i**, then

$$A_x\mathbf{B} = \mathbf{A}B_x$$
$$\mathbf{i}A_xB_x + \mathbf{j}A_xB_y + \mathbf{k}A_xB_z = \mathbf{i}A_xB_x + \mathbf{j}A_yB_x + \mathbf{k}A_zB_x. \tag{3.64}$$

By equating components we obtain

$$A_xB_x = A_xB_x,$$
$$A_xB_y = A_yB_x, \tag{3.65}$$
$$A_xB_z = A_zB_x,$$

showing that $A = cB$, in which c a constant. In other words, if multiplication with an arbitrary vector is commutative, the dyadic must be symmetric, and the coefficient of dyad pq equals the coefficient of dyad qp. Conversely, if the dyadic is symmetric, multiplication is commutative.

One of the most significant properties of a symmetric dyadic is that it can always be put in normal or diagonal form by proper choice of the coordinate axis:

$$T \rightarrow ii T_{xx}$$
$$+ jj T_{yy}$$
$$+ kk T_{zz}, \tag{3.66}$$

all the nondiagonal coefficients going to zero. The coordinate transformation that puts our dyadic in this diagonal form is known as the principal axis transformation. It is discussed at some length in Section 4.5.

There is an interesting and useful geometric interpretation of a symmetric dyadic. For simplicity let us assume that our symmetric dyadic T is already in its diagonal form. Then with r, the usual distance vector, we form the equation

$$r \cdot T \cdot r = 1, \tag{3.67}$$

which limits the length of r according to its orientation. By expanding Eq. 3.67

$$(ix + jy + kz) \cdot (ii T_{xx} + jj T_{yy} + kk T_{zz}) \cdot (ix + jy + kz) = 1$$
$$x^2 T_{xx} + y^2 T_{yy} + z^2 T_{zz} = 1. \tag{3.68}$$

This defines an ellipsoid with semiaxes a, b, and c, given by

$$a = T_{xx}^{-1/2}, \qquad b = T_{yy}^{-1/2}, \qquad c = T_{zz}^{-1/2}. \tag{3.69}$$

Diagonalizing our dyadic corresponded to orienting the dyadic ellipsoid so that the ellipsoid axes were lined up with the coordinate axes.

If U is an antisymmetric dyadic,

$$U_{xx} = 0, \text{ etc.,}$$
$$U_{xy} = - U_{yx}, \text{ etc.,}$$

then for any vector a

$$a \cdot U = - U \cdot a. \tag{3.70}$$

Multiplication of a vector and an antisymmetric dyadic follows an anticommutation rule (cf. Exercise 3.5.1).

Dyadics are rather awkward to handle in comparison with the usual tensor analysis (once the concept of transformation under coordinate rotation has been absorbed). They are quite unwieldy for representing third- or higher-rank tensors, so we shall return to tensor analysis and have nothing further to do with dyadic notation.

EXERCISES

3.5.1 If **U** is an antisymmetric dyadic and **V** a vector, show that
(a) $\mathbf{V} \cdot \mathbf{U} = -\mathbf{U} \cdot \mathbf{V}$
(b) $\mathbf{V} \cdot \mathbf{U} \cdot \mathbf{V} = 0$.

3.5.2 If **U** is a symmetric dyadic, **a** a unit vector of variable direction, and **r** the distance vector, show that **r** traces out an ellipsoid when
$$\mathbf{r} = \mathbf{U} \cdot \mathbf{a}.$$

3.5.3 The two-dimensional vectors $\mathbf{r} = \mathbf{i}x + \mathbf{j}y$ and $\mathbf{t} = -y\mathbf{i} + \mathbf{j}x$ may be related by the tensor equation $\mathbf{r}\mathbf{U} = \mathbf{t}$.
(a) Find the tensor **U**, using our earlier component description of tensors.
(b) Find **U** and treat it as a dyadic.

3.5.4 In an investigation of the interaction of molecules a dyadic is formed from the unit relative distance vectors $\mathbf{e}_{12}$ given by
$$\mathbf{e}_{12} = \frac{\mathbf{r}_2 - \mathbf{r}_1}{|\mathbf{r}_2 - \mathbf{r}_1|}$$
For
$$\mathbf{U} = \mathbf{I} - 3\mathbf{e}_{12}\mathbf{e}_{12}$$
Show that trace $\mathbf{U} \cdot \mathbf{U} = 6$.

I is the unit dyadic, that is $\mathbf{I} = \mathbf{ii} + \mathbf{jj} + \mathbf{kk}$.

3.5.5 Show that $\mathbf{I} = \mathbf{ii} + \mathbf{jj} + \mathbf{kk}$ is a *unit dyadic* in the sense that for any vector **V**,
$$\mathbf{I} \cdot \mathbf{V} = \mathbf{V}.$$

The individual dyads **ii**, etc., are specific examples of the projection operators of quantum mechanics.

3.6 Theory of Elasticity

When an elastic body is subjected to an external force or stress, it becomes deformed or strained. Our study of elasticity in terms of tensors falls naturally into three parts. First, a description of the strain or deformation of the elastic substance, second, a description of the force or stress that produces the deformation, and finally a generalized Hooke's law in tensor form, relating stress and strain.

Elastic strain: deformation.   The deformation of our elastic body may be described by giving the change in relative position of the parts of the body when the body is subjected to some external stress. Consider a point P_0 at position **r** relative to some fixed origin and a second point Q_0 displaced from P_0 by a distance $\delta \mathbf{x}$. In the unstrained state the coordinates of Q_0 *relative to* P_0 are δx_i; in the strained state, when P_0 has been displaced a distance **u** to point P_1 and Q_0 a distance **v** to Q_1, the coordinates of Q_1 relative to P_1 are $\delta y_i = \delta x_i + \delta u_i$. The change in position

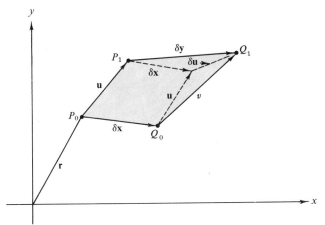

FIG. 3.3 Elastic strain

of Q *relative to* P is just δu_i. Neglecting second- and higher-order differentials, we obtain

$$\delta \mathbf{u} = \mathbf{u}(\mathbf{r} + \delta \mathbf{x}) - u(\mathbf{r}) = (\delta \mathbf{x} \cdot \nabla)\mathbf{u},$$

$$\delta u_i = \frac{\partial u_i}{\partial x_k} \delta x_k. \tag{3.71}$$

Since u_i is the component of a vector $\partial u_i / \partial x_k$ is an element of a second-rank tensor, $\nabla \mathbf{u}$. Resolving this tensor into symmetric and antisymmetric terms,

$$\delta u_i = \frac{1}{2}\left(\frac{\partial u_i}{\partial x_k} + \frac{\partial u_k}{\partial x_i}\right)\delta x_k - \frac{1}{2}\left(\frac{\partial u_k}{\partial x_i} - \frac{\partial u_i}{\partial x_k}\right)\delta x_k = \eta_{ik}\,\delta x_k - \xi_{ik}\,\delta x_k. \tag{3.72}$$

The antisymmetric part, ξ_{ik}, may be identified as a pure rotation (and not a deformation at all).

From Section 3.4 we may associate an axial vector $\boldsymbol{\xi}$ with ξ_{ij}:

$$\boldsymbol{\xi} = \tfrac{1}{2}\nabla \times \mathbf{u}. \tag{3.73}$$

The displacement $\delta \mathbf{u}$ corresponding to the antisymmetric part $-\xi_{ik}\,dx_k$ becomes

$$\delta \mathbf{u} = -\tfrac{1}{2}(\nabla \times \mathbf{u}) \times \delta \mathbf{x}. \tag{3.74}$$

This is a rotation about an instantaneous axis through P_0 in the direction $(\nabla \times \mathbf{u})$ through $-\tfrac{1}{2}\nabla \times \mathbf{u}$ radians.

The remaining symmetric part of our tensor η_{ij} is taken as a pure strain tensor. The diagonal elements ($\eta_{11}, \eta_{22}, \eta_{33}$) of η_{ik} represent stretches, whereas the non-diagonal elements represent shear strains.

This may be seen by considering Q_0 to be displaced from P_0 along the x-axis; $\delta \mathbf{x} = \mathbf{i}\,\delta x_1$. From Eq. 3.72

$$\delta u_1 = \eta_{11}\,\delta x_1,$$

$$\delta u_2 = \eta_{21}\,\delta x_1, \tag{3.75}$$

$$\delta u_3 = \eta_{31}\,\delta x_1.$$

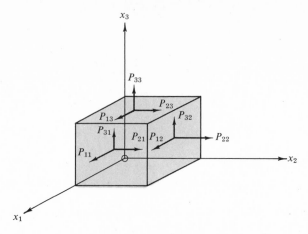

FIG. 3.4 Stresses

Hence the displacement in the strained case is

$$\delta y_1 = \delta x_1 + \delta u_1 = (1 + \eta_{11})\, \delta x_1,$$
$$\delta y_2 = \qquad \delta u_2 = \qquad \eta_{21}\, \delta x_1, \qquad\qquad (3.76)$$
$$\delta y_3 = \qquad \delta u_3 = \qquad \eta_{31}\, \delta x_1.$$

For our initial displacement, $\delta \mathbf{x} = \mathbf{i}\, \delta x_1$, the diagonal term η_{11} contributes to the 1 component of $\delta \mathbf{y}$ (stretching) and η_{21} and η_{31} contribute to δy_2 and δy_3, respectively, representing shears.

Stress-force.   The stresses or forces must be defined carefully. Referring to Fig. 3.3, which shows a differential volume, the force in the x_i-direction acting on

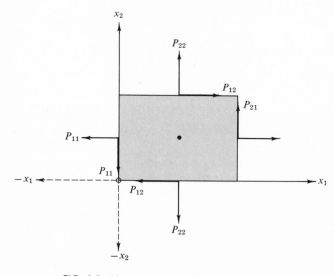

FIG. 3.5 Homogeneous stresses—sign reversal

the surface dA whose normal is in the x_j-direction is $P_{ij}\, dA$. The P_{ij}'s themselves are actually " pressures " in the sense of being force/area. Whenever the terms stress or force are used, it is understood that the P_{ij} are to be multiplied by the appropriate differential area. These are the forces acting *on* the small parallelepiped of Fig. 3.4. For clarity only the forces on the front three faces are shown. If we assume that the stresses are homogeneous, the forces on the opposite faces will be reversed in sign as shown in Fig. 3.5. Note that P_{21} is the shear (in the x_2-direction) applied to face A. For a homogeneous force face B must apply the same shearing stress P_{21} *to the outside medium*. The stress applied to face B by the outside medium is just the reverse, or P_{21} directed downward (in the $-x_2$-direction). Built into this argument are three assumptions that should be noted explicitly.

1. Homogeneous stress throughout the body.
2. Existance of static equilibrium.
3. Absence of body forces (such as gravity acting on the mass within the parallelepiped) and body torques (external magnetic field acting on magnetic domains).

These assumptions permit placement of a further restriction on the P_{ij}'s. Consider the net torque on the parallelepiped shown in Figs. 3.4 and 3.6 about the

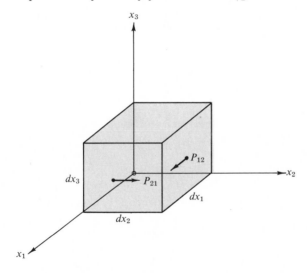

FIG. 3.6 Homogeneous stresses—balance of torques

x_3-axis. The normal pressures P_{ii} exert no net torque. The shearing stresses P_{31} and P_{32} have zero moment arm. The shearing stresses P_{13} and P_{23} are balanced by equal and opposite stresses on the bottom face ($x_3 = 0$). Remaining are the torques

$$P_{21}(dx_2\, dx_3)\, dx_1$$

and

$$P_{12}(dx_1\, dx_3)\, dx_2,$$ (3.77)

which must balance,

$$P_{21}\, dx_1\, dx_2\, dx_3 = P_{12}\, dx_1\, dx_2\, dx_3$$

in the absence of rotation about the x_3-axis. We have

$$P_{21} = P_{12} \tag{3.78}$$

and, in general, repeating the argument for the absence of rotation about x_2 and x_3,

$$P_{ij} = P_{ji}. \tag{3.79}$$

These are equalities of magnitude, not direction, which is given by the first index.

Thus the array of stresses (pressure) P_{ij} is symmetric. Now we show that this array is a tensor. We form an infinitesimal tetrahedron with a slant face of area dA, normal in the x'_j-direction, as shown in Fig. 3.7. The forces on the slant face

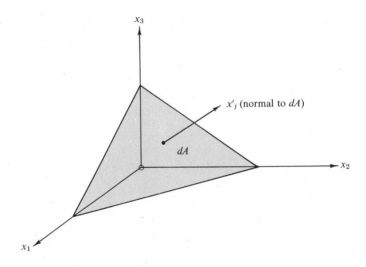

FIG. 3.7   Differential tetrahedron—balance of forces

are $P'_{ij}\, dA$. The forces on the faces $x_1 = 0$, $x_2 = 0$, and $x_3 = 0$ are, respectively,

$$P_{m1}(a_{j1}\, dA),$$

$$P_{m2}(a_{j2}\, dA),$$

and

$$P_{m3}(a_{j3}\, dA),$$

where $a_{jk}\, dA$ is the area of the face $x_k = 0$, being given by the slant area dA projected onto the plane $x_k = 0$. Our a_{jk} is the usual direction cosine, the cosine of the angle between the x'_j- and the x_k-axes.

The force $P_{m1}a_{j1}\, dA$ is along x_m. Its component in the x'_i-direction is $a_{im}a_{j1}P_{m1}\, dA$ (no summation). If we now sum over m, the foregoing expression gives us the sum of the x'_i-components of the three forces on the back face, $x_1 = 0$, in the x'_i-direction. Finally, summing over all three faces, $x_k = 0$, the total force along x'_i is

$$a_{im}a_{jk}P_{mk}\, dA = P'_{ij}\, dA \tag{3.80}$$

for static equilibrium. Since the area dA is arbitrary, we have

$$P'_{ij} = a_{im} a_{jk} P_{mk}, \tag{3.81}$$

which by definition makes P_{mk} a tensor.

Stress-strain relations: Hooke's law.   First, let us assume an isotropic elastic solid. Later we shall return to the general anisotropic case. Consider a uniform rod parallel to the x_1-axis.[1] By applying a small tensile stress P_{11},

$$E\eta_{11} = P_{11}, \tag{3.82a}$$

$$E\eta_{22} = -\sigma P_{11}, \tag{3.82b}$$

$$E\eta_{33} = -\sigma P_{11}, \tag{3.82c}$$

where E is Young's modulus and, σ is Poisson's ratio. If we add small tensile stresses P_{22} and P_{33}, Eq. 3.82a becomes

$$E\eta_{11} = P_{11} - \sigma P_{22} - \sigma P_{33}. \tag{3.83}$$

All through here we are limiting ourselves to *small* stresses and *small* strains so that the stress–strain relation will be linear. Eq. 3.83 may be rewritten

$$E\eta_{11} = (1 + \sigma)P_{11} - \sigma(P_{11} + P_{22} + P_{33}), \tag{3.84}$$

and similarly for $E\eta_{22}$ and $E\eta_{33}$.

Now η_{ij} and P_{ij} are tensors as proved earlier in this section. Because of the symmetry of our system their nondiagonal components are zero. To find the generalization of Eq. 3.84 in an arbitrarily oriented cartesian coordinate system we rotate the axes

$$\eta'_{ij} = a_{ik} a_{jk} \eta_{kk},$$
$$P'_{ij} = a_{ik} a_{jk} P_{kk}. \tag{3.85}$$

If we multiply Eq. 3.84 by $a_{i1} a_{j1}$, the corresponding equation for $E\eta_{22}$ by $a_{i2} a_{j2}$, and the equation for $E\eta_{33}$ by $a_{i3} a_{j3}$ and add all three equations, we obtain

$$E a_{ik} a_{jk} \eta_{kk} = (1 + \sigma) a_{ik} a_{jk} P_{kk} - \sigma(P_{nn}) a_{ik} a_{jk}. \tag{3.86}$$

Using Eqs. 3.85 and 3.18,

$$E\eta'_{ij} = (1 + \sigma)P'_{ij} - \sigma(P'_{mm}) \delta_{ij}, \tag{3.87}$$

where

$$(P'_{mm}) = (P_{nn}) = P_{11} + P_{22} + P_{33}, \tag{3.88}$$

the contracted (and, therefore invariant) tensor P_{ij}.

It is frequently more convenient to solve for the stresses P_{ik}. We may do this by setting $i = j$ and contracting

$$E\eta_{jj} = (1 + \sigma)P_{jj} - 3\sigma P_{jj}$$
$$= (1 - 2\sigma)P_{jj}, \tag{3.89}$$

---

[1] This special choice will start us off in a system identified in Chapter 4 as the principal axis system, the particular coordinate system in which the shearing strains vanish.

dropping the primes as superfluous. Substituting back into Eq. 3.87,

$$(1 + \sigma)P_{ij} = E\eta_{ij} + \frac{E\sigma}{1 - 2\sigma}\eta_{mm}\delta_{ij} \tag{3.90}$$

or

$$P_{ij} = 2\mu\eta_{ij} + \lambda\eta_{mm}\delta_{ij}, \tag{3.91}$$

where λ and μ, known as Lames's constants, are given by

$$\lambda = \frac{\sigma E}{(1 + \sigma)(1 - 2\sigma)}, \qquad \mu = \frac{E}{2(1 + \sigma)}. \tag{3.92}$$

The constant μ may be identified as the rigidity or shear modulus. Consider a parallelepiped fixed to the $(x_3 = 0)$-plane with a tangential stress P_{12} applied.

FIG. 3.8 Shear stress—shear strain

The displacement is $(\eta x_2, 0, 0)$. In terms of our strain tensor, $\eta_{ij} = 0$ except for $\eta_{12} = \eta_{21} = \frac{1}{2}\eta$. From Eq. 3.91

$$P_{12} = 2\mu \cdot \tfrac{1}{2}\eta = \mu\eta, \tag{3.93}$$

showing that μ is the ratio of shear stress to shear modulus η.

If the strain is spherically symmetric, as in hydrostatic pressure,

$$\eta_{11} = \eta_{22} = \eta_{33}; \qquad \eta_{12} = \eta_{13} = \eta_{23} = 0. \tag{3.94}$$

Then

$$P_{11} = 3\lambda\eta_{11} + 2\mu\eta_{11}$$
$$= 3k\eta_{11}, \tag{3.95}$$

where

$$k = \lambda + \tfrac{2}{3}\mu. \tag{3.96}$$

Since $3\eta_{11}$ is the relative change in volume to first-order, we identify k as the bulk modulus.

For the general case covering anisotropic as well as isotropic solids we express the linear stress-strain relation by a generalized Hooke's law.

$$P_{ij} = c_{ijkl}\eta_{kl}, \tag{3.97}$$

where c_{ijkl} is a fourth-rank tensor by the quotient theorem. Since the stress tensor

P_{ij} is symmetric and the strain tensor η_{kl} is likewise symmetric,

$$c_{ijkl} = c_{jikl} = c_{ijlk} = c_{jilk},\tag{3.98}$$

reducing the number of components from 81 (3^4) to 36. It may further be shown[1] that

$$c_{ijkl} = c_{klij},\tag{3.99}$$

which further reduces the number of independent components to 21.

If we apply our general tensor relation (Eq. 3.97) to an isotropic body, the elastic constant tensor c_{ijkl} must be a linear combination of the most general isotropic tensors of fourth rank. Using the results of Exercise 3.4.5, we have

$$c_{ijkl} = a\delta_{ij}\delta_{kl} + b[\delta_{ik}\delta_{jl} + \delta_{il}\delta_{jk}] + c[\delta_{ik}\delta_{jl} - \delta_{il}\delta_{jk}].\tag{3.100}$$

By substituting into Eq. 3.97,

$$P_{ij} = a\delta_{ij}\eta_{kk} + b(\eta_{ij} + \eta_{ji}) + c(\eta_{ij} - \eta_{ji})\tag{3.101}$$

as before. Since η_{ij} is symmetric, this reduces to

$$P_{ij} = a\eta_{kk}\delta_{ij} + 2b\eta_{ij}$$

in complete agreement with Eq. 3.91.

EXERCISES

3.6.1 The three-dimensional fourth-rank stress-strain tensor c_{ijkl} satisfies
$$c_{ijkl} = c_{jikl} = c_{ijlk} = c_{jilk}.$$

(a) Show that application of these symmetry conditions reduces the number of independent components or elements of c_{ijkl} from 81 to 36.

(b) If we further specify that
$$c_{ijkl} = c_{klij},$$
show that the number of independent components drops to 21.

3.7 Lorentz Covariance of Maxwell's Equations

The Lorentz transformations of special relativity involving space and time may be shown to be equivalent to rotations in a special four-dimensional space.[2] This space is Minkowski space with the fourth coordinate $x_4 = ict$. Basically, the reason for the inclusion of the imaginary i is to give a space in which the four-dimensional Pythagorean theorem has the same form as the usual three-dimensional cartesian case. This may be taken as the criterion of a cartesian system. Our immediate

---

[1] Cf. I. S. Sokolnikoff, *Mathematical Theory of Elasticity*. New York: McGraw-Hill (1956).

[2] Goldstein, *Classical Mechanics*, Chapter 6. The tensor equation for a photon $\sum x_\lambda^2 = 0$, independent of reference frame, leads to the Lorentz transformations.

problem is to rewrite Maxwell's equations in tensor form in this Minkowski space. If we can do this, then, because of the transformation properties of our tensors, consistency with special relativity will be automatic. We have

$$\mathbf{V} \times \mathbf{E} = -\frac{\partial \mathbf{B}}{\partial t}, \tag{3.102a}$$

$$\mathbf{V} \times \mathbf{H} = \frac{\partial \mathbf{D}}{\partial t} + \rho \mathbf{v}, \tag{3.102b}$$

$$\mathbf{V} \cdot \mathbf{D} = \rho, \tag{3.102c}$$

$$\mathbf{V} \cdot \mathbf{B} = 0, \tag{3.102d}$$

and the relations

$$\mathbf{D} = \varepsilon_0 \mathbf{E}, \qquad \mathbf{B} = \mu_0 \mathbf{H}. \tag{3.103}$$

The symbols have their usual meanings as given in the introduction. For simplicity we assume vacuum ($\varepsilon = \varepsilon_0$, $\mu = \mu_0$).

In terms of scalar and magnetic vector potentials, we may write

$$\begin{aligned} \mathbf{B} &= \mathbf{V} \times \mathbf{A} \\ \mathbf{E} &= -\frac{\partial \mathbf{A}}{\partial t} - \mathbf{V}\varphi. \end{aligned} \tag{3.104}$$

Equation 3.104 specifies the curl of $\mathbf{A}$; the divergence of $\mathbf{A}$ is still undefined (cf. Section 1.13 and 1.15). We may, and for future convenience we do, impose the further restriction on the vector potential $\mathbf{A}$,

$$\mathbf{V} \cdot \mathbf{A} + \varepsilon_0 \mu_0 \frac{\partial \varphi}{\partial t} = 0. \tag{3.105}$$

This is the Lorentz relation.

From Eqs. 3.102c and 3.104

$$\mathbf{V}^2\varphi + \mathbf{V} \cdot \frac{\partial \mathbf{A}}{\partial t} = -\frac{\rho}{\varepsilon_0}, \tag{3.106}$$

whereas Eqs. 3.102b) and 3.104 and Eq. 1.80 of Chapter 1 yield

$$\frac{\partial^2 \mathbf{A}}{\partial t^2} + \mathbf{V}\frac{\partial \varphi}{\partial t} + \frac{1}{\varepsilon_0 \mu_0}\{\mathbf{V}\mathbf{V} \cdot \mathbf{A} - \mathbf{V}^2\mathbf{A}\} = \frac{\rho \mathbf{v}}{\varepsilon_0}. \tag{3.107}$$

Using the Lorentz relation, Eq. 3.105 and the relation $\varepsilon_0\mu_0 = 1/c^2$,

$$\left[\mathbf{V}^2 - \frac{1}{c^2}\frac{\partial^2}{\partial t^2}\right]\mathbf{A} = -\mu_0\rho\mathbf{v},$$

$$\left[\mathbf{V}^2 - \frac{1}{c}\frac{\partial^2}{\partial t^2}\right]\varphi = -\frac{\rho}{\varepsilon_0}, \tag{3.108}$$

Now the differential operator

$$\mathbf{V}^2 - \frac{1}{c^2}\frac{\partial^2}{\partial t^2}$$

becomes in Minkowski space

$$\sum_{\lambda=1}^{4} \frac{\partial^2}{\partial x_\lambda^2}.$$

Here we adopt Greek indices, as is customary in relativity theory, to indicate a summation from 1 to 4. This summation,

$$\sum_\lambda \frac{\partial^2}{\partial x_\lambda^2},$$

is a four-dimensional Laplacian, usually called the d'Alembertian and denoted by $\square^2$. It may readily be proved a scalar (cf. Exercise 3.4.2).

For convenience we define

$$A_1 \equiv \frac{A_x}{\mu_0 c} = c\varepsilon_0 A_x,$$

$$A_2 \equiv \frac{A_y}{\mu_0 c} = c\varepsilon_0 A_y,$$

$$A_3 \equiv \frac{A_z}{\mu_0 c} = c\varepsilon_0 A_z, \tag{3.109}$$

and

$$A_4 \equiv i\varepsilon_0 \varphi.$$

If we further put

$$\frac{\rho v_x}{c} \equiv i_1, \qquad \frac{\rho v_y}{c} \equiv i_2, \qquad \frac{\rho v_z}{c} \equiv i_3, \qquad i\rho \equiv i_4, \tag{3.110}$$

then Eq. 3.108 may be written in the form

$$\sum_\lambda \frac{\partial^2}{\partial x_\lambda^2} A_\mu = -i_\mu. \tag{3.111}$$

Equation 3.111 looks like a tensor equation, but looks do not constitute proof. To prove that it is a tensor equation we start by investigating the transformation properties of the generalized current i_μ.

Since an electric charge element de is an invariant quantity, we have

$$de = \rho \, dx_1 \, dx_2 \, dx_3, \qquad \text{invariant.} \tag{3.112}$$

We saw in Section 3.4 that the four-dimensional volume element, $dx_1 \, dx_2 \, dx_3 \, dx_4$ was also invariant. Comparing this result, Eq. 3.53 with Eq. 3.112, we see that the charge density ρ must transform the same way as dx_4, the fourth component of a four-dimensional vector dx_λ. We put $i\rho = i_4$, with i_4 now established as the fourth component of a vector. The other parts of Eq. 3.110 may be expanded as

$$i_1 = \frac{\rho x_x}{c} = \frac{\rho \, dx_1}{c \, dt} = \frac{i\rho \, dx_1}{ic \, dt}$$

$$= i_4 \frac{dx_1}{dx_4}. \tag{3.113}$$

Since we have just shown that i_4 transforms as dx_4, it means that i_1 transforms as dx_1. With similar results for i_2 and i_3, we have i_λ transforming as dx_λ, proving that i_λ is a vector, a four-dimensional vector in Minkowski space.

Equation 3.111, which follows directly from Maxwell's equations, Eq. 3.102, is assumed to hold in all cartesian systems (all Lorentz frames). Then, by the quotient rule, Section 3.3, A_μ is also a vector and Eq. 3.111 is a legitimate tensor equation.

Now, working backward, Eq. 3.104 may be written

$$i\varepsilon_0 E_j = \frac{\partial A_j}{\partial x_4} - \frac{\partial A_4}{\partial x_j}, \qquad j = 1, 2, 3,$$

$$\frac{1}{\mu_0 c} B_i = \frac{\partial A_k}{\partial x_j} - \frac{\partial A_j}{\partial x_4}, \qquad (i, j, k) = (1, 2, 3) \tag{3.114}$$

and *cyclic* permutations.

We define a new tensor

$$\frac{\partial A_\lambda}{\partial x_\mu} - \frac{\partial A_\mu}{\partial x_\lambda} \equiv f_{\mu\lambda} = -f_{\lambda\mu},$$

an antisymmetric second-rank tensor, since A_λ is a vector. Written out explicitly,

$$f_{\mu\lambda} = \varepsilon_0 \begin{pmatrix} 0 & cB_z & -cB_y & -iE_x \\ -cB_z & 0 & cB_x & -iE_y \\ cB_y & -cB_x & 0 & -iE_z \\ iE_x & iE_y & iE_z & 0 \end{pmatrix}. \tag{3.115}$$

With this tensor we may write two of Maxwell's equations (3.102b) and (3.102c) combined as a tensor equation:

$$\frac{\partial f_{\lambda\mu}}{\partial x_\mu} = i_\lambda. \tag{3.116}$$

The left-hand side of Eq. 3.116 is a four-dimensional divergence of a tensor and therefore a vector. This, of course, is equivalent to contracting a third-rank tensor $\partial f_{\lambda\mu}/\partial x_\nu$ (cf. Exercise 3.2.1 and 3.2.2). The remaining two Maxwell equations (3.102a) and (3.102d) may be expressed in the tensor form

$$\frac{\partial f_{23}}{\partial x_1} + \frac{\partial f_{31}}{\partial x_2} + \frac{\partial f_{12}}{\partial x_3} = 0. \tag{3.117}$$

for Eq. 3.102d and three equations of the form

$$\frac{\partial f_{34}}{\partial x_2} + \frac{\partial f_{42}}{\partial x_3} + \frac{\partial f_{23}}{\partial x_4} = 0 \tag{3.118}$$

for Eq. 3.102a. (A second equation permutes 124, a third permutes 134.) Since

$$\frac{\partial f_{\lambda\mu}}{\partial x_\nu} \equiv t_{\lambda\mu\nu}$$

is a tensor (of third rank), Eqs. 3.102*a* and 3.102*d* are given by the tensor equation

$$t_{\lambda\mu\nu} + t_{\nu\lambda\mu} + t_{\mu\nu\lambda} = 0. \tag{3.119}$$

From Eqs. 3.117 and 3.118 the reader will understand that the indices λ, μ, and ν are supposed to be different. Actually, Eq. 3.119 automatically reduces to $0 = 0$ if any two indices coincide (cf. Exercise 3.7.4).

The establishment of the tensor equations (3.116) and (3.119) actually completes the demonstration of the Lorentz covariance of Maxwell's equations, but it is perhaps of interest to exploit the tensor properties of $f_{\lambda\mu}$ (Eq. 3.115). For the Lorentz transformation corresponding to motion along the $z(x_3)$-axis with velocity v, the "direction cosines" are[1]

$$a_{\lambda\mu} = \begin{pmatrix} 1 & 0 & 0 & 0 \\ 0 & 1 & 0 & 0 \\ 0 & 0 & \gamma & i\beta\gamma \\ 0 & 0 & -i\beta\gamma & \gamma \end{pmatrix}, \tag{3.120}$$

where

$$\beta = \frac{v}{c}$$

and

$$\gamma = (1 - \beta^2)^{-1/2} \tag{3.121}$$

Using the tensor transformation properties, we may calculate the electric and magnetic fields in the moving system in terms of the values in the original reference frame. From Eqs. 3.13, 3.115, and 3.120 we obtain

$$E'_x = \frac{1}{\sqrt{1 - \beta^2}} (E_x - vB_y),$$

$$E'_y = \frac{1}{\sqrt{1 - \beta^2}} (E_y + vB_x), \tag{3.122}$$

$$E'_z = E_z,$$

and

$$B'_x = \frac{1}{\sqrt{1 - \beta^2}} \left(B_x + \frac{v}{c^2} E_y \right),$$

$$B'_y = \frac{1}{\sqrt{1 - \beta^2}} \left(B_y - \frac{v}{c^2} E_x \right), \tag{3.123}$$

$$B'_z = B_z.$$

This coupling of **E** and **B** is to be expected. Consider, for instance, the case of zero electric field in the unprimed system

$$E_x = E_y = E_z = 0.$$

[1] Goldstein, Chapter 6.

Clearly there will be no force on a stationary charged particle. When the particle is in motion with a *small* velocity **v** along the z-axis,[1] an observer on the particle sees fields (exerting a force on his charged particle) given by

$$E'_x = -vB_y,$$

$$E'_y = vB_x,$$

where **B** is a magnetic field in the unprimed system. These equations may be put in vector form

$$\mathbf{E}' = \mathbf{v} \times \mathbf{B}$$

or   (3.124)

$$\mathbf{F} = q\mathbf{v} \times \mathbf{B},$$

which is usually taken as the operational definition of the magnetic inductance **B**.

Finally, the tensor (or vector) properties allow us to construct a multitude of invariant quantities. One of the more important is the scalar product of the two four-dimensional vectors or four vectors A_λ and i_λ. We have

$$A_\lambda i_\lambda = c\varepsilon_0 A_x \frac{\rho v_x}{c} + c\varepsilon_0 A_y \frac{\rho v_y}{c}$$

$$+ c\varepsilon_0 A_z \frac{\rho v_z}{c} + i\varepsilon_0 \varphi i \rho$$

$$= \varepsilon_0(\mathbf{A} \cdot \mathbf{j} - \rho\varphi), \qquad \text{invariant,} \qquad (3.125)$$

with **A** the usual magnetic vector potential and **j** the ordinary current density. The final term $\rho\varphi$ is the ordinary static electric coupling with dimensions of energy per unit volume. Hence our newly constructed scalar invariant is an energy density. The dynamic interaction of field and current is given by the product $\mathbf{A} \cdot \mathbf{j}$.

Other possible electromagnetic invariants appear in Exercise 3.7.3.

EXERCISES

3.7.1 The dual of a four-dimensional second-rank tensor **B** may be defined by **B***, where the elements of the dual tensor are given by

$$B^*_{ij} = \frac{1}{2!} \delta_{ijkl} B_{kl}.$$

Show that **B*** transforms as
(a) a second-rank tensor under rotations,
(b) a pseudotensor under inversions.
Note. The asterisk here does *not* mean complex conjugate.

---

[1] If the velocity is not small (so that v^2/c^2) is negligible, a relativistic transformation of force is needed.

3.7.2 Construct **f***, the dual of **f**, where **f** is the electromagnetic tensor given by Eq. 3.115.

$$\text{Ans. } \mathbf{f}^* = \varepsilon_0 \begin{pmatrix} 0 & -iE_z & iE_y & cB_x \\ iE_z & 0 & -iE_x & cB_y \\ -iE_y & iE_x & 0 & cB_z \\ -cB_x & -cB_y & -cB_z & 0 \end{pmatrix}.$$

This corresponds to

$$c\mathbf{B} \to -i\mathbf{E},$$

$$-i\mathbf{E} \to c\mathbf{B}.$$

This transformation, sometimes called a "dual transformation," leaves Maxwell's equations in vacuum ($\rho = 0$) invariant.

3.7.3 Show that
(a) $c^2B^2 - E^2$
and
(b) $\mathbf{B} \cdot \mathbf{E}$
are invariants.

3.7.4 Show that Eq. 3.119,

$$t_{\lambda\mu\nu} + t_{\nu\lambda\mu} + t_{\mu\nu\lambda} = 0,$$

is a trivial identity, $0 = 0$, unless λ, μ, and ν are all different.

3.7.5 Write the Lorentz condition (Eq. 3.105), as a tensor equation in Minkowski space.

3.7.6 Show that

$$\sum_\mu \frac{\partial i_\mu}{\partial x_\mu} = 0$$

is a statement of continuity of charge and current (cf. Section 1.7). If this equation is known to hold in all Lorentz reference frames, why does this not permit us to conclude that i_μ is a vector?

3.7.7 A gauge transformation consists of varying the scalar potential φ_1 and the vector potential A_1 according to the relation

$$\varphi_2 = \varphi_1 + \frac{\partial\chi}{\partial t},$$

$$\mathbf{A}_2 = \mathbf{A}_1 - \nabla\chi.$$

The new function χ is required to satisfy the homogeneous wave equation

$$\nabla^2\chi - \varepsilon_0\mu_0 \frac{\partial^2\chi}{\partial t^2} = 0.$$

Show the following:

(a) The Lorentz relation is unchanged.
(b) The new potentials satisfy the same inhomogeneous wave equations as did the original potentials.
(c) The fields **E** and **B** are unaltered.

The invariance of our electromagnetic theory under this transformation is called *gauge invariance*.

REFERENCES

HEITLER, W. *The Quantum Theory of Radiation*. 2nd Ed., Oxford: Oxford University Press (1947).

JEFFREYS, Harold, *Cartesian Tensors*. Cambridge: Cambridge University Press (1952). This is an excellent discussion of cartesian tensors and their application to a wide variety of fields of classical physics.

LAWDEN, Derek F., *An Introduction to Tensor Calculus and Relativity*. New York: Wiley (Methuen monograph) (1962).

MOLLER, C., *The Theory of Relativity*. Oxford: Oxford University Press (1955). Most texts on general relativity include a discussion of tensor analysis. Chapter 4 develops tensor calculus, including the topic of dual tensors. The extension to noncartesian systems, as required by general relativity, is presented in Chapter 9.

PANOFSKY, W. K. H., and M. PHILLIPS. *Classical Electricity and Magnetism*. Reading, Mass.: Addison-Wesley (1955). The Lorentz covariance of Maxwell's equations is developed for both vacuum and material media. Panofsky and Phillips use contravariant and covariant tensors rather than Minkowski space. Discussions using Minkowski space are given by Heitler and Stratton.

SOKOLNIKOFF, I. S., *Tensor Analysis—Theory and Applications*. New York: Wiley (1951). Particularly useful for its extension of tensor analysis to non-Euclidean geometries.

SPAIN, B., *Tensor Calculus*, 3rd Ed. New York: Interscience Publishers. (1960). A useful concise presentation of tensors with applications to elasticity and relativity theory.

STRATTON, J. A., *Electromagnetic Theory*. New York: McGraw-Hill (1941).

TEMPLE, George, *Cartesian Tensors*. New York: Wiley (Methuen monograph) (1960).

CHAPTER 4

MATRICES AND DETERMINANTS

4.1 Determinants

We begin our study of matrices by summarizing some properties of determinants, partly because determinants are useful in matrix analysis and partly to illustrate, by way of contrast, what matrices are not.

Properties.   A determinant is a square array of numbers or functions,

$$D = \begin{vmatrix} a_1 & b_1 & c_1 & \cdot & \cdot & \cdot \\ a_2 & b_2 & c_2 & \cdot & \cdot & \cdot \\ a_3 & b_3 & c_3 & \cdot & \cdot & \cdot \\ \cdot & & & \cdot & \cdot & \cdot \\ a_n & b_n & c_n & \cdot & \cdot & \cdot \end{vmatrix}, \tag{4.1}$$

of n rows and n columns. The value of n is sometimes called the order of the determinant. In terms of its elements, a_i, b_j, etc., the value of the determinant D is

$$D = \sum_{i,j,k\cdots} \delta_{ijk\cdots} a_i b_j c_k \cdots, \tag{4.2}$$

where $\delta_{ijk\cdots}$, analogous to the Levi-Civita symbol of Section 3.4 is $+1$ for even permutations of $(1, 2, 3, \cdots, n)$, -1 for odd permutations, and zero if any index is repeated. Specifically, for the third-order determinant,

$$D = \begin{vmatrix} a_1 & b_1 & c_1 \\ a_2 & b_2 & c_2 \\ a_3 & b_3 & c_3 \end{vmatrix}, \tag{4.3}$$

Eq. 4.2 leads to

$$D = +a_1b_2c_3 - a_1b_3c_2 + a_2b_3c_1$$
$$-a_2b_1c_3 + a_3b_1c_2 - a_3b_2c_1. \qquad (4.4)$$

The third-order determinant, then, is this particular linear combination of products. Each product contains one and only one element from each row and from each column. Each product is added in if the order represents an even permutation of rows (the colums being in a, b, c or 1, 2, 3 order) and subtracted if we have an odd permutation. Equation 4.3 may be considered shorthand notation for Eq. 4.4.

Several useful properties of the nth order determinants follow from Eq. 4.4. Again, to be specific, Eq. 4.4 for third-order determinants is used to illustrate these properties.

Laplacian development by minors.   Equation 4.4 may be written

$$D = a_1(b_2c_3 - b_3c_2) - a_2(b_1c_3 - b_3c_1) + a_3(b_1c_2 - b_2c_1)$$

$$= a_1 \begin{vmatrix} b_2 & c_2 \\ b_3 & c_3 \end{vmatrix} - a_2 \begin{vmatrix} b_1 & c_1 \\ b_3 & c_3 \end{vmatrix} + a_3 \begin{vmatrix} b_1 & c_1 \\ b_2 & c_2 \end{vmatrix}. \qquad (4.5)$$

In general, the nth order determinant may be expanded as a linear combination of the products of the elements of any row (or any column) and the $(n-1)$-order determinants formed by striking out the row and column of the original determinant in which the element appears. This reduced array (2×2 in this specific example) is called a "minor." If the element is in the ith row and the jth column, the sign associated with the product is $(-1)^{i+j}$. The minor with the sign $(-1)^{i+j}$ is called the "cofactor." If M_{ij} is used to designate the minor formed by omitting the ith row and the jth column and C_{ij} is the corresponding cofactor, Eq. 4.5 becomes

$$D = \sum_{i=1}^{3} (-1)^{i+1} a_i M_{i1} = \sum_{i=1}^{3} a_i C_{i1}.$$

In this case, expanding down the first column, we have $j = 1$ and the summation over i.

This Laplace expansion may be used to advantage in the evaluation of high-order determinants in which a lot of the elements are zero. For example, to find the value of the determinant

$$D = \begin{vmatrix} 0 & 1 & 0 & 0 \\ -1 & 0 & 0 & 0 \\ 0 & 0 & 0 & 1 \\ 0 & 0 & -1 & 0 \end{vmatrix}, \qquad (4.6)$$

we expand across the top row to obtain

$$D = (-1)^{1+2} \cdot (1) \begin{vmatrix} -1 & 0 & 0 \\ 0 & 0 & 1 \\ 0 & -1 & 0 \end{vmatrix}. \qquad (4.7)$$

Again, expanding across the top row, we get

$$D = (-1) \cdot (-1)^{1+1} \cdot (-1) \begin{vmatrix} 0 & 1 \\ -1 & 0 \end{vmatrix}$$

$$= \begin{vmatrix} 0 & 1 \\ -1 & 0 \end{vmatrix} = 1. \tag{4.8}$$

This determinant D (Eq. 4.6) is formed from one of the Dirac matrices appearing in Dirac's relativistic electron theory.

Antisymmetry. The determinant changes sign if any two rows are interchanged or if any two columns are interchanged. This follows from the even-odd character of the Levi-Civita δ in Eq. 4.2 or explicitly from the form of Eqs. 4.3 and 4.4.[1]

This property was used in Section 3.4 to develop a totally antisymmetric linear combination. It is also frequently used in quantum mechanics in the construction of a many-particle wave function that, in accordance with the Pauli exclusion principle, will be antisymmetric under the interchange of any two identical spin $\frac{1}{2}$ particles (electrons, protons, neutrons, etc.).

As a special case of antisymmetry, any determinant with two rows equal or two columns equal equals zero.

If each element in a row or each element in a column is zero, the determinant is equal to zero.

If each element in a row or each element in a column is multiplied by a constant, the determinant is multiplied by that constant.

The value of a determinant is unchanged if a multiple of one row is added (column by column) to another row or if a multiple of one column is added (row by row) to another column.

We have

$$\begin{vmatrix} a_1 & b_1 & c_1 \\ a_2 & b_2 & c_2 \\ a_3 & b_3 & c_3 \end{vmatrix} = \begin{vmatrix} a_1 + kb_1 & b_1 & c_1 \\ a_2 + kb_2 & b_2 & c_2 \\ a_3 + kb_3 & b_3 & c_3 \end{vmatrix}. \tag{4.9}$$

Using the Laplace development on the right-hand side,

$$\begin{vmatrix} a_1 + kb_1 & b_1 & c_1 \\ a_2 + kb_2 & b_2 & c_2 \\ a_3 + kb_3 & b_3 & c_3 \end{vmatrix} = \begin{vmatrix} a_1 & b_1 & c_1 \\ a_2 & b_2 & c_2 \\ a_3 & b_3 & c_3 \end{vmatrix} + k \begin{vmatrix} b_1 & b_1 & c_1 \\ b_2 & b_2 & c_2 \\ b_3 & b_3 & c_3 \end{vmatrix}, \tag{4.10}$$

then by the property of antisymmetry the second determinant on the right-hand side of Eq. 4.10 vanishes, verifying Eq. 4.9.

As a special case, a determinant is equal to zero if any two rows are proportional or any two columns are proportional.

---

[1] The sign reversal is reasonably obvious for the interchange of two adjacent rows (or columns), this clearly being an odd permutation. The reader may wish to show that the interchange of *any* two rows is still an odd permutation.

Solution of a set of homogeneous equations.   One of the major applications of determinants is in the establishment of a condition for the existence of a non-trivial solution for a set of linear homogeneous algebraic equations. Suppose we have three homogeneous equations with three unknowns (or n equations with n unknowns)

$$a_1 x + b_1 y + c_1 z = 0,$$

$$a_2 x + b_2 y + c_2 z = 0, \qquad (4.11)$$

$$a_3 x + b_3 y + c_3 z = 0.$$

The problem is to determine whether any solution, apart from the trivial one $x = 0$, $y = 0$, $z = 0$, exists.

By forming the determinant of the coefficients of Eq. 4.11 and then multiplying by x,

$$x \begin{vmatrix} a_1 & b_1 & c_1 \\ a_2 & b_2 & c_2 \\ a_3 & b_3 & c_3 \end{vmatrix} = \begin{vmatrix} a_1 x & b_1 & c_1 \\ a_2 x & b_2 & c_2 \\ a_3 x & b_3 & c_3 \end{vmatrix}$$

$$= \begin{vmatrix} a_1 x + b_1 y + c_1 z & b_1 & c_1 \\ a_2 x + b_2 y + c_2 z & b_2 & c_2 \\ a_3 x + b_3 y + c_3 z & b_3 & c_3 \end{vmatrix}. \qquad (4.12)$$

The final step follows from Eq. 4.9, but by Eq. 4.11 each element of the first column vanishes. Then

$$x \begin{vmatrix} a_1 & b_1 & c_1 \\ a_2 & b_2 & c_2 \\ a_3 & b_3 & c_3 \end{vmatrix} = \begin{vmatrix} 0 & b_1 & c_1 \\ 0 & b_2 & c_2 \\ 0 & b_3 & c_3 \end{vmatrix} = 0. \qquad (4.13)$$

Therefore x (and y and z) must be zero *unless the determinant of the coefficients vanishes.* Conversely, we can show that if the determinant of the coefficient vanishes a nontrivial solution does indeed exist. This is used in Section 7.6 to establish the linear dependence or independence of a set of functions.

EXERCISES

4.1.1 Evaluate the following determinants

(a) $\begin{vmatrix} 1 & 0 & 1 \\ 0 & 1 & 0 \\ 1 & 0 & 0 \end{vmatrix}$

(b) $\dfrac{1}{\sqrt{2}}\begin{vmatrix} 0 & \sqrt{3} & 0 & 0 \\ \sqrt{3} & 0 & 2 & 0 \\ 0 & 2 & 0 & \sqrt{3} \\ 0 & 0 & \sqrt{3} & 0 \end{vmatrix}$

(c) $\begin{vmatrix} 1 & 2 & 0 \\ 3 & 1 & 2 \\ 0 & 3 & 1 \end{vmatrix}$

4.1.2 Test the set of linear homogeneous equations

$$x + 3y + 3z = 0,$$
$$x - y + z = 0,$$
$$2x + y + 3z = 0,$$

to see if it possesses a nontrivial solution.

4.1.3 If C_{ij} is the cofactor of element a_{ij} (formed by striking out the ith row and jth column and including a sign $(-1)^{i+j}$), show that

(a) $\sum_i a_{ij} C_{ij} = \sum_i a_{ji} C_{ji} = |A|$, where $|A|$ is the determinant with the elements a_{ij},

(b) $\sum_i a_{ij} C_{ik} = \sum_i a_{ji} C_{ki} = 0, \qquad j \neq k.$

4.2 Matrices

Basic definitions. A matrix may be defined as a square or rectangular array of numbers or functions that obeys certain laws. This is a perfectly logical extension of familiar mathematical concepts. In arithmetic we deal with single numbers. In the theory of complex variables (Chapter 6) we deal with ordered pairs of numbers, $(1, 2) = 1 + 2i$, in which the ordering is important. We now consider numbers (or functions) ordered in a square or rectangular array. For convenience in later work the numbers are distinguished by two subscripts, the first indicating the row (horizontal) and the second indicating the column (vertical) in which the number appears. For instance, a_{13} is the matrix element in the first row, third column. Hence, if A is a matrix with m rows and n columns,

$$A = \begin{pmatrix} a_{11} & a_{12} & \cdot & \cdot & \cdot & a_{1n} \\ a_{21} & a_{22} & \cdot & \cdot & \cdot & a_{2n} \\ \cdot & \cdot & \cdot & \cdot & \cdot & \cdot \\ a_{m1} & a_{m2} & \cdot & \cdot & \cdot & a_{mn} \end{pmatrix}. \tag{4.14}$$

Perhaps the most important thing to note is that the elements a_{ij} are not combined with one another. The matrix is not a determinant. It is not a single number; it is an ordered array of numbers. It makes no more sense to add or multiply all the a_{ij}'s together than it does to write $1 + 2i = 3$!

The matrix A so far just an array of numbers, has the properties we assign to it. Literally, this means constructing a new form of mathematics. We postulate that matrices A, B, and C, with elements a_{ij}, b_{ij}, and c_{ij}, respectively, combine according to the following rules:

Equality.   Matrix A = Matrix B if and only if $a_{ij} = b_{ij}$ for all values of i and j. This, of course, requires that A and B each be m by n arrays (m rows, n columns).

Addition.   A + B = C if and only if $a_{ij} + b_{ij} = c_{ij}$ for all values of i and j, the elements combining according to the laws of ordinary algebra (or arithmetic if they are simple numbers). This means that A + B = B + A, commutation. Also, an associative law is satisfied (A + B) + C = A + (B + C).

Multiplication (by a scalar).   The multiplication of matrix A by the scalar quantity α is defined as

$$\alpha A = (\alpha A),$$

in which the elements of αA are αa_{ij}; that is, each element of matrix A is multiplied by the scalar factor. This is in striking contrast to the behavior of determinants in which the factor α multiplies only one column or one row and not every element of the entire determinant. A consequence of this scalar multiplication is that

$$\alpha A = A\alpha, \text{ commutation}$$

Multiplication (matrix multiplication).

$$A B = C \quad \text{if and only if} \quad c_{ij} = \sum_k a_{ik} b_{kj}. \tag{4.15}$$

The ij element of C is formed as a scalar product of the ith row of A with the jth column of B (which demands that A have the same number of columns (n) as B as rows). The dummy index k takes on all the values 1, 2, $\cdots$, n in succession, that is,

$$c_{ij} = a_{i1} b_{1j} + a_{i2} b_{2j} + a_{i3} b_{3j} \tag{4.16}$$

for $n = 3$. Obviously the dummy index k may be replaced by any other symbol that is not already in use without altering Eq. 4.15. Perhaps the situation may be clarified by stating that Eq. 4.15 defines the method of combining certain matrices. This method of combination, to give it a label, is called matrix multiplication. To illustrate, consider two matrices

$$\sigma_1 = \begin{pmatrix} 0 & 1 \\ 1 & 0 \end{pmatrix} \quad \text{and} \quad \sigma_3 = \begin{pmatrix} 1 & 0 \\ 0 & -1 \end{pmatrix}. \tag{4.17}$$

We have

$$\sigma_1 \sigma_3 = \begin{pmatrix} 0 \cdot 1 + 1 \cdot 0 & 0 \cdot 0 + 1 \cdot (-1) \\ 1 \cdot 1 + 0 \cdot 0 & 1 \cdot 0 + 0 \cdot (-1) \end{pmatrix} = \begin{pmatrix} 0 & -1 \\ 1 & 0 \end{pmatrix} \tag{4.18}$$

Here

$$(\sigma_1 \sigma_3)_{ij} = \sigma_{1_{i1}} \sigma_{3_{1j}} + \sigma_{1_{i2}} \sigma_{3_{2j}}$$

Direct application of the definition of matrix multiplication shows that

$$\sigma_3 \sigma_1 = \begin{pmatrix} 0 & 1 \\ -1 & 0 \end{pmatrix} \tag{4.19}$$

and by Eq. 4.15

$$\sigma_3\sigma_1 = -\sigma_1\sigma_3. \tag{4.20}$$

Except in special cases, matrix multiplication is not commutative.[1]

$$AB \neq BA. \tag{4.21}$$

However, from the definition of matrix multiplication we can show that an associative law does hold, $(AB)C = A(BC)$. There is also a distributive law, $A(B + C) = AB + AC$.

A number of matrices are of special interest. If the matrix has one column and n rows, it is called a column vector, $\{x\}$ with components x_i, $i = 1, 2, \cdots, n$.

Similarly, if the matrix has one row and n columns, it is called a row vector, $[x]$ with components x_i, $i = 1, 2, \cdots, n$. Clearly, if A is an $n \times n$ matrix, $\{x\}$ an n-component column vector, and $[x]$ an n-component row vector,

$$A\{x\} \quad \text{and} \quad [x]A$$

are defined by Eq. 4.15, whereas

$$A[x] \quad \text{and} \quad \{x\}A$$

are not defined.

In the remainder of this chapter we shall confine our attention to column vectors, row vectors, and square matrices.

The unit matrix 1 has elements δ_{ij}, Kronecker delta, and the property that $1A = A1 = A$ for all A.

$$1 = \begin{pmatrix} 1 & 0 & 0 & 0 & \cdot & \cdot & \cdot \\ 0 & 1 & 0 & 0 & \cdot & \cdot & \cdot \\ 0 & 0 & 1 & 0 & \cdot & \cdot & \cdot \\ 0 & 0 & 0 & 1 & \cdot & \cdot & \cdot \\ \cdot & \cdot & \cdot & \cdot & \cdot & \cdot & \cdot \end{pmatrix}. \tag{4.22}$$

If all elements are zero, the matrix is called the null matrix and is denoted by O. For all A

$$OA = AO = O.$$

$$O = \begin{pmatrix} 0 & 0 & 0 & \cdot & \cdot & \cdot \\ 0 & 0 & 0 & \cdot & \cdot & \cdot \\ 0 & 0 & 0 & \cdot & \cdot & \cdot \\ \cdot & \cdot & \cdot & \cdot & \cdot & \cdot \end{pmatrix}. \tag{4.23}$$

It should be noted that it is possible for the product of two matrices to be the null

---

[1] Commutation or the lack of it is conveniently described by the commutator bracket symbol, $[A, B] = AB - BA$. Equation 4.21 becomes $[A, B] \neq 0$.

matrix without either one being the null matrix. For example, if

$$A = \begin{pmatrix} 1 & 1 \\ 0 & 0 \end{pmatrix} \quad \text{and} \quad B = \begin{pmatrix} 1 & 0 \\ -1 & 0 \end{pmatrix},$$

$AB = O$. Once more the results of ordinary algebra do not apply directly.

Diagonal matrices.   An important special type of matrix is the square matrix in which all the nondiagonal elements are zero. Specifically, if a 3×3 matrix A is diagonal,

$$A = \begin{pmatrix} a_{11} & 0 & 0 \\ 0 & a_{22} & 0 \\ 0 & 0 & a_{33} \end{pmatrix}.$$

The physical interpretation of such diagonal matrices and the method of reducing matrices to this diagonal form are considered in Section 4.5. Here, we simply note a significant property of diagonal matrices—that multiplication of diagonal matrices is commutative,

$$AB = BA, \quad \text{if} \quad A \quad \text{and} \quad B \quad \text{are each diagonal.}$$

Trace.   In any square matrix the sum of the diagonal elements is called the *trace*. One of its interesting and useful properties is that the trace of a product of two matrices A and B is independent of the order of multiplication:

$$\text{trace}(AB) = \sum_i (AB)_{ii} = \sum_i \sum_j a_{ij} b_{ji}$$

$$= \sum_j \sum_i b_{ji} a_{ij} = \sum_i (BA)_{jj}$$

$$= \text{trace}(BA). \tag{4.24}$$

This holds even though $AB \neq BA$.

EXERCISES

4.2.1 The three Pauli spin matrices are

$$\sigma_1 = \begin{pmatrix} 0 & 1 \\ 1 & 0 \end{pmatrix}, \quad \sigma_2 = \begin{pmatrix} 0 & -i \\ i & 0 \end{pmatrix}, \quad \text{and} \quad \sigma_3 = \begin{pmatrix} 1 & 0 \\ 0 & -1 \end{pmatrix}.$$

Show that
(a) $\sigma_i^2 = 1$,
(b) $\sigma_i \sigma_j = i \sigma_k$, $(i, j, k) = (1, 2, 3), (2, 3, 1), (3, 1, 2)$ (cyclic permutation),
(c) $\sigma_i \sigma_j + \sigma_j \sigma_i = 2\delta_{ij} 1$.
These matrices were used by Pauli in the nonrelativistic theory of electron spin.

4.2.2 Given the three matrices

$$A = \begin{pmatrix} -1 & 0 \\ 0 & -1 \end{pmatrix}, \quad B = \begin{pmatrix} 0 & 1 \\ 1 & 0 \end{pmatrix}, \quad \text{and} \quad C = \begin{pmatrix} 0 & -1 \\ -1 & 0 \end{pmatrix}.$$

Find all possible products of A, B, and C, two at a time, including squares. Express your answers in terms of A, B, and C, and 1, the unit matrix.

These three matrices together with the unit matrix form a representation of a mathematical group, the *vierergruppe*.

4.2.3 One description of spin 1 particles uses the matrices

$$M_x = \frac{1}{\sqrt{2}} \begin{pmatrix} 0 & 1 & 0 \\ 1 & 0 & 1 \\ 0 & 1 & 0 \end{pmatrix}, \quad M_y = \frac{1}{\sqrt{2}} \begin{pmatrix} 0 & -i & 0 \\ i & 0 & -i \\ 0 & i & 0 \end{pmatrix},$$

and

$$M_z = \begin{pmatrix} 1 & 0 & 0 \\ 0 & 0 & 0 \\ 0 & 0 & -1 \end{pmatrix}.$$

Show that
(a) $[M_x, M_y]$ [1] $= iM_z$, etc.   (cyclic permutation of indices),
(b) $M^2 \equiv M_x^2 + M_y^2 + M_z^2 = 2\mathbf{1}$,
where **1** is the unit matrix.
(c) $[M^2, M_i] = 0$,
    $[M_z, L^+] = L^+$,
    $[L^+, L^-] = 2M_z$
where
    $L^+ \equiv M_x + iM_y$,
    $L^- \equiv M_x - iM_y$.

4.2.4 Repeat Exercise 4.2.3, using an alternate representation,

$$M_x = \begin{pmatrix} 0 & 0 & 0 \\ 0 & 0 & -i \\ 0 & i & 0 \end{pmatrix}, \quad M_y = \begin{pmatrix} 0 & 0 & i \\ 0 & 0 & 0 \\ -i & 0 & 0 \end{pmatrix},$$

and

$$M_z = \begin{pmatrix} 0 & -i & 0 \\ i & 0 & 0 \\ 0 & 0 & 0 \end{pmatrix}.$$

4.2.5 Repeat Exercise 4.2.3, using the matrices for a spin of $\frac{3}{2}$,

$$M_x = \frac{1}{\sqrt{2}} \begin{pmatrix} 0 & \sqrt{3} & 0 & 0 \\ \sqrt{3} & 0 & 2 & 0 \\ 0 & 2 & 0 & \sqrt{3} \\ 0 & 0 & \sqrt{3} & 0 \end{pmatrix}, \quad M_y = \frac{i}{\sqrt{2}} \begin{pmatrix} 0 & -\sqrt{3} & 0 & 0 \\ \sqrt{3} & 0 & -2 & 0 \\ 0 & 2 & 0 & -\sqrt{3} \\ 0 & 0 & \sqrt{3} & 0 \end{pmatrix},$$

and

$$M_z = \frac{1}{2} \begin{pmatrix} 3 & 0 & 0 & 0 \\ 0 & 1 & 0 & 0 \\ 0 & 0 & -1 & 0 \\ 0 & 0 & 0 & -3 \end{pmatrix}.$$

[1] $[A, B] \equiv AB - BA$.

4.2.6 Using the Pauli σ's of Exercise 4.2.1, show that

$$(\boldsymbol{\sigma}\cdot\mathbf{a})(\boldsymbol{\sigma}\cdot\mathbf{b}) = \mathbf{a}\cdot\mathbf{b} + i\boldsymbol{\sigma}\cdot(\mathbf{a}\times\mathbf{b}).$$

Here

$$\boldsymbol{\sigma} \equiv \mathbf{i}\sigma_x + \mathbf{j}\sigma_y + \mathbf{k}\sigma_z$$

and **a** and **b** are ordinary vectors.

4.2.7 Show that matrix multiplication is associative, (AB)C = A(BC).

4.2.8 If A is diagonal, with all diagonal elements different, and A and B commute, show that B is diagonal.

4.2.9 If A and B are diagonal, show that A and B commute.

4.2.10 If two nonsingular matrices anticommute, show that the trace of each one is zero. (Nonsingular means that the determinant of the matrix elements $\neq 0$).

4.2.11 Show that trace (ABCD) = trace (DABC).

4.2.12 If A^{-1} has elements

$$a_{ij}^{-1} = \frac{C_{ji}}{|A|}$$

where C_{ji} is the jith cofactor of $|A|$. Show that

$$A^{-1}A = 1.$$

Hence A^{-1} is the inverse of A (if $|A| \neq 0$).

4.2.13 Given

$$K = \begin{pmatrix} 0 & 0 & i \\ -i & 0 & 0 \\ 0 & -1 & 0 \end{pmatrix},$$

show that

$$K^n = KKK\cdots(n\text{ factors}) = 1$$

(with the proper choice of n, $n \neq 0$).

4.2.14 Verify the Jacobi identity

$$[A, [B, C]] = [B, [A, C]] - [C, [A, B]].$$

This is useful in matrix descriptions of elementary particles. As a mnemonic aid, the reader might note that the Jacobi identity has the same form as the *BAC-CAB* rule of Section 1.5.

4.2.15 Matrix C is the matrix product of A and B. Show that the determinant of C is the product of the determinants of A and B.

$$\det C = \det A \times \det B.$$

4.3 Orthogonal Matrices

Ordinary three-dimensional space may be described with the familiar cartesian coordinates (x, y, z). We consider a second set of cartesian coordinates (x', y', z') whose origin coincides with that of the first set but whose orientation is different. This section repeats portions of Chapters 1 and 3 in a slightly different context and with a different emphasis. In Chapters 1 and 3 attention was focused on the vector or tensor. Here emphasis is laid on the description of the coordinate rotation itself.

Direction cosines.   A unit vector along the x'-axis ($\mathbf{i}'$) may be resolved into components along the x-, y-, and z-axes by the usual projection technique.

$$\mathbf{i}' = \mathbf{i}\cos(x', x) + \mathbf{j}\cos(x', y) + \mathbf{k}\cos(x', z). \qquad (4.25)$$

For convenience these cosines, which are the direction cosines, are labeled

$$\cos(x', x) = a_{11},$$
$$\cos(x', y) = a_{12}, \qquad\qquad (4.26)$$
$$\cos(x', z) = a_{13}.$$

Continuing,

$$\cos(y', x) = a_{21}, \qquad (a_{21} \neq a_{12}),$$
$$\cos(y', y) = a_{22}, \text{ etc.} \qquad\qquad (4.27)$$

Now, Eq. 4.25 may be rewritten

$$\mathbf{i}' = \mathbf{i}a_{11} + \mathbf{j}a_{12} + \mathbf{k}a_{13}$$

and also

$$\mathbf{j}' = \mathbf{i}a_{21} + \mathbf{j}a_{22} + \mathbf{k}a_{23}, \qquad\qquad (4.28)$$
$$\mathbf{k}' = \mathbf{i}a_{31} + \mathbf{j}a_{32} + \mathbf{k}a_{33}.$$

We may also go the other way by resolving $\mathbf{i}$, $\mathbf{j}$, and $\mathbf{k}$ into components in the primed system. Then

$$\mathbf{i} = \mathbf{i}'a_{11} + \mathbf{j}'a_{21} + \mathbf{k}'a_{31},$$
$$\mathbf{j} = \mathbf{i}'a_{12} + \mathbf{j}'a_{22} + \mathbf{k}'a_{32}, \qquad\qquad (4.29)$$
$$\mathbf{k} = \mathbf{i}'a_{13} + \mathbf{j}'a_{23} + \mathbf{k}'a_{33}.$$

Associating $\mathbf{i}$ and $\mathbf{i}'$ with the subscript 1, $\mathbf{j}$ and $\mathbf{j}'$ with the subscript 2, $\mathbf{k}$ and $\mathbf{k}'$ with the subscript 3, we see that in each case the first subscript of a_{ij} refers to the

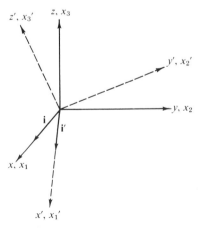

FIG. 4.1 Cartesian coordinate systems

primed unit vector ($\mathbf{i}'$, $\mathbf{j}'$, $\mathbf{k}'$), whereas the second subscript refers to the unprimed unit vector ($\mathbf{i}$, $\mathbf{j}$, $\mathbf{k}$).

Applications to vectors.   If we consider a vector whose components are functions of the position in space, then

$$\mathbf{V}(x, y, z) = \mathbf{i}V_x + \mathbf{j}V_y + \mathbf{k}V_z$$
$$= \mathbf{V}'(x', y', z') = \mathbf{i}'V'_{x'} + \mathbf{j}'V'_{y'} + \mathbf{k}'V'_{z'}, \tag{4.30}$$

since the point may be given both by the coordinates (x, y, z) and the coordinates (x', y', z'). Using Eq. 4.29 to eliminate $\mathbf{i}$, $\mathbf{j}$, and $\mathbf{k}$, Eq. 4.30 may be separated into three scalar equations.

$$V'_{x'} = a_{11}V_x + a_{12}V_y + a_{13}V_z$$
$$V'_{y'} = a_{21}V_x + a_{22}V_y + a_{23}V_z \tag{4.31}$$

and

$$V'_{z'} = a_{31}V_x + a_{32}V_y + a_{33}V_z.$$

In particular, these relations will hold for the coordinates of a point (x, y, z) and (x', y', z'), giving

$$x' = a_{11}x + a_{12}y + a_{13}z,$$
$$y' = a_{21}x + a_{22}y + a_{23}z, \tag{4.32}$$

and

$$z' = a_{31}x + a_{32}y + a_{33}z.$$

It is convenient to change the notation slightly at this point.
Let

$$x \to x_1,$$
$$y \to x_2, \tag{4.33}$$
$$z \to x_3,$$

and similarly for the primed coordinates. In this notation the set of three equations (4.32) may be written

$$x'_i = \sum_{j=1}^{3} a_{ij}x_j, \tag{4.34}$$

where i takes on the values 1, 2, and 3 and the result is three *separate* equations.

Now let us set aside these results and try a different approach to the same problem. We consider two coordinate systems (x_1, x_2, x_3) and (x'_1, x'_2, x'_3) with a common origin and one point (x_1, x_2, x_3) in the unprimed system, (x'_1, x'_2, x'_3) in the primed system. Note the usual ambiguity. The same symbol x denotes both the coordinate axis and a particular distance along that axis. Since our system is linear, x'_i must be a linear combination of the x_i's. Let

$$x'_i = \sum_{j=1}^{3} a_{ij}x_j. \tag{4.35}$$

The a_{ij} may be identified as our old friends, the direction cosines. This identification is carried out for the two-dimensional case later.

If we have two sets of quantities (V_1, V_2, V_3) in the unprimed system and (V'_1, V'_2, V'_3) in the primed system, related in the same way as the coordinates of a point in the two different systems (Eq. 4.35),

$$V'_i = \sum_{j=1}^{3} a_{ij} V_j, \tag{4.36}$$

then, as in Section 1.2, the quantities (V_1, V_2, V_3) are defined as the components of a vector; that is, a vector is defined in terms of transformation properties of its components under a rotation of the coordinate system. In a sense the coordinates of a point have been taken as a prototype vector. The power and usefulness of this definition becomes apparent in Chapter 3, in which it is extended to define pseudo-vectors and tensors.

From Eq. 4.34 we can derive interesting information about the a_{ij}'s which describe the orientation of coordinate system (x'_1, x'_2, x'_3) relative to system (x_1, x_2, x_3). The length from the origin to the point is the same in both systems. Squaring, for convenience,

$$\sum_i x_i^2 = \sum_i x_i'^2$$

$$= \sum_i (\sum_j a_{ij} x_j)(\sum_k a_{ik} x_k) \;^1$$

$$= \sum_{j,k} x_j x_k \sum_i a_{ij} a_{ik}. \tag{4.37}$$

This can be true for all points if and only if

$$\sum_i a_{ij} a_{ik} = \delta_{jk}, \qquad j, k = 1, 2, 3. \tag{4.38}$$

Verification of Eq. 4.38, if needed, may be obtained by returning to Eq. 4.37 and setting $x = (1, 0, 0)$, $(0, 1, 0)$, $(0, 0, 1)$, $(1, 1, 0)$, etc., to evaluate the nine relations given by equation 4.38. This process is valid, since Eq. 4.37 must hold for all x for a given set of a_{ij}. Equation 4.38, a consequence of requiring that the length remain constant (invariant) under rotation of the coordinate system, is called the *orthogonality condition*. The a_{ij}'s written as a matrix A, form an orthogonal matrix. Note carefully that Eq. 4.38 is *not* matrix multiplication. Rather it is interpreted later as a scalar product of two columns of A.

In matrix notation Eq. 4.34 becomes

$$\{x'\} = A\{x\}. \tag{4.39}$$

Orthogonality conditions—two-dimensional case.   A better feeling for the a_{ij}'s and the orthogonality condition may be gained by considering rotation in two dimensions in detail. (This can be thought of as a three-dimensional system with the x_1-x_2-axes rotated about x_3. From Fig. 1.6, Chapter 1,

$$x'_1 = x_1 \cos \varphi + x_2 \sin \varphi,$$

$$x'_2 = -x_1 \sin \varphi + x_2 \cos \varphi. \tag{4.40}$$

---

[1] Note that *two* independent indices j and k are used.

Therefore by Eq. 4.39

$$A = \begin{pmatrix} \cos \varphi & \sin \varphi \\ -\sin \varphi & \cos \varphi \end{pmatrix}. \tag{4.41}$$

It is clear from Fig. 1.6 that

$$a_{11} = \cos \varphi = \cos(x'_1, x_1),$$

$$a_{12} = \sin \varphi = \cos\left(\frac{\pi}{2} - \varphi\right) = \cos(x'_1, x_2), \text{ etc.} \tag{4.42}$$

thus identifying the matrix elements a_{ij} as the direction cosines. Equation 4.38, the orthogonality condition, becomes

$$\sin^2 \varphi + \cos^2 \varphi = 1,$$

$$\sin \varphi \cos \varphi - \sin \varphi \cos \varphi = 0. \tag{4.43}$$

The extension to three dimensions (rotation of the coordinates through an angle φ counterclockwise about x_3) is simply

$$A = \begin{pmatrix} \cos \varphi & \sin \varphi & 0 \\ -\sin \varphi & \cos \varphi & 0 \\ 0 & 0 & 1 \end{pmatrix}. \tag{4.44}$$

The $a_{33} = 1$ expresses the fact that $x'_3 = x_3$, since the rotation has been about the x_3-axis. The zeros guarantee that x'_1 and x'_2 do not depend on x_3 and that x'_3 does not depend on x_1 and x_2.

Inverse matrix, A^{-1}.   Returning to the general transformation matrix A, the inverse matrix A^{-1} is defined such that

$$\{x\} = A^{-1}\{x'\}; \tag{4.45}$$

that is, A^{-1} describes the reverse of the rotation given by A and returns the coordinate system to its original position. Symbolically, Eqs. 4.39 and 4.45 combine to give

$$\{x\} = A^{-1}A\{x\}, \tag{4.46}$$

and since $\{x\}$ is arbitrary

$$A^{-1}A = 1 \tag{4.47}$$

the unit matrix. Similarly

$$AA^{-1} = 1, \tag{4.48}$$

using Eqs. 4.39 and 4.45 and eliminating $\{x\}$ instead of $\{x'\}$.

Transpose matrix, $\tilde{A}$.   We can determine the elements of our postulated inverse matrix A^{-1} by employing the orthogonality condition. Equation 4.38, the orthogonality condition, does *not* conform to our definition of matrix multiplication, but it can be put in the required form by *defining* a new matrix A such that

$$\tilde{a}_{ij} = a_{ji}; \tag{4.49}$$

that is, $\tilde{A}$, is called "A transpose," is formed from A by interchanging rows and columns. Equation 4.38 becomes

$$\tilde{A}A = 1. \tag{4.50}$$

This is a restatement of the orthogonality condition and may be taken as a definition of orthogonality. Multiplying Eq. 4.50 by A^{-1} from the right and using Eq. 4.48,

$$\tilde{A} = A^{-1}. \tag{4.51}$$

This important result that the inverse equals the transpose holds only for orthogonal matrices and indeed may be taken as a further restatement of the orthogonality condition.

Multiplying Eq. 4.51 by A from the left,

$$A\tilde{A} = 1 \tag{4.52}$$

or

$$\sum_i a_{ji}a_{ki} = \delta_{jk}, \tag{4.53}$$

which is still another form of the orthogonality condition.

It is now possible to see and understand why the term *orthogonal* is appropriate for these matrices. We have the general form

$$A = \begin{pmatrix} a_{11} & a_{12} & a_{13} \\ a_{21} & a_{22} & a_{23} \\ a_{31} & a_{32} & a_{33} \end{pmatrix},$$

a matrix of direction cosines in which a_{ij} is the cosine of the angle between x'_i and x_j. Therefore a_{11}, a_{12}, a_{13} are the direction cosines of x'_1 relative to x_1, x_2, x_3. These three elements of A *define* a unit length along x'_1, that is, a unit vector $\mathbf{i}$,

$$\mathbf{i}' = \mathbf{i}a_{11} + \mathbf{j}a_{12} + \mathbf{k}a_{13}.$$

The orthogonality relation (Eq. 4.53) is simply a statement that the unit vectors $\mathbf{i}'$, $\mathbf{j}'$, and $\mathbf{k}'$ are mutually perpendicular or orthogonal. Our orthogonal transformation matrix A rotates one orthogonal coordinate system into a second orthogonal coordinate system.

The inverse of a nonorthogonal matrix (if it exists) is defined still by Eq. 4.47 or equivalently by Eq. 4.48. The necessary and sufficient conditions for its existence are that the matrix be a square $(n \times n)$ array and that its determinant, meaning the determinant of its elements, not vanish (cf. Exercise 4.2.12).

It will be noticed that the matrices have been handled in two ways in the foregoing discussion: by their components and as single entities. Each technique has its own advantages. Both are useful.

Consider the evaluation of $(ST)^{-1}$ where ST is a (product) matrix which has an inverse. Then, clearly,

$$(ST)(ST)^{-1} = 1. \tag{4.54}$$

Multiplying first by S^{-1} and then by T^{-1} successively from the left,

$$(ST)^{-1} = T^{-1}S^{-1}. \tag{4.55}$$

The inverse of a product equals the product of the inverses *in reverse order*. This may be readily generalized to any number of factors.

On the other hand, the evaluation of $(\tilde{ST})$ may perhaps best be carried out by considering the components. Let

$$u_{ik} = \sum_j s_{ij} t_{jk}$$

$$= \sum \tilde{t}_{kj} \tilde{s}_{ji},$$

$$(4.56)$$

using the definition of transpose. But

$$u_{ik} = \tilde{u}_{ki},$$

$$(4.57)$$

and Eq. 4.56 may be written

$$(\tilde{ST}) = \tilde{T}\tilde{S}.$$

$$(4.58)$$

The transpose of a product equals the product of the transposes *in reverse order*. Note that in neither of the two illustrations have we required S or T to be orthogonal.

Symmetry properties.   The transpose matrix is useful in a discussion of symmetry properties. If

$$A = \tilde{A}, \qquad a_{ij} = a_{ji},$$

$$(4.59)$$

the matrix is called *symmetric*, whereas if

$$A = -\tilde{A}, \qquad a_{ij} = -a_{ji},$$

$$(4.60)$$

it is called antisymmetric or skewsymmetric. The diagonal elements vanish. It is easy to show that any (square) matrix may be written as the sum of a symmetric matrix and an antisymmetric matrix. Consider the identity

$$A = \tfrac{1}{2}[A + \tilde{A}] + \tfrac{1}{2}[A - \tilde{A}].$$

$$(4.61)$$

$[A + \tilde{A}]$ is clearly symmetric, whereas $[A - \tilde{A}]$ is clearly antisymmetric. This is the matrix analog of Eq. 3.22, Chapter 3, for tensors.

Successive rotations, matrix multiplication.   Returning to orthogonal matrices, let the coordinate rotation

$$\{x'\} = A\{x\}$$

$$(4.62)$$

be followed by a second rotation given by matrix B such that

$$\{x''\} = B\{x'\}.$$

$$(4.63)$$

In component form

$$x_i'' = \sum_j b_{ij} x_j'$$

$$= \sum_j b_{ij} \sum_k a_{jk} x_k$$

$$= \sum_k (\sum_j b_{ij} a_{jk}) x_k.$$

$$(4.64)$$

The summation over j is matrix multiplication defining a matrix $C = BA$ such that

$$x_i'' = \sum_k c_{ik} x_k.$$

$$(4.65)$$

Again the definition of matrix multiplication is found useful and indeed *this is the justification for its existence*. The physical interpretation is that the matrix product of the two matrices, BA, is the rotation that carries the unprimed system directly into the double-primed coordinate system.

So far we have interpreted the orthogonal matrix as rotating the coordinate system. This changes the components of a fixed vector (not rotating with the coordinates) (Fig. 1.6, Chapter 1). However, Eq. 4.62 may be interpreted equally well as a rotation of the *vector* in the *opposite* direction (Fig. 4.2).

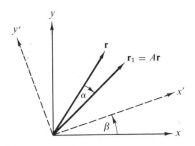

FIG. 4.2   Fixed coordinates—rotated vector

Suppose we interpret matrix A as rotating a *vector* **r** into the position shown by $\mathbf{r}_1$.

$$\mathbf{r}_1 = A\mathbf{r}. \tag{4.66}$$

Now let us rotate the *coordinates* by applying matrix B, which rotates (x, y, z) into (x', y', z')

$$B\mathbf{r}_1 = BA\mathbf{r}$$
$$= BA(B^{-1}B)\mathbf{r} \tag{4.67}$$
$$= (BAB^{-1})B\mathbf{r}.$$

$B\mathbf{r}_1$ is just $\mathbf{r}_1$ in the new coordinate system with a similar interpretation holding for $B\mathbf{r}$. Hence *in this new system* ($B\mathbf{r}$) is rotated into position ($B\mathbf{r}_1$) by the matrix BAB^{-1}; or, in other words, in the new system, the coordinates having been rotated by matrix B, A has the form A', in which

$$A' = BAB^{-1}. \tag{4.68}$$

Similarity transformation.   The transformation defined by Eq. 4.68 with B any matrix, not necessarily orthogonal, is known as a similarity transformation.

In component form Eq. 4.68 becomes

$$a'_{ij} = \sum_{k,l} b_{ik} a_{nl} b_{lj}^{-1}. \tag{4.69}$$

Now if B is orthogonal,

$$b_{lj}^{-1} = \tilde{b}_{lj} = b_{jl}, \tag{4.70}$$

and we have

$$a'_{ij} = \sum_{k,l} b_{ik} b_{jl} a_{kl}. \tag{4.71}$$

Relation to tensors.   Comparing (4.71) with the equations of Section 3.1, we see that it is the definition of a tensor of second rank. Hence a matrix that transforms by an *orthogonal* similarity transformation is, by definition, a tensor. Clearly then, any *orthogonal* matrix A, interpreted as rotating a vector (Eq. 4.66), may be called a tensor. If, however, we consider the orthogonal matrix as a collection of fixed direction cosines, giving the new orientation of a coordinate system, there is no tensor transformation involved.

The symmetry and antisymmetry properties defined earlier are preserved under *orthogonal* similarity transformations. Let A by a symmetric matrix, $A = \tilde{A}$, and

$$A' = BAB^{-1} \tag{4.72}$$

Now

$$\tilde{A}' = \widetilde{BAB^{-1}} = \widetilde{B^{-1}}\tilde{A}\tilde{B}$$
$$= B\tilde{A}B^{-1}, \tag{4.73}$$

since B is orthogonal. But $A = \tilde{A}$. Therefore

$$\tilde{A}' = BAB^{-1} = A', \tag{4.74}$$

showing that the property of symmetry is invariant under an orthogonal similarity transformation.

EXERCISES

Note. Assume all matrix elements are real.

4.3.1 Write out the matrix describing a counterclockwise rotation of the coordinate system (right-handed system) about the x_2-axis.

4.3.2 Show that the product of two orthogonal matrices is orthogonal.

4.3.3 Show that trace (ABC) = trace (CBA) if any two of the three matrices commute.

4.3.4 Show that the trace of the product of a symmetric and an antisymmetric matrix is zero.

4.3.5 If $AB = 1$, show that $BA = 1$.

4.3.6 Show that $\tilde{A} = A^{-1}$ by summing the triple product of orthogonal matrix elements
$$\sum_i \sum_k a_{ij}a_{ik}a_{kl}^{-1} = \sum_k \sum_i a_{ij}a_{ik}a_{kl}^{-1}$$
Here a_{kl}^{-1} is the kl element of A^{-1}.

4.3.7 Prove that the operations of inverse and transpose commute,
$$(\tilde{M})^{-1} = (\widetilde{M^{-1}}).$$

4.3.8 If a matrix has an inverse, show that the inverse is unique.

4.3.9 If A is antisymmetric, show that

$$\tilde{r}Ar = 0,$$

where **r** is a (column) vector.

4.3.10 Show that the trace of a matrix remains invariant under similarity transformations.

4.3.11 Show that the sum of the squares of the elements of a matrix remains invariant under orthogonal similarity transformations.

4.3.12 As a generalization of Exercise 4.3.11, show that

$$\sum_{jk} S_{jk} T_{jk} = \sum_{l,m} S'_{lm} T'_{lm},$$

where the primed and unprimed elements are related by an orthogonal similarity transformation. This result is useful in deriving invariants in electromagnetic theory (cf. Section 3.7).

4.3.13 Show that the determinant of a matrix remains invariant under similarity transformations.

4.3.14 Show that the property of antisymmetry is invariant under orthogonal similarity transformations.

4.3.15 Given AA = 1, show that symmetry implies orthogonality.

4.3.16 Given AA = 1, show that orthogonality implies symmetry.

4.3.17 If A is orthogonal, show that its determinant has unit magnitude.

4.4 Hermitian Matrices, Unitary Matrices

Definitions. Up to this point is has been generally assumed that the matrix elements were real. For many calculations in classical physics real matrix elements will suffice. However, in quantum mechanics complex variables are inescapable because of the form of the basic commutation relations (or the form of the time-dependent Schrödinger equation). With this in mind, we generalize to the case of complex matrix elements. To handle these elements, it is convenient to define, or to label, some new properties.

1. Complex conjugate, A*, formed by taking the complex conjugate $(i \rightarrow -i)$ of each element, where $i = \sqrt{-1}$.

2. Adjoint, A†, formed by transposing A*,

$$A^\dagger = \widetilde{A^*} = \tilde{A}^*. \tag{4.75}$$

3. Hermitian matrix. The matrix A is labeled Hermitian (or self-adjoint) if

$$A = A^\dagger. \tag{4.76}$$

In quantum mechanics (or matrix mechanics), matrices are usually constructed to be Hermitian.

4. Unitary matrix. Matrix U is labeled unitary if

$$U^\dagger = U^{-1}, \tag{4.77}$$

which represents a generalization of the concept of orthogonal matrix (cf. Eq. 4.51).

If the transforming matrix in a similarity transformation is unitary, the transformation is referred to as a unitary transformation,

$$A' = UAU^\dagger \tag{4.78}$$

Just as the product of two orthogonal matrices is found to be orthogonal (Exercise 4.3.2), so we can show that the product of two unitary matrices is unitary. Let U_1 and U_2 be unitary. Then

$$\begin{aligned} 1 &= (U_1 U_2)(U_1 U_2)^{-1} \\ &= U_1 U_2 U_2^{-1} U_1^{-1} \\ &= U_1 U_2 U_2^\dagger U_1^\dagger, \end{aligned} \tag{4.79}$$

using the unitary property. Since the operation of adjoint is the same as transpose (except for the complex conjugate),

$$(U_1 U_2)^\dagger = U_2^\dagger U_1^\dagger, \tag{4.80}$$

(Exercise 4.4.2). Substituting into Eq. 4.79 we have

$$1 = (U_1 U_2)(U_1 U_2)^\dagger \tag{4.81}$$

Multiplying from the left by $(U_1 U_2)^{-1}$, we obtain

$$(U_1 U_2)^{-1} = (U_1 U_2)^\dagger, \tag{4.82}$$

which shows that the product of two unitary matrices is itself unitary. Other properties and applications of these concepts are included in the exercises at the end of this chapter.

Pauli matrices.   Four by four complex matrices have been used extensively in relativistic theories of the electron. A convenient starting point for developing the 4×4 matrices is the set of three 2×2 Pauli matrices

$$\sigma_1 = \begin{pmatrix} 0 & 1 \\ 1 & 0 \end{pmatrix}, \quad \sigma_2 = \begin{pmatrix} 0 & -i \\ i & 0 \end{pmatrix}, \quad \sigma_3 = \begin{pmatrix} 1 & 0 \\ 0 & -1 \end{pmatrix} \tag{4.83}$$

These were introduced by W. Pauli to describe a particle of spin one half (nonrelativistic theory). It can readily be shown that (cf. Exercise 4.2.1) the Pauli σ's satisfy

$$\sigma_i \sigma_j + \sigma_j \sigma_i = 2\delta_{ij} 1, \qquad \text{anticommutation} \tag{4.84}$$

$$\sigma_i \sigma_j = i\sigma_k, \qquad \text{cyclic permutation of indices} \tag{4.85}$$

$$(\sigma_i)^2 = 1. \tag{4.86}$$

Dirac matrices.   In 1927 P. A. M. Dirac extended this formalism. Dirac required a set of four anticommuting matrices. The three Pauli matrices plus the unit matrix form a complete set; that is, any constant 2×2 matrix M may be written

$$M = c_0 1 + c_1 \sigma_1 + c_2 \sigma_2 + c_3 \sigma_3, \qquad (4.87)$$

where c_0, c_1, c_2, and c_3 are constants. Hence the Pauli 2×2 matrices were inadequate; no fourth anticommuting matrix exists. We can show that 3×3 matrices likewise cannot furnish an anticommuting set of four matrices.

Turning to 4×4 matrices, we can build up a complete set from the Pauli matrices. Let

$$\sigma_i = \begin{pmatrix} (\sigma_i) & (0) \\ (0) & (\sigma_i) \end{pmatrix} \quad \text{and} \quad \rho_1 = \begin{pmatrix} (0) & (1) \\ (1) & (0) \end{pmatrix}, \qquad (4.88)$$

in which each element of the 2×2 matrices is itself a 2×2 matrix.[1] For example,

$$\sigma_1 = \begin{pmatrix} 0 & 1 & 0 & 0 \\ 1 & 0 & 0 & 0 \\ 0 & 0 & 0 & 1 \\ 0 & 0 & 1 & 0 \end{pmatrix}, \rho_1 = \begin{pmatrix} 0 & 0 & 1 & 0 \\ 0 & 0 & 0 & 1 \\ 1 & 0 & 0 & 0 \\ 0 & 1 & 0 & 0 \end{pmatrix}. \qquad (4.89)$$

Dirac originally chose to use a set of four matrices labeled a_1, a_2, a_3 with

$$a_i = \rho_1 \sigma_i, \quad a_4 \equiv \rho_3 = \begin{pmatrix} 1 & 0 & 0 & 0 \\ 0 & 1 & 0 & 0 \\ 0 & 0 & -1 & 0 \\ 0 & 0 & 0 & -1 \end{pmatrix}. \qquad (4.90)$$

If we add a matrix ρ_2, given by

$$\rho_2 = \begin{pmatrix} (0) & -i(1) \\ i(1) & (0) \end{pmatrix} = \begin{pmatrix} 0 & 0 & -i & 0 \\ 0 & 0 & 0 & -i \\ i & 0 & 0 & 0 \\ 0 & i & 0 & 0 \end{pmatrix}, \qquad (4.91)$$

we can show that these 4×4 matrices satisfy the relations

$$\begin{aligned} \sigma_i \sigma_j + \sigma_j \sigma_i &= 2\delta_{ij} 1, \\ \rho_i \rho_j + \rho_j \rho_i &= 2\delta_{ij} 1, \end{aligned} \qquad \text{anticommutation,} \qquad (4.92)$$

$$\sigma_i \rho_j - \rho_j \sigma_i \equiv [\sigma_i, \rho_j] = 0, \quad \text{commutation,} \qquad (4.93)$$

and

$$\begin{aligned} \sigma_i \sigma_j &= i\sigma_k, \\ \rho_i \rho_j &= i\rho_k, \end{aligned} \qquad \text{cyclic permutation of indices.} \qquad (4.94)$$

It is now possible to set up a matrix multiplication table (Table 4.1).

[1] This result is often labeled a *direct* or *tensor* product.

TABLE 4.1

Dirac Matrices

	1	σ_1	σ_2	σ_3
1	$\begin{pmatrix} 1 & 0 & 0 & 0 \\ 0 & 1 & 0 & 0 \\ 0 & 0 & 1 & 0 \\ 0 & 0 & 0 & 1 \end{pmatrix}$ 1	$\begin{pmatrix} 0 & 1 & 0 & 0 \\ 1 & 0 & 0 & 0 \\ 0 & 0 & 0 & 1 \\ 0 & 0 & 1 & 0 \end{pmatrix}$ σ_1	$\begin{pmatrix} 0 & -i & 0 & 0 \\ i & 0 & 0 & 0 \\ 0 & 0 & 0 & -i \\ 0 & 0 & i & 0 \end{pmatrix}$ σ_2	$\begin{pmatrix} 1 & 0 & 0 & 0 \\ 0 & -1 & 0 & 0 \\ 0 & 0 & 1 & 0 \\ 0 & 0 & 0 & -1 \end{pmatrix}$ σ_3
ρ_1	$\begin{pmatrix} 0 & 0 & 1 & 0 \\ 0 & 0 & 0 & 1 \\ 1 & 0 & 0 & 0 \\ 0 & 1 & 0 & 0 \end{pmatrix}$ $\rho_1, -\gamma_5$	$\begin{pmatrix} 0 & 0 & 0 & 1 \\ 0 & 0 & 1 & 0 \\ 0 & 1 & 0 & 0 \\ 1 & 0 & 0 & 0 \end{pmatrix}$ α_1	$\begin{pmatrix} 0 & 0 & 0 & -i \\ 0 & 0 & i & 0 \\ 0 & -i & 0 & 0 \\ i & 0 & 0 & 0 \end{pmatrix}$ α_2	$\begin{pmatrix} 0 & 0 & 1 & 0 \\ 0 & 0 & 0 & -1 \\ 1 & 0 & 0 & 0 \\ 0 & -1 & 0 & 0 \end{pmatrix}$ α_3
ρ_2	$\begin{pmatrix} 0 & 0 & -i & 0 \\ 0 & 0 & 0 & -i \\ i & 0 & 0 & 0 \\ 0 & i & 0 & 0 \end{pmatrix}$ ρ_2, α_5	$\begin{pmatrix} 0 & 0 & 0 & -i \\ 0 & 0 & -i & 0 \\ 0 & i & 0 & 0 \\ i & 0 & 0 & 0 \end{pmatrix}$ γ_1	$\begin{pmatrix} 0 & 0 & 0 & -1 \\ 0 & 0 & 1 & 0 \\ 0 & 1 & 0 & 0 \\ -1 & 0 & 0 & 0 \end{pmatrix}$ γ_2	$\begin{pmatrix} 0 & 0 & -i & 0 \\ 0 & 0 & 0 & i \\ i & 0 & 0 & 0 \\ 0 & -i & 0 & 0 \end{pmatrix}$ γ_3
ρ_3	$\begin{pmatrix} 1 & 0 & 0 & 0 \\ 0 & 1 & 0 & 0 \\ 0 & 0 & -1 & 0 \\ 0 & 0 & 0 & -1 \end{pmatrix}$ $\rho_3, \alpha_4, \gamma_4, \beta$	$\begin{pmatrix} 0 & 1 & 0 & 0 \\ 1 & 0 & 0 & 0 \\ 0 & 0 & 0 & -1 \\ 0 & 0 & -1 & 0 \end{pmatrix}$ δ_1	$\begin{pmatrix} 0 & -i & 0 & 0 \\ i & 0 & 0 & 0 \\ 0 & 0 & 0 & i \\ 0 & 0 & -i & 0 \end{pmatrix}$ δ_2	$\begin{pmatrix} 1 & 0 & 0 & 0 \\ 0 & -1 & 0 & 0 \\ 0 & 0 & -1 & 0 \\ 0 & 0 & 0 & 1 \end{pmatrix}$ δ_3

These 4×4 Dirac matrices may be referred to as E_{ij}, in which

$$E_{ij} = \rho_i \sigma_j.$$

With the understanding that $\rho_0 = \sigma_0 = 1$, the unit matrix, we let the indices i and j range from 0 to 3. These 16 matrices E_{ij} have a number of interesting properties:

1. $E_{ij}^2 = 1$.

2. $E_{ij} = E_{ij}^\dagger$; all are Hermitian and then, by property 1, unitary.

3. The 16 E_{ij} matrices *almost* form a mathematical group.[1] Any two of them multiplied together yield a member of the set within a factor of -1 or $\pm i$.

[1] The E_{ij} can be modified so that they satisfy the group property exactly, but then they are no longer Hermitian and unitary.

4. The 16 E_{ij} are linearly independent. No one can be written as a linear sum of the other 15.

5. The 16 E_{ij} form a complete set. Any 4×4 matrix (with constant elements) may be written as a linear combination of these 16,

$$A = \sum_{i,j=0}^{3} c_{ij} E_{ij},$$

where the coefficients c_{ij} are constants, real or complex.

Anticommuting sets. From these 16 Hermitian matrices we can form six anticommuting sets of five matrices each. Using the labels shown in Table 4.1 these sets are the following:

1. a_1, a_2, a_3, a_4, a_5.

2. $\gamma_1, \gamma_2, \gamma_3, \gamma_4, \gamma_5$.

3. $\delta_1, \delta_2, \delta_3, \rho_1, \rho_2$

4. $a_1, \gamma_1, \delta_1, \sigma_2, \sigma_3$. (4.95)

5. $a_2, \gamma_2, \delta_2, \sigma_1, \delta_3$.

6. $a_3, \gamma_3, \delta_3, \sigma_1, \sigma_2$.

In addition to the set of a's, the set of γ's has been used extensively in relativistic quantum theory.

The discussion of orthogonal matrices in Section 4.3 and unitary matrices in this section is only a bare beginning. The further extensions are of vital concern in modern "elementary" particle physics. With the Pauli and Dirac matrices we can develop *spinors* for describing electrons, protons, and other spin one half particles. The coordinate system rotations lead to $\mathcal{D}$, the rotation group, usually represented by matrices in which the elements are functions of the angles describing the rotation. The special unitary group SU_n has been used with considerable success to describe mesons and baryons, the more massive particles being interpreted as rotational states of the less massive ones.

EXERCISES

4.4.1 Show that $(AB)^+ = B^+ A^+$.

4.4.2 If A and B are Hermitian matrices, show that $(AB + BA)$ and $i(AB - BA)$ are also Hermitian.

4.4.3 Show that the reciprocal of a unitary matrix is unitary.

4.4.4   Show that a Hermitian matrix remains Hermitian under unitary similarity transformations.

4.4.5   Matrix $C = S^\dagger S$. Show that the trace is positive definite unless S is the null matrix in which case trace $(C) = 0$.

4.4.6   Show that all 4×4 matrices (whose elements are complex numbers) may be formed as a linear combination of 1, γ_1, γ_2, γ_3, γ_4, and *products* of the γ's.

4.4.7   Denoting the 16 Dirac matrices by $E_{ij} = \rho_i \sigma_j$ $(\rho_0 = \sigma_0 = 1)$, show that
(a) $E_{ij}^2 = 1$ for all i and j,
(b) $E_{ij} = E_{ij}^\dagger$ (Hermitian).
Hint. Use the known properties of ρ_i and σ_j.

4.4.8   Verify Eqs. 4.92, 4.93, and 4.94 for the 4×4 σ and ρ matrices.

4.4.9   Using Eqs. 4.93 and 4.94, show that each of the six sets of Dirac matrices listed in Eq. 4.95 is actually an anticommuting set.

4.4.10   Using Eqs. 4.93 and 4.94 show that
(a) $a_1 a_2 a_3 a_4 a_5 = +1$,
(b) $\gamma_1 \gamma_2 \gamma_3 \gamma_4 \gamma_5 = +1$.

4.4.11   If $M = \frac{1}{2}(1 + \gamma_5)$, show that
$$M^2 = M.$$

Note that γ_5 may be replaced by any other Dirac matrix (any E_{ij} of Table 4.1.)

4.5   Diagonalization of Matrices

Moment of inertia matrix.   In many physical problems involving matrices it is desirable to carry out a (real) orthogonal similarity transformation or a unitary transformation to reduce the matrix to a diagonal form, nondiagonal elements all equal to zero. One particularly direct example of this is the moment of inertia matrix I, of a rigid body. From the definition of angular momentum **L** we have

$$\mathbf{L} = \mathsf{I}\boldsymbol{\omega} \tag{4.96}$$

ω being the angular velocity. The inertia matrix I is found to have diagonal components

$$I_{xx} = \sum_i m_i(r_i^2 - x_i^2), \text{ etc.,} \tag{4.97}$$

the subscript i referring to the mass m_i. For the nondiagonal components we have the products of inertia

$$I_{xy} = -\sum_i m_i x_i y_i = I_{yx}. \tag{4.98}$$

By inspection matrix I is symmetric. Also, since I appears in a physical equation of the form (4.96), which holds for all orientations of the coordinate system, it may be considered to be a tensor.

The problem now is to orient the coordinate axes in space so that the I_{xy} and the other nondiagonal elements will vanish. A consequence of this orientation and an indication of it is that if the angular velocity is along one such realigned axis the angular velocity and the angular momentum will be parallel.

Geometrical picture—ellipsoid.   It is perhaps instructive to consider a geometrical picture of this problem. If the inertia matrix I is multiplied from each side
by a unit vector of variable direction, $\mathbf{n} = (\alpha, \beta, \gamma)$,

$$[n]I\{n\} = \mathbf{I}, \tag{4.99}$$

where I is a number (scalar) whose magnitude depends on the choice of direction
of $\mathbf{n}$. Carrying out the multiplication,

$$\mathbf{I} = I_{xx}\alpha^2 + I_{yy}\beta^2 + I_{zz}\gamma^2 + 2I_{xy}\alpha\beta + 2I_{xz}\alpha\gamma + 2I_{yz}\beta\gamma. \tag{4.100}$$

To throw this into one of the standard forms for an ellipsoid we introduce

$$\boldsymbol{\rho} = \frac{\mathbf{n}}{\sqrt{\mathbf{I}}}, \tag{4.101}$$

in which $\boldsymbol{\rho}$ is variable in direction *and* magnitude. Equation 4.100 becomes

$$1 = I_{xx}\rho_1^2 + I_{yy}\rho_2^2 + I_{zz}\rho_3^2 + 2I_{xy}\rho_1\rho_2 + 2I_{xz}\rho_1\rho_3 + 2I_{yz}\rho_2\rho_3. \tag{4.102}$$

This is the general form of an ellipsoid relative to the coordinates ρ_1, ρ_2, ρ_3.
However, from analytic geometry it is known that the coordinate axes can always
be rotated to coincide with the axes of our ellipsoid. Then

$$1 = I_1\rho_1'^2 + I_2\rho_2'^2 + I_3\rho_3'^2, \tag{4.103}$$

in which $\rho_1', \rho_2', \rho_3'$ is the new set of coordinates.

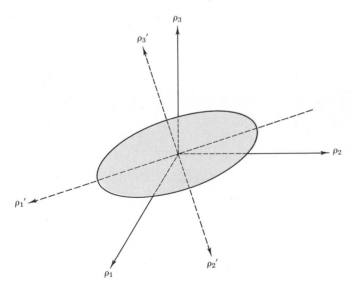

FIG. 4.3   Moment of inertia ellipsoid

Principal axes.   In many elementary cases, especially when symmetry is
present, these new axes, called the *principal axes*, can be found by inspection. We
now proceed to develop a general method of finding the diagonal elements and the
principal axes.

Hermitian matrices.   First, an important theorem about the diagonal elements and the principal axes. In the equation

$$\mathbf{Ar} = \lambda \mathbf{r} \tag{4.104}$$

λ, a number (scalar), is known as the eigenvalue; $\mathbf{r}$, the corresponding vector, is the eigenvector.[1] The terms were introduced from the early German literature on quantum mechanics. We will now show that if $\mathbf{A}$ is a Hermitian matrix,[2] its eigenvalues are real and its eigenvectors orthogonal.

Let λ_i and λ_j be two eigenvalues and $\mathbf{r}_i$ and $\mathbf{r}_j$, the corresponding eigenvectors of $\mathbf{A}$, a Hermitian matrix. Then

$$\mathbf{Ar}_i = \lambda_i \mathbf{r}_i \tag{4.105}$$

$$\mathbf{Ar}_j = \lambda_j \mathbf{r}_j . \tag{4.106}$$

Equation 4.105 is multiplied by $\mathbf{r}_j^\dagger$ to give

$$\mathbf{r}_j^\dagger \mathbf{Ar}_i = \lambda_i \mathbf{r}_j^\dagger \mathbf{r}_i . \tag{4.107}$$

(Note that if $\mathbf{r}$ is a column vector $\mathbf{r}^\dagger$ is a row vector.) Equation 4.106 is multiplied by $\mathbf{r}_i^\dagger$ to give

$$\mathbf{r}_i^\dagger \mathbf{Ar}_j = \lambda_j \mathbf{r}_i^\dagger \mathbf{r}_j . \tag{4.108}$$

Taking the adjoint of this equation

$$\mathbf{r}_j^\dagger \mathbf{A}^\dagger \mathbf{r}_i = \lambda_j^* \mathbf{r}_j^\dagger \mathbf{r}_i \tag{4.109}$$

or

$$\mathbf{r}_j^\dagger \mathbf{Ar}_i = \lambda_j^* \mathbf{r}_j^\dagger \mathbf{r}_i , \tag{4.110}$$

since $\mathbf{A}$ is Hermitian. Subtracting Eq. 4.110 from Eq. 4.107, we obtain

$$(\lambda_i - \lambda_j^*)\mathbf{r}_j^\dagger \mathbf{r}_i = 0. \tag{4.111}$$

This is a general result for all possible combinations of i and j. First, let $i = j$. Then Eq. 4.111 becomes

$$(\lambda_i - \lambda_i^*)|\mathbf{r}_i|^2 = 0. \tag{4.112}$$

Since $|\mathbf{r}_i| = 0$ would be a trivial solution of Eq. 4.112, we conclude that

$$\lambda_i = \lambda_i^*, \tag{4.113}$$

or λ_i is real, for all i.

Second, for $i \neq j$, and $\lambda_i \neq \lambda_j$,

$$(\lambda_i - \lambda_j)\mathbf{r}_j^\dagger \mathbf{r}_i = 0 \tag{4.114}$$

or

$$\mathbf{r}_j^\dagger \mathbf{r}_i = 0, \tag{4.115}$$

which means that the eigenvectors of *distinct* eigenvalues are orthogonal, Eq. 4.115 being our generalization of orthogonality in this complex space.[3]

[1] Equation 4.96 will take on this form when $\boldsymbol{\omega}$ is along one of the principal axes. Then $\mathbf{L} = \lambda \boldsymbol{\omega}$ and $\mathbf{I}\boldsymbol{\omega} = \lambda \boldsymbol{\omega}$.

[2] If $\mathbf{A}$ is real, the Hermitian requirement is replaced by a requirement of symmetry.

[3] The corresponding theory for differential operators (Sturm-Liouville theory) appears in Section 9.2. The integral equation analog (Hilbert-Schmidt theory) is given in Section 16.4.

If $\lambda_i = \lambda_j$ (degenerate case), $\mathbf{r}_i$ is not automatically orthogonal to $\mathbf{r}_j$, but it may be *made* orthogonal. Consider the physical problem of the moment of inertia matrix again. If x_1 is an axis of rotational symmetry, then we will find that $\lambda_2 = \lambda_3$. Eigenvectors $\mathbf{r}_2$ and $\mathbf{r}_3$ are each perpendicular to the symmetry axis, $\mathbf{r}_1$, but they lie anywhere in the plane perpendicular to $\mathbf{r}_1$; that is, any linear combination of $\mathbf{r}_2$ and $\mathbf{r}_3$ is also an eigenvector. Consider $(a_2\mathbf{r}_2 + a_3\mathbf{r}_3)$ with a_2 and a_3 constants. Then

$$A(a_2\mathbf{r}_2 + a_3\mathbf{r}_3) = a_2\lambda_2\mathbf{r}_2 + a_3\lambda_3\mathbf{r}_3$$

$$= \lambda_2(a_2\mathbf{r}_2 + a_3\mathbf{r}_3), \qquad (4.116)$$

as is to be expected, for x_1 is an axis of rotational symmetry. Therefore, if $\mathbf{r}_1$ and $\mathbf{r}_2$ are fixed, $\mathbf{r}_3$ may simply be chosen to lie in the plane perpendicular to $\mathbf{r}_1$ and also perpendicular to $\mathbf{r}_2$. A general method of orthogonalizing solutions, the Schmidt process, is applied to functions in Section 9.3.

The foregoing is essentially an existence theorem. To determine the eigenvalues λ_i and the eigenvectors $\mathbf{r}_i$ actually we return to Eq. 4.104. Assuming $\mathbf{r}$ to be multiplied by the unit matrix, we may rewrite Eq. 4.104

$$(A - \lambda 1)\mathbf{r} = 0, \qquad (4.117)$$

in which 1 is the unit matrix. This is a set of simultaneous, homogeneous, linear equations. By Section 4.1 it has nontrivial solutions only if the determinant of the coefficient vanishes,

$$|A - \lambda 1| = 0. \qquad (4.118)$$

Let us consider the case in which A is a 3×3 Hermitian matrix. Then

$$\begin{vmatrix} a_{11} - \lambda & a_{12} & a_{13} \\ a_{21} & a_{22} - \lambda & a_{23} \\ a_{31} & a_{32} & a_{33} - \lambda \end{vmatrix} = 0. \qquad (4.119)$$

Because of its applications in astronomical theories Eq. 4.119 is usually called the *secular equation*. Equation 4.119 yields a cubic equation in λ, which, of course, has three roots. By Eq. 4.113 we know that these roots are real. Substituting one root at a time back into Eq. 4.117, we can find the corresponding eigenvectors.

EXAMPLE 4.5.1

Let

$$A = \begin{pmatrix} 0 & 1 & 0 \\ 1 & 0 & 0 \\ 0 & 0 & 0 \end{pmatrix}. \qquad (4.120)$$

The secular equation is

$$\begin{vmatrix} -\lambda & 1 & 0 \\ 1 & -\lambda & 0 \\ 0 & 0 & -\lambda \end{vmatrix} = 0 \qquad (4.121)$$

or
$$-\lambda(\lambda^2 - 1) = 0, \tag{4.122}$$

expanding by minors. The roots are $\lambda = -1, 0, 1$. To find the eigenvector corresponding to $\lambda = -1$, we substitute this value back into the eigenvalue equation Eq. 4.117

$$\begin{pmatrix} -\lambda & 1 & 0 \\ 1 & -\lambda & 0 \\ 0 & 0 & -\lambda \end{pmatrix} \begin{pmatrix} x \\ y \\ z \end{pmatrix} = \begin{pmatrix} 0 \\ 0 \\ 0 \end{pmatrix}. \tag{4.123}$$

With $\lambda = -1$, this yields
$$x + y = 0,$$
$$z = 0. \tag{4.124}$$

Within an arbitrary scale factor, and an arbitrary sign (or phase factor), $\mathbf{r}_1 = (1, -1, 0)$. Note carefully that (for real $\mathbf{r}$ in ordinary space) the eigenvector singles out a line in space. The positive or negative sense is not determined. This indeterminancy could be expected if we noted that Eq. 4.117 is homogeneous in $\mathbf{r}$. For convenience we will require that the eigenvectors be normalized to unity, $|\mathbf{r}_1| = 1$. With this choice of sign,

$$\mathbf{r}_1 = \left(\frac{1}{\sqrt{2}}, \frac{-1}{\sqrt{2}}, 0 \right). \tag{4.125}$$

is fixed. For $\lambda = 0$, Eq. 4.117 yields
$$y = 0,$$
$$x = 0. \tag{4.126}$$

$\mathbf{r}_2 = (0, 0, 1)$ is a suitable eigenvector. Finally for $\lambda = 1$, we get

$$-x + y = 0.$$
$$z = 0, \tag{4.127}$$

or

$$\mathbf{r}_3 = \left(\frac{1}{\sqrt{2}}, \frac{1}{\sqrt{2}}, 0 \right). \tag{4.128}$$

The orthogonality of $\mathbf{r}_1$, $\mathbf{r}_2$, and $\mathbf{r}_3$, corresponding to three distinct eigenvalues, may be easily verified.

EXAMPLE 4.5.2

Consider

$$A = \begin{pmatrix} 1 & 0 & 0 \\ 0 & 0 & 1 \\ 0 & 1 & 0 \end{pmatrix}. \tag{4.129}$$

The secular equation is

$$\begin{vmatrix} 1 - \lambda & 0 & 0 \\ 0 & -\lambda & 1 \\ 0 & 1 & -\lambda \end{vmatrix} = 0 \qquad (4.130)$$

or

$$(1 - \lambda)(\lambda^2 - 1) = 0, \qquad \lambda = -1, 1, 1, \qquad (4.131)$$

a degenerate case. If $\lambda = -1$, the eigenvalue equation (4.117) yields

$$2x = 0.$$
$$y + z = 0. \qquad (4.132)$$

A suitable normalized eigenvector is

$$\mathbf{r}_1 = \left(0, \frac{1}{\sqrt{2}}, \frac{-1}{\sqrt{2}} \right). \qquad (4.133)$$

For $\lambda = 1$, we get

$$-y + z = 0 \qquad (4.134)$$

and no further information. We have an infinite number of choices. Suppose, as one possible choice, $\mathbf{r}_2$ is taken as

$$\mathbf{r}_2 = \left(0, \frac{1}{\sqrt{2}}, \frac{1}{\sqrt{2}} \right), \qquad (4.135)$$

which clearly satisfies Eq. 4.134. Then $\mathbf{r}_3$ must be perpendicular to $\mathbf{r}_1$ and may be made perpendicular to $\mathbf{r}_2$ by

$$\mathbf{r}_3 = \mathbf{r}_1 \times \mathbf{r}_2 = (1, 0, 0). \qquad (4.136)$$

Diagonalization.   The equations, developed on page 168 for our existence theorem can be used to form a transformation matrix which will convert our Hermitian matrix A into diagonal form. Let R be a matrix formed from the three orthonormal *column* vectors $\mathbf{r}_1$, $\mathbf{r}_2$, and $\mathbf{r}_3$ in any desired order.

$$R = \begin{pmatrix} x_1 & x_2 & x_3 \\ y_1 & y_2 & y_3 \\ z_1 & z_2 & z_3 \end{pmatrix}, \qquad (4.137)$$

in which each column $\{x_i, y_i, z_i\}$ is an eigenvector $\mathbf{r}_i$. Since

$$\mathbf{r}_i^\dagger \mathbf{r}_j = \delta_{ij} \qquad (4.138)$$

R is unitary (or simply orthogonal if A, and therefore $\mathbf{r}_i$ are real). Then, forming

$R^\dagger AR$, we have

$$R^\dagger AR = \begin{pmatrix} [\ r_1^* \ ] \\ [\ r_2^* \ ] \\ [\ r_3^* \ ] \end{pmatrix} \begin{pmatrix} & A & \end{pmatrix} \left(\begin{pmatrix} r_1 \end{pmatrix} \begin{pmatrix} r_2 \end{pmatrix} \begin{pmatrix} r_3 \end{pmatrix} \right)$$

$$= \begin{pmatrix} [\ r_1^* \ ] \\ [\ r_2^* \ ] \\ [\ r_3^* \ ] \end{pmatrix} \left(\begin{pmatrix} \lambda r_1 \end{pmatrix} \begin{pmatrix} \lambda_2 r_2 \end{pmatrix} \begin{pmatrix} \lambda_3 r_3 \end{pmatrix} \right)$$

$$= \begin{pmatrix} \lambda_1 & 0 & 0 \\ 0 & \lambda_2 & 0 \\ 0 & 0 & \lambda_3 \end{pmatrix}. \tag{4.139}$$

Hence $R^\dagger AR$ is a diagonal matrix with eigenvalues λ_i, the order of the eigenvalues corresponding to the order of the column vectors r_i in R. To develop the geometrical picture consider A, a real (symmetric) matrix with real eigenvalues and real eigenvectors. Matrix R corresponds to B^{-1} in Eq. 4.68 or better, $\tilde{R}$ corresponds to B, $\tilde{R}$ being composed of the eigenvectors r_i written as row vectors.

$$\begin{pmatrix} [r_2] \\ [r_3] \\ [r_3] \end{pmatrix} = \begin{pmatrix} x_1 & y_1 & z_1 \\ x_2 & y_2 & z_2 \\ x_3 & y_3 & z_3 \end{pmatrix} = \begin{pmatrix} b_{11} & b_{12} & b_{13} \\ b_{12} & b_{22} & b_{23} \\ b_{31} & b_{32} & b_{33} \end{pmatrix}. \tag{4.140}$$

Now, the row (b_{i1}, b_{i2}, b_{i3}), which defines a unit vector r_i in relation to the original coordinate system. specifies the three direction cosines of r_i with the original axes. Remembering that matrix B rotates the coordinate system into a new system in which (here) A is diagonal, we see that this new system is specified by the three eigenvectors $r_i = (x_i, y_i, z_i)$. They are the unit vectors along the principal axes, the axes in relation to which A is diagonal.

The analysis of this section has the advantage of exhibiting and clarifying conceptual relationships in the diagonalization of matrices. However, for matrices larger than 3×3 or perhaps 4×4, the process rapidly becomes so cumbersome that we turn gratefully to high-speed computers and iterative techniques.

EXERCISES

4.5.1 Show that the eigenvalues of a matrix are unaltered if the matrix is transformed by a similarity transformation.

4.5.2 Assuming a unitary matrix U to satisfy an eigenvalue equation $Ur = \lambda r$, show that the eigenvalues of the unitary matrix have unit magnitude.

4.5.3 The same similarity transformation diagonalizes each of two matrices. Show that the original matrices must commute. (This is particularly important in the matrix (Heisenberg) formulation of quantum mechanics.)

4.5.4 Two Hermitian matrices A and B have the same eigenvalues. Show that A and B are related by a unitary similarity transformation.

4.5.5 Find the transformation matrix that relates the spin 1 representations of exercise 4.2.4 to those of 4.2.3 (similarity transformation). *Hint.* Remember that the phase factor for the eigenvectors is at your disposal.

4.5.6 Find the eigenvalues and form the matrices R and R^{-1} that will diagonalize $A' = R^{-1} AR$ when matrix A is σ_1 or σ_2 from the set of Pauli spin matrices of Exercise 4.2.1.

4.5.7 Find the eigenvalues and an orthonormal (orthogonal and normalized) set of eigenvectors for the matrices of Exercise 4.2.3.

4.5.8 Repeat for the matrices of Exercise 4.2.4.

4.5.9 Repeat for the matrices of Exercises 4.2.5.

4.5.10 Find the eigenvalues and corresponding orthonormal eigenvectors of the following matrices

$$A = \begin{pmatrix} 1 & 0 & 1 \\ 0 & 1 & 0 \\ 1 & 0 & 1 \end{pmatrix}.$$ *Ans.* $\lambda = 0, 1, 2.$

4.5.11

$$A = \begin{pmatrix} 3 & 4 & -6 \\ 4 & 3 & -6 \\ -6 & -6 & -14 \end{pmatrix}.$$ *Ans.* $\lambda = -17, -1, 10.$

4.5.12

$$A = \begin{pmatrix} 1 & \sqrt{2} & 0 \\ \sqrt{2} & 0 & 0 \\ 0 & 0 & 0 \end{pmatrix}.$$ *Ans.* $\lambda = -1, 0, 2.$

4.5.13

$$A = \begin{pmatrix} 1 & 1 & 0 \\ 1 & 0 & 1 \\ 0 & 1 & 1 \end{pmatrix}.$$ *Ans.* $\lambda = -1, 1, 2.$

4.5.14

$$A = \begin{pmatrix} 1 & \sqrt{8} & 0 \\ \sqrt{8} & 1 & \sqrt{8} \\ 0 & \sqrt{8} & 1 \end{pmatrix}.$$ *Ans.* $\lambda = -3, 1, 5.$

4.5.15

$$A = \begin{pmatrix} 1 & 0 & 0 \\ 0 & 1 & 1 \\ 0 & 1 & 1 \end{pmatrix}.$$ *Ans.* $\lambda = 0, 1, 2.$

4.5.16

$$A = \begin{pmatrix} 1 & 0 & 0 \\ 0 & 1 & \sqrt{2} \\ 0 & \sqrt{2} & 0 \end{pmatrix}.$$ *Ans.* $\lambda = -1, 1, 2.$

4.5.17

$$A = \begin{pmatrix} 0 & 1 & 0 \\ 1 & 0 & 1 \\ 0 & 1 & 0 \end{pmatrix}.$$ *Ans.* $\lambda = -\sqrt{2}, 0, \sqrt{2}.$

174   4 MATRICES AND DETERMINANTS

4.5.18
$$A = \begin{pmatrix} 2 & 0 & 0 \\ 0 & 1 & 1 \\ 0 & 1 & 1 \end{pmatrix}.$$
Ans. $\lambda = 0, 2, 2.$

4.5.19
$$A = \begin{pmatrix} 0 & 1 & 1 \\ 1 & 0 & 1 \\ 1 & 1 & 0 \end{pmatrix}.$$
Ans. $\lambda = -1, -1, 2.$

4.5.20
$$A = \begin{pmatrix} 1 & -1 & -1 \\ -1 & 1 & -1 \\ -1 & -1 & -1 \end{pmatrix}.$$
Ans. $\lambda = -1, 2, 2.$

4.5.21
$$A = \begin{pmatrix} 1 & 1 & 1 \\ 1 & 1 & 1 \\ 1 & 1 & 1 \end{pmatrix}.$$
Ans. $\lambda = 0, 0, 3.$

4.5.22
$$A = \begin{pmatrix} 1 & 0 & 0 \\ 0 & 5 & 2 \\ 0 & 2 & 2 \end{pmatrix}.$$
Ans. $\lambda = 1, 1, 6.$

4.5.23
$$A = \begin{pmatrix} 5 & 0 & 2 \\ 0 & 1 & 0 \\ 2 & 0 & 2 \end{pmatrix}.$$
Ans. $\lambda = 1, 1, 6.$

4.5.24
$$A = \begin{pmatrix} 1 & 1 & 0 \\ 1 & 1 & 0 \\ 0 & 0 & 0 \end{pmatrix}.$$
Ans. $\lambda = 0, 0, 2.$

4.5.25
$$A = \begin{pmatrix} 5 & 0 & \sqrt{3} \\ 0 & 3 & 0 \\ \sqrt{3} & 0 & 3 \end{pmatrix}.$$
Ans. $\lambda = 2, 3, 6.$

4.5.26 A certain rigid body may be represented by three point masses:
$$\begin{aligned} m_1 &= 1 \quad \text{at} \quad (1, 1, -2) \\ m_2 &= 2 \quad \text{at} \quad (-1, -1, 0) \\ m_3 &= 1 \quad \text{at} \quad (1, 1, 2). \end{aligned}$$

(a) Find the inertia matrix.
(b) Diagonalize the inertia matrix obtaining the eigenvalues and the principal axes (as orthonormal eigenvectors).

4.5.27 Show that a real matrix that is not symmetric cannot be diagonized by an orthogonal similarity transformation.
Hint. Assume that the nonsymmetric real matrix can be diagonized and develop a contradiction.

4.5.28 A square matrix with zero determinant is labeled *singular*.
(a) If A is singular, show that there is at least one nonzero column vector **v** such that
$$A\mathbf{v} = 0.$$
(b) If there is a vector **v** such that
$$A\mathbf{v} = 0,$$
show that A is a singular matrix.

REFERENCES

AITKEN, A. C., *Determinants and Matrices*. New York: Interscience Publishers (1956). A readable introduction to determinants and matrices.

BICKLEY, W. G., and R. S. H. G. THOMPSON, *Matrices—Their Meaning and Manipulation*. Princeton, New Jersey: Van Nostrand (1964). A comprehensive account of the occurrence of matrices in physical problems, their analytic properties, and numerical techniques.

MICHAEL, A. D., *Matrix and Tensor Calculus with Applications to Mechanics, Elasticity and Aeronautics*. New York: Wiley (1947). An unusually clear exposition of matrices and tensors and the development of a calculus of matrices and tensors.

WIGNER, EUGENE P., *Group Theory and Its Application to the Quantum Mechanics of Atomic Spectra*. Translated by J. J. Griffin. New York: Academic Press (1959). The first three chapters of this book present the elements of vector and matrix analysis in a concise but readable and meaningful form. As the title suggests, quantum mechanical applications are a determining factor in the selection of subject matter.

CHAPTER 5

INFINITE SERIES

5.1 Fundamental Concepts

Infinite series, literally summations of an infinite number of terms, occur frequently in both pure and applied mathematics. They may be used by the pure mathematician to define functions as a fundamental approach to the theory of functions. They may be used also for calculating accurate values of transcendental constants and transcendental functions. In the mathematics of science and engineering infinite series are ubiquitous, for they appear in the evaluation of integrals (Sections 5.6 and 5.7), in the solution of differential equations (Sections 8.4 and 8.5), and as Fourier series (Chapter 14) and compete with integral representations for the description of a host of special functions (Chapters 11, 12, and 13).

Right at the start we face the problem of attaching meaning to the sum of an infinite number of terms. The usual approach is on partial sums. If we have a sequence of finite terms $u_1, u_2, u_3, u_4, u_5, \ldots$, we define the ith partial sum as

$$s_i = \sum_{n=1}^{i} u_n. \tag{5.1}$$

This is a finite summation and offers no difficulties. If the partial sums s_i converge to a (finite) limit as $i \to \infty$,

$$\lim_{i \to \infty} s_i = S, \tag{5.2}$$

the infinite series $\sum_{n=1}^{\infty} u_n$ is said to be *convergent* and to have the value S. Note carefully that we reasonably, plausibly, but still arbitrarily *define* the infinite series as equal to S. The reader should also note that a necessary condition for this convergence to a limit is that $\lim_{n \to \infty} u_n = 0$. This condition, however, is not sufficient to guarantee convergence.

176

Our partial sums s_i may not converge to a single limit but may oscillate, as in the case

$$\sum_{n=1}^{\infty} u_n = 1 - 1 + 1 - 1 + 1 + \cdots - (-1)^n + \cdots. \qquad (5.3)$$

Clearly, $s_i = 1$ for i odd but 0 for i even. There is no convergence to a limit, and series such as this one are labeled oscillatory.

For the series

$$\sum_{n=1}^{\infty} 1 + 2 + 3 + \cdots + n + \cdots \qquad (5.4)$$

we have

$$s_n = \frac{n(n + 1)}{2}. \qquad (5.5)$$

As $n \to \infty$

$$\lim_{n \to \infty} s_n = \infty. \qquad (5.6)$$

Whenever the sequence of partial sums diverges (approaches $\pm\infty$), the infinite series is said to *diverge*. Often the term divergent is extended to include oscillatory series as well.

Because we evaluate the partial sums by ordinary arithmetic, the convergent series, defined in terms of a limit of the partial sums, assume a position of supreme importance. Two examples may clarify the nature of convergence or divergence of a series and will also serve as a basis for a further detailed investigation in the next section.

The geometrical sequence, starting with a and with a ratio r $(r \geqslant 0)$, is given by

$$a, ar, ar^2, ar^3, \ldots, ar^{n-1}, \ldots$$

The nth partial sum is given by

$$s_n = a \frac{1 - r^n}{1 - r}. \qquad (5.7)$$

Taking the limit as $n \to \infty$,

$$\lim_{n \to \infty} s_n = \frac{a}{1 - r}, \qquad \text{for } r < 1. \qquad (5.8)$$

Hence, by definition, the infinite geometric series converges for $r < 1$ and is given by

$$\sum_{n=1}^{\infty} ar^{n-1} = \frac{a}{1 - r}. \qquad (5.9)$$

On the other hand, if $r \geqslant 1$, the necessary condition $u_n \to 0$ is not satisfied and the infinite series diverges.

As a second and more involved example, we consider the harmonic series

$$\sum_{n=1}^{\infty} n^{-1} = 1 + \frac{1}{2} + \frac{1}{3} + \frac{1}{4} + \cdots + \frac{1}{n} + \cdots. \qquad (5.10)$$

We have the $\lim_{n \to \infty} u_n = \lim_{n \to \infty} 1/n = 0$, but this is not sufficient. If we group the terms (no change in order) as

$$1 + \tfrac{1}{2} + (\tfrac{1}{3} + \tfrac{1}{4}) + \ (\tfrac{1}{5} + \tfrac{1}{6} + \tfrac{1}{7} + \tfrac{1}{8}) + (\tfrac{1}{9} + \cdots + \tfrac{1}{16}) + \cdots, \qquad (5.11)$$

it will be seen that each pair of parentheses encloses p terms of the form

$$\frac{1}{p+1} + \frac{1}{p+2} + \cdots + \frac{1}{p+p} > \frac{p}{2p} = \frac{1}{2}. \qquad (5.12)$$

Forming partial sums by adding the parenthetical groups one by one, we obtain

$$s_1 = 1, \qquad s_4 > \frac{5}{2},$$

$$s_2 = \frac{3}{2}, \qquad s_5 > \frac{6}{2}, \qquad (5.13)$$

$$s_3 > \frac{4}{2}, \qquad s_n > \frac{n+1}{2}.$$

The haromonic series considered in this way is certainly divergent. An alternate and independent demonstration of its divergence appears in Section 5.2.

Using the binomial theorem[1] (Section 5.6), we may expand the function $(1 + x)^{-1}$:

$$\frac{1}{1+x} = 1 - x + x^2 - x^3 + \cdots + (-x)^{n-1} + \cdots. \qquad (5.14)$$

If we let $x \to 1$, this series becomes

$$1 - 1 + 1 - 1 + 1 - 1 + \cdots, \qquad (5.15)$$

a series that we labeled oscillatory earlier in this section. Although it does not converge in the usual sense, it is possible to attach meaning to this series. Euler, for example, assigned a value of $\tfrac{1}{2}$ to this oscillatory sequence on the basis of the correspondence between this series and the well-defined function $(1 + x)^{-1}$. Unfortunately, such correspondence between series and function is not unique and this approach must be refined. Other methods of assigning a meaning to a divergent or oscillatory series, methods of defining a sum, have been developed. In general, however, this aspect of infinite series is of relatively little interest to the scientist or the engineer. An exception to this statement, the very important asymptotic or semiconvergent series, is considered in Section 5.10.

5.2   Convergence Tests

Although nonconvergent series may be useful in certain special cases, (cf. Section 5.10), we usually insist, as a matter of convenience if not necessity, that our series be convergent. It therefore becomes a matter of extreme importance to be able to tell whether a given series is convergent. We shall develop a number of

---

[1] Actually Eq. 5.14 may be taken as an identity and verified by multiplying both sides by $1 + x$.

possible tests, starting with the simple and relatively insensitive tests and working up to the more complicated but quite sensitive tests.

For the present let us consider a series of positive terms, $a_n > 0$, postponing negative terms until the next section.

Comparison test.   If, term by term, a series of terms $u_n \leqslant a_n$, in which the a_n form a convergent series, the series $\sum_n u_n$ is also convergent.

If term by term a series of terms $v_n \geqslant b_n$, in which the b_n form a divergent series, the series $\sum_n v_n$ is also divergent. Note that comparisons of u_n with b_n or v_n with a_n yield no information.

For the convergent series a_n we already have the geometric series, whereas the harmonic series will serve as the divergent series b_n. As other series are identified as either convergent or divergent, they may be used for the known series in this comparison test.

EXAMPLE 5.2.1

Test $\sum_n n^{-p}$, $p = 0.999$, for convergence. Since $n^{-0.999} > n^{-1}$, and $b_n = n^{-1}$ forms the divergent harmonic series, the comparison test shows that $\sum_n n^{-0.999}$ is divergent. Generalizing, $\sum_n n^{-p}$ is seen to be divergent for all $p \leqslant 1$.

Cauchy root test.   If $(a_n)^{1/n} \leqslant r < 1$ for all sufficiently large n, with r independent of n, then $\sum_n a_n$ is convergent. If $(a_n)^{1/n} \geqslant 1$ for all sufficiently large n, then $\sum_n a_n$ is divergent.

The first part of this test is verified easily by raising $(a_n)^{1/n} \leqslant r$ to the nth power. We get

$$a_n \leqslant r^n < 1.$$

Since r^n is just the nth term in a convergent geometric series, $\sum_n a_n$ is convergent by the comparison test. Conversely, if $(a_n)^{1/n} \geqslant 1$, then $a_n \geqslant 1$ and the series must diverge. This root test is particularly useful in establishing the properties of power series (Section 5.7).

D'Alembert or Cauchy ratio test.   If $a_{n+1}/a_n \leqslant r < 1$ for all sufficiently large n, and r is independent of n, then $\sum_n a_n$ is convergent. If $a_{n+1}/a_n \geqslant 1$ for all sufficiently large n, then $\sum_n a_n$ is divergent.

Convergence is proved by direct comparison with the geometric series $a_n(1 + r + r^2 + \cdots)$. In the second part $a_{n+1} \geqslant a_n$ and divergence should be reasonably obvious. Although not quite so sensitive as the Cauchy root test, this D'Alembert ratio test is one of the easiest to apply and is widely used. An alternate statement of the ratio test is in the form of a limit:

If

$$\lim_{n \to \infty} \frac{a_{n+1}}{a_n} < 1, \qquad \text{convergence,}$$
$$> 1, \qquad \text{divergence,}$$
$$= 1, \qquad \text{indeterminant.} \qquad (5.16)$$

Because of this final indeterminant possibility, the ratio test is likely to fail at crucial points, and more delicate, more sensitive tests are necessary.

The alert reader may wonder how this indeterminacy arose. Actually it was concealed in the first statement $a_{n+1}/a_n \leqslant r < 1$. We might encounter $a_{n+1}/a_n < 1$ but be unable to choose an $r < 1$ *and independent of n* such that $a_{n+1}/a_n \leqslant r$ for all sufficiently large n. An example is provided by the harmonic series

$$\frac{a_{n+1}}{a_n} = \frac{n}{n+1} < 1. \tag{5.17}$$

Since

$$\lim_{n \to \infty} \frac{a_{n+1}}{a_n} = 1, \tag{5.18}$$

no fixed ratio $r < 1$ exists and the ratio test fails.

EXAMPLE 5.2.2

Test $\sum_n n/2^n$ for convergence.

$$\frac{a_{n+1}}{a_n} = \frac{(n+1)/2^{n+1}}{n/2^n} = \frac{1}{2} \cdot \frac{n+1}{n}. \tag{5.19}$$

Since

$$\frac{a_{n+1}}{a_n} \leqslant \frac{3}{4} \quad \text{for } n \geqslant 2, \tag{5.20}$$

we have convergence. Alternatively,

$$\lim_{n \to \infty} \frac{a_{n+1}}{a_n} = \frac{1}{2} \tag{5.21}$$

and again—convergence.

Cauchy or Maclaurin integral test.   This is another sort of comparison test in which we compare a series with an integral. Geometrically we compare the area of a series of unit-width rectangles with the area under a curve.

Let $f(x)$ be a continuous, monotonic decreasing function in which $f(n) = a_n$. Then $\sum_n a_n$ converges if $\int_1^\infty f(x)\, dx$ is finite and diverges if the integral is infinite. For the ith partial sum

$$s_i = \sum_{n=1}^{i} a_n = \sum_{n=1}^{i} f(n). \tag{5.22}$$

But

$$s_i > \int_1^{i+1} f(x)\, dx \tag{5.23}$$

by Fig. 5.1a, $f(x)$ being monotonic decreasing. On the other hand, from Fig. 5.1b,

$$s_{i+1} - a_1 < \int_1^{i} f(x)\, dx, \tag{5.24}$$

in which the series is represented by the inscribed rectangles. Taking the limit as

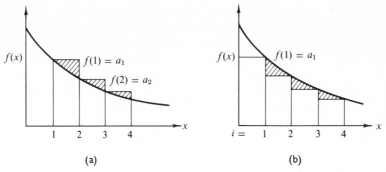

FIG. 5.1(a) Comparison of integral and sum-blocks leading. (b) Comparison of integral and sum-blocks lagging

$i \to \infty$, we have

$$\int_1^\infty f(x)\, dx < \sum_{n=1}^\infty a_n < \int_1^\infty f(x)\, dx + a_1. \tag{5.25}$$

Hence the infinite series converges or diverges as the corresponding integral converges or diverges.

EXAMPLE 5.2.3

The Riemann zeta function is defined by

$$\zeta(p) = \sum_{n=1}^\infty n^{-p}. \tag{5.26}$$

We may take $f(x) = x^{-p}$ and then

$$\int_1^\infty x^{-p}\, dx = \left. \frac{x^{-p+1}}{-p+1} \right|_1^\infty, \qquad p \neq 1$$

$$= \ln x \, \big|_1^\infty, \qquad p = 1. \tag{5.27}$$

The integral and therefore the series are divergent for $p \leqslant 1$, convergent for $p > 1$. This, incidentally, is an independent proof that the harmonic series $(p = 1)$ diverges and diverges logarithmically. The sum of the first million terms $\sum^{1,000,000} n^{-1}$, is only 14.392 726 ....

This integral comparison may also be used to set an upper limit to the Euler-Mascheroni constant C defined by

$$C = \lim_{n \to \infty} \left(\sum_{m=1}^n m^{-1} - \ln n \right). \tag{5.28}$$

Returning to partial sums,

$$s_n = \sum_{m=1}^n m^{-1} - \ln n < \int_1^n \frac{dx}{x} - \ln n + 1. \tag{5.29}$$

Evaluating the integral on the right, $s_n < 1$ for all n and therefore $C < 1$. Actually the Euler-Mascheroni constant is 0.577 215 66 ... .

Kummer's test.   This is the first of three tests which are somewhat more difficult to apply than the preceding tests. Their importance lies in their power and sensitivity. Frequently, at least one of the three will work when the simpler easier tests are indecisive. It must be remembered, however, that these tests, like those previously discussed, are ultimately based on comparisons. It can be shown that there is no most slowly converging convergent series and no most slowly diverging divergent series. This means that all of the convergence tests given here, including Kummer's, may fail sometime.

We consider a series of positive terms u_i and a series of finite positive constants a_i. If

$$a_n \frac{u_n}{u_{n+1}} - a_{n+1} \geqslant C > 0 \tag{5.30}$$

for all $n \geqslant N$, some fixed number, then $\sum_{i=1}^{\infty} u_i$ converges. If

$$a_n \frac{u_n}{u_{n+1}} - a_{n+1} \leqslant 0 \tag{5.31}$$

and $\sum_{i=1}^{\infty} a_i^{-1}$ diverges, then $\sum_{i=1}^{\infty} u_i$ diverges.

The proof of this powerful test is remarkably simple. From Eq. 5.30, with C some positive constant,

$$Cu_{N+1} \leqslant a_N u_N \qquad - a_{N+1} u_{N+1}$$

$$Cu_{N+2} \leqslant a_{N+1} u_{N+1} - a_{N+2} u_{N+2} \tag{5.32}$$

$$\cdots\cdots\cdots\cdots\cdots\cdots\cdots\cdots\cdots\cdots\cdots .$$

$$Cu_n \leqslant a_{n-1} u_{n-1} \qquad - a_n u_n$$

Adding and dividing by C, $(C \neq 0)$,

$$\sum_{i=N+1}^{n} \leqslant \frac{a_N u_N}{C} - \frac{a_n u_n}{C} . \tag{5.33}$$

Hence for the partial sum, s_n,

$$s_n \leqslant \sum_{i=1}^{N} u_i + \frac{a_N u_N}{C} - \frac{a_n u_n}{C}$$

$$< \sum_{i=1}^{N} u_i + \frac{a_N u_N}{C} , \qquad \text{a constant, independent of } n. \tag{5.34}$$

The partial sums therefore have an upper bound. With zero as an obvious lower bound, the series $\sum_i u_i$ must converge.

Divergence is shown as follows. From Eq. 5.31

$$a_n u_n \geqslant a_{n-1} u_{n-1} \geqslant \cdots \geqslant a_N u_N . \tag{5.35}$$

Thus

$$u_n \geqslant \frac{a_N u_N}{a_n} \tag{5.36}$$

and

$$\sum_{i=N+1}^{\infty} u_i \geqslant a_N u_N \sum_{i=N+1}^{\infty} a_n^{-1} . \tag{5.37}$$

By the comparison test $\sum_i u_i$ diverges.

Equations 5.30 and 5.31 are often given in a limit form:

$$\lim_{n \to \infty} \left(a_n \frac{u_n}{u_{n+1}} - a_{n+1} \right) = C. \tag{5.38}$$

Thus for $C > 0$ we have convergence, whereas for $C < 0$ (and $\sum_i a_i^{-1}$ divergent) we have divergence. It is perhaps useful to show the equivalence of Eq. 5.38 and Eqs. 5.30 and 5.31 and to show why indeterminacy creeps in when the limit $C = 0$. From the definition of limit

$$\left| a_n \frac{u_n}{u_{n+1}} - a_{n+1} - C \right| < \varepsilon \tag{5.39}$$

for all $n \geqslant N$ and all $\varepsilon > 0$, no matter how small ε may be. When the absolute value signs are removed,

$$C - \varepsilon < a_n \frac{u_n}{u_{n+1}} - a_{n+1} < C + \varepsilon. \tag{5.40}$$

Now if $C > 0$, Eq. 5.30 follows from ε sufficiently small. On the other hand, if $C < 0$, Eq. 5.31 follows. However, if $C = 0$, the center term $a_n(u_n/u_{n+1}) - a_{n+1}$ may be either positive or negative and the proof fails. The primary use of Kummer's test is to prove other tests such as Raabe's (cf. also Exercise 5.2.12).

If the positive constants a_n of Kummer's test are chosen $a_n = n$, we have Raabe's test.

Raabe's test.   If $u_n > 0$ and if

$$n\left(\frac{u_n}{u_{n+1}} - 1 \right) \geqslant P > 1 \tag{5.41}$$

for all $n \geqslant N$, where N is a positive integer independent of n, then $\sum_i u_i$ converges. If

$$n\left(\frac{u_n}{u_{n+1}} - 1 \right) \leqslant 1, \tag{5.42}$$

then $\sum_i u_i$ diverges.

The limit form of Raabe's test is

$$\lim_{n \to \infty} n\left(\frac{u_n}{u_{n+1}} - 1 \right) = P. \tag{5.43}$$

We have convergence for $P > 1$, divergence for $P < 1$, and no test for $P = 1$ exactly as with the Kummer test. This indeterminacy is pointed up by Exercise 5.2.13, which presents a convergent series and a divergent series with both series yielding $P = 1$ in Eq. 5.43.

Raabe's test is more sensitive than the d'Alembert ratio test because $\sum_{n=1}^{\infty} n^{-1}$ diverges more slowly than $\sum_{n=1}^{\infty} 1$. We obtain a still more sensitive test (and one that is relatively easy to apply) by choosing $a_n = n \ln n$. This is Gauss's test.

Gauss's test.   If $u_n > 0$ for all finite n and

$$\frac{u_n}{u_{n+1}} = 1 + \frac{h}{n} + \frac{B(n)}{n^2}, \tag{5.44}$$

in which $B(n)$ is a bound function of n for $n \to \infty$, then $\sum_i u_i$ converges for $h > 1$ and diverges for $h \leqslant 1$. For $h > 1$ or $h < 1$ the proof follows directly from Raabe's test.

$$\lim_{n \to \infty} n\left[1 + \frac{h}{n} + \frac{B(n)}{n^2} - 1\right] = \lim_{n \to \infty}\left[h + \frac{B(n)}{n}\right]$$

$$= h. \tag{5.45}$$

If $h = 1$, Raabe's test fails. However, if we return to Kummer's test and use $a_n = n \ln n$, Eq. 5.31 leads to

$$\lim_{n \to \infty}\left\{n \ln n\left[1 + \frac{1}{n} + \frac{B(n)}{n^2}\right] - (n+1)\ln(n+1)\right\}$$

$$= \lim_{n \to \infty}\left[n \ln n \cdot \frac{(n+1)}{n} - (n+1)\ln(n+1)\right]$$

$$= \lim_{n \to \infty}(n+1)\left[\ln n - \ln n - \ln\left(1 + \frac{1}{n}\right)\right]. \tag{5.46}$$

Borrowing a result from Section 5.6 (which is not dependent on Gauss's test), we have

$$\lim_{n \to \infty} -(n+1)\ln\left(1 + \frac{1}{n}\right) = \lim_{n \to \infty} -(n+1)\left(\frac{1}{n} - \frac{1}{2n^2} + \frac{1}{3n^3} \cdots\right)$$

$$= -1 < 0. \tag{5.47}$$

Hence we have divergence for $h = 1$. This is an example of a successful application of Kummer's test in which Raabe's test had failed.

EXAMPLE 5.2.4

The recurrence relation for the series solution of Legendre's equation (Section 8.4) may be put in the form

$$\frac{a_{2j+2}}{a_{2j}} = \frac{2j(2j+1) - n(n+1)}{(2j+1)(2j+2)}. \tag{5.48}$$

This is equivalent to u_{2j+2}/u_{2j} for $x = +1$. For $j \gg n$,[1]

$$\frac{u_{2j}}{u_{2j+2}} \to \frac{(2j+1)(2j+2)}{2j(2j+1)} = \frac{2j+2}{2j}$$

$$= 1 + \frac{1}{j}. \tag{5.49}$$

---

[1] The n dependence enters $B(n)$ but does not affect h.

By Eq. 5.44 the series is divergent. Later we shall demand that the Legendre series be finite at $x = 1$. We shall eliminate the divergence by setting the parameter $n = 2j_0$, an even integer.

All of this section so far has been concerned with establishing convergence as an abstract mathematical property. In practice, the *rate* of convergence may be of extreme importance. We might, for instance, be attempting to estimate the convergence limit. A method of increasing the *rate* of convergence has been given by Kummer. If we have a (slowly converging) series S and a known series S', we may write

$$S = S' + (S - S').$$

The point of this simple-minded rearrangement is that by proper choice of S' the new series $(S - S')$ may converge *more rapidly* than the original S.

EXAMPLE 5.2.5

Let $S = \sum_{n=1}^{\infty} n^{-3}$. In Section 5.8 this is identified as $\zeta(3)$. Choose

$$S' = \sum_{n=2}^{\infty} \frac{1}{(n-1)n(n+1)} = \frac{1}{4}.$$

Then

$$\sum_{n=1}^{\infty} n^{-3} = \frac{1}{4} + 1 + \sum_{n=2}^{\infty} \left(\frac{1}{n^3} - \frac{1}{n^3 - n} \right) \tag{5.50}$$

$$= \frac{5}{4} - \sum_{n=2}^{\infty} \frac{1}{n^3(n^2 - 1)},$$

which converges as n^{-5}, obviously faster than the original n^{-3}.

For problems in numerical approximation of a series limit Kummer's method can be very useful indeed.

EXERCISES

5.2.1 (a) Prove that if

$$\lim_{n \to \infty} n^p u_n \to A < \infty; \quad p > 1$$

the series $\sum_{n=1}^{\infty} u_n$ converges.

(b) Prove that if

$$\lim_{n \to \infty} n u_n = A > 0$$

the series diverges. (The test fails for $A = 0$.)

These two tests, known as limit tests, are often convenient for establishing the convergence or divergence of a series. They may be treated as comparison tests, comparing with

$$\sum n^{-q}, \qquad 1 \leqslant q < p.$$

5.2.2 Test for convergence

(a) $\sum_{n=2}^{\infty} (\ln n)^{-1}$.

(d) $\sum_{n=1}^{\infty} [n(n+1)]^{-1/2}$.

(b) $\sum_{n=1}^{\infty} \frac{n!}{10^n}$.

(e) $\sum_{n=0}^{\infty} \frac{1}{2n+1}$.

(c) $\sum_{n=1}^{\infty} \frac{1}{2n(2n-1)}$.

5.2.3 Test for convergence

(a) $\sum_{n=1}^{\infty} \frac{1}{n(n+1)}$

(d) $\sum_{n=1}^{\infty} \ln\left(1 + \frac{1}{n}\right)$

(b) $\sum_{n=2}^{\infty} \frac{1}{n \ln n}$

(e) $\sum_{n=1}^{\infty} \frac{1}{n \cdot n^{1/n}}$

(c) $\sum_{n=1}^{\infty} \frac{1}{n 2^n}$

5.2.4 For what values of p and q will be the following series converge?

$$\sum_{n=2}^{\infty} \frac{1}{n^p (\ln n)^p},$$

Ans. Convergent for $\begin{cases} p > 1, & \text{all } q, \\ p = 1, & q > 1, \end{cases}$

divergent for $\begin{cases} p < 1, & \text{all } q, \\ p = 1, & q \leqslant 1. \end{cases}$

5.2.5 Determine the range of convergence for Gauss's hypergeometric series

$$F(\alpha, \beta, \gamma; x) = 1 + \frac{\alpha\beta}{1!\,\gamma}x + \frac{\alpha(\alpha+1)\beta(\beta+1)}{2!\,\gamma(\gamma+1)}x^2 + \cdots.$$

Hint. Gauss developed Gauss's test for the specific purpose of establishing the convergence of this series.   *Ans.* Convergent for $-1 < x < 1$ and for $x = 1$ if $\gamma > \alpha + \beta$.

5.2.6 A simple machine calculation yields

$$\sum_{n=1}^{100} n^{-3} = 1.202\,007.$$

Show that

$$1.202\,056 \leqslant \sum_{n=1}^{\infty} n^{-3} \leqslant 1.202\,057.$$

Hint. Use integrals to set upper and lower bounds on $\sum_{n=101}^{\infty} n^{-3}$.

Comment. A more exact value for summation $\sum_{1}^{\infty} n^{-3}$ is $1.202\,056\,903 \cdots$.

5.2.7 Prove that

$$\lim_{n\to\infty} \left[\sum_{m=2}^{n} \frac{1}{m \ln m} - \ln(\ln n) \right]$$

is finite. See if rough upper and lower bounds can be established.

5.2.8 The Legendre series, $\sum_{j \text{ even}} u_j(x)$, satisfies the recurrence relations

$$u_{j+2}(x) = \frac{j(j+1) - n(n+1)}{(j+1)(j+2)} x^2 \, u_j(x)$$

in which the index j is even and n is some constant (but, in this problem, *not* a non-negative even integer). Find the range of values of x for which this Legendre series is convergent. Test the endpoints carefully. *Ans.* $-1 < x < 1$.

5.2.9 Show whether $\sum_{n=2}^{\infty} 1/(\ln n)^n$ is convergent or divergent by the Cauchy root test.

5.2.10 Prove that the series

$$\sum_{n=3}^{\infty} \frac{1}{n \ln n [\ln (\ln n)]^r}$$

is convergent for $r > 1$, divergent for $r \leqslant 1$.

5.2.11 (From Olber's paradox.) Assume a static universe in which the stars are uniformly distributed. Divide all space into shells of constant thickness; the stars in any one shell by themselves subtend a solid angle of ω_0. *Allowing for the blocking out of distant stars by nearer stars*, show that the total net solid angle subtended by all stars, shells extending to infinity, is *exactly* 4π. (Therefore the night sky should be ablaze with light.)

5.2.12 Show that the complete d'Alembert ratio test follows directly from Kummer's test with $a_i = 1$.

5.2.13 Show that Raabe's test is indecisive for $P = 1$ by establishing that $P = 1$ for the series

(a) $u_n = \dfrac{1}{n \ln n}$ and that this series diverges.

(b) $u_n = \dfrac{1}{n(\ln n)^2}$ and that this series converges.

5.2.14 Gauss's test is often given in the form of a test of the ratio

$$\frac{u_n}{u_{n+1}} = \frac{n^2 + a_1 n + a_0}{n^2 + b_1 n + b_0}.$$

For what values of the parameters a_1 and b_1 is there convergence? Divergence?

5.2.15 Test for convergence

$$\sum_{n=1}^{\infty} \left[\frac{1 \cdot 3 \cdot 5 \cdots (2n-1)}{2 \cdot 4 \cdot 6 \cdots (2n)} \right]^2 = \frac{1}{4} + \frac{9}{64} + \frac{25}{256} + \cdots .$$

5.2.16 If

$$\lim_{n \to \infty} \frac{b_n}{a_n} = K,$$

a constant with $0 < K < \infty$, show that $\sum b_n$ converges or diverges with $\sum a_n$.
Hint. If $\sum a_n$ converges, use

$$b_n' = \frac{1}{2K} b_n .$$

If $\sum a_n$ diverges, use

$$b_n'' = \frac{2}{K} b_n .$$

5.2.17 Show that

$$\sum_{n=1}^{\infty} \frac{1}{(2n-1)(2n+1)} = \frac{1}{2}.$$

Hint. Show (by mathematical induction) that $s_n = n/(2n+1)$.

5.2.18 Show that

$$\sum_{n=1}^{\infty} \frac{1}{n(n+1)} = 1.$$

5.2.19 Show that

$$\sum_{n=1}^{\infty} \frac{1}{n(n+1)(n+2)\cdots(n+p)} = \frac{1}{p} \cdot \frac{1}{p!}$$

5.3 Alternating Series

In Section 5.2 we limited ourselves to series of positive terms. Now, in contrast, we consider infinite series in which the signs alternate. The partial cancellation due to alternating signs makes convergence more rapid and much easier to identify. We shall prove the Leibnitz criterion, a general condition for the convergence of an alternating series.

Leibnitz criterion.   With $a_n > 0$, take $\sum_{n=1}^{\infty} (-1)^{n+1} a_n$. If we further have a_n monotonically decreasing for sufficiently large n and $\lim_{n \to \infty} a_n = 0$, then from the partial sums

$$s_{2n} = a_1 - a_2 + a_3 - \cdots - a_{2n},$$

$$s_{2n+2} = s_{2n} + (a_{2n+1} - a_{2n+2}). \tag{5.51}$$

Since $a_{2n+1} > a_{2n+2}$, we have

$$s_{2n+2} > s_{2n}. \tag{5.52}$$

On the other hand,

$$s_{2n+2} = a_1 - (a_2 - a_3) - (a_4 - a_5) - \cdots - a_{2n+2}. \tag{5.53}$$

Hence, with each pair of terms $a_{2p} - a_{2p+1} > 0$,

$$s_{2n+2} < a_1. \tag{5.54}$$

With the even partial sums bounded $s_{2n} < s_{2n+2} < a_1$ and the terms a_n decreasing monotonically and approaching zero, this alternating series converges.

One further important result can be extracted from the partial sums. From the difference between the series limit S and the partial sum s_n

$$S - s_n = a_{n+1} - a_{n+2} + a_{n+3} - a_{n+5} + \cdots$$

$$= a_{n+1} - (a_{n+2} - a_{n+3}) - (a_{n+4} - a_{n+5}) - \cdots \tag{5.55}$$

or

$$S - s_n < a_{n+1}. \tag{5.56}$$

Equation 5.56 says that the error in cutting off an alternating series after n terms is less than a_{n+1}, the first term dropped. A knowledge of the error obtained this way may be of great practical importance.

Absolute convergence.   Given a series of terms u_n in which u_n may vary in sign, if $\sum |u_n|$ converges, then $\sum u_n$ is said to be absolutely convergent. If $\sum u_n$ converges but $\sum |u_n|$ diverges, the convergence is called conditional.

The alternating harmonic series is a simple example of this conditional convergence. We have

$$\sum_{n=1}^{\infty}(-1)^{n-1}n^{-1} = 1 - \frac{1}{2} + \frac{1}{3} - \frac{1}{4} + \cdots + \frac{1}{n} - \cdots, \tag{5.57}$$

convergent by the Leibnitz criterion; but

$$\sum_{n=1}^{\infty}n^{-1} = 1 + \frac{1}{2} + \frac{1}{3} + \frac{1}{4} + \cdots + \frac{1}{n} + \cdots \tag{5.58}$$

has been shown to be divergent in Sections 5.1 and 5.2.

The reader will note that all the tests developed in Section 5.2 assume a series of positive terms. Therefore all the tests in that section guarantee absolute convergence.

EXERCISES

5.3.1   Test $\sum_k(-1)^k k^\alpha e^{k\beta}$ for convergence (absolute or conditional) for all values of the parameters α and β.

5.3.2   Show by direct numerical computation that the sum of the first ten terms of

$$\lim_{x \to 1} \ln(1 + x) = \ln 2 = \sum_{n=1}^{\infty}(-1)^{n-1}n^{-1}$$

differs from ln 2 by less than the eleventh term: $\ln 2 = 0.69314\ 71806\cdots$.

5.4   Algebra of Series

The establishment of absolute convergence is important because it can be proved that absolutely convergent series may be handled according to the ordinary familiar rules of algebra or arithmetic.

1. If an infinite series is absolutely convergent, the series sum is independent of the order in which the terms are added.

2. The series may be multiplied with another absolutely convergent series. The limit of the product will be the product of the individual series limits. The product series, a double series, will also converge absolutely.

No such guarantees can be given for conditionally convergent series. Again consider the alternating harmonic series. If we write

$$1 - \tfrac{1}{2} + \tfrac{1}{3} - \tfrac{1}{4} + \cdots = 1 - (\tfrac{1}{2} - \tfrac{1}{3}) - (\tfrac{1}{4} - \tfrac{1}{5}) - \cdots, \tag{5.59}$$

it is clear that the sum

$$\sum_{n=1}^{\infty}(-1)^{n-1}n^{-1}<1. \tag{5.60}$$

However, if we rearrange the terms slightly, we may make the alternating harmonic series converge to $\frac{3}{2}$. We regroup the terms of Eq. 5.59, taking

$$(1+\tfrac{1}{3}+\tfrac{1}{5})-(\tfrac{1}{2})+(\tfrac{1}{7}+\tfrac{1}{9}+\tfrac{1}{11}+\tfrac{1}{13}+\tfrac{1}{15})-(\tfrac{1}{4})$$

$$+(\tfrac{1}{17}+\cdots+\tfrac{1}{25})-(\tfrac{1}{6})+(\tfrac{1}{27}+\cdots+\tfrac{1}{35})-(\tfrac{1}{8})+\cdots. \tag{5.61}$$

Treating the terms grouped in parenthesis as single terms for convenience, we obtain the partial sums

$$s_1 = 1.5333 \qquad s_2 = 1.0333$$

$$s_3 = 1.5218 \qquad s_4 = 1.2718$$

$$s_5 = 1.5143 \qquad s_6 = 1.3476$$

$$s_7 = 1.5103 \qquad s_8 = 1.3853$$

$$s_9 = 1.5078 \qquad s_{10} = 1.4078$$

$$\cdots$$

From this tabulation of s_n and the plot of s_n versus n in Fig. 5.2 the convergence

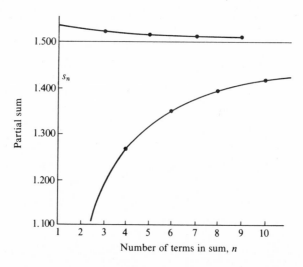

FIG. 5.2   Alternating harmonic series—terms rearranged to give convergence to 1.5

to $\frac{3}{2}$ is fairly clear. We have rearranged the terms, taking positive terms until the partial sum was equal to or greater than $\frac{3}{2}$, then adding in negative terms until the partial sum just fell below $\frac{3}{2}$, and so on. As the series extends to infinity, all of the original terms will eventually appear, but the partial sums of this rearranged alternating harmonic series converge to $\frac{3}{2}$.

By a suitable rearrangement of terms a conditionally convergent series may be made to converge to any desired value or even to diverge. This statement is sometimes given as Riemann's theorem. Obviously, conditionally convergent series must be treated with caution.

Another aspect of the rearrangement of series appears in the treatment of double series

$$\sum_{m=0}^{\infty} \sum_{n=0}^{\infty} a_{n,m}.$$

Let us substitute

$$n = q \geqslant 0,$$

$$m = p - q \geqslant 0$$

$$(q \leqslant p).$$

This results in the identity

$$\sum_{m=0}^{\infty} \sum_{n=0}^{\infty} a_{n,m} = \sum_{p=0}^{\infty} \sum_{q=0}^{p} a_{q,p-q}. \tag{5.62a}$$

The substitution

$$n = s \geqslant 0,$$

$$m = r - 2s \geqslant 0$$

$$\left(s \leqslant \frac{r}{2}\right),$$

leads to

$$\sum_{m=0}^{\infty} \sum_{n=0}^{\infty} a_{n,m} = \sum_{r=0}^{\infty} \sum_{s=0}^{[r/2]} a_{s,r-2s} \tag{5.62b}$$

FIG. 5.3 Double series—summation over n indicated by vertical dashed lines

	$p = 0$	1	2	3
$q = 0$	a_{00}	a_{01}	a_{02}	a_{03}
1		a_{10}	a_{11}	a_{12}
2			a_{20}	a_{21}
3				a_{30}

FIG. 5.4   Double series—again the first summation is represented by vertical dashed lines but these vertical lines correspond to diagonals in Fig. 5.3

with $[r/2] = r/2$ for r even, $(r - 1)/2$ for r odd. Equations 5.62a and b are represented in Fig. 5.3.

	$r = 0$	1	2	3	4
$s = 0$	a_{00}	a_{01}	a_{02}	a_{03}	a_{04}
1			a_{10}	a_{11}	a_{12}
2					a_{20}

FIG. 5.5   Double Series. The summation over s corresponds to a summation along the almost horizontal slanted lines in Fig. 5.3.

Equations 5.62a and b are clearly rearrangements of the array of coefficients a_{nm}, rearrangements that are valid as long as we have absolute convergence.

The combination of Eqs. 5.62a and b,

$$\sum_{p=0}^{\infty} \sum_{q=0}^{p} a_{q,p-q} = \sum_{r=0}^{\infty} \sum_{s=0}^{[r/2]} a_{s,r-2s}, \tag{5.62c}$$

is used in Section 12.1 in the determination of the series form of the Legendre polynomials.

EXERCISES

5.4.1   Given the series

$$\ln (1 + x) = x - \frac{x^2}{2} + \frac{x^3}{3} - \frac{x^4}{4} \cdots$$

show that

(a) $\ln(1-x) = -x - \dfrac{x^2}{2} - \dfrac{x^3}{3} - \dfrac{x^4}{4} \cdots$

(b) $\ln\left(\dfrac{1+x}{1-x}\right) = 2\left(x + \dfrac{x^3}{3} + \dfrac{x^5}{5} + \cdots\right)$.

The second series is useful in developing a second solution for Legendre's differential equation (Section 12.9).

5.5 Series of Functions

We extend our concept of infinite series to include the possibility that each term u_n may be a function of some variable, $u_n = u_n(x)$. The partial sums become functions of the variable x

$$s_n(x) = u_1(x) + u_2(x) + \cdots + u_n(x), \qquad (5.63)$$

as does the series sum, defined as the limit of the partial sums

$$\sum_{n=1}^{\infty} u_n(x) = S(x) = \lim_{n \to \infty} s_n(x). \qquad (5.64)$$

So far we have concerned ourselves with the behavior of the partial sums as a function of n. Now we consider how the foregoing quantities depend on x. The key concept here is that of uniform convergence.

Uniform convergence. If for any small $\varepsilon > 0$ there exists a number N, *independent of x* in the interval $[a, b]$ $(a \leqslant x \leqslant b)$ such that

$$|S(x) - s_n(x)| < \varepsilon, \qquad \text{for all } n \geqslant N, \qquad (5.65)$$

the series is said to be uniformly convergent in the interval $[a, b]$.

This condition, Eq. 5.65, which defines uniform convergence, is illustrated in Fig. 5.6. The point is that no matter how small ε is taken to be we can always choose

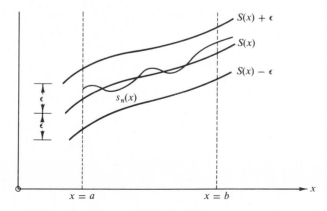

FIG. 5.6 Uniform convergence

n large enough so that the absolute magnitude of the difference between $S(x)$ and $s_n(x)$ is less than ε for all x, $a \leqslant x \leqslant b$. If this cannot be done, then $\sum u_n(x)$ is *not* uniformly convergent in $[a, b]$.

EXAMPLE 5.5.1

$$\sum_{n=1}^{\infty} u_n(x) = \sum_{n=1}^{\infty} \frac{x}{[(n-1)x+1][nx+1]} \tag{5.66}$$

The partial sum $s_n(x) = nx(nx+1)^{-1}$ as may be verified by mathematical induction. By inspection this expression for $s_n(x)$ holds for $n = 1, 2$. We assume it holds for n terms and then prove it holds for $n + 1$ terms.

$$s_{n+1}(x) = s_n(x) + \frac{x}{[nx+1][(n+1)x+1]}$$

$$= \frac{nx}{[nx+1]} + \frac{x}{[nx+1][(n+1)x+1]} \tag{5.67}$$

$$= \frac{(n+1)x}{(n+1)x+1},$$

completing the proof.

Letting n approach infinity, we obtain

$$S(0) = \lim_{n \to \infty} s_n(0) = 0,$$

$$S(x \neq 0) = \lim_{n \to \infty} s_n(x \neq 0) = 1. \tag{5.68}$$

We have a discontinuity in our series limit at $x = 0$. However, $s_n(x)$ is a continuous function of x, $0 \leqslant x \leqslant 1$, for all finite n. Equation 5.65 with ε sufficiently small, will be violated for all *finite* n. Our series does not converge uniformly.

Weierstrass M test. The most commonly encountered test for uniform convergence is the Weierstrass M test. If we can construct a series of numbers $\sum_1^{\infty} M_i$, in which $M_i \geqslant |u_i(x)|$ for all x in the interval $[a, b]$ and $\sum_1^{\infty} M_i$ is convergent, our series $\sum_1^{\infty} u_i(x)$ will be *uniformly* convergent in $[a, b]$.

The proof of this Weierstrass M test is direct and simple. Since $\sum_i M_i$ converges, some number N exists such that for $n + 1 \geqslant N$,

$$\sum_{i=n+1}^{\infty} M_i < \varepsilon. \tag{5.69}$$

This follows from our definition of convergence. Then, with $|u_i(x)| \leqslant M_i$ for all x in the interval $a \leqslant x \leqslant b$,

$$\sum_{i=n+1}^{\infty} |u_i(x)| < \varepsilon. \tag{5.70}$$

Hence

$$|S(x) - s_n(x)| = \left| \sum_{i=n+1}^{\infty} u_i(x) \right| < \varepsilon, \tag{5.71}$$

and by definition $\sum_{i=1}^{\infty} u_i(x)$ is uniformly convergent in $[a, b]$. Since we have speci-fied absolute values in the statement of the Weierstrass M test, the series $\sum_{i=1}^{\infty} u_i(x)$ is also seen to be *absolutely* convergent.

The reader should note carefully that uniform convergence and absolute con-vergence are independent properties. Neither implies the other. For specific examples,

$$\sum_{n=1}^{\infty} \frac{(-1)^n}{n + x^2}, \qquad -\infty < x < \infty \tag{5.72}$$

and

$$\sum_{n=1}^{\infty} (-1)^{n-1} \frac{x^n}{n} = \ln(1 + x), \qquad 0 \leqslant x \leqslant 1 \tag{5.73}$$

converge uniformly in the indicated intervals but do not converge absolutely. On the other hand,

$$\sum_{n=0}^{\infty} (1 - x)x^n = 1, \qquad 0 \leqslant x < 1$$
$$= 0, \qquad x = 1 \tag{5.74}$$

converges absolutely but does not converge uniformly in $[0, 1]$.

From the definition of uniform convergence we may show that any series

$$f(x) = \sum_{n=1}^{\infty} u_n(x) \tag{5.75}$$

cannot converge uniformly in any interval that includes a discontinuity of $f(x)$.

Since the Weierstrass M test establishes both uniform and absolute convergence, it will necessarily fail for series that are uniformly but conditionally convergent. A somewhat more delicate test for uniform convergence has been given by Abel. If

$$u_n(x) = a_n f_n(x),$$

$$\sum a_n = A, \quad \text{convergent},$$

and the functions $f_n(x)$ are monotonic and bounded, $0 \leqslant f_n(x) \leqslant M$, for all x in $[a, b]$, then $\sum u_n(x)$ converges uniformly in $[a, b]$.

This test is expecially useful in analyzing power series (cf. Section 5.7). Details of the proof of Abel's test and other tests for uniform convergence are given in the references listed at the end of this chapter.

Uniformly convergent series have three particularly useful properties.

1. If the individual terms $u_n(x)$ are continuous, the series sum

$$f(x) = \sum_{n=1}^{\infty} u_n(x) \tag{5.76}$$

is also continuous.

2. If the individual terms $u_n(x)$ are continuous, the series may be integrated term by term. The sum of the integrals is equal to the integral of the sum.

$$\int_a^b f(x)\,dx = \sum_{n=1}^{\infty} \int_a^b u_n(x)\,dx. \tag{5.77}$$

3. The derivative of the series sum $f(x)$ equals the sum of the individual term derivatives,

$$\frac{d}{dx}f(x) = \sum_{n=1}^{\infty} \frac{d}{dx}u_n(x), \tag{5.78}$$

provided the following conditions are satisfied.

$$u_n(x) \quad \text{and} \quad \frac{du_n(x)}{dx} \quad \text{are continuous in } [a,b].$$

$$\sum_{n=1}^{\infty} \frac{du_n(x)}{dx} \quad \text{is uniformly convergent in } [a,b].$$

Term-by-term integration of a series, usually valid, requires only uniform convergence and continuity of the individual terms. These conditions are almost always satisfied in physical applications. Term-by-term differentiation of a series is often not valid because more restrictive conditions must be satisfied. Indeed, we shall encounter cases in Chapter 14, Fourier Series, in which term-by-term differentiation of a uniformly convergent series leads to a divergent series.

EXERCISES

5.5.1   Find the range of *uniform* convergence of

(a) $\displaystyle\sum_{n=1}^{\infty} \frac{(-1)^{n-1}}{n^x}$

(b) $\displaystyle\sum_{n=1}^{\infty} \frac{1}{n^x}$ *Ans.* (a) $1 \leqslant x < \infty$.
                                                                      (b) $1 < s \leqslant x < \infty$.

5.5.2   Assume that the two Fourier series,

(a) $\displaystyle\frac{\pi - x}{2} = \sum_{n=1}^{\infty} \frac{\sin nx}{n}$,   (b) $\displaystyle -2\ln\left(2\sin\left(\frac{x}{2}\right)\right) = \sum_{n=1}^{\infty} \frac{\cos nx}{n}$,

may be shown uniformly convergent in the range $s \leqslant x \leqslant 2\pi - s$ where $s > 0$. Is term-by-term differentiation of these two series justified? How about term-by-term integration?

5.5.3 For what range of x is the geometric series $\sum\limits_{n=0}^{\infty} x^n$ uniformly convergent?

$$\text{Ans. } -1 < -s \leqslant x \leqslant s < 1$$

5.5.4 For what range of positive values of x is $\sum\limits_{n=0}^{\infty} 1/(1 + x^n)$

(a) Convergent?   (b) Uniformly convergent?

5.5.5 If the series of the coefficients $\sum a_n$ and $\sum b_n$ are absolutely convergent, show that the Fourier series

$$\sum (a_n \cos nx + b_n \sin nx)$$

is *uniformly* convergent for $-\infty < x < \infty$.

5.6 Taylor's Expansion

This is an expansion of a function into an infinite series or into a finite series plus a remainder term. The coefficients of the successive terms of the series involve the successive derivatives of the function. We have already used Taylor's expansion in the establishment of a physical interpretation of divergence (Section 1.7) and in other sections of Chapters 1 and 2. Now we derive the Taylor expansion.

We assume that our function $f(x)$ has a continuous nth derivative[1] in the interval $a \leqslant x \leqslant b$. Then, integrating this nth derivative n times,

$$\int_a^x f^{(n)}(x)\,dx = f^{(n-1)}(x) \Big|_a^x = f^{(n-1)}(x) - f^{(n-1)}(a)$$

$$\int_a^x \left(\int_a^x f^{(n)}(x)\,dx \right) dx = \int_a^x [f^{(n-1)}(x) - f^{(n-1)}(a)]\,dx \qquad (5.79)$$

$$= f^{(n-2)}(x) - f^{(n-2)}(a) - (x-a)f^{(n-1)}(a).$$

Continuing, we obtain

$$\int_a^x\!\!\int\!\!\int f^{(n)}(x)\,(dx)^3 = f^{(n-3)}(x) - f^{(n-3)}(a) - (x-a)f^{(n-2)}a$$

$$-\frac{(x-a)^2}{2} f^{(n-1)}a. \qquad (5.80)$$

Finally, on integrating for the nth time,

$$\int_a^x \cdots \int f^{(n)}(x)\,(dx)^n = f(x) - f(a) - (x-a)f'(a)$$

$$-\frac{(x-a)^2}{2!} f''(a) - \cdots - \frac{(x-a)^{n-1}}{(n-1)!} f^{(n-1)}(a). \qquad (5.81)$$

---

[1] Taylor's expansion may be derived under slightly less restrictive conditions, cf. *Mathematical Physics*, Jeffreys and Jeffreys, Section 1.133.

Note that this expression is exact. No terms have been dropped, no approximations made. Now, solving for $f(x)$, we have

$$f(x) = f(a) + (x - a)f'(a) + \frac{(x - a)^2}{2!} f''(a) + \cdots + \frac{(x - a)^{n-1}}{(n-1)!} f^{(n-1)}(a) + R_n.$$
(5.82)

The remainder, R_n, is given by the n-fold integral

$$R_n = \int_a^x \cdots \int f^{(n)}(x) \, (dx)^n.$$
(5.83)

This remainder, Eq. 5.83, may be put into perhaps more intelligible form by using the mean value theorem of differential calculus.

$$\int_a^x g(x) \, dx = (x - a) \, g(\xi),$$
(5.84)

with $a \leqslant \xi \leqslant x$. By integrating n times we get the Lagrangian form of the remainder:

$$R_n = \frac{(x - a)^n}{n!} f^{(n)}(\xi).$$
(5.85)

With Taylor's expansion in this form we are not concerned with any questions of infinite series convergence. This series is finite, and the only questions concern the magnitude of the remainder.

When the function $f(x)$ is such that

$$\lim_{n \to \infty} R_n = 0,$$
(5.86)

Eq. 5.82 becomes Taylor's series

$$f(x) = f(a) + (x - a)f'(a) + \frac{(x - a)^2}{2!} f''(a) + \cdots$$

$$= \sum_{n=0}^{\infty} \frac{(x - a)^n}{n!} f^{(n)}(a).[1]$$
(5.87)

Maclaurin theorem.   If we expand about the origin ($a = 0$), Eq. 5.87 is known as Maclaurin's series

$$f(x) = f(0) + x f'(0) + \frac{x^2}{2!} f''(0) + \cdots$$
(5.88)

$$= \sum_{n=0}^{\infty} \frac{x^n}{n!} f^{(n)}(0).$$

An immediate application of the Maclaurin series (or the Taylor series) is in the expansion of various transcendental functions into infinite series.

[1] Note that $0! = 1$ (cf. Section 10.1).

EXAMPLE 5.6.1

Let $f(x) = e^x$. Differentiating,

$$f^{(n)}(0) = 1 \qquad (5.89)$$

for all n, $n = 1, 2, 3, \ldots$. Then, by Eq. 5.88, we have

$$e^x = 1 + x + \frac{x^2}{2!} + \frac{x^3}{3!} + \cdots$$

$$= \sum_{n=0}^{\infty} \frac{x^n}{n!}. \qquad (5.90)$$

This is the series expansion of the exponential function. Some authors use this series to define the exponential function.

Although this series is clearly convergent for all x, we should check the remainder term, R_n. By Eq. 5.85 we have

$$R_n = \frac{x^n}{n!} f^{(n)}(\xi)$$

$$= \frac{x^n}{n!} e^\xi, \qquad 0 \leqslant \xi \leqslant x. \qquad (5.91)$$

Therefore

$$R_n \leqslant \frac{x^n e^x}{n!} \qquad (5.92)$$

and

$$\lim_{n \to \infty} R_n = 0 \qquad (5.93)$$

for all *finite* values of x, which indicates that this Maclaurin expansion of e^x is valid over the range $-\infty < x < \infty$.

EXAMPLE 5.6.2

Let $f(x) = \ln(1 + x)$. By differentiating we obtain

$$f'(x) = (1 + x)^{-1},$$
$$f^{(n)}(x) = (-1)^{n-1}(n - 1)!(1 + x)^{-n}. \qquad (5.94)$$

The Maclaurin expansion (Eq. 5.88) yields

$$\ln(1 + x) = x - \frac{x^2}{2} + \frac{x^3}{3} - \frac{x^4}{4} + \cdots + R_n$$

$$= \sum_{p=1}^{n} (-1)^{p-1} \frac{(x)^p}{p} + R_n. \qquad (5.95)$$

In this case our remainder is given by

$$R_n = \frac{x^n}{n!} f^{(n)}(\xi), \qquad 0 \leqslant \xi \leqslant x$$

$$\leqslant \frac{x^n}{n}, \qquad 0 \leqslant \xi \leqslant x \leqslant 1. \qquad (5.96)$$

Now the remainder approaches zero as n is increased indefinitely, provided $0 \leqslant x \leqslant 1$.[1] As an infinite series

$$\ln(1 + x) = \sum_{n=1}^{\infty} (-1)^{n-1} \frac{x^n}{n}, \tag{5.97}$$

which converges for $-1 < x \leqslant 1$. The range $-1 < x < 1$ is easily established by the d'Alembert ratio test (Section 5.2). Convergence at $x = 1$ follows by the Leibnitz criterion (Section 5.3). In particular, at $x = 1$, we have

$$\ln 2 = 1 - \tfrac{1}{2} + \tfrac{1}{3} - \tfrac{1}{4} + \tfrac{1}{5} - \cdots$$

$$= \sum_{n=1}^{\infty} (-1)^{n-1} n^{-1}, \tag{5.98}$$

the conditionally convergent alternating harmonic series.

Binomial theorem.   A second, extremely important application of the Taylor and Maclaurin expansions is the derivation of the binomial theorem for negative and/or nonintegral powers.

Let $f(x) = (1 + x)^m$, in which m may be negative and is not limited to integral values. Direct application of Eq. 5.88 gives

$$(1 + x)^m = 1 + mx + \frac{m(m - 1)}{2!} x^2 + \cdots + R_n. \tag{5.99}$$

For this function the remainder is

$$R_n = \frac{x^n}{n!} (1 + \xi)^{m-n} \times m(m - 1) \cdots (m - n + 1) \tag{5.100}$$

and ξ lies between 0 and x, $0 \leqslant \xi \leqslant x$. Now, for $n > m$, $(1 + \xi)^{m-n}$ is a maximum for $\xi = 0$. Therefore

$$R_n \leqslant \frac{x^n}{n!} \times m(m - 1) \cdots (m - n + 1). \tag{5.101}$$

Note that the m dependent factors do not yield a zero unless m is a non-negative integer; R_n tends to zero as $n \to \infty$ if x is restricted to the range $0 \leqslant x < 1$.
The binomial expansion therefore is shown to be

$$(1 + x)^m = 1 + mx + \frac{m(m - 1)}{2!} x^2 + \frac{m(m - 1)(m - 2)}{3!} x^3 + \cdots. \tag{5.102}$$

Although we have only shown that the remainder vanishes,

$$\lim_{n \to \infty} R_n = 0,$$

for $0 \leqslant x < 1$, the series in Eq. 5.102 actually may be shown to be convergent for the extended range $-1 < x < 1$.

[1] This range can easily be extended to $-1 < x \leqslant 1$ but not to $x = -1$.

EXAMPLE 5.6.3

The total relativistic energy of a particle is

$$E = mc^2\left(1 - \frac{v^2}{c^2}\right)^{-1/2} \tag{5.103}$$

Compare this equation with the classical kinetic energy, $\frac{1}{2}mv^2$.

By Eq. 5.102 with $x = -v^2/c^2$ and $m = -\frac{1}{2}$ we have

$$E = mc^2\left[1 - \frac{1}{2}\left(-\frac{v^2}{c^2}\right) + \frac{(-1/2)(-3/2)}{2!}\left(-\frac{v^2}{c^2}\right)^2\right.$$

$$\left. + \frac{(-1/2)(-3/2)(-5/2)}{3!}\left(-\frac{v^2}{c^2}\right)^3 + \cdots\right] \tag{5.104}$$

or

$$E = mc^2 + \frac{1}{2}mv^2 + \frac{3}{8}mv^2 \cdot \frac{v^2}{c^2} + \frac{5}{16}mv^2 \cdot \left(\frac{v^2}{c^2}\right)^2 + \cdots. \tag{5.105}$$

The first term, mc^2, is identified as the rest mass energy. Then

$$E_{\text{kinetic}} = \frac{1}{2}mv^2\left[1 + \frac{3}{4}\frac{v^2}{c^2} + \frac{5}{8}\left(\frac{v^2}{c^2}\right)^2 + \cdots\right]. \tag{5.106}$$

For particle velocity $v \ll c$, the velocity of light, the expression in the brackets reduces to unity and we see that the kinetic portion of the total relativistic energy agrees with the classical result.

For polynomials we can generalize the binomial expansion to

$$(a_1 + a_2 + \cdots + a_m)^n = \sum \frac{n!}{n_1!n_2!\ldots n_m!} a_1^{n_1}a_2^{n_2}\cdots a_m^{n_m},$$

where the summation includes all different combinations of $n_1, n_2, \ldots, n_m$ with $\sum_{i=1}^m n_i = n$. Here n_i and n are all integral. This generalization finds considerable use in statistical mechanics.

If the function f has more than one independent variable, say $f = f(x, y)$, the Taylor expansion becomes

$$f(x, y) = f(a, b) + (x - a)\frac{\partial f}{\partial x} + (y - b)\frac{\partial f}{\partial y}$$

$$+ \frac{1}{2!}\left[(x - a)^2\frac{\partial^2 f}{\partial x^2} + 2(x - a)(y - b)\frac{\partial^2 f}{\partial x\,\partial y} + (y - b)^2\frac{\partial^2 f}{\partial y^2}\right]$$

$$+ \frac{1}{3!}\left[(x - a)^3\frac{\partial^3 f}{\partial x^2} + 3(x - a)^2(y - b)\frac{\partial^3 f}{\partial x^2\,\partial y}\right.$$

$$\left. + 3(x - a)(y - b)^2\frac{\partial^3 f}{\partial x\,\partial y^2} + (y - b)^3\frac{\partial^3 f}{\partial y^3}\right] + \cdots, \tag{5.107}$$

with all derivatives evaluated at the point (a, b). Using $\alpha_j t = x_j - x_{j0}$, we may write the Taylor expansion for m independent variables in the symbolic form

$$f(x_j) = \sum_{n=0}^{\infty} \frac{t^n}{n!} \left(\sum_{i=1}^{m} \alpha_i \frac{\partial}{\partial x_i} \right)^n f(x_k) \Bigg|_{x_k = x_{k0}} \tag{5.108}$$

EXERCISES

5.6.1 Show, by a Taylor expansion about $\theta_0 = \pi/2$, that

$$\sin\left(\frac{\pi}{2} + \theta\right) = +\cos\theta.$$

5.6.2 With $n > 1$, show that

(a) $\dfrac{1}{n} - \ln\left(\dfrac{n}{n-1}\right) < 0,$ (b) $\dfrac{1}{n} - \ln\left(\dfrac{n+1}{n}\right) > 0.$

Use these inequalities to show that the limit defining the Euler-Mascheroni constant is finite.

5.6.3 Using binomial expansions compare the three Doppler shift formulas:

(a) $v' = v\left(1 \mp \dfrac{v}{c}\right)^{-1}$ moving source;   (c) $v' = v\left(1 \pm \dfrac{v}{c}\right)\left(1 - \dfrac{v^2}{c^2}\right)^{-1/2}$,   relativistic;

(b) $v' = v\left(1 \pm \dfrac{v}{c}\right)$,   moving observer;

Note that the relativistic formula agrees with the classical formulas if terms of order v^2/c^2 can be neglected.

5.6.4 The relativistic sum w of two velocities u and v is given by

$$\frac{w}{c} = \frac{u/c + v/c}{1 + uv/c^2}.$$

If

$$\frac{v}{c} = \frac{u}{c} = 1 - \alpha,$$

where $0 \leqslant \alpha \leqslant 1$, find w/c in powers of α through terms in α^3.

5.6.5 The displacement x of a particle of rest mass m_0, resulting from a constant force $m_0 g$ along the x-axis, is

$$x = \frac{c^2}{g}\left\{ \left[1 + \left(g\frac{t}{c}\right)^2\right]^{1/2} - 1 \right\},$$

including relativistic effects. Find the displacement x as a power series in time t. Compare with the classical result

$$x = \tfrac{1}{2}gt^2.$$

5.6.6 The Raabe test for $\sum (n \ln n)^{-1}$ leads to

$$\lim_{n \to \infty} n \left[\frac{(n+1) \ln (n+1)}{n \ln n} - 1 \right].$$

Show that this limit is unity (which means that the Raabe test here is indeterminant).

5.6.7 Show by series expansion that

$$\ln\frac{\eta_0 + 1}{\eta_0 - 1} = \coth^{-1}\eta_0$$

This identity is used to obtain a second solution for Legendre's equation (Section 12.9).

5.6.8 Given that

$$\int_0^1 \frac{dx}{1 + x^2} = \tan^{-1}x \Big|_0^1 = \frac{\pi}{4},$$

expand the integrand into a series and integrate term by term obtaining

$$\frac{\pi}{4} = 1 - \tfrac{1}{3} + \tfrac{1}{5} - \tfrac{1}{7} + \tfrac{1}{9} - \cdots + (-1)^n \frac{1}{2n + 1} + \cdots,$$

which is Leibnitz' formula for π. Compare the convergence (or lack of it) of the integrand series and the integrated series at $x = 1$.

Leibnitz' formula converges so slowly that it is quite useless for numerical work; π has been computed to 100,000 decimals [D. Shanks and J. W. Wrench, Jr., Mathematics of Computation **16**, 76 (1962)] by using expressions such as

$$\pi = 24\tan^{-1}\tfrac{1}{8} + 8\tan^{-1}\tfrac{1}{57} + 4\tan^{-1}\tfrac{1}{239},$$

$$\pi = 48\tan^{-1}\tfrac{1}{18} + 32\tan^{-1}\tfrac{1}{57} - 20\tan^{-1}\tfrac{1}{239}.$$

5.6.9 Expand the incomplete factorial function

$$\int_0^x e^{-t}t^n \, dt$$

in a series of powers of x for small values of x. What is the range of convergence of the resulting series? Why was x specified to be small?

Ans. $\displaystyle\int_0^x e^{-t}t^n \, dt = x^{n+1}\left[\frac{1}{(n+1)} - \frac{x}{(n+2)} + \frac{x^2}{2!(n+3)} - \cdots \frac{(-1)^p x^p}{p!(n+p+1)} + \cdots\right].$

5.6.10 By use of Dirac's relativistic theory the fine structure formula of atomic spectroscopy is given by

$$E = mc^2\left[1 + \frac{\gamma^2}{(s + n - |k|)^2}\right]^{-1/2},$$

where

$$s = (|k|^2 - \gamma^2)^{1/2}, \qquad k = \pm 1, \pm 2, \pm 3, \ldots.$$

Expand in powers of γ^2 through order γ^4. ($\gamma^2 = Ze^2/\hbar c$, with Z the atomic number.) This expansion is useful in comparing the predictions of the Dirac electron theory with those of a relativistic Schrödinger electron theory. Experimental results support the Dirac theory.

5.6.11 Show that the series

$$(1 - k^2\sin^2\varphi)^{-1/2} = 1 + \frac{1}{2}k^2\sin^2\varphi + \frac{1\cdot 3}{2\cdot 4}k^4\sin^4\varphi + \cdots,$$

with $0 \leqslant k < 1$ is uniformly convergent for all (real) values of the angle φ.

5.6.12 The period of a pendulum with an amplitude of angle α and length l is given by

$$T = 4\left(\frac{l}{g}\right)^{1/2}\int_0^{\pi/2}\frac{d\varphi}{(1 - k^2\sin^2\varphi)^{1/2}},$$

in which $k^2 = \sin^2(\alpha/2)$. Expand T in powers of k^2. (The integral is the complete elliptic integral of the first kind.)

Hint.
$$\int_0^{\pi/2} \sin^{2n} \varphi \, d\varphi = \frac{1 \cdot 3 \cdot 5 \cdots (2n-1)}{2 \cdot 4 \cdot 6 \cdots (2n)} \cdot \frac{\pi}{2}$$

$$= \frac{(2n)!}{2^{2n}(n!)^2} \cdot \frac{\pi}{2}.$$

Ans. $T = 2\pi \left(\dfrac{l}{g}\right)^{1/2} \left(1 + \dfrac{1}{4}k^2 + \dfrac{9}{64}k^4 + \cdots\right).$

5.6.13 The ellipse $x^2/a^2 + y^2/b^2 = 1$ may be represented parametrically by $x = a \sin \varphi$, $y = b \cos \varphi$. The length of arc within the first quadrant is then

$$a \int_0^{\pi/2} (1 - k^2 \sin^2 \varphi)^{1/2} \, d\varphi$$

where

$$k^2 = \frac{a^2 - b^2}{a^2} < 1.$$

Expand the integral in a series of powers of k^2. (The integral is known as the complete elliptic integral of the second kind.)

5.6.14 Expand $(1 - 2tz + t^2)^{-1/2}$ in powers of t. Assume that t is small. Collect the coefficients of t^0, t^1, and t^2.   *Ans.* $a_0 = P_0(z) = 1$,

$$a_1 = P_1(z) = z,$$

$$a_2 = P_2(z) = \tfrac{1}{2}(3z^2 - 1),$$

where $a_n = P_n(z)$, the nth Legendre polynomial.

5.6.15 Show that

(a) $\sin x = \displaystyle\sum_{n=0}^{\infty} (-1)^n \frac{x^{2n+1}}{(2n+1)!}$,   (b) $\cos x = \displaystyle\sum_{n=0}^{\infty} (-1)^n \frac{x^{2n}}{(2n)!}$.

In Section 6.1 e^{ix} is *defined* by a series expansion such that

$$e^{ix} = \cos x + i \sin x.$$

This is the basis for the polar representation of complex quantities. As a special case we find, with $x = \pi$,

$$e^{i\pi} = -1.$$

5.6.16 By *multiplying* series expansions for $\sin x$ and $\cos x$ show that

$$\sin 2x = 2 \sin x \cos x.$$

5.6.17 Derive a series expansion of $\cot x$ in increasing powers of x by dividing $\cos x$ by $\sin x$. *Note.* The resultant series which starts with $1/x$ is actually a Laurent series (Section 6.4). Although the two series for $\sin x$ and $\cos x$ were valid for all x, the convergence of the series for $\cot x$ is limited by the zeros of the denominator, $\sin x$.

5.6.18 Show that $f(x) = x^{1/2}$ (a) has no Maclaurin expansion but (b) has a Taylor expansion about any point $x_0 \neq 0$. Find the range of convergence of the Taylor expansion about $x = x_0$.

5.6.19 Set upper and lower bounds on $\sum_{n=1}^{1,000,000} n^{-1}$, assuming that (a) the Euler-Mascheroni constant is known.   *Ans.* $14.392\,726 < \sum_{n=1}^{1,000,000} n^{-1} < 14.392\,727$.

(b) The Euler-Mascheroni constant is unknown.

5.6.20 Given $\sum_{n=1}^{1,000} n^{-1} = 7.485\,470 \cdots$, set upper and lower bounds on the Euler-Mascheroni constant.   *Ans.* $0.5767 < C < 0.5778$.

5.6.21 In the theory of general relativity there are various ways of relating (defining) a velocity of recession of a galaxy to its red shift, δ. Milne's model (kinematic relativity) gives

(a) $v_1 = c \, \delta(1 + \tfrac{1}{2}\delta)$,

(b) $v_2 = c \, \delta(1 + \tfrac{1}{2}\delta)(1 + \delta)^{-2}$ (c) $1 + \delta = \left[\dfrac{1 + v_3/c}{1 - v_3/c}\right]^{1/2}$

1. Show that for $\delta \ll 1$ (and $v_3/c \ll 1$) all three formulas reduce to $v = c\delta$.

2. Compare the three velocities through terms of order δ^2.

5.6.22 Neutrons are created (by a nuclear reaction) inside a hollow sphere of radius R. The newly created neutrons are uniformly distributed over the spherical volume. Assuming that all directions are equally probable (isotropy), what is the average distance a neutron will travel before striking the surface of the sphere? Assume straight line motion, no collisions.

(a) Show that

$$\bar{r} = \tfrac{3}{2} R \int_0^1 \int_0^\pi \sqrt{1 - k^2 \sin^2 \theta}\, k^2 \, dk \, \sin \theta \, d\theta.$$

(b) Expand the integrand as a series and integrate to obtain

$$\bar{r} = R \left[1 - 4 \sum_{n=1}^{\infty} \frac{1}{(2n-1)(2n+1)(2n+3)} \right].$$

(c) Show that the sum of this infinite series is $\tfrac{1}{12}$, giving $\bar{r} = \tfrac{3}{4} R$. *Hint.* Show that $s_n = \tfrac{1}{12} - [4(2n+1)(2n+3)]^{-1}$ by mathematical induction. Then let $n \to \infty$.

5.6.23 Let x be an approximation for a zero of $f(x)$ and Δx, the correction. Show that by neglecting terms of order $(\Delta x)^2$

$$\Delta x = - \frac{f(x)}{f'(x)}$$

This is Newton's formula for finding a root.

5.6.24 Approximating the integral by

$$\int_{-1}^{1} f(x) \, dx = a_{-1} f(-1) + a_0 f(0) + a_1 f(1),$$

derive Simpson's integration formula

$$\int_{-1}^{1} f(x) \, dx = \tfrac{1}{3}[f(-1) + 4f(0) + f(+1)].$$

Hint. Use a Taylor (Maclaurin) expansion on both sides of the equation.

5.6.25 In a Taylor expansion of $y(x)$ replace d/dx by the operator D and develop the *operator equation*

$$\Delta = e^{hD} - 1.$$

Here Δ is the increment in $y(x)$, whereas h is the increment in x. This result is one of the basic formulas in the calculus of finite differences leading to interpolation formulas, numerical integration formulas, etc.

5.6.26 Expand a function $\Phi(x, y, z)$ by Taylor's expansion. Evaluate $\bar{\Phi}$, the average value of Φ, averaged over a small cube of side a centered on the origin and show that the Laplacian of Φ is a measure of deviation of $\bar{\Phi}$ from $\Phi(0, 0, 0)$. *Ans.* $\nabla^2 \Phi |_{0,0,0} = \dfrac{24}{a^2} [\bar{\Phi} - \Phi(0, 0, 0)]$.

5.7 Power Series

The power series is a special and extremely useful type of infinite series of the form

$$f(x) = a_0 + a_1 x + a_2 x^2 + a_3 x^3 + \cdots$$
$$= \sum_{n=0}^{\infty} a_n x^n \tag{5.109}$$

where the coefficients a_i are constants, independent of x.[1]

[1] Equation 5.109 may be rewritten with $z = x + iy$, replacing x. The following sections will then yield uniform convergence, integrability, and differentiability in a region of a complex plane in place of an interval on the x-axis.

Convergence.   Equation 5.109 may readily be tested for convergence by either the Cauchy root test or the d'Alembert ratio test (Section 5.2). If

$$\lim_{n \to \infty} \frac{a_{n+1}}{a_n} = R^{-1},$$

(5.110)

the series converges for $-R < x < R$. This is the interval or radius of convergence. Since the root and ratio tests fail when the limit is unity, the end points of the interval require special attention.

For instance, if $a_n = n^{-1}$, then $R = 1$ and, from Sections 5.1, 5.2, and 5.3, the series converges for $x = -1$ but diverges for $x = +1$. If $a_n = n!$, then $R = 0$ and the series diverges for all $x \neq 0$.

Uniform and absolute convergence.   Suppose our power series (Eq. 5.109) has been found convergent for $-R < x < R$; then it will be uniformly and absolutely convergent in any *interior* interval, $-S \leqslant x \leqslant S$, where $0 < S < R$.

This may be proved directly by the Weierstrass M test (Section 5.5) by using $M_i = |a_i| = S^i$.

Continuity.   Since each of the terms $u_n(x) = a_n x^n$ is a continuous function of x and $f(x) = \sum a_n x^n$ converges uniformly for $-S \leqslant x \leqslant S$, $f(x)$ must be a continuous function in the interval of uniform convergence.

This behavior is to be contrasted with the strikingly different behavior of Fourier series (Chapter 14), in which the Fourier series is used frequently to represent discontinuous functions such as sawtooth and square waves.

Differentiation and integration.   With $u_n(x)$ continuous and $\sum a_n x^n$ uniformly convergent, we find that the differentiated series is a power series with continuous functions and the same radius of convergence as the original series. The new factors introduced by differentiation (or integration) do not affect either the root or the ratio test. Therefore our power series may be differentiated or integrated as often as desired within the interval of uniform convergence (Exercise 5.7.9).

In view of the rather severe restrictions placed on differentiation (Section 5.5), this is a remarkable and valuable result.

Uniqueness theorem.   In the preceding section, using the Maclaurin series, we expanded e^x and $\ln (1 + x)$ into infinite series. In the succeeding chapters functions are frequently represented or perhaps defined by infinite series. We now establish that the power-series representation is unique.

If

$$f(x) = \sum_{n=0}^{\infty} a_n x^n, \qquad -R_a < x < R_a$$

$$= \sum_{n=0}^{\infty} b_n x^n, \qquad -R_b < x < R_b,$$

(5.111)

with overlapping intervals of convergence, including the origin, then

$$a_n = b_n$$

(5.112)

for all n; that is, we assume two (different) power-series representations and then proceed to show that the two are actually identical.

From Eq. 5.111

$$\sum_{n=0}^{\infty} a_n x^n = \sum_{n=0}^{\infty} b_n x^n, \qquad -R < x < R, \qquad (5.113)$$

where R is the smaller of R_a, R_b. By setting $x = 0$ to eliminate all but the constant terms, we obtain

$$a_0 = b_0. \qquad (5.114)$$

Now, exploiting the differentiability of our power series, we differentiate Eq. 5.113, getting

$$\sum_{n=1}^{\infty} n a_n x^{n-1} = \sum_{n=1}^{\infty} n b_n x^{n-1}. \qquad (5.115)$$

We again set $x = 0$ to isolate the new constant terms and find

$$a_1 = b_1. \qquad (5.116)$$

By repeating this process n times, we get

$$a_n = b_n, \qquad (5.117)$$

which shows that the two series coincide. Therefore our power-series representation is unique.

This will be a crucial point in Chapter 8, in which we use a power series to develop solutions of differential equations. The power-series representation of functions is often useful in evaluating indeterminate forms, particularly when l'Hospital's rule may be awkward to apply (Exercise 5.7.1).

EXAMPLE 5.7.1

Evaluate

$$\lim_{x \to 0} \frac{1 - \cos x}{x^2}. \qquad (5.118)$$

Replacing $\cos x$ by its Maclaurin series expansion,

$$\frac{1 - \cos x}{x^2} = \frac{1 - (1 - x^2/2! + x^4/4! - \cdots)}{x^2}$$

$$= \frac{x^2/2! - x^4/4! + \cdots}{x^2} \qquad (5.119)$$

$$= 1/2! - x^2/4! + \cdots.$$

Letting $x \to 0$,

$$\lim_{x \to 0} \frac{1 - \cos x}{x^2} = \frac{1}{2}. \qquad (5.120)$$

Reversion (inversion) of power series.   Suppose we are given a series

$$y - y_0 = a_1(x - x_0) + a_2(x - x_0)^2 + \cdots$$

$$= \sum_{n=1}^{\infty} a_n(x - x_0)^n. \tag{5.121}$$

This gives $(y - y_0)$ in terms of $(x - x_0)$. However, it may be desirable to have an explicit expression for $(x - x_0)$ in terms of $(y - y_0)$. We may solve Eq. 5.121 for $x - x_0$ by reversion (or inversion) of our series. Assume that

$$x - x_0 = \sum_{n=1}^{\infty} b_n(y - y_0)^n, \tag{5.122}$$

with the b_n to be determined in terms of the assumed known a_n. A brute-force approach, which is perfectly adequate for the first few coefficients, is simply to substitute Eq. 5.121 into Eq. 5.122. By equating coefficients of $(x - x_0)^n$ on both sides of Eq. 5.122, since the power series is unique, we obtain

$$b_1 = \frac{1}{a_1},$$

$$b_2 = -\frac{a_2}{a_1^3},$$

$$b_3 = \frac{1}{a_1^5}(2a_2^2 - a_1 a_3), \tag{5.123}$$

$$b_4 = \frac{1}{a_1^7}(5a_1 a_2 a_3 - a_1^2 a_4 - 5a_2^3), \qquad \text{etc.}$$

Some of the higher coefficients are listed by Dwight.[1] In Section 7.3 a more general and much more elegant approach is developed by the use of complex variables.

EXERCISES

5.7.1   Evaluate

(a) $\displaystyle \lim_{x \to 0} \frac{\sin(\tan x) - \tan(\sin x)}{x^7}$,

(b) $\displaystyle \lim_{x \to 0} x^{-n} j_n(x)$ for $n = 3$,

---

[1] H. B. Dwight, *Tables of Integrals and Other Mathematical Data*. Rev. Ed. New York: Macmillan (1947). (Cf. Formula No. 50.)

where $j_n(x)$ is a spherical Bessel function (Section 11.6) defined by

$$j_n(x) = (-1)^n x^n \left(\frac{d}{x\,dx}\right)^n \left(\frac{\sin x}{x}\right).$$

Ans. (a) $\dfrac{1}{30}$,

(b) $\dfrac{1}{1 \cdot 3 \cdot 5 \cdots (2n+1)} \to \dfrac{1}{105}$ for $n = 3$.

5.7.2 The classical Langevin theory of paramagnetism leads to an expression for the magnetic polarization

$$P(x) = C\left(\frac{\cosh x}{\sinh x} - \frac{1}{x}\right).$$

Expand $P(x)$ as a power series for small x (low fields, high temperature).

5.7.3 The analysis of the diffraction pattern of a circular opening involves

$$\int_0^{2\pi} \cos(c \cos \varphi)\,d\varphi.$$

Expand the integrand in a series and integrate by using

$$\int_0^{2\pi} \cos^{2n}\varphi\,d\varphi = \frac{(2n)!}{2^{2n}(n!)^2} \cdot 2\pi,$$

$$\int_0^{2\pi} \cos^{2n+1}\varphi\,d\varphi = 0.$$

The result is 2 times the Bessel function $J_0(c)$.

5.7.4 Neutron transport theory gives the following expression for the inverse neutron diffusion length of k:

$$\frac{a-b}{k}\,\tanh^{-1}\left(\frac{k}{a}\right) = 1.$$

By series inversion or otherwise, determine k^2 as a series of powers of b/a. Give the first two terms of the series.

Ans. $k^2 = 3ab\left(1 - \dfrac{4}{5}\dfrac{b}{a}\right).$

5.7.5 Develop a series expansion of $\sinh^{-1} x$ in powers of x by
(a) reversion of the series for $\sinh y$,
(b) a direct Maclaurin expansion.

5.7.6 Find the first three terms in a series solution for ζ, ($\zeta \approx r$), where ζ satisfies

$$(\alpha\zeta + 1)(\zeta^2 - r^2) = r\zeta^4.$$

(This equation appears in the calculation of the force exerted by a point charge on a conducting, charged sphere.)

Ans. $\zeta = r\left(1 + \dfrac{1}{2\alpha^{1/2}} + \cdots\right).$

5.7.7 The depolarizing factor L for an oblate ellipsoid in a uniform electric field parallel to the axis of rotation (Section 12.10) is

$$L = \frac{1}{\varepsilon_0}(1 + \zeta_0^2)(1 - \zeta_0 \cot^{-1} \zeta_0),$$

where ζ_0 defines an oblate ellipsoid in oblate spheroidal coordinates (ξ, ζ, φ). Show that

$$\lim_{\zeta_0 \to \infty} L = \frac{1}{3\varepsilon_0} \quad \text{(sphere)},$$

$$\lim_{\zeta_0 \to 0} L = \frac{1}{\varepsilon_0} \quad \text{(thin sheet)}.$$

5.7.8 The corresponding depolarizing factor (Exercise 5.7.7) for a prolate ellipsoid is

$$L = \frac{1}{\varepsilon_0}(\eta_0^2 - 1)\left(\frac{1}{2}\,\eta_0\,\ln\frac{\eta_0 + 1}{\eta_0 - 1} - 1\right).$$

Show that

$$\lim_{\eta_0\to\infty} L = \frac{1}{3\varepsilon_0} \qquad \text{(sphere)},$$

$$\lim_{\eta_0\to 1} L = 0 \qquad \text{(long needle)}.$$

5.7.9 A power series given by

$$f(x) = \sum_{n=0}^{\infty} a_n x^n$$

converges for $-R < x < R$. Show that the differentiated series and the integrated series have the same interval of convergence. (Do not bother about the end points $x = \pm R$.)

5.7.10 The photoionization cross section of hydrogen in the $1S$ state involves the function

$$f(x) = 2\pi x^{-1/2}\,\frac{e^{-4\xi\cot^{-1}\xi}}{1 - e^{-2\pi\xi}},$$

where

$$\xi = (x - 1)^{-1/2}$$

$$x = \frac{\text{photon energy}}{\text{threshold energy}}.$$

Expand $f(x)$ in (a) negative powers of $x^{1/2}$ (high photon energy), (b) positive powers of $(x-1) = \xi^{-2}$ (near threshold), giving the first three terms only.

Ans. (a) $f(x) = 1 - \pi x^{-1/2} + \left(\frac{7}{2} + \frac{\pi^2}{3}\right)x^{-1} + \cdots,$

(b) $f(x) = 2\pi e^{-4}x^{-1/2}\left[1 + \frac{4}{3}(x - 1) + \frac{4}{45}(x - 1)^2 + \cdots\right]$

or

$$f(x) = 2\pi e^{-4}\,x^{5/6}\left(1 - \frac{2}{15}(x - 1)^2 + \cdots\right).$$

5.8 Bernoulli Numbers

The Bernoulli numbers were introduced by Jacques (James, Jacob) Bernoulli. There are several equivalent definitions, but extreme care must be taken, for some authors introduce variations in numbering or in algebraic signs. One relatively simple approach is to define the Bernoulli numbers by the series

$$\frac{x}{e^x - 1} = \sum_{n=0}^{\infty} \frac{B_n x^n}{n!}. \tag{5.124}$$

By differentiating this power series repeatedly and then setting $x = 0$, we obtain

$$B_n = \left[\frac{d^n}{dx^n}\left(\frac{x}{e^x - 1}\right)\right]_{x=0}. \tag{5.125}$$

Specifically,

$$B_1 = \frac{d}{dx}\left(\frac{x}{e^x - 1}\right)\bigg|_{x=0} = \frac{1}{e^x - 1} - \frac{xe^x}{(e^x - 1)^2}\bigg|_{x=0}$$

$$= -\frac{1}{2}, \tag{5.126}$$

as may be seen by series expansion of the denominators.

Since these derivatives are awkward to evaluate, we may introduce instead a series expansion into the defining expression (Eq. 5.124), to obtain

$$\frac{1}{x}\left(x + \frac{x^2}{2!} + \frac{x^3}{3!} + \cdots\right)\left(B_0 + B_1 x + B_2 \frac{x^2}{2!} + \cdots\right) = 1. \qquad (5.127)$$

Using the power-series uniqueness theorem (Section 5.7) with the coefficient of x^0 equal to unity and the coefficient of $x^n (n \neq 0)$ equal to zero, we obtain

$$B_0 = 1$$

$$\frac{1}{2!} B_0 + B_1 = 0, \qquad\qquad B_1 = -\frac{1}{2} \qquad\qquad (5.128)$$

$$\frac{1}{3!} B_0 + \frac{1}{2!} B_1 + \frac{B_2}{2!} = 0, \qquad\qquad B_2 = \frac{1}{6}.$$

Continuing,

$$B_4 = -\frac{1}{30} \qquad B_{2n+1} = 0 \qquad n = 1, 2, 3 \cdots,$$

$$B_6 = \frac{1}{42} \qquad\qquad\qquad\qquad\qquad (5.129)$$

$$B_8 = -\frac{1}{30}$$

$$B_{10} = \frac{5}{66}$$

$$B_{12} = -\frac{691}{2730}, \text{ etc.}$$

An alternate (and equivalent) definition of B_{2n} is given by the expression

$$x \cot x = \sum_{n=0}^{\infty} (-1)^n B_{2n} \frac{(2x)^{2n}}{(2n)!}, \qquad -\pi < x < \pi. \qquad (5.130)$$

Using the method of residues (Section 7.3) or working from the infinite product representation of $\sin x$ (Section 5.9), we find that

$$B_{2n} = \frac{(-1)^{n-1} 2(2n)!}{(2\pi)^{2n}} \sum_{p=1}^{\infty} p^{-2n}, \qquad n = 1, 2, 3 \cdots. \qquad (5.131)$$

This representation of the Bernoulli numbers was discovered by Euler. It is readily seen from Eq. 5.131 that $|B_{2n}|$ increases without limit as $n \to \infty$. Numerical values have been calculated by Glaisher.[1] Illustrating the divergent behavior of the Bernoulli numbers, we have

$$B_{20} = 5.291 \times 10^2$$

$$\qquad\qquad\qquad\qquad\qquad (5.132)$$

$$B_{200} = 3.647 \times 10^{215}.$$

[1] *Trans. Cambridge Phil. Soc.* **XII**, 390 (1871–1879).

Some authors prefer to define the Bernoulli numbers with a modified version of Eq. 5.131 by using

$$B_n = \frac{2(2n)!}{(2\pi)^{2n}} \sum_{p=1}^{\infty} p^{-2n} \tag{5.133}$$

the subscript being just half of our subscript and all signs are positive. Again, when using other texts or references, the reader must check carefully to see exactly how the Bernoulli numbers are defined.

The Bernoulli numbers occur frequently in number theory. The von Standt-Clausen theorem states that

$$B_{2n} = A_n - \frac{1}{p_1} - \frac{1}{p_2} - \frac{1}{p_3} - \cdots - \frac{1}{p_k}, \tag{5.134}$$

in which A_n is an integer and $p_1, p_2, \cdots, p_k$ are prime numbers which exceed by 1 a divisor of $2n$. It may readily be verified that this holds for

$$B_6(A_3 = 1, \quad p = 2, \ 3, \ 7),$$
$$B_8(A_4 = 1, \quad p = 2, 3, 5), \tag{5.135}$$
$$B_{10}(A_5 = 1, \quad p = 2, 3, 11),$$

and other special cases.

The Bernoulli numbers appear in the summation of integral powers of the integers,

$$\sum_{j=1}^{N} j^p, \quad p \text{ integral},$$

and in numerous series expansion of the transcendental functions, including

$$\tan x,$$
$$\cot x,$$
$$\csc x,$$
$$\ln |\sin x|,$$
$$\ln |\cos x|,$$
$$\ln |\tan x|,$$
$$\tanh x,$$
$$\coth x,$$

and

$$\operatorname{csch} x.$$

In Section 10.3 we shall again encounter Bernoulli numbers in developing an asymptotic series expansion of the gamma function. The Bernoulli numbers are likely to come in such series expansions because of the defining equations (5.124) and (5.130) and because of their relation to the Riemann zeta function

$$\zeta(2n) = \sum_{p=1}^{\infty} p^{-2n}. \tag{5.136}$$

Riemann zeta function.   This series $\sum_{p=1}^{\infty} p^{-2n}$ was used as a comparison series for testing convergence (Section 5.2) and in Eq. 5.131 as one definition of the Bernoulli numbers, B_{2n}. It also serves to define the Riemann zeta function by

$$\zeta(s) \equiv \sum_{n=1}^{\infty} n^{-s}, \quad s > 1. \tag{5.137}$$

Figure 5.7 is a plot of $\zeta(s) - 1$. An integral expression for this Riemann zeta function appears in Section 10.2 as part of the development of the gamma function.

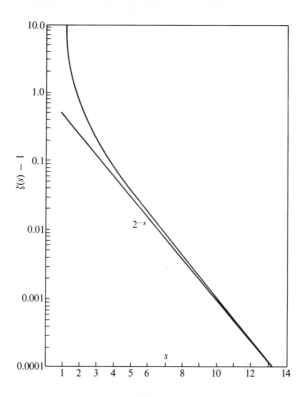

FIG. 5.7 Riemann zeta function, $\zeta(s) - 1$ versus s

Another interesting expression for the Riemann zeta function may be derived as follows:

$$\zeta(s)(1 - 2^{-s}) = 1 = \frac{1}{2^s} + \frac{1}{3^s} + \cdots$$
$$- \left(\frac{1}{2^s} + \frac{1}{4^s} + \frac{1}{6^s} + \cdots \right),$$

(5.138)

eliminating all the n^{-s} where n is a multiple of 2. Then

$$\zeta(s)(1 - 2^{-s})(1 - 3^{-s}) = 1 + \frac{1}{3^s} + \frac{1}{5^s} + \frac{1}{7^s} + \frac{1}{9^s} + \cdots$$
$$- \left(\frac{1}{3^s} + \frac{1}{9^s} + \frac{1}{15^s} + \cdots \right),$$

(5.139)

eliminating all the remaining terms in which n is a multiple of 3. Continuing, $\zeta(s)(1 - 2^{-s})(1 - 3^{-s})(1 - 5^{-s})\cdots(1 - P^{-s})$, where P is a prime number, and all terms n^{-s}, in which n is a multiple of any integer up through P, are cancelled out. As $P \to \infty$,

$$\zeta(s)(1 - 2^{-s})(1 - 3^{-s}) \cdots (1 - P^{-s}) = \zeta(s) \prod_{p(\text{prime})=2}^{\infty} (1 - P^{-s})$$

$$= 1. \qquad (5.140)$$

Therefore

$$\zeta(s) = \left[\prod_{p(\text{prime})=2}^{\infty} (1 - P^{-s}) \right]^{-1} \qquad (5.141)$$

giving $\zeta(s)$ as an infinite product.

A table of values of the Riemann zeta function is included in Section 10.2.

EXERCISES

5.8.1 Show that

(a) $\displaystyle\int_0^1 \frac{\ln(1 + x)}{x}\, dx = \frac{1}{2}\, \zeta(2)$ (b) $\displaystyle\lim_{a \to 1} \int_0^a \frac{\ln(1 - x)}{x}\, dx = \zeta(2)$.

From Exercise 5.8.7, $\zeta(2) = \pi^2/6$. Note that the integrand in part (b) diverges for $a = 1$ but that the *integrated* series is convergent.

5.8.2 For "small" values of x

$$\ln(x!) = -Cx + \sum_{n=2}^{\infty} (-1)^n \frac{\zeta(n)}{n}\, x^n,$$

where C is the Euler-Mascheroni constant and $\zeta(n)$ the Riemann zeta function. For what values of x does this series converge?   *Ans.* $-1 < x \leqslant 1$.

Note that if $x = 1$, we obtain

$$C = \sum_{n=2}^{\infty} (-1)^n \frac{\zeta(n)}{n},$$

a series for the Euler-Mascheroni constant.

5.8.3 Show that the series expansion of $\ln(x!)$ (Exercise 5.8.2) may be written as

(a) $\ln(x!) = \dfrac{1}{2} \ln\left(\dfrac{\pi x}{\sin \pi x}\right) - Cx - \displaystyle\sum_{n=1}^{\infty} \frac{\zeta(2n + 1)}{2n + 1}\, x^{2n+1}$

(b) $\ln(x!) = \dfrac{1}{2} \ln\left(\dfrac{\pi x}{\sin \pi x}\right) - \dfrac{1}{2} \ln\left(\dfrac{1 + x}{1 - x}\right) + (1 - C)x - \displaystyle\sum_{n=1}^{\infty} [\zeta(2n + 1) - 1] \frac{x^{2n+1}}{2n + 1}$.

Determine the range of convergence of each of these expressions.

5.8.4 The integral

$$\int_0^1 [\ln(1 - x)]^2\, \frac{dx}{x}$$

appears in the fourth-order correction to the magnetic moment of the electron. Show that it equals $2\, \zeta(3)$. *Hint.* Let $1 - x = e^{-t}$.

5.8.5   Planck's black-body radiation law involves the integral

$$\int_0^\infty \frac{x^3 \, dx}{e^x - 1}.$$

Show that this equals 6 $\zeta(4)$. From Exercise 5.8.7

$$\zeta(4) = \frac{\pi^4}{90}.$$

5.8.6   Show that Eq. 5.124 (with the B_1 term subtracted from both sides) and Eq. 5.130 are consistent.

5.8.7   From

$$B_{2n} = (-1)^{n-1} \frac{2(2n)!}{(2\pi)^{2n}} \zeta(2n).$$

Show that

(a) $\zeta(2) \quad = \dfrac{\pi^2}{6}$

(d) $\zeta(8) \quad = \dfrac{\pi^8}{9450}$

(b) $\zeta(4) \quad = \dfrac{\pi^4}{90}$

(e) $\zeta(10) = \dfrac{\pi^{10}}{93,555}$

(c) $\zeta(6) \quad = \dfrac{\pi^6}{945}$

5.8.8   Show that

$$\int_0^\infty \frac{(\ln z)^2}{1 + z^2} \, dz = 4 \left(1 - \frac{1}{3^3} + \frac{1}{5^3} - \frac{1}{7^3} + \cdots \right).$$

By contour integration (Chapter 7), this may be shown equal to $\pi^3/8$.

5.8.9   The Bloch-Gruneissen approximation for the resistance in a monovalent metal is

$$\rho = C \frac{T^5}{\Theta^6} \int_0^{\Theta/T} \frac{x^5 \, dx}{(e^x - 1)(1 - e^{-x})},$$

where Θ is the Debye temperature characteristic of the metal.

(a) For $T \to \infty$ show that

$$\rho \approx \frac{C}{4} \cdot \frac{T}{\Theta^2}.$$

(b) For $T \to 0$, show that

$$\rho \approx 5 \, \zeta(5) C \frac{T^5}{\Theta^6}.$$

5.9   Infinite Products

Consider a succession of positive factors $f_1 \cdot f_2 \cdot f_3 \cdot f_4 \cdots f_n$, $(f_i > 0)$. Using capital pi to indicate product, as capital sigma indicates a sum, we have

$$f_1 \cdot f_2 \cdot f_3 \cdots f_n = \prod_{i=1}^n f_i. \tag{5.142}$$

We define p_n, a partial product, in analogy with s_n the partial sum,

$$p_n = \prod_{i=1}^n f_i \tag{5.143}$$

and then investigate the limit

$$\lim_{n \to \infty} p_n = P. \tag{5.144}$$

If P is finite (but not zero), we say the infinite product is convergent. If P is infinite *or zero*, the infinite product is labeled divergent.

Since the product will diverge to infinity if

$$\lim_{n=\infty} f_n > 1 \qquad (5.145)$$

or to zero for

$$\lim_{n=\infty} f_n < 1, \qquad (\text{and} > 0), \qquad (5.146)$$

it is convenient to write our infinite product as

$$\prod_{n=1}^{\infty}(1 + a_n).$$

The condition $a_n \to 0$ is then a necessary (but not sufficient) condition for convergence.

The infinite product may be related to an infinite series by the obvious method of taking the logarithm

$$\ln \prod_{n=1}^{\infty}(1 + a_n) = \sum_{n=1}^{\infty} \ln(1 + a_n). \qquad (5.147)$$

A more useful relationship is stated by the following theorem.

Convergence of infinite product. If $0 \le a_n < 1$, the infinite products $\prod_{n=1}^{\infty}(1 + a_n)$ and $\prod_{n=1}^{\infty}(1 - a_n)$ converge if $\sum_{n=1}^{\infty} a_n$ converges and diverge if $\sum_{n=1}^{\infty} a_n$ diverges.

Considering the term $1 + a_n$, we see from Eq. 5.90

$$1 + a_n \le e^{a_n}. \qquad (5.148)$$

Therefore for the partial product p_n

$$p_n \le e^{s_n} \qquad (5.149)$$

and, letting $n \to \infty$,

$$\prod_{n=1}^{\infty}(1 + a_n) \le \exp \sum_{n=1}^{\infty} a_n, \qquad (5.150)$$

thus establishing an upper bound for the infinite product.

To develop a lower bound we note that

$$p_n = 1 + \sum_{i=1}^{n} a_i + \sum_{i=1}^{n}\sum_{j=1}^{n} a_i a_j + \cdots, \qquad > s_n, \qquad (5.151)$$

since $a_i \ge 0$. Hence

$$\prod_{n=1}^{\infty}(1 + a_n) \ge \sum_{n=1}^{\infty} a_n. \qquad (5.152)$$

If the infinite sum remains finite, the infinite product will also. If the infinite sum diverges, so will the infinite product.

The case of $\prod(1 - a_n)$ is complicated by the negative signs, but a proof that depends on the foregoing proof may be developed by noting that for $a_n < \frac{1}{2}$ (remember $a_n \to 0$ for convergence)

$$(1 - a_n) \le (1 + a_n)^{-1}$$

and

$$(1 - a_n) \ge (1 + 2a_n)^{-1}. \qquad (5.153)$$

The reader will recognize that an nth order polynomial $P_n(x)$ with n real roots may be written as a product of n factors.

$$P_n(x) = (x - x_1)(x - x_2)\cdots(x - x_n) = \prod_{i=1}^{n}(x - x_i). \qquad (5.154)$$

sin x, cos, and gamma function. In much the same way we may expect that a function with an infinite number of roots may be written as an infinite product, one factor for each root. This is indeed the case for the trigonometric functions. We have the two very useful infinite product representations,

$$\sin x = x \prod_{n=1}^{\infty}\left(1 - \frac{x^2}{n^2\pi^2}\right) \qquad (5.155a)$$

$$\cos x = \prod_{n=1}^{\infty}\left[1 - \frac{4x^2}{(2n-1)^2\pi^2}\right]. \qquad (5.155b)$$

The most convenient and perhaps most elegant derivation of these two expressions is by the use of complex variables. The derivation is given in Section 7.3. By our theorem of convergence, Eqs. 5.115a and 5.155b are convergent for all finite values of x. Specifically, for the infinite product for sin x, $a_n = x^2/n^2\pi^2$,

$$\sum_{n=1}^{\infty} a_n = \frac{x^2}{\pi^2} \sum_{n=1}^{\infty} n^{-2} = \frac{x^2}{\pi^2} \zeta(2)$$

$$= \frac{x^2}{6} \qquad (5.156)$$

by Exercise 5.8.7. The series corresponding to Eq. 5.155b behaves in a similar manner.

Equations 5.155a leads to two interesting results. First, if we set $x = \pi/2$, we obtain

$$1 = \frac{\pi}{2} \prod_{n=1}^{\infty}\left[1 - \frac{1}{(2n)^2}\right] = \frac{\pi}{2} \prod_{n=1}^{\infty}\left[\frac{(2n)^2 - 1}{(2n)^2}\right]. \qquad (5.157)$$

Solving for $\pi/2$,

$$\frac{\pi}{2} = \prod_{n=1}^{\infty}\left[\frac{(2n)^2}{(2n-1)(2n+1)}\right] \qquad (5.158)$$

$$= \frac{2\cdot2}{1\cdot3}\cdot\frac{4\cdot4}{3\cdot5}\cdot\frac{6\cdot6}{5\cdot7}\cdots,$$

which is Wallis' famous formula for $\pi/2$.

The second result involves the gamma or factorial function (Chapter 10). One definition of the gamma function is

$$\Gamma(x) = \left[xe^{Cx}\prod_{n=1}^{\infty}\left(1 + \frac{x}{r}\right)e^{-x/r}\right]^{-1}, \qquad (5.159)$$

where C is the usual Euler-Mascheroni constant (cf. Section 5.2). If we take the product of $\Gamma(x)$ and $\Gamma(-x)$, Eq. 5.159 leads to

$$\Gamma(x)\,\Gamma(-x) = -\left[xe^{Cx}\prod\left(1+\frac{x}{r}\right)e^{-x/r}xe^{-Cx}\prod\left(1-\frac{x}{r}\right)e^{x/r}\right]^{-1}$$

$$= -\left[x^2\prod_{r=1}^{\infty}\left(1-\frac{x^2}{r^2}\right)\right]^{-1}. \tag{5.160}$$

Using Eq. 5.155a with x replaced by πx, this becomes

$$\Gamma(x)\,\Gamma(-x) = -\frac{\pi}{x\,\sin\,\pi x}. \tag{5.161}$$

Anticipating a recurrence relation developed in Section 10.1, $-x\,\Gamma(-x) = \Gamma(1-x)$, Eq. 5.161 may be written

$$\Gamma(x)\,\Gamma(1-x) = \frac{\pi}{\sin\,\pi x}. \tag{5.162}$$

This will be useful in treating the gamma function (Chapter 10).

EXERCISES

5.9.1 Using

$$\ln\prod_{n=1}^{\infty}(1\pm a_n) = \sum_{n=1}^{\infty}\ln(1\pm a_n)$$

and the Maclaurin expansion of $\ln(1\pm a_n)$, show that the infinite product $\prod_{n=1}^{\infty}(1\pm a_n)$ converges or diverges with the infinite series $\sum_{n=1}^{\infty}a_n$.

5.9.2 Show that the infinite product representations of $\sin x$ and $\cos x$ are consistent with the identity $2\sin x\cos x = \sin 2x$.

5.9.3 Determine the limit to which

$$\prod_{n=2}^{\infty}\left(1+\frac{(-1)^n}{n}\right)$$

converges.

5.9.4 Show that

$$\prod_{n=2}^{\infty}\left[1-\frac{2}{n(n+1)}\right] = \frac{1}{3}.$$

5.9.5 Using the infinite product representations of $\sin x$, show that

$$x\cot x = 1 - 2\sum_{m,n=1}^{\infty}\left(\frac{x}{n\pi}\right)^{2m},$$

hence that the Bernoulli number

$$B_{2n} = (-1)^{n-1}\frac{2(2n)!}{(2\pi)^{2n}}\,\zeta(2n),$$

where $\zeta(2n)$ is the Riemann zeta function. *Hint.* Develop an infinite series representation of ln sin x and differentiate to get a series for cot x.

5.9.6 Given that

$$\int_{-\pi/2}^{\pi/2} \sin^n x \, dx = \frac{1 \cdot 3 \cdot 5 \cdots (n-1)}{2 \cdot 4 \cdot 6 \cdots n} \, \pi, \qquad (n \text{ even}),$$

what happens to the infinite product

$$\frac{1 \cdot 3 \cdot 5 \cdots (n-1)}{2 \cdot 4 \cdot 6 \cdots n}$$

as $n \to \infty$?

(a) Justify your answer in terms of infinite product or infinite series convergence theorems.

(b) Justify your answer in terms of the given definite integral.

5.9.7 The integral $\int_{-1}^{1} (1 - x^2)^{1/2} x^{2p} \, dx$ may be shown equal to the ratio

$$\frac{1 \cdot 3 \cdot 5 \cdots (2p-1)}{4 \cdot 6 \cdot 8 \cdots (2p+2)} \cdot \frac{\pi}{2}.$$

Express this as a product by using the Π notation and test what happens as $p \to \infty$. Explain your result by sketching the integrand in the interval [0, 1] with $p \to \infty$. *Note.* This integral is needed for the Schmidt construction of Chebyshev polynomials (Section 9.3).

5.9.8 Starting with the infinite product representation of sin x, show that

$$B_{2n} = (-1)^{n-1} \frac{2(2n)!}{(2\pi)^{2n}} \zeta(2n),$$

which is Eq. 5.131 of Section 5.8; B_{2n} is the Bernoulli polynomial and $\zeta(2n)$ is the Riemann zeta function. *Hint.* $d/dx \ln (\sin x) = \cot x$.

5.9.9 Verify the Euler identity

$$\prod_{p=1}^{\infty} (1 + z^p) = \prod_{q=1}^{\infty} (1 - z^{2q-1})^{-1}, \qquad |z| > 1.$$

5.10 Asymptotic or Semiconvergent Series

Incomplete gamma function.   The nature of an asymptotic series is perhaps best illustrated by a specific example. Suppose that we have the logarithmic integral function[1]

$$Ei(x) = \int_{-\infty}^{x} \frac{e^u}{u} \, du, \qquad (5.163)$$

or

$$-Ei(-x) = \int_{x}^{\infty} \frac{e^{-u}}{u} \, du = E_1(x), \qquad (5.164)$$

to be evaluated for large values of x. Better still, let us take a generalization of the incomplete factorial function (incomplete gamma function),[2]

$$I(x, p) = \int_{x}^{\infty} e^{-u} u^{-p} \, du, \qquad (5.165)$$

---

[1] This function occurs frequently in astrophysical problems involving gas with a Maxwell-Boltzmann energy distribution.

[2] See also Section 10.5.

in which x and p are positive. Again we seek to evaluate it for large values of x.
Integrating by parts, we obtain

$$I(x, p) = \frac{e^{-x}}{x^p} - p \int_x^\infty e^{-u} u^{-p-1} \, du$$

$$= \frac{e^{-x}}{x^p} - \frac{pe^{-x}}{x^{p+1}} + p(p+1) \int_x^\infty e^{-u} u^{-p-2} \, du. \tag{5.166}$$

Continuing to integrate by parts, we develop the series

$$I(x, p) = e^{-x}\left(\frac{1}{x^p} - \frac{p}{x^{p+1}} + \frac{p(p+1)}{x^{p+2}} - \cdots\right) + (-1)^n \frac{(p+n-1)!}{(p-1)!} \int_x^\infty e^{-u} u^{-p-n} \, du. \tag{5.167}$$

This is a remarkable series. Checking the convergence by the d'Alembert ratio test, we find

$$\lim_{n \to \infty} \frac{|u_{n+1}|}{|u_n|} = \lim_{n \to \infty} \frac{(p+n)!}{(p+n-1)!} \cdot \frac{1}{x}$$

$$= \lim_{n \to \infty} \frac{p+n}{x}$$

$$= \infty, \tag{5.168}$$

for all finite values of x. Therefore our series as an infinite series diverges everywhere! Before discarding Eq. 5.167 as worthless, let us see how well a given partial sum approximates the incomplete factorial function, $I(x, p)$.

$$I(x, p) - s_n(x, p) = (-1)^{n+1} \frac{(p+n)!}{(p-1)!} \int_x^\infty e^{-u} u^{-p-n-1} \, du. \tag{5.169}$$

In absolute value

$$|I(x, p) - s_n(x, p)| \leq \frac{(p+n)!}{(p-1)!} \int_x^\infty u^{-p-n-1} \, du$$

$$\leq \frac{(p+n-1)!}{(p-1)!} \cdot \frac{1}{x^{p+n}}. \tag{5.170}$$

This means that if we take x large enough, our partial sum s_n is an arbitrarily good approximation to the desired function, $I(x, p)$. Our divergent series (Eq. 5.167), is therefore perfectly good for computations. For this reason it is sometimes called a semiconvergent series.

Since the remainder $R_n(x, p)$ alternates in sign, the successive partial sums give alternately upper and lower bounds for $I(x, p)$. The behavior of the series (with $p = 1$) as a function of the number of terms included is shown in Fig. 5.8. We have

$$e^x E_1(x) = e^x \int_x^\infty \frac{e^{-u}}{u} \, du$$

$$= \frac{1}{x} - \frac{1!}{x^2} + \frac{2!}{x^3} - \frac{3!}{x^4} + \cdots, \tag{5.171}$$

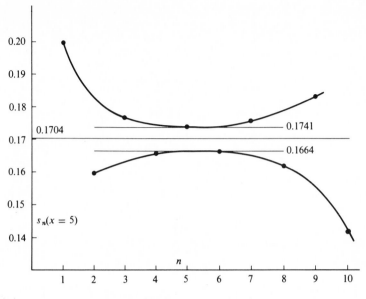

FIG. 5.8 Partial sums of $e^x E_1(x)|_{x=5}$

which is evaluated at $x = 5$. For a given value of x the successive upper and lower bounds given by the partial sums first converge and then diverge. The optimum determination of $e^x E_1(x)$ is then given by the closest approach of the upper and lower bounds, that is, between $s_4 = s_6 = 0.1664$ and $s_5 = 0.1741$ for $x = 5$. Therefore

$$0.1664 \leqslant e^x E_1(x)|_{x=5} \leqslant 0.1741. \tag{5.172}$$

Actually, from tables,

$$e^x E_1(x)|_{x=5} = 0.1704, \tag{5.173}$$

within the limits established by our asymptotic expansion. Inclusion of additional terms in the series expansion beyond the optimum point literally reduces the accuracy of the representation.

As x is increased, the spread between the lowest upper bound and the highest lower bound will diminish. By taking x large enough $e^x E_1(x)$ may be computed to any desired degree of accuracy.

This behavior is consistent with the defining properties of an asymptotic series. Following Poincaré, we take

$$x^n R_n(x) = x^n[f(x) - s_n(x)], \tag{5.174}$$

where

$$s_n(x) = a_0 + \frac{a_1}{x} + \frac{a_2}{x^2} + \cdots + \frac{a_n}{x^n}. \tag{5.175}$$

The asymptotic expansion of $f(x)$ has the properties that

$$\lim_{n \to \infty} x^n R_n(x) = 0, \qquad \text{for fixed } n, \tag{5.176}$$

and

$$\lim_{n \to \infty} x^n R_n(x) = \infty, \qquad \text{for fixed } x.\ [1] \qquad (5.177)$$

With conditions (5.176) and (5.177) satisfied, we write

$$f(x) \approx \sum_{n=0}^{\infty} a_n x^{-n}. \qquad (5.178)$$

Note the use of $\approx$ in place of $=$. The function $f(x)$ is equal to the series only in the limit as $x \to \infty$.

Asymptotic expansions of two functions may be multiplied together and the result will be an asymptotic expansion of the product of the two functions.

The asymptotic expansion of a given function $f(t)$ may be integrated term by term (just as in a uniformly convergent series of continuous functions) from $x \leqslant t < \infty$ and the result will be an asymptotic expansion of $\int_x^\infty f(t)\, dt$. In Chapter 11 a similar integration will be used to develop an asymptotic series for the modified Bessel function, $K_\nu(z)$. Term-by-term differentiation, however, is valid only under very special conditions.

A function may not possess an asymptotic expansion; e^x is an example of such a function. However, if a function has an asymptotic expansion, it has only one. The correspondence is not one-to-one; many functions may have the same asymptotic expansion.

Finally, one of the most useful and powerful methods of generating asymptotic expansions, the method of steepest descents, will be developed in Chapter 7. Applications include the derivation of Stirling's formula for the (complete) factorial function (Section 10.3) and the asymptotic forms of the various Bessel functions (Section 11.5).

EXERCISES

5.10.1 Stirling's formula for the logarithm of the factorial function is

$$\ln (x!) = \frac{1}{2} \ln 2\pi + \left(x + \frac{1}{2}\right) \ln x - x - \sum_{n=1}^{\infty} \frac{B_{2n}}{(2n)(2n-1)} x^{1-2n}.$$

The B_{2n} are the Bernoulli numbers (Section 5.8). Show that Stirling's formula is an *asymptotic* expansion.

5.10.2 Integrating by parts, develop asymptotic expansions of the Fresnel integrals.

(a) $C(x) = \displaystyle\int_0^x \cos \frac{\pi u^2}{2}\, du,$ (b) $S(x) = \displaystyle\int_0^x \sin \frac{\pi u^2}{2}\, du.$

These integrals appear in the analysis of a knife-edge diffraction pattern.

---

[1] This excludes convergent series of inverse powers of x. Some writers feel that this distinction, this exclusion, is artificial and unnecessary.

5.10.3 Derive the asymptotic expansion of the Gauss error function

$$Erf(x) = \int_0^x e^{-t^2}\, dt$$

$$= \frac{\sqrt{\pi}}{2} - \frac{e^{-x^2}}{2x}\left(1 - \frac{1}{2x^2} + \frac{1\cdot 3}{2^2 x^4} - \frac{1\cdot 3\cdot 5}{2^3 x^6} + \cdots\right).$$

This function plays an important role in probability theory. *Hint.*

$$Erf(x) = \int_0^\infty e^{-t^2}\, dt - \int_x^\infty e^{-t^2}\, dt.$$

5.10.4 The fraction of black-body radiation in the range $0 \leqslant \nu \leqslant \nu_0$ is given by

$$f(x_0) = \int_0^{x_0} \frac{x^3\, dx}{e^x - 1} \bigg/ \int_0^\infty \frac{x^3\, dx}{e^x - 1},$$

where $x_0 = h\nu_0/kT$. Show that

$$f(x_0) = 1 - \frac{e^{-x_0}}{6}(x_0^3 + 3x_0^2 + 6x_0 + 6).$$

Is this an asymptotic expansion?

REFERENCES

HARDY, G. H., *Divergent Series*. Oxford: Clarendon Press (1956). A standard, comprehensive work on methods of treating divergent series. Hardy includes an instructive account of the gradual development of the concepts of convergence and divergence.

HYSLOP, J. M., *Infinite Series*. 5th Ed. New York: Interscience Publishers (1959). An excellent presentation of infinite series and infinite products.

KNOPP, Konrad, *Theory and Application of Infinite Series*. London: Blackie and Son (reprinted 1946). This is a thorough, comprehensive, and authoritative work, which covers infinite series and products. Proofs of almost all of the statements not proved in Chapter 5 will be found in this book.

SMAIL, L. L., *Elements of the Theory of Infinite Processes*. New York: McGraw-Hill (1923). An older reference but still one of the best for independent study of infinite series and infinite products.

SOKOLNIKOFF, I. S., and R. M. REDHEFFER, *Mathematics of Physics and Modern Engineering*. New York: McGraw-Hill (1958). A long Chapter 2 (101 pages) presents infinite series in a thorough but very readable form. Extensions to the solutions of differential equations, to complex series, and to Fourier series are included.

The topic of infinite series is treated in most texts on advanced calculus. Among the better references is
WIDDER, David V., *Advanced Calculus*, 2nd Ed. Englewood Cliffs, New Jersey: Prentice-Hall (1961).

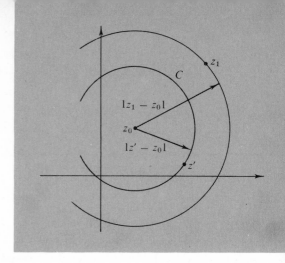

CHAPTER 6

FUNCTIONS OF

A COMPLEX VARIABLE I

ANALYTIC PROPERTIES

CONFORMAL MAPPING

> *The imaginary numbers are a wonderful flight of God's spirit;*
> *they are almost an amphibian between being and not being.*
> GOTTFRIED WILHELM VON LEIBNITZ, 1702

We turn now to a study of functions of a complex variable. In this area we develop some of the most powerful and widely useful tools in all of mathematical analysis. To indicate, at least partly, why complex variables are important, we mention briefly three areas of application.

1. For many pairs of functions u and v, both u and v satisfy Laplace's equation

$$\nabla^2\psi = \frac{\partial^2\psi(x, y)}{\partial x^2} + \frac{\partial^2\psi(x, y)}{\partial y^2} = 0.$$

Hence either u or v may be used to describe a two-dimensional electrostatic potential. The other function which gives a family of curves orthogonal to those of the first function, may then be used to describe the electric field **E**. A similar situation holds for the hydrodynamics of an ideal fluid in irrotational motion. The function u might describe the velocity potential, whereas the function v would then be the stream function.

In many cases in which the functions u and v are unknown mapping or transforming in the complex plane permits us to create a coordinate system tailored to the particular problem.

2. It will be seen in Chapter 8 that the differential equations of interest in physics may be solved by power series. The same power series may be used in the complex plane to replace x by the complex variable z. The dependence of the solution $f(z)$ at a given z_0 on the behavior of $f(z)$ elsewhere gives us greater insight into the behavior of our solution and a powerful tool (analytic continuation) for extending the region in which our solution is valid.

3. Integrals in the complex plane have a wide variety of useful applications.

a. Evaluating definite integrals.
b. Inverting power series.
c. Forming infinite products.
d. Obtaining solutions of differential equations for large values of the variable (asymptotic solutions).
e. Investigating the stability of potentially oscillatory systems.

6.1 Cauchy-Riemann Conditions

A complex number is nothing more than an ordered pair of two ordinary numbers, (a, b) or $a + ib$, in which i is $(-1)^{1/2}$. Similarly, a complex variable is an ordered pair of two real variables,

$$z = (x, y) = x + iy. \tag{6.1}$$

The reader will see that the ordering is significant, that in general $a + ib$ is not equal to $b + ia$ and $x + iy$ is not equal to $y + ix$.

It is frequently convenient to employ a graphical representation of the complex variable. By plotting x, the real part of z, as the abscissa and y, the imaginary part of z, as the ordinate, we have the complex plane or Argand plane shown in Fig. 6.1.

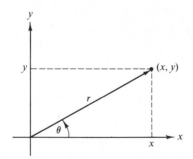

FIG. 6.1   Complex plane—Argand diagram

If we assign specific values to x and y, then z corresponds to a point (x, y) in the plane. In terms of the ordering mentioned before, it is obvious that the point (x, y) does not coincide with the point (y, x) except for the special case of $x = y$.

From Fig. 6.1,

$$x = r \cos \theta$$
$$y = r \sin \theta \tag{6.2}$$

and

$$z = r(\cos \theta + i \sin \theta) \tag{6.3}$$

Using a result that is suggested (but not rigorously proved)[1] by Section 5.6, we have the very useful polar representation

$$z = re^{i\theta}. \tag{6.4}$$

In this representation r is called the modulus or magnitude of z and the angle θ is labeled the argument or phase of z.

The reader will note the very close analogy to two-dimensional vectors, (Chapter 1), for a vector may also be defined by a point (x, y). This analogy is exploited in Section 6.2 to derive Cauchy's integral theorem.

From our complex variable z complex functions $f(z)$ or $w(z)$ may be constructed. These complex functions may then be resolved into real and imaginary parts

$$w(z) = u(x, y) + i\,v(x, y), \tag{6.5}$$

in which the separate functions $u(x, y)$ and $v(x, y)$ are pure real. For example if $f(z) = z^2$, we have

$$f(z) = (x + iy)^2$$
$$= (x^2 - y^2) + i\,2\,xy$$

In all these steps, complex number, variable, and function, the operation of replacing i by $-i$ is called "taking the complex conjugate." The complex conjugate of z is denoted by z^* where[2]

$$z^* = x - iy. \tag{6.6}$$

The complex variable z and its complex conjugate z^* are mirror images of each other

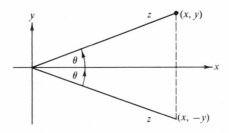

FIG. 6.2 Complex conjugate points

reflected in the x-axis, that is, inversion of the y-axis (cf. Fig. 6.2). The product zz^* leads to

$$zz^* = (x + iy)(x - iy) = x^2 + y^2$$
$$= r^2.$$

---

[1] Strictly speaking, Chapter 5 was limited to real variables. However, we can define e^z as $\sum_{n=0}^{\infty} z^n/n!$ for complex z. The development of power series expansions for complex functions is taken up in Section 6.4 (Laurent expansion).

[2] The complex conjugate is often denoted by $\bar{z}$. Here the bar will be reserved for averaged values, as in Section 15.6.

Hence

$$(zz^*)^{1/2} = |z|,$$

the magnitude of z.

Having established complex functions of a complex variable we now proceed to differentiate them. The derivative of $f(z)$, like that of a real function, is defined by

$$\lim_{\delta z \to 0} \frac{f(z + \delta z) - f(z)}{z + \delta z - z} = \lim_{\delta z \to 0} \frac{\delta f(z)}{\delta z}$$

$$= \frac{df}{dz} \quad \text{or} \quad f'(z), \tag{6.7}$$

provided that the limit is *independent* of the particular approach to the point z.

Consider increments δx and δy of the variables x and y, respectively. Then

$$\delta z = \delta x + i \, \delta y. \tag{6.8}$$

Also

$$\delta f = \delta u + i \, \delta v, \tag{6.9}$$

so that

$$\frac{\delta f}{\delta z} = \frac{\delta u + i \, \delta v}{\delta x + i \, \delta y}. \tag{6.10}$$

Let us take the limit indicated in Eq. 6.7 by two different approaches. First, with $\delta y = 0$, we let $\delta x \to 0$. Equation 6.7 yields

$$\lim_{\delta z \to 0} \frac{\delta f}{\delta z} = \lim_{\delta x = 0} \left(\frac{\delta u}{\delta x} + i \frac{\delta v}{\delta x} \right)$$

$$= \frac{\partial u}{\partial x} + i \frac{\partial v}{\partial x}, \tag{6.11}$$

assuming the partial derivatives exist. For a second approach, we set $\delta x = 0$ and then let $\delta y \to 0$. This leads to

$$\lim_{\delta z \to 0} \frac{\delta f}{\delta z} = \lim_{\delta y \to 0} \left(-i \frac{\delta u}{\delta y} + \frac{\delta v}{\delta y} \right)$$

$$= -i \frac{\partial u}{\partial y} + \frac{\partial v}{\partial y}. \tag{6.12}$$

If we are to have a derivative df/dz, Eqs. 6.11 and 6.12 must be identical. Equating real parts to real parts and imaginary parts to imaginary parts (like components of vectors), we obtain

$$\frac{\partial u}{\partial x} = \frac{\partial v}{\partial y}, \qquad \frac{\partial u}{\partial y} = -\frac{\partial v}{\partial x}. \tag{6.13}$$

These are the famous Cauchy-Riemann conditions. They were discovered by Cauchy and used extensively by Riemann in his theory of analytic functions. These Cauchy-Riemann conditions are necessary for the existence of a derivative of $f(z)$, that is, if df/dz exists, the Cauchy-Riemann conditions must hold.

Conversely, if the Cauchy-Riemann conditions are satisfied and the partial derivatives are continuous, the derivative exists. This may be shown by writing

$$\delta f = \left(\frac{\partial u}{\partial x} + i\,\frac{\partial v}{\partial x}\right)\delta x + \left(\frac{\partial u}{\partial y} + i\,\frac{\partial v}{\partial y}\right)\delta y \tag{6.14}$$

and then

$$\frac{\partial f}{\delta z} = \frac{\partial u/\partial x + i(\partial v/\partial x)}{1 + i(\delta y/\delta x)}\left[1 + i\,\frac{\partial y}{\delta x}\left(\frac{\partial v/\partial y - i(\partial u/\partial y)}{\partial u/\partial x + i(\partial v/\partial x)}\right)\right], \tag{6.15}$$

having divided numerator and denominator by the differential of x. Using the Cauchy-Riemann conditions (Eq. 6.13), we have

$$\frac{\partial v/\partial y - i(\partial u/\partial y)}{\partial u/\partial x + i(\partial v/\partial x)} = 1 \tag{6.16}$$

and

$$\frac{\delta f}{\delta z} = \frac{\partial u}{\partial x} + i\,\frac{\partial v}{\partial x}, \tag{6.17}$$

which shows that $\lim_{\delta z \to 0} \partial f/\partial z$ is independent of the direction of approach in the complex plane as long as the partial derivatives are continuous.

It is well worth noting that the Cauchy-Riemann conditions guarantee that the curves $u = c_1$ will be orthogonal to the curves $v = c_2$ (cf. Section 2.1). This is fundamental in application to potential problems in a variety of areas of physics. If $u = c_1$ is a line of electric force, then $v = c_2$ is an equipotential line (surface), and vice versa. A further implication for potential theory is developed in Exercise 6.1.3.

Analytic functions.   Finally, if $f(z)$ is differentiable at $z = z_0$ and in some small region around z_0, we say that $f(z)$ is *analytic* at $z = z_0$. Our theory of complex variables here is essentially one of analytic functions of complex variables, which points up the crucial importance of the Cauchy-Riemann conditions. The concept of analyticity carried on in advanced theories of modern physics plays a crucial role in dispersion theory (of elementary particles). If $f'(z)$ does not exist at $z = z_0$, then z_0 is labeled a singular point and consideration of it is postponed until Section 7.1.

To illustrate the Cauchy-Riemann conditions, consider two very simple examples.

EXAMPLE 6.1.1

Let $f(z) = z^2$. Then the real part $u(x, y) = x^2 - y^2$ and the imaginary part $v(x, y) = 2xy$. Following Eq. 6.13,

$$\frac{\partial u}{\partial x} = 2x = \frac{\partial v}{\partial y},$$

$$\frac{\partial u}{\partial y} = -2y = -\frac{\partial v}{\partial x}.$$

We see that $f(z) = z^2$ satisfies the Cauchy-Riemann conditions throughout the complex plane. Since the partial derivatives are clearly continuous, we conclude that $f(z) = z^2$ is analytic.

EXAMPLE 6.1.2

Let $f(z) = z^*$. Now $u = x$ and $v = -y$. Applying the Cauchy-Riemann conditions, we obtain

$$\frac{\partial u}{\partial x} = 1 \neq \frac{\partial v}{\partial y}.$$

The Cauchy-Riemann conditions are *not* satisfied and $f(z) = z^*$ is not an analytic function of z.

EXERCISES

6.1.1 Using $f(re^{i\theta}) = R(r, \theta)e^{i\Theta(r,\theta)}$, in which $R(r, \theta)$ and $\Theta(r, \theta)$ are differentiable real functions of r and θ, show that the Cauchy-Riemann conditions in polar coordinates become

(a) $\dfrac{\partial R}{\partial r} = \dfrac{R}{r} \dfrac{\partial \Theta}{\partial \theta}$,

(b) $\dfrac{\partial R}{r \, \partial \theta} = - R \dfrac{\partial \Theta}{\partial r}$.

6.1.2 Let $A = \partial^2 w / \partial x^2$, $B = \partial^2 w / \partial x \, \partial y$, $C = \partial^2 w / \partial y^2$. From the calculus of functions of *two* variables, $w(x, y)$, we have a saddle point if

$$B^2 - 4AC > 0.$$

With $f(z) = u(x, y) + iv(x, y)$, apply the Cauchy-Riemann conditions and show that neither $u(x, y)$ nor $v(x, y)$ has a maximum or a minimum in a finite region of the complex plane.

6.1.3 The functions $u(x, y)$ and $v(x, y)$ are the real and imaginary parts, respectively, of an analytic function $w(z)$.
(a) Assuming that the required derivatives exist, show that

$$\nabla^2 u = \nabla^2 v = 0.$$

(b) Show that

$$\frac{\partial u}{\partial x} \frac{\partial u}{\partial y} + \frac{\partial v}{\partial x} \frac{\partial v}{\partial y} = 0.$$

and give a geometric interpretation.

6.1.4 Having shown that the real part $u(x, y)$ and the imaginary part $v(x, y)$ of an analytic function $w(z)$ each satisfy Laplace's equation, show that $u(x, y)$ and $v(x, y)$ cannot have either a maximum or a minimum in the interior of any region in which $w(z)$ is analytic. (They can have saddle points.)

6.1.5 Find the analytic functions
$$w(z) = u(x, y) + i\,v(x, y)$$
if
(a) $u(x, y) = x^3 - 3xy^2$,
(b) $v(x, y) = e^{-y} \sin x$.

6.1.6 Resolve the following functions into real and imaginary parts $[u(x, y) + i\,v(x, y)]$:
(a) $z^2 + 2\bar{z} + 1$,
(b) $\dfrac{1}{z}$,
(c) $\dfrac{z-1}{z+1}$.

6.1.7 Show that complex numbers have square roots and that the square roots are contained in the complex plane. What are the square roots of i?

6.1.8 If there is some common region in which $w_1 = u(x, y) + iv(x, y)$ and $w_2 = w_1^* = u(x, y) - i\,v(x, y)$ are both analytic, prove that $u(x, y)$ and $v(x, y)$ are constants.

6.1.9 From the polar representation of complex quantities derive De Moivre's formula
$$(\cos\theta + i\sin\theta)^n = \cos n\theta + i\sin n\theta,$$
in which n is an integer.

6.1.10 Assume that the trigonometric functions and the hyperbolic functions are defined for complex argument by the appropriate power series
$$\sin z = \sum_{n=1,\text{odd}}^{\infty} (-1)^{(n-1)/2} \frac{z^n}{n!},$$
$$\cos z = \sum_{n=0,\text{even}}^{\infty} (-1)^{n/2} \frac{z^n}{n!},$$
$$\sinh z = \sum_{n=1,\text{odd}}^{\infty} \frac{z^n}{n!},$$
$$\cosh z = \sum_{n=0,\text{even}}^{\infty} \frac{z^n}{n!}.$$
(a) show that
$$i \sin z = \sinh iz, \qquad \sin iz = i \sinh z,$$
$$\cos z = \cosh iz, \qquad \cos iz = \cosh z.$$
(b) Verify that familiar functional relations, such as
$$\cosh z = \frac{e^z + e^{-z}}{2},$$
$$\sin(z_1 + z_2) = \sin z_1 \cos z_2 + \sin z_2 \cos z_1,$$
still hold in the complex plane.

6.1.11 Using the identities
$$\cos z = \frac{e^{iz} + e^{-iz}}{2},$$
$$\sin z = \frac{e^{iz} - e^{-iz}}{2i},$$
established from comparison of power series, show that
(a) $\sin(x + iy) = \sin x \cosh y + i \cos x \sinh y$,
    $\cos(x + iy) = \cos x \cosh y - i \sin x \sinh y$,
(b) $|\sin z|^2 = \sin^2 x + \sinh^2 y$,
    $|\cos z|^2 = \cos^2 x + \sinh^2 y$.
This demonstrates that we may have $\sin z$, $\cos z > 1$ in the complex plane.

6.1.12 Find all the zeros of
(a) $\sin z$,
(b) $\cos z$,
(c) $\sinh z$,
(d) $\cosh z$.

6.1.13 Show that

(a) $\sin^{-1}z = -i\ln(iz \pm \sqrt{1-z^2})$,

(d) $\sinh^{-1}z = \ln(z + \sqrt{z^2+1})$,

(b) $\cos^{-1}z = -i\ln(z \pm \sqrt{z^2-1})$,

(e) $\cosh^{-1} = \ln(z + \sqrt{z^2-1})$,

(c) $\tan^{-1}z = \dfrac{i}{2}\ln\left(\dfrac{i+z}{i-z}\right)$,

(f) $\tanh^{-1}z = \dfrac{1}{2}\ln\left(\dfrac{1+z}{1-z}\right)$.

Hint. 1. Express the trigonometric and hyperbolic functions in terms of exponentials. 2. Solve for the exponential and then for the exponent.

6.1.14 Prove that

(a) $\displaystyle\sum_{n=0}^{N-1} \cos nx = \frac{\sin N(x/2)}{\sin x/2}\cos(N-1)\frac{x}{2}$,

(b) $\displaystyle\sum_{n=0}^{N-1} \sin nx = \frac{\sin N(x/2)}{\sin x/2}\sin(N-1)\frac{x}{2}$.

These series occur in the analysis of the multiple-slit diffraction pattern.

6.1.15 For $-1 < p < 1$ prove that

(a) $\displaystyle\sum_{n=0}^{\infty} p^n \cos nx = \frac{1-p\cos x}{1-2p\cos x + p^2}$,

(b) $\displaystyle\sum_{n=0}^{\infty} p^n \sin nx = \frac{p\sin x}{1-2p\cos x + p^2}$.

These series occur in the theory of the Fabry-Perot interferometer.

6.1.16 The complex quantities $a = u + iv$ and $b = x + iy$ may also be represented as two-dimensional vectors, $\mathbf{a} = \mathbf{i}u + \mathbf{j}v$, $\mathbf{b} = \mathbf{i}x + \mathbf{j}y$. Show that

$$a^*b = \mathbf{a}\cdot\mathbf{b} + i|\mathbf{a}\times\mathbf{b}|.$$

6.1.17 Find the complete analytic function $w(z) = u(x,y) + i\,v(x,y)$ if $u(x,y) = \ln(x^2+y^2)^{1/2}$.

6.1.18 In the quantum theory of the photoionization we encounter the identity

$$\left(\frac{ia-1}{ia+1}\right)^{ib} = e^{-2b\cot^{-1}a},$$

in which a and b are real. Verify this identity.

6.1.19 Prove algebraically that the magnitude of $z_1 + z_2$ is no greater than the magnitude of z_1 plus the magnitude of z_2.

$$|z_1 + z_2| \leqslant |z_1| + |z_2|.$$

Interpret this result in terms of vectors.

6.1.20 A plane wave of light of angular frequency ω is represented by

$$e^{i\omega(t-nx/c)}$$

In a certain substance the simple real index of refraction n is replaced by the complex quantity $n - ik$. What is the effect of k on the wave? What does k correspond to physically?

6.2. Cauchy's Integral Theorem

This is the first of two basic theorems in the theory of the behavior of functions of a complex variable. First, a proof under relatively restrictive conditions— conditions that are intolerable to the mathematician developing a beautiful abstract theory but that are usually satisfied in physical problems.

If a function $f(z)$ is analytic (therefore single-valued) and its partial derivatives are continuous throughout some simply connected region R,[1] for every closed path

---

[1] A simply connected region or domain is one in which every closed contour in that region encloses only the points contained in it. If a region is not simply connected, it is called multiply connected. As an example of a multiply connected region, consider the z-plane with the interior of the unit circle *excluded*.

FIG. 6.3 A closed contour C within a simply connected region

C in R the line integral of $f(z)$ around C is zero or

$$\int_C f(z)\,dz = \oint_C f(z)\,dz = 0. \tag{6.18}$$

The symbol $\oint$ is used to emphasize that the path is closed. The reader will recall that in Section 1.13 such a function $f(z)$, identified as a force, was labeled conservative.

In this form the Cauchy integral theorem may be proved by direct application of Stokes's theorem (Section 1.12). With $f(z) = u(x, y) + i\,v(x, y)$,

$$\oint_C f(z)\,dx = \oint_C (u + iv)(dx + i\,dy)$$

$$= \oint_C (u\,dx - v\,dy) + i\oint(v\,dx + u\,dy). \tag{6.19}$$

These two line integrals may be converted to surface integrals by Stokes's theorem, a procedure that is justified if the partial derivatives are continuous within C. Using

$$\mathbf{V} = \mathbf{i}V_x + \mathbf{j}V_y,$$

we have

$$\oint_C (V_x\,dx + V_y\,dy) = \int\left(\frac{\partial V_y}{\partial x} - \frac{\partial V_x}{\partial y}\right)dx\,dy.$$

For the first integral in the last part of Eq. 6.19 let $V_x = u$, $V_y = -v$, and for the second integral let $V_x = v$, $V_y = u$. Then

$$\oint f(z)\,dz = -\int\left(\frac{\partial v}{\partial x} + \frac{\partial u}{\partial y}\right)dx\,dy + i\int\left(\frac{\partial u}{\partial x} - \frac{\partial v}{\partial y}\right)dx\,dy$$

$$= 0 \tag{6.20}$$

on application of the Cauchy-Riemann conditions which must hold, since $f(z)$ is assumed analytic.

This completes the proof of Cauchy's integral theorem. However, the proof is marred from a theoretical point of view by the need for continuity of the first partial derivatives. Actually, this requirement is not essential. By dividing the region interior to the curve C into infinitesimal rectangles and considering the line integrals around them (a sort of circulation of infinitesimal loop currents), Goursat showed that the theorem can be stated:

If a function $f(z)$ is analytic on and within a closed path C,

$$\oint_C f(z)\, dz = 0. \tag{6.21}$$

Details of the proof of this significantly more general and more powerful form can be found in Churchill and in the other references cited. Actually, we can still prove the theorem for $f(z)$ analytic within the interior of C and only continuous on C.

The consequence of the Cauchy integral theorem is that for analytic functions the line integral is a function only of its end points;

$$\int_{z_1}^{z_2} f(z)\, dz = F(z_2) - F(z_1) = -\int_{z_2}^{z_1} f(z)\, dz, \tag{6.22}$$

again exactly like the case of a conservative force.

The original statement of our theorem demanded a simply connected region. This restriction may easily be relaxed by the creation of a barrier, a cut line. Consider the multiply connected region of Fig. 6.4, in which $f(z)$ is not defined for the interior

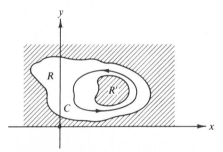

FIG. 6.4 A closed contour C in a multiply connected region

FIG. 6.5 Conversion of a multiply connected region into a simply connected region

R'. Cauchy's integral theorem is not valid for the contour C, as shown, but we can construct a contour C' for which the theorem holds. We cut from the interior forbidden region R' to the forbidden region exterior to R and then run a new contour C', as shown in Fig. 6.5.

The new contour C' through $ABDEFGA$ never crosses the cut line which literally converts R into a simply connected region. The three-dimensional analog of this technique was used in Section 1.14 to prove Gauss's law. By Eq. 6.22

$$\int_G^A f(z)\, dz = -\int_E^D f(z)\, dz, \tag{6.23}$$

$f(z)$ having been continuous across the cut line and line segments DE and GA arbitrarily close together. Then

$$\oint_{C'} f(z)\, dz = \int_{ABD} f(z)\, dz + \int_{EFG} f(z)\, dz$$

$$= 0 \tag{6.24}$$

by Cauchy's integral theorem, with region R now simply connected. Applying Eq. 6.22 once again with $ABD \rightarrow C_1'$ and $EFG \rightarrow -C_2'$, we obtain

$$\oint_{C_1'} f(z)\, dz = \int_{C_2'} f(z)\, dz, \tag{6.25}$$

in which C_1' and C_2' are both traversed in the same (counterclockwise) direction.

EXERCISES

6.2.1 Using the Cauchy-Riemann conditions (not just quoting the Cauchy integral theorem), show that

$$\oint_C (z+2)^{-1}\, dz = 0, \quad \text{for} \quad C \text{ the unit circle.}$$

6.2.2 Show that

$$\oint \frac{dz}{z^2 + z} = 0,$$

in which the contour C is a circle defined by $|z| = R > 1$. In Section 7.2 it is shown that the integral yields $2\pi i$ for $R < 1$.

6.2.3 Verify that

$$\int_{0,0}^{1,1} z^* \, dz$$

does depend on the path by evaluating the integral for the two paths shown in Fig 6.6. Recall that $f(z) = z^*$ is not an analytic function of z and that Cauchy's integral theorem therefore does not apply.

6.3 Cauchy's Integral Formula

As in the preceding section, we consider a function $f(z)$ that is analytic on a closed contour C and within the interior region bounded by C. We seek to prove that

$$\oint_C \frac{f(z)}{z - z_0}\, dz = 2\pi i\, f(z_0), \tag{6.26}$$

in which z_0 is some point in the interior region bounded by C. This is the second of the two basic theorems mentioned in Section 6.2.

Although $f(z)$ is assumed analytic, the integrand is $f(z)/(z - z_0)$ and this is *not* analytic at $z = z_0$. If the contour is deformed as shown in Fig. 6.7 (or Fig. 6.5, Section 6.2), Cauchy's integral theorem applies. By Eq. 6.25

$$\oint_C \frac{f(z)}{z - z_0}\, dz = \oint_{C_2} \frac{f(z)}{z - z_0}\, dz, \tag{6.27}$$

where C is the original outer contour and C_2 is the circle surrounding the point z_0

FIG. 6.6

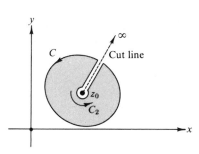

FIG. 6.7   Exclusion of a singular point

traversed in a *counterclockwise* direction. Let $z = z_0 + re^{i\theta}$, using the polar representation because of the circular shape of the path around z_0. Here r is small and will eventually be made to approach zero. We have

$$\oint_{C_2} \frac{f(z)}{z - z_0}\, dz = \oint \frac{f(z_0 + re^{i\theta})}{re^{i\theta}} rie^{i\theta}\, d\theta.$$

Taking the limit as $r \to 0$,

$$\oint_{C_2} \frac{f(z)}{z - z_0}\, dz = i f(z_0) \oint_{C_2} d\theta$$

$$= 2\pi i f(z_0), \qquad (6.28)$$

since $f(z)$ is analytic and therefore continuous at $z = z_0$. This proves the Cauchy integral formula.

Here is a remarkable result. The value of an analytic function $f(z)$ is given at an interior point $z = z_0$ once the values on the boundary C are specified. This is closely analogous to a two-dimensional form of Gauss's law (Section 1.14) in which the magnitude of an interior line charge would be given in terms of the cylindrical surface integral of the electric field **E**.

Cauchy's integral formula may be used to obtain an expression for the derivative of $f(z)$. From Eq. 6.26, with $f(z)$ analytic,

$$\frac{f(z_0 + \delta z) - f(z_0)}{\delta z} = \frac{1}{2\pi i\, \delta z}\left(\oint \frac{f(z)}{z - z_0 - \delta z}\, dz - \oint \frac{f(z)}{z - z_0}\, dz \right).$$

Then, by definition of derivative (Eq. 6.7),

$$f'(z_0) = \lim_{\delta z \to 0} \frac{1}{2\pi i\, \delta z} \oint \frac{\delta z\, f(z)}{(z - z_0 - \delta z)(z - z_0)}\, dz$$

$$= \frac{1}{2\pi i} \oint \frac{f(z)}{(z - z_0)^2}\, dz. \qquad (6.29)$$

The alert reader will see that this result could have been obtained by differentiating Eq. 6.26 under the integral sign with respect to z_0. This formal or turning-the-crank approach is valid, but the justification for it is contained in the analysis just presented.

This process of differentiation may be repeated to obtain

$$f^{(n)}(z_0) = \frac{n!}{2\pi i} \oint \frac{f(z)\, dz}{(z - z_0)^{n+1}} ; \tag{6.30}$$

that is, the requirement that $f(z)$ be analytic not only guarantees a first derivative but derivatives of *all* orders as well! The derivatives of $f(z)$ are automatically analytic. The reader should notice that this statement assumes the Goursat version of the Cauchy integral theorem. This is why Goursat's contribution is so significant in the development of the theory of complex variables.

Morera's theorem.   A further application of Cauchy's integral formula is in the proof of Morera's theorem, which is the converse of Cauchy's integral theorem. The theorem states the following:

If a function $f(z)$ is continuous in a simply connected region R and $\oint_C f(z)\, dz = 0$ for every closed contour C within R, then $f(z)$ is analytic throughout R.

Let us integrate $f(z)$ from z_1 to z_2. Since every closed path integral of $f(z)$ vanishes, the integral is independent of path and depends only on its end points. We label the result of the integration $F(z)$, with

$$F(z_2) - F(z_1) = \int_{z_1}^{z_2} f(z)\, dz. \tag{6.31}$$

As an identity,

$$\frac{F(z_2) - F(z_1)}{z_2 - z_1} - f(z_1) = \frac{\int_{z_1}^{z_2} [f(t) - f(z_1)]\, dt}{z_2 - z_1}, \tag{6.32}$$

using t as another complex variable. Now we take the limit as $z_2 \to z_1$.

$$\lim_{z_2 \to z_1} \frac{\int_{z_2}^{z_2} [f(t) - f(z_1)]\, dt}{z_2 - z_1} = 0, \tag{6.33}$$

since $f(t)$ is continous.[1] Therefore

$$\lim_{z_2 \to z_1} \frac{F(z_2) - F(z_1)}{z_2 - z_1} = F'(z)\Big|_{z=z_1} = f(z_1) \tag{6.34}$$

by definition of derivative (Eq. 6.7). We have proved that $F'(z)$ at $z = z_1$ exists and equals $f(z_1)$. Since z_1 is any point in R, we see that $F(z)$ is analytic. Then by Cauchy's integral formula (cf. Eq. 6.30) $F'(z) = f(z)$ is also analytic, proving Morera's theorem.

Drawing once more on our electrostatic analog, $f(z)$ might be used to represent the electrostatic field **E**. If the net charge within every closed region in R is zero (Gauss's law), the charge density is everywhere zero in R. Alternatively, in terms of the analysis of Section 1.13, $f(z)$ represents a conservative force (by definition

---

[1] We can quote the mean value theorem of calculus here.

of conservative), and then we find that it is always possible to express it as the derivative of a potential function $F(z)$.

Verification of Fourier inverse transform.   Let $f(z)$ and $g(z)$ be analytic functions of z in the region of interest. The two functions are related by

$$f_a(z) = \frac{1}{\sqrt{2\pi}} \int_{-a}^{a} e^{izw} g(w) \, dw. \tag{6.35}$$

In Chapter 15 $f(z)$ is labeled the Fourier transform[1] of $g(w)$.
We now proceed to show, using the Cauchy integral formula, that

$$g(t) = \frac{1}{\sqrt{2\pi}} \int_{-\infty}^{\infty} e^{-izt} f_a(z) \, dz. \tag{6.36}$$

First note that $g(w)$ is analytic. This permits a deformation of the contour off the real axis. Two possibilities are shown in Fig. 6.8. Next, we evaluate $g(t)$ by

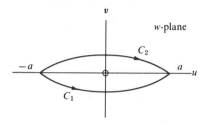

FIG. 6.8

substituting $f_a(z)$ from Eq. 6.35 into Eq. 6.36, obtaining

$$I = \frac{1}{2\pi} \int_{-\infty}^{\infty} e^{-izt} \, dz \int_{a}^{-a} e^{izw} g(w) \, dw.$$

The z integration is split into two parts and the order of integration is interchanged so that

$$I = \frac{1}{2\pi} \int_{-a}^{a} {}_{C_1} g(w) \, dw \int_{-\infty}^{\infty} e^{iz(w-t)} \, dz + \frac{1}{2\pi} \int_{-a}^{a} {}_{C_2} g(w) \, dw \int_{0}^{\infty} e^{iz(w-t)} \, dz. \tag{6.37}$$

In the first term on the right the w integration is carried over the contour C_1, whereas C_2 is chosen for the w integration in the second term. Integrating with respect to z first (because we can do it) by inspection, we obtain

$$I = \frac{1}{2\pi i} \int_{C_1} g(w) \, dw \left. \frac{e^{iz(w-t)}}{w-t} \right|_{-\infty}^{0} + \frac{1}{2\pi i} \int_{C_2} g(w) \, dw \left. \frac{e^{iz(w-t)}}{w-t} \right|_{0}^{\infty}. \tag{6.38}$$

The exponential may be written as $e^{-zv} e^{iz(u-t)}$, in which w is replaced by $u + iv$. Now, because of the choice of contour in the w-plane, we have $I.P.(w) = v$, negative for C_1, positive for C_2. Our choice of contour guarantees that $e^{iz(w-t)}$ vanishes as

[1] We shall take $\lim a \to \infty$.

$e^{-\infty}$ for $z \to \pm\infty$. Equation 6.38 becomes

$$I = \frac{1}{2\pi i}\left[\int_{C_1} \frac{g(w)}{w - t}\, dw - \int_{C_2} \frac{g(w)}{w - t}\, dw\right]$$

$$= \frac{1}{2\pi i}\oint \frac{g(w)}{w - t}\, dw.$$

For $-a < t < a$, t is within the closed contour, and by Cauchy's integral formula

$$I = \frac{1}{\sqrt{2\pi}}\int_{-\infty}^{\infty} e^{-izt} f_a(z)\, dz = g(w). \tag{6.39}$$

This result (Equation 6.39) (with $a \to \infty$) is the Fourier inverse transform.

EXERCISES

6.3.1 Show that

$$\oint_C (z - z_0)^n\, dz = \begin{cases} 2\pi i, & n = -1, \\ 0, & n \neq -1, \end{cases}$$

where the contour C encircles the point $z = z_0$ in a positive (counterclockwise) sense. The exponent n is an integer.

6.3.2 Show that

$$|f^n(z_0)| \leq \frac{Mn!}{R^n},$$

where R is the radius of a circle centered at $z = z_0$ and M is the maximum value of $|f(z)|$ on that circle. Assume that $f(z)$ is analytic on and within the circle.

6.3.3 If $f(z)$ is analytic and bounded [$f(z) \leq M$, a constant] for all z, show that $f(z)$ must be a constant. This is Liouville's theorem.

6.3.4 Solve Exercise 6.2.2 by separating the integrand into partial fractions and then applying Cauchy's integral theorem for multiply connected regions.

6.3.5 Evaluate

$$\oint \frac{\sin z}{z}\, dz,$$

where C is any contour enclosing the origin in a positive sense.

6.3.6 Assuming that $f(z)$ is analytic on and within a closed contour C and that the point z_0 is within C, show that

$$\oint_C \frac{f'(z)}{(z - z_0)}\, dz = \oint_C \frac{f(z)}{(z - z_0)^2}\, dz.$$

6.3.7 (a) A function $f(z)$ is analytic within a closed contour C (and continuous on C). If $f(z) \neq 0$ within C and $|f(z)| \geq M$ on C, show that

$$|f(z)| > M$$

for all points within C. *Hint.* Consider $w(z) = 1/f(z)$.

(b) If $f(z) = 0$ within the contour C, show that the foregoing result does not hold, that it is possible to have $|f(z)| = 0$ at one or more points in the interior with $|f(z)| > 0$ over the entire bounding contour. Cite a specific example of an analytic function that behaves this way.

6.3.8 Show that

$$\frac{1}{2\pi i} \oint z^{m-n-1} \, dz, \qquad m \text{ and } n \text{ integers}$$

(with the contour encircling the origin once counterclockwise), is a representation of the Kronecker delta $\delta_{m,n}$.

6.4 Laurent Expansion

Taylor expansion. The Cauchy integral formula of the preceding section opens up the way for another derivation of Taylor's series (Section 5.6) but this time for functions of a complex variable. Suppose we are trying to expand $f(z)$ about $z = z_0$ and we have $z = z_1$ as the nearest point on the Argand diagram for

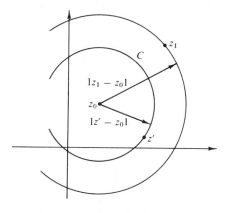

FIG. 6.9

which $f(z)$ is not analytic. We construct a circle C centered at $z = z_0$ with radius $|z' - z_0| < |z_1 - z_0|$. Since z_1 was assumed to be the nearest point at which $f(z)$ was not analytic, $f(z)$ is necessarily analytic on and within C.

From Equation 6.26, the Cauchy integral formula,

$$(z) = \frac{1}{2\pi i} \oint_C \frac{f(z') \, dz'}{z' - z}$$

$$= \frac{1}{2\pi i} \oint_C \frac{f(z') \, dz'}{(z' - z_0) - (z - z_0)}$$

$$= \frac{1}{2\pi i} \oint_C \frac{f(z') \, dz'}{(z' - z_0)[1 - (z - z_0)/(z' - z_0)]} \qquad (6.40)$$

Here z' is a point on the contour C and z is any point interior to C. It is not quite rigorously legal to expand the denominator of the integrand in Eq. 6.40 by the binomial theorem, for we have not yet proved the binomial theorem for complex variables. Instead, we note the identity

$$\frac{1}{1-t} = 1 + t + t^2 + t^3 + \cdots = \sum_{n=0}^{\infty} t^n, \qquad (6.41)$$

which may easily be verified by multiplying both sides by $1 - t$. The infinite series, following the methods of Section 5.2, is convergent for $|t| < 1$.

Now for point z interior to C, $|z - z_0| < |z' - z_0|$, and, using Eq. 6.41, Eq. 6.40 becomes

$$f(z) = \frac{1}{2\pi i} \oint_C \sum_{n=0}^{\infty} \frac{(z - z_0)^n f(z')\, dz'}{(z' - z_0)^{n+1}} \qquad (6.42)$$

Interchanging the order of integration and summation (valid since Eq. 6.41 is uniformly convergent for $|t| < 1$), we obtain

$$f(z) = \frac{1}{2\pi i} \sum_{n=0}^{\infty} (z - z_0)^n \oint_C \frac{f(z')\, dz'}{(z' - z_0)^{n+1}} . \qquad (6.43)$$

Referring to Eq. 6.35, we get

$$f(z) = \sum_{n=0}^{\infty} (z - z_0)^n \frac{f^{(n)}(z_0)}{n!}, \qquad (6.44)$$

which is our desired Taylor expansion. Note that it is based only on the assumption that $f(z)$ is analytic for $|z - z_0| < |z_1 - z_0|$. Just as for real variable power series (Section 5.7), this expansion is unique for a given z_0.

Analytic continuation.   In the foregoing discussion we assumed that $f(z)$ has an isolated nonanalytic or singular point at $z = z_1$ (Fig. 6.9). For a specific example of this behavior consider

$$f(z) = \frac{1}{1 + z}, \qquad (6.45)$$

which becomes infinite at $z = -1$. Therefore $f(z)$ is nonanalytic at $z_1 = -1$ or $z_1 = -1$ is our singular point. By Eq. 6.44 or the binomial theorem for complex functions that follows directly from it,

$$\frac{1}{1+z} = 1 - z + z^2 - z^3 + \cdots = \sum_{n=0}^{\infty} (-1)^n z^n \qquad (6.46)$$

convergent for $|z| < 1$. If we label this circle of convergence C_1, Eq. 6.46 holds for $f(z)$ in the interior of C, which we label region S_1.

The situation is that $f(z)$ expanded about the origin holds only in S_1 (and on C_1 excluding $z_1 = -1$), but we know from the form of $f(z)$ that it is well defined and analytic elsewhere in the complex plane outside S_1. Analytic continuation is a process of extending the region in which a function such as the series in Eq. 6.46 is defined. For instance, suppose we expand $f(z)$ about the point $z = i$. We have

$$f(z) = \frac{1}{1 + z} = \frac{1}{1 + i + (z - i)}$$

$$= \frac{1}{1 + i}\left(1 + \frac{z - i}{1 + i}\right)^{-1} \qquad (6.47)$$

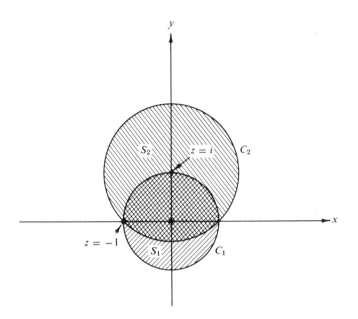

FIG. 6.10 Analytic continuation

By Eq. 6.44 again

$$f(z) = \frac{1}{1+i}\left[1 - \frac{z-i}{1+i} + \left(\frac{z-i}{1+i}\right)^2 - \cdots\right], \tag{6.48}$$

convergent for $|z - i| < |1 + i| = |\sqrt{2}$. Our circle of convergence is C_2 and the region bounded by C_2 is labeled S_2. Now $f(z)$ is defined by the expansion (Eq. 6.48) for S_2, which overlaps S_1 and extends out further in the complex plane.[1] This extension is an analytic continuation, and when we have only isolated singular points to contend with the function can be extended indefinitely. As an example, we shall use a recurrence relation in Chapter 10 to extend the factorial function around the isolated singular points, $z = -n$, $n = 1, 2, 3 \ldots$.

All of our elementary functions, e^z, $\sin z$, etc., can be extended into the complex plane (cf. Exercise 6.1.10). For instance, they can be *defined* by power-series expansions such as

$$e^z = 1 + \frac{z}{1!} + \frac{z^2}{2!} + \cdots = \sum_{n=0}^{\infty} \frac{z^n}{n!} \tag{6.49}$$

---

[1] One of the most powerful and beautiful results of the more abstract theory of functions of a complex variable is that if two analytic functions coincide in any region, such as the overlap of S_1 and S_2, or coincide on any line segment they are the same function in the sense that they will coincide everywhere as long as they are both well defined. In this case the agreement of the expansions (Eqs. 6.46 and 6.48) over the region common to S_1 and S_2 would establish the identity of the functions these expansions represent. Then Eq. 6.48 would represent an analytic continuation or extension of $f(z)$ into regions not covered by Eq. 6.46. We could equally well say that $f(z) = 1/(1 + z)$ is itself an analytic continuation of either of the series given by Eqs. 6.46 and 6.48.

for the exponential. Such definitions agree with the real variable definitions along the real x-axis and literally constitute an analytic continuation of the corresponding real functions into the complex plane.

Laurent series.   We frequently encounter functions that are analytic in an annular region, say of inner radius r and outer radius R, as shown in Fig. 6.11.

FIG. 6.11   Laurent expansion, $f(z)$ analytic for $r < |z - z_0| < R$

Drawing an imaginary cut line to convert our region into a simply connected region, we apply Cauchy's integral formula, and for two circles, C_2 and C_1, centered at $z = z_0$ and with radii r_2 and r_1 respectively, where $r < r_2 < r_1 < R$, we have[1]

$$f(z) = \frac{1}{2\pi i} \oint_{C_1} \frac{f(z')\, dz'}{z' - z} - \frac{1}{2\pi i} \oint_{C_2} \frac{f(z')\, dz'}{z' - z}. \tag{6.50}$$

Note carefully that in Eq. 6.50 an explicit minus sign has been introduced so that contour C_2 (like C_1) is to be traversed in the *positive* (counterclockwise) sense. The treatment of Eq. 6.50 now proceeds exactly like that of Eq. 6.40 in the development of the Taylor series. Each denominator is written as $(z' - z_0) - (z - z_0)$ and expanded by the binomial theorem which now follows from the Taylor series (Eq. 6.44).

We find

$$f(z) = \frac{1}{2\pi i} \sum_{n=0}^{\infty} (z - z_0)^n \oint_{C_1} \frac{f(z')\, dz'}{(z' - z_0)^{n+1}}$$

$$+ \frac{1}{2\pi i} \sum_{n=1}^{\infty} (z - z_0)^{-n} \oint (z' - z_0)^{n-1} f(z')\, dz'. \tag{6.51}$$

The minus sign of Eq. 6.50 has been absorbed by the binomial expansion. Labeling the first series S_1 and the second S_2,

$$S_1 = \frac{1}{2\pi i} \sum_{n=0}^{\infty} (z - z_0)^n \oint_{C_1} \frac{f(z')\, dz'}{(z' - z_0)^{n+1}}, \tag{6.52}$$

[1] We may take r_2 arbitrarily close to r and r_1 arbitrarily close to R, maximizing the area enclosed between C_1 and C_2.

which is the regular Taylor expansion, convergent for $|z - z_0| < |z' - z_0| = r_1$, that is, for all z *interior* to the larger circle, C_1. For the second series in Eq. 6.51 we have

$$S_2 = \frac{1}{2\pi i} \sum_{n=0}^{\infty} (z - z_0)^{-n} \oint_{C_2} (z' - z_0)^{n-1} f(z') \, dz' \qquad (6.53)$$

convergent for $|z - z_0| > |z' - z_0| = r_2$, that is, for all z *exterior* to the smaller circle C_2.

These two series may be combined into one series (a Laurent series) by

$$f(z) = \sum_{n=-\infty}^{\infty} a_n (z - z_0)^n, \qquad (6.54)$$

where

$$a_n = \frac{1}{2\pi i} \oint_C \frac{f(z') \, dz'}{(z' - z_0)^{n+1}}. \qquad (6.55)$$

Here C is any contour within the annular region $r < |z - z_0| < R$ encircling z_0 once in a counterclockwise sense. If we assume that such an annular region of convergence does exist, Eq. 6.54 is the Laurent series or Laurent expansion of $f(z)$.

Numerous examples of Laurent series appear in Chapter 7. We limit ourselves here to one simple example to illustrate the application of Eq. 6.54.

EXAMPLE 6.4.1

Let $f(z) = [z(z - 1)]^{-1}$. If we choose $z_0 = 0$, then $r = 0$ and $R = 1$, $f(z)$ diverging at $z = 1$. From Eqs. 6.55 and 6.41

$$a_n = \frac{1}{2\pi_i} \oint \frac{dz'}{(z')^{n+2}(z' - 1)}$$

$$= \frac{-1}{2\pi i} \oint \sum_{m=0}^{\infty} (z')^m \frac{dz'}{(z')^{n+2}}. \qquad (6.56)$$

Again interchanging the order of summation and integration (uniformly convergent series),

$$a_n = -\frac{1}{2\pi i} \sum_{m=0}^{\infty} \oint \frac{dz'}{(z')^{n+2-m}}. \qquad (6.57)$$

If we employ the polar form, as in Eq. 6.30 (or cf. Exercise 6.3.1),

$$a_n = -\frac{1}{2\pi i} \sum_{m=0}^{\infty} \oint \frac{r i e^{i\theta} \, d\theta}{r^{n+2-m} e^{i(n+2-m)\theta}}$$

$$= -\frac{1}{2\pi i} \cdot 2\pi i \sum_{m=0}^{\infty} \delta_{n+2-m, 1}. \qquad (6.58)$$

In other words,

$$a_n = \begin{cases} -1 & \text{for } n \geqslant -1, \\ 0 & \text{for } n < -1. \end{cases} \qquad (6.59)$$

The Laurent expansion (Eq. 6.54) becomes

$$\frac{1}{z(z-1)} = -\frac{1}{z} - 1 - z - z^2 - z^3 - \cdots$$

$$= -\sum_{n=-1}^{\infty} z^n. \tag{6.60}$$

For this simple function the Laurent series can, of course, be obtained by a direct binomial expansion.

The Laurent series differs from the Taylor series by the obvious feature of negative powers of $(z - z_0)$. For this reason the Laurent series will always diverge at least at $z = z_0$ and perhaps as far out as some distance r (Fig. 6.11).

EXERCISES

6.4.1 (a) Develop a Laurent expansion of $f(z) = [z(z-1)]^{-1}$ about the point $z = 1$ valid for small values of $|z - 1|$. Specify the exact range over which your expansion holds. This is an analytic continuation of Eq. 6.60.
(b) Determine the Laurent expansion of $f(z)$ about $z = 1$ but for $|z - 1|$ large.

6.4.2 A function $f(z)$ is analytic on and within the unit circle. Also $|f(z)| \leqslant 1$ for $|z| \leqslant 1$ and
$f(0) = 0$. Show that $|f(z)| \leqslant |z|$ for $|z| \leqslant 1$.

6.4.3 Develop the Taylor expansion of $\ln(1 + z)$. $Ans.\ \sum\limits_{n=1}^{\infty} (-1)^{n-1} \dfrac{z^n}{n}.$

6.4.4 Prove that the Laurent expansion of a given function about a given point is unique; that is, if

$$f(z) = \sum_{n=-N}^{\infty} a_n(z - z_0)^n = \sum_{n=-N}^{\infty} b_n(z - z_0)^n,$$

show that $a_n = b_n$ for all n.   *Hint.* Use the Cauchy integral formula.

6.4.5 Expand the following functions in a Laurent series about the origin. Give the first three nonvanishing coefficients.
(a) cot z,
(b) $(e^z - 1)^{-1}$.

6.4.6 Derive the binomial expansion

$$(1 + z)^m = 1 + mz + \frac{m(m-1)}{1\cdot 2} z^2 + \cdots$$

for m any real number.

6.4.7 A function $f(z)$ can be expanded in a Laurent series about the origin with the coefficients a_n real. Show that the complex conjugate of this function of z is the same function of the complex conjugate of z; that is,

$$f^*(z) = f(z^*).$$

Verify this explicitly for
(a) $f(z) = z^n$, $\quad n$ an integer,
(b) $f(z) = \sin z$.
If $f(z) = iz$, $(a_1 = i)$, show that the foregoing statement does *not* hold.

6.4.8 If $f(z)$ is a real function of the complex variable z and the Laurent expansion about the origin, $f(z) = \sum a_n z^n$, has $a_n = 0$ for $n < -N$, show that all of the coefficients, a_n, are real.

6.5 Mapping

In the preceding sections we have defined analytic functions and developed some of their main features. From these developments the integral relations of Chapter 7 follow directly. Here we introduce some of the more geometric aspects of functions of complex variables, aspects that will be useful in visualizing the integral operations in Chapter 7 and that are valuable in their own right in solving Laplace's equation in two-dimensional systems.

In ordinary analytic geometry we may take $y = f(x)$ and then plot y versus x. Our problem here is more complicated, for z is a function of two variables x and y. We shall use the notation

$$w = f(z) = u(x, y) + i\, v(x, y). \tag{6.61}$$

Then for a point in the z-plane (specific values for x *and* y) there may correspond specific values for $u(x, y)$ and $v(x, y)$ which then yield a point in the w-plane. As points in the z-plane transform or are mapped into points in the w-plane, so lines or areas in the z-plane will be mapped into lines or areas in the w-plane. Our immediate purpose is to see how lines and areas map from the z-plane to the w-plane for a number of simple functions.

Translation.

$$w = z + z_0 \tag{6.62}$$

The function w is equal to the variable z plus a constant, $z_0 = x_0 + iy_0$. By Eqs. 6.1 and 6.61

$$u = x + x_0,$$
$$v = y + y_0, \tag{6.63}$$

representing a pure translation of the coordinate axes as shown in Fig. 6.12.

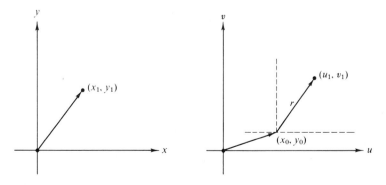

FIG. 6.12 Translation

Rotation.

$$w = zz_0. \tag{6.64}$$

Here it is convenient to return to the polar representation, using

$$w = \rho e^{i\varphi}, \qquad z = re^{i\theta}, \quad \text{and} \quad z_0 = r_0 e^{i\theta_0}, \tag{6.65}$$

then

$$\rho e^{i\varphi} = rr_0 e^{i(\theta + \theta_0)} \tag{6.66}$$

or

$$\rho = rr_0, \\ \varphi = \theta + \theta_0. \tag{6.67}$$

Two things have occurred. First, the modulus r has been modified, either expanded or contracted, by the factor r_0. Second, the argument θ has been increased by the additive constant θ_0. This represents a *rotation* of the complex variable through an angle θ_0. For the special case of $z_0 = i$, we have a pure rotation through $\pi/2$ radians.

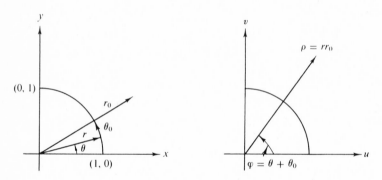

FIG. 6.13   Rotation

Inversion.

$$w = \frac{1}{z}. \tag{6.68}$$

Again, using the polar form,

$$\rho e^{i\varphi} = \frac{1}{re^{i\theta}} = \frac{1}{r} e^{-i\theta} \tag{6.69}$$

shows that

$$\rho = \frac{1}{r}, \qquad \varphi = -\theta. \tag{6.70}$$

The first part of Eq. 6.70 shows the inversion clearly. The interior of the unit circle is mapped onto the exterior and vice versa. In addition, the second part of Eq. 6.70 shows that the polar angle is reversed in sign. Equation 6.68 therefore also involves a reflection of the y-axis exactly like the complex conjugate equation.

To see how lines in the z-plane transform into the w-plane it is convenient to return to the cartesian form:

$$u + iv = \frac{1}{x + iy}. \tag{6.71}$$

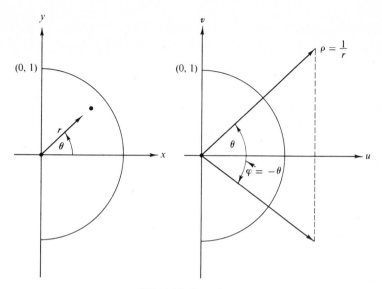

FIG. 6.14 Inversion

Rationalizing the right-hand side by multiplying numerator and denominator by z^* and then equating the real parts and the imaginary parts, we have

$$u = \frac{x}{x^2 + y^2}, \qquad x = \frac{u}{u^2 + v^2}$$

$$v = -\frac{y}{x^2 + y^2}, \qquad y = -\frac{v}{u^2 + v^2}.$$

(6.72)

A circle centered at the origin in the z-plane has the form

$$x^2 + y^2 = r^2$$

(6.73)

and by Eq. 6.72 transforms into

$$\frac{u^2}{(u^2 + v^2)^2} + \frac{v^2}{(u^2 + v^2)^2} = r^2.$$

(6.74)

Simplifying Eq. 6.74, we obtain

$$u^2 + v^2 = \frac{1}{r^2} = \rho^2,$$

(6.75)

which describes a circle in the w-plane also centered at the origin.

The horizontal line $y = c_1$ transforms into

$$\frac{-v}{u^2 + v^2} = c_1$$

(6.76)

or

$$u^2 + v^2 + \frac{v}{c_1} + \frac{1}{(2c_1)^2} = \frac{1}{(2c_1)^2},$$

(6.77)

which describes a circle in the z-plane of radius $1/2c_1$ and centered at $u = 0$, $v = -1/2c_1$ (Fig. 6.15).

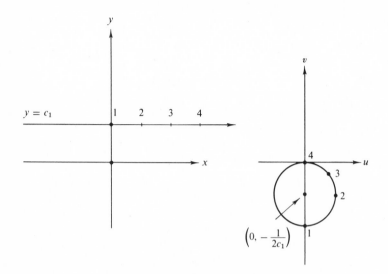

FIG. 6.15   Inversion, line $\leftrightarrow$ circle

The reader may pick up the other three possibilities, $x = \pm c_1$, $y = -c_1$, by rotating the xy-axes. In general, any straight line or circle in the z-plane will transform into a straight line or a circle in the w-plane (cf. Exercise 6.5.2).

The three transformations just discussed have all involved one-to-one correspondence of points in the z-plane to points in the w-plane. Now to illustrate the variety of transformations possible and the problems that can arise we introduce first a two-to-one correspondence and then a many-to-one correspondence. Finally, we take up the inverses of these two transformations.

Consider first the transformation

$$w = z^2, \tag{6.78}$$

which leads to

$$\rho = r^2, \qquad \varphi = 2\theta. \tag{6.79}$$

Clearly our transformation is nonlinear, for the modulus is squared, but the significant feature of Eq. 6.79 is that the phase angle or argument is doubled. This means that the

first quadrant of z, $0 \leqslant \theta < \dfrac{\pi}{2} \rightarrow$ upper half plane of w, $0 \leqslant \varphi < \pi$,

upper half plane of z, $0 \leqslant \theta < \pi \rightarrow$ whole plane of w, $0 \leqslant \varphi < 2\pi$.

The lower half plane of z maps into the already covered entire plane of w, thus covering the w-plane a *second* time. This is our two-to-one correspondence, two distinct points in the z-plane, z_0 and $z_0 e^{i\pi} = -z_0$, corresponding to the single point $w = z_0^2$.

In cartesian representation

$$u + iv = (x + iy)^2$$
$$= x^2 - y^2 + i2xy, \tag{6.80}$$

leading to

$$u = x^2 - y^2,$$
$$v = 2xy. \tag{6.81}$$

Hence the lines $u = c_1$, $v = c_2$ in the w-plane correspond to $x^2 - y^2 = c_1$, $2xy = c_2$, rectangular (and orthogonal) hyperbolas in the z-plane (Fig. 6.16). To every point

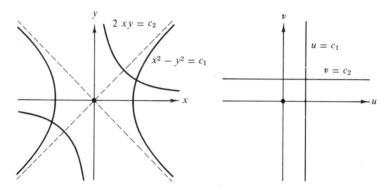

FIG. 6.16   Mapping—hyperbolic coordinates

on the hyperbola $x^2 - y^2 = c_1$ in the right half plane, $x > 0$, one point on the line $u = c_1$ corresponds and vice versa. However, every point on the line $u = c_1$ also corresponds to a point on the hyperbola $x^2 - y^2 = c_1$ in the left half plane, $x < 0$, as already explained.

It will be shown in Section 6.6 that if lines in the w-plane are orthogonal the corresponding lines in the z-plane are also orthogonal, as long as the transformation is analytic. Since $u = c_1$ and $v = c_2$ are constructed perpendicular to each other, the corresponding hyperbolas in the z-plane are orthogonal. We have literally constructed a new orthogonal system of hyperbolic lines (or surfaces if we add an axis perpendicular to x and y). Exercise 2.1.4 was an analysis of this system.

The transformation

$$w = e^z \tag{6.82}$$

leads to

$$\rho e^{i\varphi} = e^{x+iy} \tag{6.83}$$

or

$$\rho = e^x,$$
$$\varphi = y. \tag{6.84}$$

If y ranges from $0 \leqslant y < 2\pi$ (or $-\pi \leqslant y < \pi$), then φ covers the same range. But this is the whole w-plane. In other words, a horizontal strip in the z-plane of width 2π maps into the entire w-plane. Further, any point $x + i(y + 2n\pi)$, in which n is any integer, maps into the same point (by Eq. 6.84), in the w-plane. We have a many-(infinitely many)-to-one correspondence.

The inverse of the fourth transformation (Eq. 6.78) is

$$w = z^{1/2}. \tag{6.85}$$

From the relation

$$\rho e^{i\varphi} = r^{1/2} e^{i\theta/2} \tag{6.86}$$

and

$$2\varphi = \theta \tag{6.87}$$

we now have two points in the w-plane (arguments φ and $\varphi + \pi$) corresponding to one point in the z-plane(except for the point $z = 0$). Or, to put it another way, θ and $\theta + 2\pi$ correspond to φ and $\varphi + \pi$, two distinct points in the w-plane. This is the complex variable analog of the simple real variable equation $y^2 = x$, in which two values of y, plus and minus, correspond to each value of x.

The important point here is that we can make the function w of Eq. 6.85 a single-valued function instead of a double-valued function if we agree to restrict θ to a range such as $0 \leqslant \theta < 2\pi$. This may be done by agreeing never to cross the line $\theta = 0$ in the z-plane (Fig. 6.17). Such a line of demarcation is called a cut line. The point of termination ($z = 0$, here) in a multivalued function is known as a branch point. It is a form of a singular point (cf. Section 7.1), $f(z)$ not being analytic at $z = 0$.

Any line running from $z = 0$ out to infinity would serve equally well. The purpose of the cut line is to restrict the argument of z. The points z_0 and $z_0 e^{2\pi i}$ coincide in the z-plane but yield different points w and $we^{i\pi} = -w$ in the w-plane. Hence in the absence of a cut line the function $w = z^{1/2}$ is ambiguous.

We shall encounter branch points and cut lines frequently in Chapter 7.

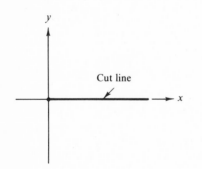

FIG. 6.17   A cut line

FIG. 6.18   Ln z, a multivalued function

Finally, as the inverse of the fifth transformation (Eq. 6.82) we have

$$w = \ln z. \tag{6.88}$$

By expanding it we obtain

$$u + iv = \ln re^{i\theta}$$
$$= \ln r + i\theta. \tag{6.89}$$

For a given point z_0 in the z-plane the argument θ is unspecified within an integral multiple of 2π. This means that

$$v = \theta + 2n\pi \qquad (6.90)$$

and as in the exponential transformation we have an infinitely many-to-one correspondence.

Equation 6.88 has a nice physical representation. If we go around the unit circle in the z-plane, $r = 1$ and by Eq. 6.89 $u = \ln r = 0$; but $v = \theta$, and θ is steadily increasing and continues to increase as θ continues, past 2π. The behavior in the w-plane as we go around and around the unit circle in the z-plane is like the advance of a screw as it is rotated or the ascent of a person walking up a spiral staircase.

As in the preceding example, we make the correspondence unique (and Eq. 6.88 unambiguous) by restricting θ to a range such as $0 \leqslant \theta < 2\pi$ by taking the line $\theta = 0$ (positive real axis) as a cut line. This is equivalent to taking one and only one complete turn of the spiral staircase.

It is because of the multivalued nature of $\ln z$ that the contour integral

$$\oint \frac{dz}{z} = 2\pi i, \qquad \neq 0,$$

integrating about the origin. This property appears in Exercises 6.3.1 and 6.3.8 and is the basis for the entire calculus of residues (Chapter 7).

EXERCISES

6.5.1 Show that negative numbers have logarithms in the complex plane. In particular, find $\ln(-1)$. *Ans.* $\ln(-1) = i\pi$.

6.5.2 How do circles centered on the origin in the z-plane transform for

(a) $w_1(z) = z + \dfrac{1}{z}$,   (b) $w_2(z) = z - \dfrac{1}{z}$ $(z \neq 0)$?

What happens when $|z| \to 1$?

6.5.3 Discuss the transformations
(a) $w(z) = \sin z$,   (c) $w(z) = \sinh z$,
(b) $w(z) = \cos z$,   (d) $w(z) = \cosh z$.
Show how the lines $x = c_1$, $y = c_2$ map into the w-plane. Note that the last three transformations can be obtained from the first one by appropriate translation and/or rotation.

6.5.4 Show why
(a) $w(z) = z^{1/2}$,   (b) $w(z) = \ln z$
do not possess Laurent expansions about the origin.

6.5.5 Show that the function

$$w(z) = (z^2 - 1)^{1/2}$$

is analytic if we take
(a) $-1 \leqslant x \leqslant 1, \quad y = 0$
or
(b) $-\infty < x \leqslant -1$ and $1 \leqslant x < \infty, \quad y = 0$
as cut lines.

6.5.6 What part of the z-plane corresponds to the interior of the unit circle in the w-plane if

(a) $w = \dfrac{z-1}{z+1}$,   (b) $w = \dfrac{z-i}{z+i}$?

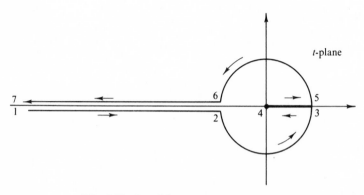

FIG. 6.19   Bessel function integration contour

6.5.7 An integral representation of the Bessel function follows the contour in the t-plane shown below. Map this contour into the θ-plane with $t = e^\theta$. Many additional examples of mapping are given in Chapters 11, 12, and 13.

6.6 Conformal Mapping

In Section 6.5 hyperbolas were mapped into straight lines and straight lines were mapped into circles. Yet in all these transformations one feature stayed constant. This constancy was a result of all of the transformations of Section 6.5 being analytic.

As long as $w = f(z)$ is an analytic function, we have

$$\frac{df}{dz} = \frac{dw}{dz} = \lim_{\Delta z \to 0} \frac{\Delta w}{\Delta z}. \tag{6.91}$$

Assuming that this equation is in polar form, we may equate modulus to modulus and argument to argument. For the latter (assuming that $df/dz \neq 0$)

$$\arg \lim_{\Delta z \to 0} \frac{\Delta w}{\Delta z} = \lim_{\Delta z \to 0} \arg \frac{\Delta w}{\Delta z}$$

$$\lim_{\Delta z \to 0} \arg \Delta w - \lim_{\Delta z \to 0} \arg \Delta z$$

$$= \arg \frac{df}{dz} = \alpha, \tag{6.92}$$

where α, the argument of the derivative, may depend on z but is a constant for a fixed z, independent of the direction of approach. To see the significance of this, consider two curves, C_z in the z-plane and the corresponding curve C_w in the w-plane (Fig. 6.20). The increment Δz is shown at an angle of θ relative to the real

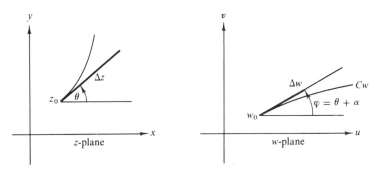

FIG. 6.20   Conformal mapping—preservation of angles

(x) axis whereas the corresponding increment Δw forms an angle of φ with the real (u) axis. From Eq. 6.92

$$\varphi = \theta + \alpha, \tag{6.93}$$

or any line in the z-plane is rotated through an angle α in the w-plane as long as w is an analytic transformation and the derivative is not zero.[1]

Since this result holds for any line through z_0, it will hold for a pair of lines. Then for the angle between these two lines

$$\varphi_2 - \varphi_1 = (\theta_2 + \alpha) - (\theta_1 + \alpha) = \theta_2 - \theta_1, \tag{6.94}$$

which shows that the included angle is preserved under an analytic transformation. Such angle-preserving transformations are called *conformal*. The rotation angle α will, in general, depend on z. In addition $|f'(z)|$ will, in general, be a function of z. Thus, although angles are preserved, the coordinate lines may be deformed. Indeed this is the basis for creating new coordinate systems as discussed later in this section.

The importance of conformal transformations to scientists and engineers is in their application to the solution of Laplace's equation for problems of electrostatics, hydrodynamics, heat flow, and so on. Suppose we have the physically absurd but mathematically simple problem of determining the electric field lines and the equipotential lines (surfaces) between two hyperbolic surfaces with cross sections $x^2 - y^2 = c_1$ at potential V_1 and $x^2 - y^2 = c_2$ at potential V_2 [2] (Fig. 6.21). We know that there will be equipotential lines and electric fields perpendicular to

[1] If $df/dz = 0$, its argument or phase is undefined and the (analytic) transformation will not necessarily preserve angles.

[2] Our complex variable analysis is two-dimensional. The electrostatic force is three-dimensional. We reconcile them by considering a cross-sectional plane of a cylindrical system; that is, we assume a dimension t perpendicular to x and y and assume that *nothing* depends on t.

them, roughly as shown in Fig. 6.21, but with these unusual boundary conditions let us pretend that the analytical forms of the equipotentials and of the force

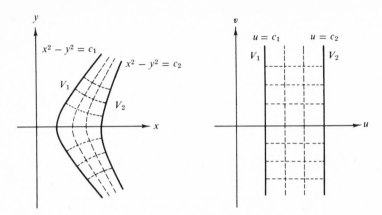

FIG. 6.21 Conformal mapping—hyperbolic coordinates

lines are unknown. This is equivalent to saying that we do not know the solutions of Laplace's equation, $\nabla^2 \psi = 0$, that satisfy these boundary conditions.

If we transform to the w-plane by $w = z^2$, (cf. Eq. 6.78 et seq.), the equipotential line V_1 becomes the vertical line $u = c_1$ and the equipotential line V_2 becomes the vertical line $u = c_2$. In the w-plane Laplace's equation may be solved by inspection to yield the rectangular net $u = c_i$ for the equipotentials and $v = c_j$ for the electric field lines. By transforming back to the z-plane we find that all the right angles are preserved, since $z = w^{1/2}$ is also analytic (except at $w = 0$). In analytic form we have

$$u = x^2 - y^2 = c_i \qquad \text{equipotentials,}$$
$$v = 2xy = c_j \qquad \text{electric field lines.} \tag{6.95}$$

The net result is that a problem that we at least pretended to be unable to solve in the z-plane has been transformed into the w-plane. Here, with a custom-tailored coordinate system literally designed to simplify this particular problem, the problem has been solved by inspection. Finally, the solution is transformed back to the original z-plane as Eq. 6.95.

At the risk of belaboring the obvious, let us prove that a solution of Laplace's equation in the w-plane $\Psi(u, v)$ is still a solution when transformed back into the z-plane, provided only that $w = f(z)$ is analytic. As a fringe benefit, the proof points up the usefulness of the Cauchy-Riemann conditions. We have

$$z\text{-plane, coordinates } x, y, \psi = \psi(x, y),$$
$$w\text{-plane, coordinates } u, v, \Psi = \Psi(u, v), \tag{6.96}$$

where the curve $\Psi(u, v) = a$ in the w-plane corresponds to the curve $\psi(x, y) = a$ in the z-plane; that is,

$$\Psi(u, v) = \Psi[u(x, y), v(x, y)] = \psi(x, y). \tag{6.97}$$

Differentiating $\Psi(u, v)$ with respect to x, we obtain

$$\frac{\partial \Psi(u, v)}{\partial x} = \frac{\partial u}{\partial x} \frac{\partial \Psi}{\partial u} + \frac{\partial v}{\partial x} \frac{\partial \Psi}{\partial v}$$

$$\frac{\partial^2 \Psi}{\partial x^2} = \frac{\partial^2 u}{\partial x^2} \frac{\partial \Psi}{\partial u} + \left(\frac{\partial u}{\partial x}\right)^2 \frac{\partial^2 \Psi}{\partial u^2}$$

$$+ 2 \frac{\partial u}{\partial x} \frac{\partial v}{\partial x} \frac{\partial^2 \Psi}{\partial u \, \partial v} + \frac{\partial^2 v}{\partial x^2} \frac{\partial \Psi}{\partial v} + \left(\frac{\partial v}{\partial x}\right)^2 \frac{\partial^2 \Psi}{\partial v^2}. \qquad (6.98)$$

A similar result holds for $\partial^2 \Psi / \partial y^2$. Then

$$\frac{\partial^2 \psi(x, y)}{\partial x^2} + \frac{\partial^2 \psi(x, y)}{\partial y^2} = \frac{\partial^2 \Psi(u, v)}{\partial x^2} + \frac{\partial^2 \Psi(u, v)}{\partial y^2} = \left(\frac{\partial^2 u}{\partial x^2} + \frac{\partial^2 u}{\partial y^2}\right) \frac{\partial \Psi}{\partial u}$$

$$+ \left(\frac{\partial^2 v}{\partial x^2} + \frac{\partial^2 v}{\partial y^2}\right) \frac{\partial \Psi}{\partial v} + 2 \left(\frac{\partial u}{\partial x} \frac{\partial v}{\partial x} + \frac{\partial u}{\partial y} \frac{\partial v}{\partial y}\right) \frac{\partial^2 \Psi}{\partial u \, \partial v} \qquad (6.99)$$

$$+ \left[\left(\frac{\partial u}{\partial x}\right)^2 + \left(\frac{\partial u}{\partial y}\right)^2\right] \frac{\partial^2 \Psi}{\partial u^2} + \left[\left(\frac{\partial v}{\partial x}\right)^2 + \left(\frac{\partial v}{\partial y}\right)^2\right] \frac{\partial^2 \Psi}{\partial v^2}.$$

On the right-hand side of Eq. 6.99, the first two parentheses vanish, for u and v both satisfy Laplace's equation when w is analytic (cf. Exercise 6.1.3). The third parentheses yields zero from the Cauchy-Riemann conditions, and the same conditions show that the two square brackets are equal. The result is that

$$\nabla^2 \psi(x, y) = \left[\left(\frac{\partial u}{\partial x}\right)^2 + \left(\frac{\partial u}{\partial y}\right)^2\right] \nabla^2 \Psi(u, v)$$

$$= 0, \qquad (6.100)$$

since $\Psi(u, v)$ is known to satisfy Laplace's equation in the w-plane. Therefore, when a solution of Laplace's equation is subjected to an analytic transformation, it remains a solution of Laplace's equation.

EXAMPLE 6.6.1

A perhaps more realistic and more interesting example of this technique is provided by a conducting circular cylinder parallel to an infinite metal plane (Fig. 6.22).

The transformation relating the z- and w-planes is

$$z = ia \tan \frac{w}{2}$$

$$= -a \tanh \frac{w}{2}, \qquad (6.101)$$

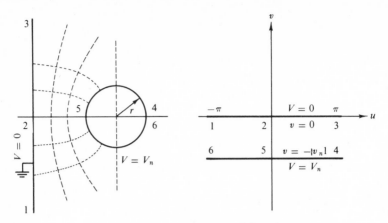

FIG. 6.22　Infinite cylinder parallel to plane

as the reader may verify.[1] Equation 6.101 leads to

$$x = -a\,\frac{\sinh v}{\cosh v - \cos u},$$

$$y = a\,\frac{\sin u}{\cosh v - \cos u}.$$

Eliminating u, we see that the circle is centered at $x = d = -a \coth v_n$, $y = 0$ and has a radius of $r = -a \operatorname{csch} v_n$. This means that $v_n = -\cosh^{-1}(d/r)$, choosing the negative sign since v_n is negative. In the w-plane, by inspection,[2] the electrostatic potential V is

$$V = +V_n\,\frac{v}{v_n}, \qquad -|v_n| \leqslant v \leqslant 0$$

$$= \frac{-vV_n}{\cosh^{-1}(d/r)}. \tag{6.102}$$

Now, if we invert Eq. 6.101, obtain v in terms of z, and substitute into Eq. 6.102, we will have the equipotentials in the z-plane. Solving Eq. 6.101 for w, we obtain

---

[1] Verification is not too difficult, but how about derivation? Some of the transformation needed may be built up from combinations of elementary functions. Equation 6.101 could be built up from exponentials and trigonometric functions with some difficulty. The usual "derivation" of a transform comes from a dictionary of transforms. Among the better, more complete dictionaries of transforms are Z. Nehari, *Conformal Mapping*. New York: McGraw-Hill (1952), and H. Kober, *Dictionary of Conformal Representations*. New York: Dover (1952).

[2] This deserves more than just a quick glance. The boundary lines (surfaces) in the w-plane are finite, $-\pi \leqslant u \leqslant \pi$. However, $u = \pi$, $v = v$ corresponds to the same point in the z-plane as $u = -\pi$, $v = v$, so that there are no end effects after all. The coordinate u is defined only for $-\pi \leqslant u \leqslant \pi$.

$$w = -2 \tan^{-1}\left(-\frac{iz}{a}\right),$$

$$v = \text{I.P.}\left[2 \tan^{-1}\left(\frac{iz}{a}\right)\right] \tag{6.103}$$

$$= -\text{R.P.}\left[2 \tanh^{-1}\left(\frac{z}{a}\right)\right].$$

Therefore the potential in the right-hand z-plane ($x \geqslant 0$) is

$$V = +\text{R.P.}\frac{[2 \tanh^{-1}(z/a)]V_n}{\cosh^{-1}(d/a)} \tag{6.104}$$

all negative signs cancelling. This can be put in better form. Comparison with Section 2.9 shows that Eq. 6.101 *generates* a bipolar coordinate system. The equipotentials are the coordinate circles[1]

$$(x + a \coth v)^2 + y^2 = a^2 \operatorname{csch}^2 v. \tag{6.105}$$

The electrostatic problem is not quite complete. There is still the question of the capacitance between the two equipotential surfaces (per unit length normal to the xy-plane). We have

$$w(z) = u(x, y) + i\,v(x, y), \tag{6.106}$$

with $u(x, y)$ describing the equipotentials and its conjugate function $v(x, y)$ describing the field lines or vice versa. The choice is arbitrary but to be consistent with Eq. 6.103, which is a specific form of Eq. 6.106, let us take $v(x, y)$ to describe the equipotentials and its conjugate function $u(x, y)$ to describe the field lines.

The capacitance per unit length is defined by

$$C = \frac{\text{charge per unit length}}{\text{potential difference}} = \frac{q}{v_2 - v_1}. \tag{6.107}$$

The electric charge per unit length (on one conductor) may be calculated, starting from Gauss's law (Section 1.14).

$$q = \varepsilon_0 \int \mathbf{E} \cdot d\mathbf{s} = -\varepsilon_0 \int \nabla v \cdot d\mathbf{s}. \tag{6.108}$$

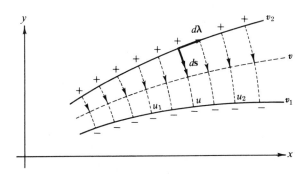

FIG. 6.23 Electrostatic capacitance

[1] This is the final step in identifying r and d in terms of v_n.

Now

$$\nabla v = \mathbf{i}\frac{\partial v}{\partial x} + \mathbf{j}\frac{\partial v}{\partial y}$$

$$= -\mathbf{i}\frac{\partial u}{\partial y} + \mathbf{j}\frac{\partial u}{\partial x} \tag{6.109}$$

from the Cauchy-Riemann conditions. If we replace the area element $d\mathbf{s}$ by

$$d\mathbf{s} = -\mathbf{k} \times d\boldsymbol{\lambda}, \tag{6.110}$$

where $d\boldsymbol{\lambda}$ is the direction of increasing u (Fig. 6.23) and $\mathbf{k}$ is given by $\mathbf{i} \times \mathbf{j}$,

$$q = \varepsilon_0 \int_{u_1}^{u_2} \left(-\mathbf{i}\frac{\partial u}{\partial y} + \mathbf{j}\frac{\partial u}{\partial x} \right) \cdot \mathbf{k} \times d\boldsymbol{\lambda}$$

$$= \varepsilon_0 \int_{u_1}^{u_2} \left(\mathbf{i}\frac{\partial u}{\partial x} + \mathbf{j}\frac{\partial u}{\partial y} \right) \cdot d\boldsymbol{\lambda}$$

$$= \varepsilon_0 (u_2 - u_1). \tag{6.111}$$

When Eq. 6.111 for the charge per unit length (between u_1 and u_2) is substituted into Eq. 6.107, we obtain

$$C = \varepsilon_0 \frac{u_2 - u_1}{v_2 - v_1}. \tag{6.112}$$

If we apply Eq. 6.112 to the foregoing plane and cylinder problem, the capacitance per unit length is found to be

$$C = \varepsilon_0 \frac{2\pi}{(-)v_n} = \frac{2\pi\varepsilon_0}{\cosh^{-1}(d/r)}. \tag{6.113}$$

One final example of the use of conformal transformations.

EXAMPLE 6.6.2

A potential difference $2V_0$ is established between two surfaces or semicircular cross sections shown in Fig. 6.24. We want the potential at any point between the curved surfaces.

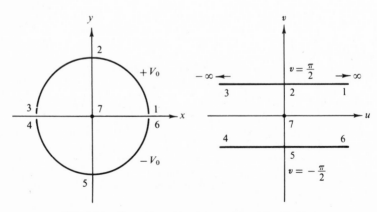

FIG. 6.24 Charged, conducting, semicircular cylinders

The semicircles in the z-plane ($x^2 + y^2 = 1$, unit radius) may be mapped into parallel straight lines in the w-plane by[1]

$$w = \ln \left(\frac{1 + z}{1 - z} \right).$$ (6.114)

We have

$$u + iv = \ln \frac{1 + x + iy}{1 - x - iy} = \ln \frac{1 - x^2 - y^2 + 2iy}{1 - 2x + x^2 + y^2}.$$ (6.115)

Replacing $(1 - x^2 - y^2 + 2iy)/(1 - 2x + x^2 + y^2)$ by $Re^{i\alpha}$,

$$u + iv = \ln R + i\alpha,$$ (6.116)

where

$$v = \alpha = \tan^{-1} \frac{2y}{1 - (x^2 + y^2)}.$$ (6.117)

To map the semicircular boundaries

$$\lim_{\substack{x^2 + y^2 \to 1 \\ y > 0}} \tan^{-1} \frac{2y}{1 - (x^2 + y^2)} = \frac{\pi}{2},$$

$$\lim_{\substack{x^2 + y^2 \to 1 \\ y < 0}} \tan^{-1} \frac{2y}{1 - (x^2 + y^2)} = -\frac{\pi}{2},$$ (6.118)

as shown in Fig. 6.24. The potential is obtained (by inspection) as

$$V = \frac{2V_0}{\pi} v$$

$$= \frac{2V_0}{\pi} \tan^{-1} \left[\frac{2y}{1 - (x^2 + y^2)} \right]$$ (6.119)

$$= \frac{2V_0}{\pi} \tan^{-1} \left(\frac{2r \sin \theta}{1 - r^2} \right), \qquad 0 \leqslant r \leqslant 1.$$

This particular problem may be solved easily by separating variables in circular cylindrical coordinates. We obtain an infinite series solution for the potential. A possible advantage of the conformal mapping approach is that the solution is given in closed form.

The reader may show that the range of u is $-\infty < u < \infty$, which means that the capacitance is infinite!

---

[1] Solving for z, $z = \tanh w/2$, so that we are really using Eq. 6.101 again in a different form and in a different context.

EXERCISES

6.6.1 Show that the transformation
$$w = e^z + z$$
maps the infinite lines $y = \pm\pi$ into semi-infinite lines $u \leqslant u_0$, $v = \pm\pi$. This is equivalent to transforming an infinite or edgeless parallel plate capacitor (z-plane) into a parallel plate capacitor (w-plane). Sketch the equipotentials in the w-plane near the edge of the capacitor plates.

Find the electric field at the plane midway between the two plates (at $v = 0$) as a function of u.

6.6.2 In the transformation
$$e^z = \frac{a - w}{a + w}.$$
how do the coordinate lines in the z-plane transform? What coordinate system of Chapter 2 have you constructed?

6.6.3 Develop the transformations that create each of the four cylindrical coordinate systems:
(a) Circular cylindrical $x = \rho \cos\varphi,$
                             $y = \rho \sin\varphi.$
(b) Elliptic cylindrical $x = a \cosh u \cos v,$
                             $y = a \sinh u \sin v.$
(c) Parabolic cylindrical $x = \xi\eta,$
                             $y = \frac{1}{2}(\eta^2 - \xi^2).$
(d) Bipolar $x = \dfrac{a \sinh\eta}{\cosh\eta - \cos\xi},$

                             $y = \dfrac{a \sin\xi}{\cosh\eta - \cos\xi}.$

Note. These transformations are not necessarily analytic.

6.6.4 In an electrostatic problem the equipotentials are given by $u(x, y) = c_i$, in which u is the real part of $w(z)$ and $w(z)$ is analytic. Show that the magnitude of the electric field $\mathbf{E}$ is given by
$$|\mathbf{E}| = \left| \frac{dw(z)}{dz} \right|.$$

6.6.5 The function $w(z)$ is analytic and has a nonvanishing derivative at $w_0 = w(z_0)$. Prove that there is an inverse function $z = z(w)$ with the followng properties:
$$z_0 = z(w_0),$$
$$w = w[z(w)], \qquad z = z[w(z)],$$
$$\frac{dz}{dw} = \left(\frac{dw}{dz} \right)^{-1}.$$

6.6.6 (a) A conducting cylinder of unit radius is placed in a uniform electric field, $\mathbf{E}_0$. The axis of the cylinder is perpendicular to the direction of the original field. Using the transformation
$$w = z + \frac{1}{z},$$
find the perturbed electrostatic potential.

(b) How is the transformation function modified if the radius of the cylinder is r_0 with $r_0 \neq 1$?

6.6.7 Two cylindrical conductors, one of radius r_1 and the other of radius r_2, are separated by a center-to-center distance D. What is their capacitance per unit length if
(a) $D > r_1 + r_2$ (b) $0 < D < |r_1 - r_2|$?

6.6.8 A thin, flat conducting strip of width $2a$ is raised to a potential V_0 above ground. Find the following:
(a) The lines of constant potential.
(b) The electric field lines.
(c) The distribution of electric charge as a function of distance from the center line of the strip.
(d) The capacitance per unit length.

6.6.9 Show how the transformation Eq. 6.88

$$w = a \ln z$$

can represent the (two-dimensional) field of a line charge, the line being perpendicular to the xy-plane. Renormalize your transformation so that it describes unit charge (per unit length.)

6.6.10 The two analytic transformations

$$z = a \sin w$$

$$z = -a \tanh \frac{iw}{2}$$

develop sets of equipotentials and field lines corresponding to $u = c_i$ and $v = c_j$, with the line segment $-a \leqslant x \leqslant a, y = 0$ as a possible equipotential when $v = 0$.
(a) Sketch the orthogonal system resulting from each of the two transformations.
(b) What is the difference between these two cases from a physical point of view?

6.7 Schwarz-Christoffel Transformation

The Schwarz-Christoffel transformation may be set up to map the real axis of the w-plane into any desired polygon in the z-plane, the upper half ($v > 0$) of the w-plane being mapped into the interior of the polygon. The inverse transformation then maps the z-plane polygon into the upper half of the w-plane. This provides us with a systematic way of deriving a useful conformal transformation for polygon-type figures, including various degenerate cases.

To develop the Schwarz-Christoffel transformation, consider first the function $z'(w)$:

$$\frac{dz}{dw} = A(w - w_1)^{-k_1}, \tag{6.120}$$

in which A is a complex constant, k_1 is a real constant, and w_1 is a point on the real (u) axis. The phase or argument is given by

$$\arg \frac{dz}{dw} = \begin{cases} \arg A - k_1\pi, & w < w_1, \\ \arg A, & w > w_1, \end{cases} \tag{6.121}$$

for w moving along the real axis. We have $\arg(w - w_1) = \pi$ for $w < w_1$, and $\arg(w - w_1) = 0$ for $w > w_1$; that is, as w moves along the u-axis in the positive sense the argument of dz/dw discontinuously jumps by an amount $k_1\pi$ when w

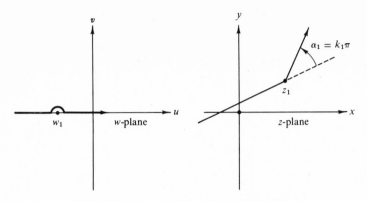

FIG. 6.25   Schwarz-Christoffel transformation

passes point w_1. Referring to Section 6.6, especially Fig. 6.20, we note that $\arg \Delta w = 0$ constant. Therefore

$$\arg \Delta z = \begin{cases} \arg A - k_1\pi, & w < w_1, \\ \arg A, & w > w_1. \end{cases} \qquad (6.122)$$

Since A is a constant (at our disposal), $\arg A$ is a constant and z therefore is a pair of straight-line segments which form an exterior angle $\alpha_1 = k_1\pi$.

From the factor $(w - w_1)^{-k_1}$, Eq. 6.120 we obtain one vertex of a polygon. By including n factors of this form we may construct an n vertex polygon:

$$\frac{dz}{dw} = A(w - w_1)^{-k_1}(w - w_2)^{-k_2} \cdots (w - w_n)^{-k_n}, \qquad (6.123)$$

with the constraint

$$\sum_{i=1}^{n} k_i = 2, \qquad (6.124)$$

so that the sum of the exterior angles will be 2π.[1]

By integrating Eq. 6.123 we have

$$z = A \int^w (w - w_1)^{-k_1}(w - w_2)^{-k_2} \cdots (w - w_n)^{-k_n}\, dw + B. \qquad (6.125)$$

The complex constant A permits us to rotate and orient our z-plane polygon as desired and the complex constant of integration B is available for any needed translational displacement. In the z-plane the polygon may be specified by giving the locations of the n vertices which means fixing $2n$ constants. However, Eq. 6.125 has $2n + 4$ parameters,

$$
\begin{array}{rl}
n & w_i\text{'s} \\
n & k_i\text{'s} \\
\underline{4} & A \text{ and } B \\
2n + 4 &
\end{array}
$$

[1] If treated in terms of the closed contours of Chapter 7, this guarantees that the infinite semicircle in the upper half w-plane which closes the contour will contribute nothing to the integral.

from which we deduct one for the constraint of Eq. 6.124 to yield $2n + 3$ parameters. Hence three of the singularities w_i may be chosen arbitrarily, after which the remainder is uniquely determined. Usually the three arbitrary w_i's are chosen to facilitate the evaluation of the integral (Eq. 6.125).

EXAMPLE 6.7.1

Map the real w-axis into the "triangle" shown in Fig. 6.26. From the diagram

FIG. 6.26   Schwarz-Christoffel mapping of a degenerate triangle

$$\alpha_1 \to \frac{\pi}{2}, \quad k_1 \to \frac{1}{2}$$

$$\alpha_2 = \frac{\pi}{2}, \quad k_2 = \frac{1}{2} \qquad (6.126)$$

$$\alpha_3 \to \pi, \quad k_3 \to 1.$$

For convenience we let $w_1 = -1$, $w_2 = +1$, and $w_3 \to \infty$, with A available to compensate for w_3. Then, by Eq. 6.125,

$$z = A \int^w (w + 1)^{-1/2} (w - 1)^{-1/2} \, dw + B$$

$$= A \int^w (w^2 - 1)^{-1/2} + B. \qquad (6.127)$$

Integrating

$$z = A \cosh^{-1} w + B$$

$$w = \cosh\left(\frac{z - B}{A}\right). \qquad (6.128)$$

The constants A and B are evaluated by noting that when $w = -1$, $z = ia$, and when $w = +1$, $z = 0$. From the latter condition, $B = 0$. From the former

$$\cosh \frac{ia}{A} = \cos \frac{a}{A} = -1, \qquad (6.129)$$

which shows that $A = a/\pi$. Hence

$$w = \cosh \frac{\pi z}{a}. \tag{6.130}$$

The upper half of the w-plane is mapped into the interior of the semi-infinite strip.

EXAMPLE 6.7.2

Map the real w-axis into the "triangle" shown in Fig. 6.27. From this diagram

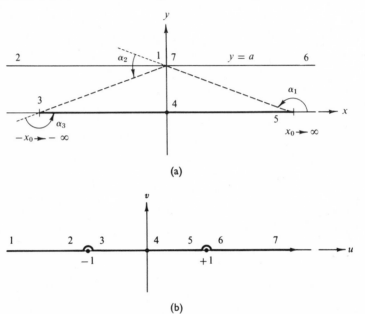

(a)

(b)

FIG. 6.27   Schwarz-Christoffel mapping of a second degenerate triangle

$$\alpha_1 \to \pi, \qquad k_1 \to 1,$$
$$\alpha_3 \to \pi, \qquad k_3 \to 1, \tag{6.131}$$

and, since $\alpha_2 \to 0$, $k_2 \to 0$, and this factor may be dropped. As in the preceding example, we arbitrarily place the singularities at -1 and $+1$. Then

$$z = A \int^{w} (w - 1)^{-1}(w + 1)^{-1} \, dw + B$$

$$= \frac{A}{2} \ln \frac{w - 1}{w + 1} + B. \tag{6.132}$$

The constants A and B are evaluated by requiring that $w = 0$ correspond to $z = 0$, or

$$\frac{A}{2} \ln(-1) + B = \frac{i\pi A}{2} + B = 0. \tag{6.133}$$

Also, as $w \to \pm\infty$, $z = ia$ or

$$ia = \frac{A}{2} \ln 1 + B = B. \tag{6.134}$$

Therefore

$$z = -\frac{a}{\pi} \ln\left(\frac{w-1}{w+1}\right) + ia. \tag{6.135}$$

It should be noted that the choice of singularities ($w_3 = -1$, $w_1 = +1$) forces the correspondence of

$$-1 < u < 1, \qquad v = 0 \quad \text{and} \quad -\infty < x < \infty, \qquad y = 0,$$

$$-\infty < u < -1, \quad v = 0 \quad \text{and} \quad -\infty < x < 0, \qquad y = a,$$

$$1 < u < \infty, \qquad v = 0 \quad \text{and} \qquad 0 < x < \infty, \qquad y = a,$$

shown by the position numbers on the z- and w-planes. A different choice of singularities would have led to a different transformation and a different correspondence. In some exercises Eq. 6.135 may be used to take the Schwarz-Christoffel transformation of a polygon and map it into two parallel infinite lines so that Laplace's equation may be solved by inspection.

EXERCISES

6.7.1 Derive the parallel plate capacitor transformation
$$w = e^z + z$$
(Exercise 6.6.1) by using the Schwarz-Christoffel transformation.

6.7.2 Using the Schwarz-Christoffel procedure, map the "polygon" bounded by the three lines $x = -a$, $y = 0$, $x = +a$ into the u-axis (w-plane) with singularities at $u = \pm 1$, $v = 0$.

6.7.3 The real axis in the z-plane between $y = -a$ and $y = +a$ is held at a potential of 100 volts. The remainder of the real axis is grounded. Find the potential for any point of $y = 0$. What is the capacitance (per unit length) of this system?

6.7.4 Derive the transformation $w = z^2$ (which maps the first quadrant of the z-plane into the upper half of the w-plane) by using the Schwarz-Christoffel transformation.

6.7.5 Find the electrostatic potential at any point $x > 0$, $y > 0$, if the real (x) axis is grounded, $V = 0$, and the imaginary (y) axis is held at $V = 100$.

REFERENCES

CHURCHILL, R. V., *Complex Variables and Applications*. 2nd Ed. New York: McGraw-Hill (1960). For both the beginning and the advanced student this is an excellent text. It is readable and quite complete. A detailed proof of the Cauchy-Goursat theorem is given in Chapter 5.

LASS, H., *Elements of Pure and Applied Mathematics*, New York: McGraw-Hill (1957). Chapter 4 is a useful presentation of complex-variable theory.

MORSE, P. M., and FESBACH, H., *Methods of Theoretical Physics*. New York: McGraw-Hill (1953). Chapter 4 is a presentation of portions of the theory of functions of a complex variable of interest to theoretical physicists.

SMITH, L. P., *Mathematical Methods for Scientists and Engineers*. New York: Prentice-Hall (1953). Smith uses complex variables extensively in the development of power series, series of functions, theory of functions, conformal mapping, and calculus of residues. Chapter 9 includes some involved but realistic applications of the Schwarz-Christoffel transformation.

SOKOLNIKOFF, I. S., and REDHEFFER, R. M., *Mathematics of Physics and Modern Engineering*. New York: McGraw-Hill (1958). Chapter 7 covers complex variables.

WATSON, G. N., *Complex Integration and Cauchy's Theorem*. New York: Hafner (orig. 1917). A short work containing a rigorous development of the Cauchy integral theorem and integral formula. Applications to the calculus of residues are included. *Cambridge Tracts in Mathematics, and Mathematical Physics*, No. 15.

Other references are given at the end of Chapter 15.

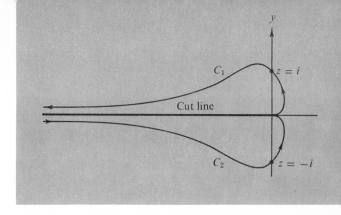

CHAPTER 7

FUNCTIONS OF
A COMPLEX VARIABLE II

CALCULUS OF RESIDUES

7.1 Singularities

In this chapter we return to the line of analysis that started with the Cauchy-Riemann conditions in Chapter 6 and led on through the Laurent expansion (Section 6.4). The Laurent expansion represents a generalization of the Taylor series in the presence of singularities. We define the point z_0 as an isolated singular point of the function $f(z)$ if $f(z)$ is not analytic at $z = z_0$ but is analytic at neighboring points.

Poles.   In the Laurent expansion of $f(z)$ about z_0

$$f(z) = \sum_{n=-\infty}^{\infty} a_n(z - z_0)^n. \tag{7.1}$$

If $a_n = 0$ for $n < -m < 0$ and $a_{-m} \neq 0$, we say that z_0 is a pole of order m. For instance, if $m = 1$, that is, if $a_{-1}/(z - z_0)$ is the first nonvanishing term in the Laurent series, we have a pole of order one, often called a simple pole.

If, on the other hand, the summation continues to $n = -\infty$, the z_0 is a pole of infinite order and is called an essential singularity. These essential singularities have many pathological features. For instance, we can show that in any small neighborhood of an essential singularity of $f(z)$ the function $f(z)$ comes arbitrarily close to any (and therefore every) preselected complex quantity w_0. Literally, the entire w-plane is mapped into the neighborhood of the point z_0. One point of fundamental difference between a pole of finite order and an essential singularity is that a pole of order m can be removed by multiplying $f(z)$ by $(z - z_0)^m$. This obviously cannot be done for an essential singularity.

The behavior of $f(z)$ as $z \to \infty$ is defined in terms of the behavior of $f(1/t)$ as $t \to 0$. Consider the function

$$\sin z = \sum_{n=0}^{\infty} \frac{(-1)^n z^{2n+1}}{(2n+1)!}. \tag{7.2}$$

As $z \to \infty$, we replace the z by $1/t$ to obtain

$$\sin\left(\frac{1}{t}\right) = \sum_{n=0}^{\infty} \frac{(-1)^n}{(2n+1)! \, t^{2n+1}}. \tag{7.3}$$

Clearly, from the definition, $\sin z$ has an essential singularity at infinity. This result could be anticipated from Exercise 6.1.10 since

$$\sin z = \sin iy, \qquad \text{when } x = 0,$$

$$= i \sinh y,$$

which approaches infinity exponentially as $y \to \infty$.

Branch points.   There is another sort of singularity that will be important in the later sections of this chapter. Consider

$$f(z) = z^a,$$

in which a is not an integer.[1] As z moves around the unit circle from e^0 to $e^{2\pi i}$,

$$f(z) \to e^{2\pi a i} \neq e^{0i},$$

for nonintegral a. As in Section 6.5, we have a branch point. The points e^{0i} and $e^{2\pi i}$ in the z-plane coincide but these coincident points lead to *different* values of $f(z)$; that is, $f(z)$ is a multivalued function. The problem is resolved by constructing a cut line so that $f(z)$ will be uniquely specified for a given point in the z-plane.

Note carefully that a function with a branch point and a required cut line will not be continuous across the cut line. Hence line integrals on either side of the cut line will not, in general, cancel each other.

EXAMPLE 7.1.1

Consider the function

$$f(z) = (z^2 - 1)^{1/2} = (z + 1)^{1/2}(z - 1)^{1/2}.$$

The first factor on the right-hand side, $(z + 1)^{1/2}$, has a branch point at $z = -1$. The second factor has a branch point at $z = +1$. To check on the possibility of taking the line segment joining $z = +1$ and $z = -1$ as a cut line let us follow the phases of these two factors as we move along the contour shown in Fig. 7.1.

Starting at point 1 where both $(z + 1)$ and $(z - 1)$ have a phase of zero, we can

---

[1] $z = 0$ is technically a singular point, for z^a has only a finite number of derivatives, whereas an analytic function is guaranteed an infinite number of derivatives (Section 6.3).

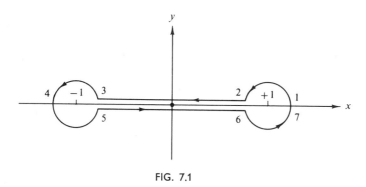

FIG. 7.1

build up Table 7.1.

TABLE 7.1

		Phase Angle	
Point	$(z+1)$	$(z-1)$	$(z+1)^{1/2}(z-1)^{1/2}$
1	0	0	0
2	0	π	$\pi/2$
3	0	π	$\pi/2$
4	π	π	π
5	2π	π	$3\pi/2$
6	2π	π	$3\pi/2$
7	2π	2π	2π

Moving from point 1 to point 2 the phase of $(z-1)$ increases by π, that is, $z-1$ becomes negative. The phase of $z-1$ then stays constant until the circle is completed, moving from 6 to 7. The phase of $(z+1)$ shows a similar behavior increasing by 2π as we move from 3 to 5. The phase of $f(z) = (z+1)^{1/2}(z-1)^{1/2}$ tabulated in the final column is one half the sum of the two preceding columns.

Two features emerge;

1. The phase at points 5 and 6 is not the same as the phase at points 2 and 3. This behavior can be expected at a cut line.
2. The phase at point 7 exceeds that at point 1 by 2π and the function $f(z) = (z^2-1)^{1/2}$ is therefore *single-valued* for the contour shown, encircling *both* branch points.

If we take the x-axis $-1 \leqslant x \leqslant 1$ as a cut line, $f(z)$ is uniquely specified.

As a final note on singularites, Liouville's theorem (Exercise 6.3.3) states "A function which is everywhere finite (bounded) and analytic must be a constant." This is readily proved by the use of Cauchy's integral formula. Conversely, the slightest deviation of an analytic function from a constant value implies that there must be at least one singularity somewhere in the infinite complex plane. Apart from the trivial constant functions, then, singularities are a fact of life, and we must learn to live with them. But we shall do more than that. We shall use singularities to develop the powerful and useful calculus of residues.

EXERCISES

7.1.1 The function $f(z)$ expanded in a Laurent series exhibits a pole of order m at $z = z_0$. Show that the coefficient of $(z - z_0)^{-1}$, a_{-1}, is given by

$$a_{-1} = \frac{1}{(m-1)!} \frac{d^{m-1}}{dz^{m-1}} \left[(z - z_0)^m f(z) \right]_{z=z_0},$$

with

$$a_{-1} = [(z - z_0) f(z)]_{z=z_0},$$

when the pole is a simple pole ($m = 1$).

7.1.2 A function $f(z)$ can be represented by

$$f(z) = \frac{f_1(z)}{f_2(z)},$$

in which $f_1(z)$ and $f_2(z)$ are analytic. The denominator $f_2(z)$ vanishes at $z = z_0$ showing that $f(z)$ has a pole at $z = z_0$. However, $f_1(z_0) \neq 0$, $f_2'(z_0) \neq 0$. Show that a_{-1}, the coefficient of $(z - z_0)^{-1}$ in a Laurent expansion of $f(z)$ at $z = z_0$, is given by

$$a_{-1} = \frac{f_1(z_0)}{f_2'(z_0)}.$$

7.2 Calculus of Residues

If the Laurent expansion of a function is integrated term by term by using a closed contour that encircles one isolated singular point z_0 once in a counterclockwise sense, we obtain

$$a_n \oint (z - z_0)^n \, dz = a_n \frac{(z - z_0)^{n+1}}{n+1} \bigg|_{z_1}^{z_1}$$

$$= 0 \quad \text{for} \quad n \neq -1. \tag{7.4}$$

However, if $n = -1$,

$$a_{-1} \oint (z - z_0)^{-1} \, dz = a_{-1} \oint \frac{ire^{i\theta} \, d\theta}{re^{i\theta}} = 2\pi i a_{-1}. \tag{7.5}$$

Summarizing Eqs. 7.4 and 7.5, we have

$$\frac{1}{2\pi i} \oint f(z) \, dz = a_{-1}. \tag{7.6}$$

The constant a_{-1}, the coefficient of $(z - z_0)^{-1}$ in the Laurent expansion, is called the *residue* of $f(z)$ at $z = z_0$.

A set of isolated singularities can be handled very nicely by deforming our

FIG. 7.2 Excluding isolated singularities

contour as shown in Fig. 7.2. Cauchy's integral theorem (Section 6.2) leads to

$$\oint_C f(z)\,dz + \oint_{C_0} f(z)\,dz + \oint_{C_1} f(z)\,dz + \oint_{C_2} f(z)\,dz + \cdots = 0. \qquad (7.7)$$

The circular integral around any given singular point is given by Eq. 7.6.

$$\oint_{C_i} f(z)\,dz = -2\pi i\, a_{-1}(z = z_i), \qquad (7.8)$$

assuming a Laurent expansion about the singular point, $z = z_i$. The negative sign comes from the clockwise integration as shown in Fig. 7.2. Combining Eqs. 7.7 and 7.8, we have

$$\oint_C f(z)\,dz = 2\pi i (a_{-1_{z_0}} + a_{-1_{z_1}} + a_{-1_{z_2}} + \cdots)$$

$$= 2\pi i \quad \text{(sum of enclosed residues)}. \qquad (7.9)$$

This is the residue theorem.

Occasionally an isolated first-order pole will be directly on the contour of integration. In this case we may deform the contour to include or exclude the residue as desired by including a semicircular detour of infinitesimal radius.

FIG. 7.3 By-passing singular points

This is shown in Fig. 7.3. The integration over the semicircle then gives

$$\pi i a_{-1} \quad \text{if counterclockwise,}$$

$$-\pi i a_{-1} \quad \text{if clockwise.}$$

This contribution, $+$ or $-$, appears on the left-hand side of Eq. 7.9. If our detour were clockwise, the residue would not be enclosed and there would be no corresponding term on the right-hand side of Eq. 7.9. However, if our detour were counterclockwise, this residue would be enclosed by the contour C and term $2\pi i a_{-1}$ would appear on the right-hand side of Eq. 7.9. The net result for either clockwise or counterclockwise detour is that a simple pole on the contour is counted as one half what it would be if it were within the contour. This corresponds to taking the Cauchy principle value.

An alternate treatment moves the pole off the contour and then considers the limiting behavior as it is brought back. This technique is illustrated in Example 7.2.5, in which the singular points are moved off the contour in such a way that the solution is forced into the form desired to satisfy the boundary conditions of the physical problem.

EXAMPLE 7.2.1

Evaluate

$$I = \int_{-\infty}^{\infty} \frac{dx}{1 + x^2}. \qquad (7.10)$$

In our complex plane this becomes

$$I = \int_{x=-\infty}^{x=\infty} \frac{dz}{1 + z^2}. \qquad (7.11)$$

Here and in every other similar problem we have two immediate questions. First, where are the poles? Rewriting the integrand as

$$\frac{1}{z^2 + 1} = \frac{1}{z + i} \cdot \frac{1}{z - i}, \qquad (7.12)$$

we see that there are simple poles (order 1) at $z = i$ and $z = -i$.

A simple pole at $z = z_0$ indicates (and is indicated by) a Laurent expansion of the form

$$f(z) = \frac{a_{-1}}{z - z_0} + a_0 + \sum_{n=1}^{\infty} a_n(z - z_0)^n. \qquad (7.12a)$$

The residue a_{-1} is easily isolated as

$$a_{-1} = (z - z_0) f(z) |_{z = z_0}. \qquad (7.12b)$$

Using Eq. 7.12b, we find that the residue at $z = i$ is $1/2i$, whereas that at $z = -i$ is $-1/2i$.

The second question is, how can we complete the contour in such a way that the additional line integral will contribute a known amount or, preferably, zero? This closing of the contour is a necessary step for applying the residue theorem. For the integral in Eq. 7.11 the contour may be completed by a semicircle in either the upper or lower half planes, as indicated in Fig. 7.4. Then

$$\oint \frac{dz}{1 + z^2} = \lim_{R \to \infty} \int_{-R}^{R} \frac{dx}{1 + x^2} + \lim_{R \to \infty} \int_{0}^{\pi} \frac{iRe^{i\theta} d\theta}{1 + R^2 e^{2i\theta}}, \qquad (7.13)$$

choosing the upper semicircle. If we take the limit as $R \to \infty$, the second term on the right, the integral over the infinite semicircle vanishes because the integrand goes to zero.

FIG. 7.4 Closing the contour with an
infinite radius semicircle

The final step is to apply the residue theorem (Eq. 7.9), which yields

$$\oint \frac{dz}{1+z^2} = \int_{-\infty}^{\infty} \frac{dx}{1+x^2}$$

$$= 2\pi i \cdot \frac{1}{2i} = \pi. \tag{7.14}$$

Here we have used $a_{-1} = 1/2i$ for the residue of the one included pole at $z = i$. The reader should satisfy himself that it is possible to use the lower semicircle and that this choice will lead to the same result, $I = \pi$. A somewhat more delicate problem is provided by the next example.

EXAMPLE 7.2.2

Evaluate

$$I = \int_0^{\infty} \frac{\sin x}{x} dx. \tag{7.15}$$

This may be taken as one half the imaginary part[1] of

$$I_z = \int_{-\infty}^{\infty} \frac{e^{iz} dz}{z}. \tag{7.16}$$

Now the only pole is a simple pole at $z = 0$ and the residue there by Eq. 7.12b is $a_{-1} = 1$. We choose the contour shown in Fig. 7.5 (a) to avoid the pole, (b) to

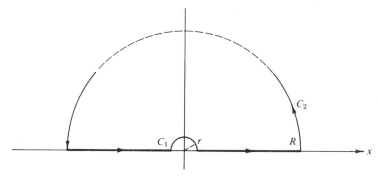

FIG. 7.5

[1] One can use $\int[(e^{iz} - e^{-iz})/2iz]dz$, but then two different contours will be needed for the two exponentials (cf. Example 7.2.4).

include the real axis, and (c) to yield a vanishingly small integrand for $z = iy$, $y \to \infty$. Note that in this case a semicircle in the lower half plane would be disastrous. We have

$$\oint \frac{e^{iz}\,dz}{z} = \int_{-R}^{-r} e^{ix}\frac{dx}{x} + \int_{C_1} \frac{e^{iz}\,dz}{z} + \int_{r}^{R} \frac{e^{ix}\,dx}{x} + \int_{C_2} \frac{e^{iz}\,dz}{z} = 0, \qquad (7.17)$$

the final zero coming from the residue theorem (Eq. 7.9). Taking the limit as $r \to 0$, $R \to \infty$,

$$\int_{-\infty}^{\infty} \frac{e^{ix}\,dx}{x} = \int_{0}^{\pi} i\,d\theta - \lim_{R \to \infty} \int_{0}^{\pi} e^{iR\cos\theta} e^{-R\sin\theta}\, \frac{iRe^{i\theta}\,d\theta}{Re^{i\theta}}. \qquad (7.18)$$

In the limit as $R \to \infty$ the final integrand vanishes for $0 < \theta < \pi$ (though not at $\theta = 0, \pi$). Since the integrand is at most of unit magnitude, and this over a vanishingly small range, the final integral is seen to be zero. Taking the imaginary parts, Eq. 7.18 yields

$$\int_{-\infty}^{\infty} \frac{\sin x}{x}\,dx = \pi, \qquad (7.19)$$

or

$$\int_{0}^{\infty} \frac{\sin x}{x}\,dx = \frac{\pi}{2}. \qquad (7.20)$$

The alert reader will see that this technique of setting and taking limits is again equivalent to taking a Cauchy principle value. In particular, we have taken the improper integral

$$\int_{-\infty}^{\infty} \frac{\cos x}{x}\,dx$$

to be zero.

The contour of Fig. 7.5, although convenient, is not at all unique. Another choice of contour for evaluating Eq. 7.15 is presented as Exercise 2.2.11.

As a third example we consider an integral that will be quite useful in developing a relation between $z!$ and $(-z)!$.

EXAMPLE 7.2.3

Evaluate

$$I = \int_{-\infty}^{\infty} \frac{e^{ax}}{1+e^x}\,dx, \qquad 0 < a < 1. \qquad (7.21)$$

FIG. 7.6

The limits on a are necessary (and sufficient) to prevent the integral from diverging as $x \to \pm\infty$. This integral (Eq. 7.21) may be handled by replacing the real variable x by the complex variable z and integrating around the contour shown in Fig. 7.6. If we take the limit as $R \to \infty$, the real axis, of course, leads to the integral we want. The return path along $\lambda = 2\pi$ is chosen to leave the denominator of the integral invariant, at the same time introducing a constant factor $e^{i2\pi a}$ in the numerator. We have, in the complex plane,

$$\oint \frac{e^{az}}{1 + e^z}\, dz = \lim_{R \to \infty} \left(\int_{-R}^{R} \frac{e^{ax}}{1 + e^x}\, dx - e^{i2\pi a} \int_{-R}^{R} \frac{e^{ax}}{1 + e^x}\, dx \right)$$

$$= (1 - e^{i2\pi a}) \int_{-\infty}^{\infty} \frac{e^{ax}}{1 + e^x}\, dx. \tag{7.22}$$

In addition there are two vertical sections $(0 \leqslant y \leqslant 2\pi)$, which vanish (exponentially) as $R \to \infty$.

Now where are the poles and what are the residues? We have a pole when

$$e^z = e^x e^{iy} = -1. \tag{7.23}$$

Equation 7.23 is satisfied at $z = 0 + i\pi$. By a Laurent expansion in powers of $(z - i\pi)$ the pole is seen to be a simple pole with a residue of $-e^{i\pi a}$. Then, applying the residue theorem once more,

$$(1 - e^{i2\pi a}) \int_{-\infty}^{\infty} \frac{e^{ax}}{1 + e^x}\, dx = 2\pi i(-e^{i\pi a}). \tag{7.24}$$

This quickly reduces to

$$\int_{-\infty}^{\infty} \frac{e^{ax}}{1 + e^x}\, dx = \frac{\pi}{\sin a\pi}, \qquad 0 < a < 1. \tag{7.25}$$

Using the beta function (Section 10.4), the integral can be shown to be equal to the product $(a - 1)!\, (-a)!$. This results in the interesting and useful factorial function relation

$$a!(-a)! = \frac{\pi a}{\sin \pi a}. \tag{7.26}$$

Although Eq. 7.25 holds for real a, $0 < a < 1$, Eq. 7.26 may be extended by analytic continuation to all values of a, real and complex, excluding only real integral values.

EXAMPLE 7.2.4

The quantum mechanical analysis of scattering leads to the function

$$I(\sigma) = \int_{-\infty}^{\infty} \frac{x \sin x\, dx}{x^2 - \sigma^2}, \tag{7.27}$$

where σ is real and positive. From the physical conditions of the problem there is a further requirement: $I(\sigma)$ is to have the form $e^{i\sigma}$ so that it will represent an outgoing scattered wave.

Using

$$\sin z = \frac{1}{i} \sinh iz$$

$$= \frac{1}{2i} e^{iz} - \frac{1}{2i} e^{-iz}, \qquad (7.28)$$

we write Eq. 7.27 in the complex plane as

$$I(\sigma) = I_1 + I_2, \qquad (7.29)$$

with

$$I_1 = \frac{1}{2i} \int_{-\infty}^{\infty} \frac{ze^{iz}}{z^2 - \sigma^2} \, dz,$$

$$I_2 = -\frac{1}{2i} \int_{-\infty}^{\infty} \frac{ze^{-iz}}{z^2 - \sigma^2} \, dz. \qquad (7.30)$$

Integral I_1 is similar to Example 7.2.2 and, as in that case, we may complete the contour by an infinite semicircle in the upper half plane. For I_2 the exponential is negative and we complete the contour by an infinite semicircle in the lower half plane, as shown in Fig. 7.7. As in Example 7.2.2, neither semicircle contributes anything to the integral.

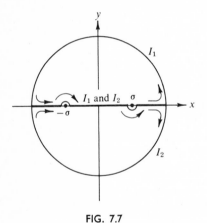

FIG. 7.7

There is still the problem of locating the poles and evaluating the residues. We find poles at $z = +\sigma$ and $z = -\sigma$ *on the contour of integration*. The residues are

	$z = \sigma$	$z = -\sigma$
I_1	$\dfrac{e^{i\sigma}}{2}$	$\dfrac{e^{-i\sigma}}{2}$
I_2	$\dfrac{e^{-i\sigma}}{2}$	$\dfrac{e^{i\sigma}}{2}$

Detouring around the poles, as shown in Fig. 7.7 (it matters little whether we go above or below), the residue theorem leads to

$$I_1 - \pi i \left(\frac{1}{2i}\right)\frac{e^{-i\sigma}}{2} + \pi i \left(\frac{1}{2i}\right)\frac{e^{i\sigma}}{2} = 2\pi i \left(\frac{1}{2i}\right)\frac{e^{i\sigma}}{2}, \qquad (7.31)$$

for we have enclosed the singularity at $z = \sigma$ but excluded the one at $z = -\sigma$. In similar fashion, but noting that the contour for I_2 is *clockwise*,

$$I_2 - \pi i \left(\frac{-1}{2i}\right)\frac{e^{i\sigma}}{2} + \pi i \left(\frac{-1}{2i}\right)\frac{e^{-i\sigma}}{2} = -2\pi i \left(\frac{-1}{2i}\right)\frac{e^{i\sigma}}{2}. \qquad (7.32)$$

Adding Eqs. 7.31 and 7.32, we have

$$I(\sigma) = I_1 + I_2 = \frac{\pi}{2}(e^{i\sigma} + e^{-i\sigma}) = \pi \cosh i\sigma$$

$$= \pi \cos \sigma. \tag{7.33}$$

This is a perfectly good evaluation of Eq. 7.27, but unfortunately the cosine dependence is appropriate for a standing wave and not for the outgoing scattered wave as specified.

To obtain the desired form we try a different technique. Instead of dodging around the singular points, let us move them off the real axis. Specifically, let $\sigma \to \sigma + i\gamma$, $-\sigma \to -\sigma - i\gamma$, where γ is positive but small and will eventually be made to approach zero, that is,

$$I(\sigma) = \lim_{\gamma \to 0} I(\sigma + i\gamma). \tag{7.34}$$

With this simple substitution, the first integral I_1 becomes

$$I_1(\sigma + i\gamma) = 2\pi i \left(\frac{1}{2i}\right) \frac{e^{i(\sigma+i\gamma)}}{2} \tag{7.35}$$

by direct application of the residue theorem. Also

$$I_2(\sigma + i\gamma) = -2\pi i \left(\frac{-1}{2i}\right) \frac{e^{i(\sigma+i\gamma)}}{2}. \tag{7.36}$$

Adding Eqs. 7.35 and 7.36 and then letting $\gamma \to 0$, we obtain

$$I(\sigma) = \lim_{\gamma \to 0} [I_1(\sigma + i\gamma) + I_2(\sigma + i\gamma)]$$

$$= \lim_{\gamma \to 0} \pi e^{i(\sigma+i\gamma)} = \pi e^{i\sigma}, \tag{7.37}$$

a result that does fit the boundary conditions of our scattering problem.

It is perhaps interesting to note that the substitution $\sigma \to \sigma - i\gamma$ would have led to

$$I(\sigma) = \pi e^{-i\sigma}, \tag{7.38}$$

which could represent an incoming wave. Our earlier result (Eq. 7.33) is seen to be the arithmetic average of Eqs. 7.37 and 7.38. This average is the Cauchy principle value of the integral. Note that we have these possibilities (Eqs. 7.33, 7.37 and 7.38) because our integral is an improper integral. It is not uniquely defined until we specify the particular limiting process (or average) to be used.

In Section 5.8 the Bernoulli numbers were defined by the expansion

$$\frac{x}{e^x - 1} = \sum_{n=0}^{\infty} \frac{B_n}{n!} x^n. \tag{7.39}$$

Replacing x with z, we have a Taylor series with

$$B_n = \frac{n!}{2\pi i} \oint_{C_0} \frac{z}{e^z - 1} \frac{dz}{z^{n+1}}, \tag{7.40}$$

where the contour C_0 is around the origin counterclockwise with $|z| < 2\pi$.

For $n = 0$ we have a simple pole at $z = 0$ with a residue of $+1$. Hence by Eq. 7.9

$$B_0 = \frac{0!}{2\pi i} \cdot 2\pi i(1) = 1. \tag{7.41}$$

For $n = 1$ the singularity at $z = 0$ becomes a second-order pole. The residue may be shown to be $-\frac{1}{2}$ by series expansion of the exponential, followed by a binomial expansion. This results in

$$B_1 = \frac{1!}{2\pi i} \cdot 2\pi i \left(-\frac{1}{2}\right) = -\frac{1}{2}. \tag{7.42}$$

For $n \geqslant 2$ this procedure becomes rather tedious, and we resort to a different means of evaluating Eq. 7.40. The contour is deformed, as shown in Fig. 7.8.

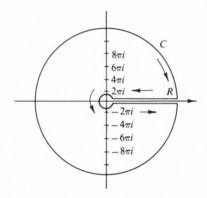

FIG. 7.8 Contour of integration for Bernoulli numbers

The new contour C still encircles the origin, as required, but now it also encircles (in a negative direction) an infinite series of singular points along the imaginary axis at $z = \pm p2\pi i$, $p = 1, 2, 3, \ldots$. The integration back and forth along the x-axis cancels out and for $R \to \infty$, the integration over the infinite circle, yields zero. Remember that $n \geqslant 2$. Therefore

$$\oint_{C_0} \frac{z}{e^z - 1} \frac{dz}{z^{n+1}} = -2\pi i \sum_{p=1}^{\infty} \text{residues} \qquad (z = \pm p2\pi i). \tag{7.43}$$

At $z = p2\pi i$ we have a simple pole with a residue $(p2\pi i)^{-n}$. When n is odd, the residue from $z = p2\pi i$ exactly cancels that from $z = -p2\pi i$ and $B_{n \text{ odd}} = 0$, $n = 3, 5, 7$, etc. For n even the residues add, giving

$$B_n = \frac{n!}{2\pi i}(-2\pi i)2 \sum_{p=1}^{\infty} \frac{1}{p^n(2\pi i)^n}$$

$$= -\frac{(-1)^{n/2}2n!}{(2\pi)^n} \sum_{p=1}^{\infty} p^{-n}$$

$$= -\frac{(-1)^{n/2}2n!}{(2\pi)^n} \zeta(n), \tag{7.44}$$

where $\zeta(n)$ is the Riemann zeta function introduced in Section 5.8. Equation 7.44 corresponds to Eq. 5.131 of Section 5.8.

EXERCISES

7.2.1 Determine the nature of the singularities of each of the following functions and evaluate the residues $(a > 0)$.

(a) $\dfrac{1}{z^2 + a^2}$.

(b) $\dfrac{1}{(z^2 + a^2)^2}$.

(c) $\dfrac{z^2}{(z^2 + a^2)^2}$.

(d) $\dfrac{\sin 1/z}{z^2 + a^2}$.

(e) $\dfrac{ze^{+iz}}{z^2 + a^2}$.

(f) $\dfrac{ze^{+iz}}{z^2 - a^2}$.

(g) $\dfrac{e^{+iz}}{z^2 - a^2}$.

(h) $\dfrac{z^{-k}}{z+1}$, $0 < k < 1$.

7.2.2 Evaluate the following definite integrals by the calculus of residues $(a > 0)$.

(a) $\displaystyle\int_{-\infty}^{\infty} \dfrac{dx}{(x^2 + a^2)^2}$.

Ans. $\dfrac{\pi}{2a^3}$.

(b) $\displaystyle\int_{-\infty}^{\infty} \dfrac{x^2\, dx}{(x^2 + a^2)^2}$.

Ans. $\dfrac{\pi}{2a}$.

(c) $\displaystyle\int_{-\infty}^{\infty} \dfrac{x^2\, dx}{(x^2 + a^2)^3}$.

Ans. $\dfrac{\pi}{8a^3}$.

(d) $\displaystyle\int_{-\infty}^{\infty} \dfrac{dx}{x^4 + a^4}$.

Ans. $\dfrac{\pi}{\sqrt{2}\, a^3}$.

7.2.3 The statement that the integral half way around a singular point is equal to one half the integral all the way around was limited to simple poles. Show, by a specific example, that

$$\int_{\text{Semicircle}} f(z)\, dz = \frac{1}{2} \oint_{\text{Circle}} f(z)\, dz$$

does not necessarily hold if the integral encircles a pole of higher order. *Hint.* Try $f(z) = z^{-2}$.

7.2.4 Show that

$$\int_0^{\infty} \frac{x^{-a}}{x + 1}\, dx = \frac{\pi}{\sin a\pi},$$

where $0 < a < 1$. This opens up another way of deriving the factorial function relation given by Eq. 7.26. *Hint.* You have a branch point and you will need a cut line. Recall that $z^{-a} = w$ in polar form is

$$[re^{i(\theta + 2\pi n)}]^{-a} = \rho e^{i\varphi},$$

which leads to $-a\theta - 2an\pi = \varphi$.

You must restrict n to zero (or any other single integer) in order that φ may be uniquely specified. Try the contour shown in Fig. 7.9.

7.2.5　In the quantum theory of atomic collisions we encounter the integral

$$I = \int_{-\infty}^{\infty} \frac{\sin t}{t} e^{ipt} \, dt$$

in which p is real. Show that

$$I = 0, \qquad |p| > 1$$
$$I = \pi, \qquad |p| < 1.$$

What happens if $p = \pm 1$?

7.2.6　If $f(z)$ is analytic for $y \geqslant 0$, except for isolated poles at $y > 0$, and $\lim_{|z| \to \infty} z f(z) = 0$, $0 \leqslant \arg z \leqslant \pi$, show that

$$\int_{-\infty}^{\infty} f(x) \, dx = 2\pi i \, \Sigma \text{ residues } (y > 0).$$

This would apply directly to all the integrals in Exercise 7.2.2.

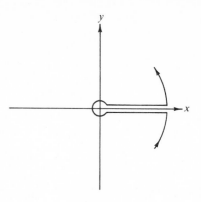

FIG. 7.9

7.2.7　Show that $(a > 0)$

(a) $\displaystyle \int_{-\infty}^{\infty} \frac{\cos x}{x^2 + a^2} \, dx = \pi e^{-a}.$

How is the right side modified if cos x is replaced by cos kx?

(b) $\displaystyle \int_{-\infty}^{\infty} \frac{x \sin x}{x^2 + a^2} \, dx = \pi e^{-a}.$

How is the right side modified if sin x is replaced by sin kx?

7.2.8　Use the calculus of residues to show that

$$\int_0^\pi \sin^{2n}\theta \, d\theta = \pi \frac{(2n)!}{2^{2n}(n!)^2}, \qquad n = 0, 1, 2, \ldots .$$

7.2.9　Prove that

$$\int_0^\infty \frac{\sin^2 x}{x^2} \, dx = \frac{\pi}{2}.$$

7.2.10　Apply the calculus of residues to show that

$$\int_0^{2\pi} \frac{d\theta}{1 + \varepsilon \cos \theta} = \frac{2\pi}{\sqrt{1 - \varepsilon^2}},$$

where $0 \leqslant \varepsilon < 1$.

7.2.11　Use the contour shown (Fig. 7.10) with $R \to \infty$ to prove that

$$\int_{-\infty}^{\infty} \frac{\sin x}{x} \, dx = \pi.$$

7.2.12　Show that

$$\int_0^\infty \frac{x^a}{(x+1)^2} \, dx = \frac{\pi a}{\sin \pi a},$$

where $-1 < a < 1$. Here is still another way of deriving Eq. 7.26. *Hint.* Use the contour shown in Fig. 7.11, noting that $z = 0$ is a branch point and the positive x-axis is a cut line.

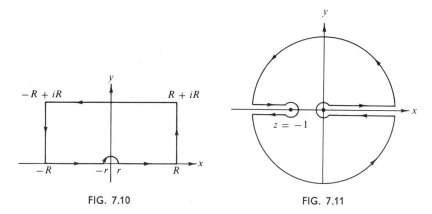

FIG. 7.10   FIG. 7.11

7.2.13 Evaluate $\oint e^{-z^2} dz$ over a sector bounded by $0 \leqslant \theta \leqslant \pi/4$, radius R, with $R \to \infty$. Show that

$$\int_0^\infty \cos(x^2)\, dx = \int_0^\infty \sin(x^2)\, dx = \frac{\sqrt{\pi}}{2\sqrt{2}}.$$

These are the Fresnel integrals. *Hint.*

$$\int_0^\infty e^{-x2}\, dx = \frac{\sqrt{\pi}}{2}.$$

7.2.14 Evaluate

$$\int_0^\infty \frac{(\ln x)^2}{1 + x^2}\, dx.$$

(a) by appropriate series expansion of the integrand to obtain

$$4 \sum_{n=0}^\infty (-1)^n (2n+1)^{-3},$$

(b) by contour integration to obtain

$$\frac{\pi^3}{8}.$$

FIG. 7.12

Hint. $x \to z = e^t$. Try the contour shown in Fig. 7.12, letting $R \to \infty$.

7.2.15 Show that

$$\int_0^{2\pi} \frac{d\theta}{1 - 2t \cos\theta + t^2} = \frac{2\pi}{1 - t^2}.$$

What limits are placed on the parameter t? Why?

7.3 Applications of the Calculus of Residues

Inversion of power series.   In Section 5.7 the problem of taking a known series expansion

$$w = a_1 z + a_2 z^2 + a_3 z^3 + \cdots \tag{7.45}$$

and rewriting it as

$$z = b_1 w + b_2 w^2 + b_3 w^3 + \cdots \tag{7.46}$$

was investigated. The first few coefficients b_i were found in terms of the known a_i

by a direct substitution procedure. We can now rederive these coefficients by a more powerful and more elegant method.

We need the equality

$$z(w) = \frac{1}{2\pi i} \int_C \frac{t(dw/dt)}{w(t) - w(z)} \, dt, \tag{7.47}$$

where t is a (complex) variable of integration. To verify Eq. 7.47 we calculate the residue at $t = z$. Using Exercise 7.1.1 with $m = 1$ and a Taylor expansion of $w(t)$ about the point $t = z$ we find that the residue of the integrand is

$$a_{-1} = \lim_{t \to z} \frac{(t - z)t(dw/dt)}{w(t) - w(z)}$$

$$= \lim_{t \to z} \frac{(t - z)z(dw/dt)}{w(z) + (t - z)(dw/dt) + [(t - z)^2/2!](d^2w/dt^2) + \cdots - w(z)}. \tag{7.48}$$

In the limit as $t \to z$, Eq. 7.48 reduces to $a_{-1} = z$ verifying Eq. 7.47.

The contour C in Eq. 7.47 is chosen so that $w(t) \neq 0$ on and within the contour except for the zero of $w(t)$ at the origin. Then z is restricted to keep $|w(z)| < |w(t)|$ over the entire contour. With this restriction the integrand may be expanded by the binomial theorem to yield

$$z(w) = \frac{1}{2\pi i} \oint \frac{t(dw/dt)}{w(t)} \sum_{n=0}^{\infty} \left[\frac{w(z)}{w(t)}\right]^n dt$$

$$= \sum_{n=0}^{\infty} [w(z)]^n \frac{1}{2\pi i} \oint \frac{t(dw/dt)}{[w(t)]^{n+1}} \, dt. \tag{7.49}$$

Comparing Eqs. 7.46 and 7.49, we equate coefficients of equal powers of $w(z)$ to obtain

$$b_n = \frac{1}{2\pi i} \oint \frac{t(dw/dt)}{[w(t)]^{n+1}} \, dt \tag{7.50}$$

Now the problem reduces to an evaluation of the integral in Eq. 7.50. From Eq. 7.45 the integrand I of Eq. 7.50 becomes

$$I = \frac{t(a_1 + 2a_2 t + \cdots)}{t^{n+1}(a_1 + a_2 t + \cdots)^{n+1}}, \tag{7.51}$$

showing a pole of order n at $t = 0$. Since $t = 0$ is the only zero of $w(t)$ on and within contour C,

$$b_n = \frac{1}{(n-1)!} \frac{d^{n-1}}{dt^{n-1}} \left[\frac{t^{n+1}(dw/dt)}{[w(t)]^{n+1}}\right]_{t=0} \tag{7.52}$$

by Exercise 7.1.1.

In an alternate procedure we integrate Eq. 7.50 by parts to obtain

$$b_n = \frac{1}{2\pi i} \oint \frac{t(dw/dt)}{w^{n+1}} \, dt = -\frac{1}{2\pi n i} \oint t \frac{d}{dt} [w^{-n}] \, dt$$

$$= \frac{1}{2\pi n i} \oint \frac{dt}{w^n}. \tag{7.53}$$

There is no "integrated part" because we have integrated a single-valued function over a closed loop. Now, applying the residue theorem, we have

$$b_n = \frac{1}{n!} \left[\frac{d^{n-1}}{dt^{n-1}} \left(\frac{t}{w(t)} \right)^n \right]_{t=0}. \tag{7.54}$$

This method of inverting a series is particularly useful when $w(t)$ can be expressed in closed form so that Eqs. 7.52 or 7.54 can be differentiated directly.

If the series expansion of $w(t)$ is used, we get the new coefficients b_i in terms of the original known a_j. The first few coefficients are

$$
\begin{aligned}
b_1 &= a_1^{-1}, \\
b_2 &= -a_2 a_1^{-3}, \\
b_3 &= a_1^{-3}(2a_2^2 a_1^{-2} - a_3 a_1^{-1}), \\
b_4 &= a_1^{-4}(-5a_2^3 a_1^{-3} + 5a_2 a_3 a_1^{-2} - a_4 a_1^{-1}),
\end{aligned}
\tag{7.55}
$$

in agreement with the results of Section 5.7.

Infinite products.   By Cauchy's integral formula (Section 6.3) and the residue theorem

$$\frac{1}{2\pi i} \oint_{C_m} \frac{f(z)}{z - z_0} \, dz = f(z_0) + \sum_{k=1}^{m} a_{-1}(z = z_k). \tag{7.56}$$

Here $f(z)$ is a function that is analytic everywhere except at isolated (first-order) poles, $z = z_k$, $k = 1, 2, 3, \dots, m$. The index k is ordered so that $|z_1| \leqslant |z_2| \leqslant |z_3| \leqslant \dots$. The contour C_m is a circle centered at the origin and enclosing poles at $z = z_1, z_2, \dots, z_m$. Equation 7.56 follows by deforming C_m, as shown in Fig. 7.13.

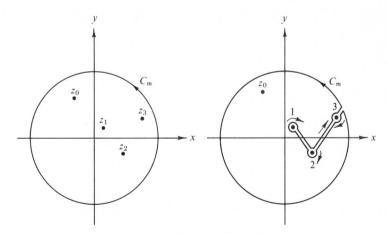

FIG. 7.13   Excluding isolated singularities

The residue of $f(z)/(z - z_0)$ at $z = z_k$ is just

$$a_{-1} = \lim_{z \to z_k} \frac{(z - z_k) f(z)}{z - z_0} = \frac{b_{-1}(z = z_k)}{z_k - z_0}, \tag{7.57}$$

where b_{-1} is the residue of $f(z)$ at $z = z_k$. Therefore Eq. 7.56 may be rewritten as

$$f(z_0) = \frac{1}{2\pi i} \oint_{C_m} \frac{f(z)}{z - z_0} dz + \sum_{k=1}^{m} \frac{b_{-1}(z = z_k)}{z_0 - z_k}, \qquad (7.58)$$

Returning to our original integral, we have the identity

$$\frac{1}{2\pi i} \oint_{C_m} \frac{f(z)}{z - z_0} dz = \frac{1}{2\pi i} \oint_{C_m} \frac{f(z)\, dz}{z} + \frac{1}{2\pi i} \oint_{C_m} \frac{z_0 f(z)\, dz}{z(z - z_0)}, \qquad (7.59)$$

Applying Eq. 7.58 to the first integral on the right side of Eq. 7.59, $z_0 = 0$, we obtain

$$\frac{1}{2\pi i} \oint_{C_m} \frac{f(z)}{z} dz = f(0) + \sum_{k=1}^{m} \frac{b_{-1}(z = z_k)}{z_k}. \qquad (7.60)$$

Now if $f(z)/z^2$ falls off faster than $|z|^{-1}$ as $|z| \to \infty$, the second integral on the right-hand side of Eq. 7.59 will vanish as the radius of C_m is extended to infinity ($m \to \infty$). Then, substituting Eq. 7.60 into Eq. 7.59 and the result into Eq. 7.58, we have

$$f(z_0) = f(0) + \sum_{k=1}^{\infty} b_{-1}\left(\frac{1}{z_0 - z_k} + \frac{1}{z_k}\right). \qquad (7.61)$$

The next step is to replace $f(z)$ by a function that is more convenient to handle. Suppose $g(z)$ is a function that is everywhere analytic in the finite complex plane and has simple zeros at isolated points $z = z_k$. We construct

$$f(z) = \frac{dg(z)/dz}{g(z)} = \frac{g'}{g}, \qquad (7.62)$$

and this function $f(z)$ will satisfy the conditions of Eq. 7.56. With b_{-1}, the residue of g'/g; equal to unity at all poles, z_k (Eq. 7.61), becomes

$$\frac{g'(z)}{g(z)} = \frac{g'(0)}{g(0)} + \sum_{k=1}^{\infty} \left(\frac{1}{z - z_k} + \frac{1}{z_k}\right). \qquad (7.63)$$

The subscript zero of the z_0 has been dropped as no longer necessary. By integrating Eq. 7.63 from 0 to z we obtain

$$\ln g(z) = \ln g(0) + \frac{g'(0)}{g(0)} z + \sum_{k=1}^{\infty} \left[\ln\left(1 - \frac{z}{z_k}\right) + \frac{z}{z_k}\right]. \qquad (7.64)$$

Converting to exponential form, we have

$$g(z) = g(0) \exp\left\{\frac{g'(0)}{g(0)} z + \sum_{k=1}^{\infty} \left[\ln\left(1 - \frac{z}{z_k}\right) + \frac{z}{z_k}\right]\right\} \qquad (7.65)$$

$$= g(0) \exp\left(\frac{g'(0)}{g(0)} z\right) \prod_{k=1}^{\infty} \left[\left(1 - \frac{z}{z_k}\right) e^{z/z_k}\right],$$

giving $g(z)$ as an infinite product.

This final result (Eq. 7.65) is sometimes called the Weierstrass factor theorem. In using this equation it should be remembered that $g(z)$ is required to be analytic in the entire (finite) complex plane and that it has (simple) zeros at $z = z_k$. Also $g'(z)/zg(z)$ must vanish as $|z| \to \infty$.

EXAMPLE 7.3.1

Expand $(\sin z)/z$ as an infinite product. We note that $g(z) = (\sin z)/z$ has no singularities in the finite plane and that it has simple zeros at $z = \pm k\pi$, $k = 1, 2, 3, \ldots$. Therefore $z_k = \pm k\pi$. Since

$$g(0) = 1 \quad \text{and} \quad g'(0) = 0, \tag{7.66}$$

Eq. 7.65 yields

$$\frac{\sin z}{z} = \prod_{k=1}^{\infty} \left(1 - \frac{z}{k\pi}\right) e^{z/k\pi} \left(1 + \frac{z}{k\pi}\right) e^{-z/k\pi}$$

$$= \prod_{k=1}^{\infty} \left(1 - \frac{z^2}{k^2 \pi^2}\right). \tag{7.67}$$

This is the origin of Eq. 5.155 of Section 5.9.

Stability of amplifying circuits. An amplifier with feedback can be represented by a diagram (Fig. 7.14). The original signal is E_s and the final output E_0.

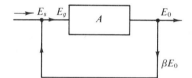

FIG. 7.14 Feedback circuit

Some of the output, βE_0, in which β may be a complex quantity, is fed back to join the signal E_s. The sum E_g is the actual input to the amplifying stage. We have

$$E_g = E_s + \beta E_0. \tag{7.68}$$

Also

$$E_0 = AE_g, \tag{7.69}$$

where A is the amplification. Like β, A may be complex. Both A and β may depend on the angular frequency ω of the input (and output) signals. Eliminating E_g, we have

$$E_0 = AE_s + A\beta E_0. \tag{7.70}$$

Instability (oscillation, etc.) is characterized by an output without any input, that is, $E_s = 0$, $E_0 \neq 0$. From Eq. 7.70 the condition for instability becomes

$$1 - A(\omega)\,\beta(\omega) = 0, \tag{7.71}$$

in which the real part of ω is greater than zero to correspond to a physically attainable frequency.

If $f(z) = 1 - A(z)\beta(z) = 0$ has a solution on the positive real axis, we have an exponentially increasing instability. If there is a complex solution in the right half of the complex plane, an oscillatory instability will result. So we try to determine whether $1 - A\beta$ has any solutions or roots anywhere in the right half of the complex plane.

Now the number of zeros (N), each multiplied by its multiplicity, minus the number of poles (P), each multiplied by its order or multiplicity, of a function $f(z)$ is given by[1]

$$\frac{1}{2\pi i} \oint \frac{f'(z)}{f(z)} \, dz = N - P. \tag{7.72}$$

Here N and P include the zeros and poles within the contour C. To prove Eq. 7.72 consider a zero of order n of $f(z)$ at $z = z_1$. Then

$$f(z) = (z - z_1)^n \, g(z). \tag{7.73}$$

Differentiating, we obtain

$$f'(z) = n(z - z_1)^{n-1} \, g(z) + (z - z_1)^n \, g'(z) \tag{7.74}$$

and the integrand of Eq. 7.72 becomes

$$\frac{f'(z)}{f(z)} = \frac{n}{z - z_1} + \frac{g'(z)}{g(z)}. \tag{7.75}$$

Integrating around z_1, we have

$$\frac{1}{2\pi i} \oint_{C_1} \frac{f'(z)}{f(z)} \, dz = n, \tag{7.76}$$

the multiplicity of the zero.

For a pole of order m at $z = z_2$

$$f(z) = (z - z_2)^{-m} \, h(z). \tag{7.77}$$

This time the integrand becomes

$$\frac{f'(z)}{f(z)} = \frac{-m}{z - z_2} + \frac{h'(z)}{h(z)}, \tag{7.78}$$

and integrating around the pole at z_2

$$\frac{1}{2\pi i} \oint_{C_2} \frac{f'(z)}{f(z)} \, dz = -m, \tag{7.79}$$

the negative of the order of the pole. Combining Eqs. 7.76 and 7.79, we obtain Eq. 7.72.

We shall assume that our function $f(z) = 1 - A\beta$ has no poles for R.P. (ω) $\geqslant 0$. Then, if we integrate $f'(z)/f(z)$ around the right side of the complex plane, Eq. 7.72 will indicate whether we have included any zeros. If

$$\oint_C \frac{f'(z)}{f(z)} \, dz = 0, \tag{7.80}$$

[1] This is a special case of a more general integral sometimes known as Cauchy's integral.

then $N = 0$ and our system is stable. Here C is the imaginary axis and an (infinite) semicircle enclosing the right side of the z-plane.

To evaluate Eq. 7.72, that is, to check on Eq. 7.80, let

$$f(z) = re^{i\theta},$$
$$\ln f(z) = \ln r + i\theta. \tag{7.81}$$

Then

$$\frac{f'(z)}{f(z)} = \frac{d}{dz} \ln f(z) = \frac{1}{r} \frac{dr}{dz} + i \frac{d\theta}{dz}. \tag{7.82}$$

Substituting into Eq. 7.72, we obtain

$$\oint_C \frac{f'(z)}{f(z)} dz = \oint \frac{dr}{r} + i \oint d\theta. \tag{7.83}$$

Since C is a closed contour, the first integral on the right (which yields $\ln r$) vanishes. The second integral yields 2π or zero, depending on whether the origin is included or excluded. We therefore conclude that the stability of our amplifier depends on whether a polar plot of $f(z) = 1 - A(z)\beta(z)$ excludes the origin as z ranges along the imaginary axis from $-i\infty$ to $+i\infty$.[1] If the origin is *not* included,

$$\oint d\theta = 0, \tag{7.84}$$

$$\frac{1}{2\pi i} \oint_C \frac{f'(z)}{f(z)} dz = N = 0, \tag{7.85}$$

and there are no zeros in the right half plane. Hence the amplifier is stable. This is the Nyquist stability criterion.

EXERCISES

7.3.1 The quantum mechanical theory of the photoionization of hydrogen involves the contour integral

$$J = \oint \left(z + \frac{1}{2}\right)^{-in-2} \left(z - \frac{1}{2}\right)^{in-2} \left(z - \frac{in}{2}\right)^{-2} dz,$$

where n is real but *not* an integer. The contour encircles the two branch points $z = \pm 1/2$ as shown in the diagram. The contour may be extended as shown in Fig. 7.15.
(a) Justify this extension of the original contour.
(b) Using the extended contour, evaluate the integral J.

$$Ans. \ a_{-1} = \frac{i64n}{(n^2 + 1)^3} \left(\frac{in - 1}{in + 1}\right)^{in},$$

$$J = \frac{128n\pi}{(n^2 + 1)^3} e^{-2n\cot^{-1}n}.$$

[1] For $\omega \to \infty$, $A \to 0$. Hence the infinite semicircle maps into the point $f(z) = 1$.

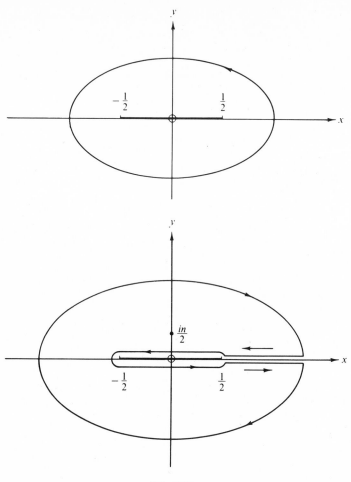

FIG. 7.15

7.3.2 The Riemann zeta function may be represented by the integral

$$\zeta(s) = \frac{1}{(s-1)!} \int_0^\infty \frac{x^{s-1} e^{-x}}{1 - e^{-x}} \, dx, \qquad \text{R.P.}(s) > 1.$$

From a consideration of

$$\int_C \frac{(-z)^{s-1} e^{-z}}{1 - e^{-z}} \, dz$$

show that

$$\zeta(s) = -\frac{(-s)!}{2\pi i} \int_C \frac{(-z)^{s-1} e^{-z}}{1 - e^{-z}} \, dz,$$

which is valid for all s in the complex s-plane except the discrete points $s = 1, 2, 3, \ldots$. The contour C is shown in Fig. 7.16. This represents an analytic continuation of $\zeta(s)$ over the entire complex plane.

7.3.3 Derive the infinite product representation

$$\cos x = \prod_{n=1}^\infty \left[1 - \frac{4x^2}{(2n-1)^2 \pi^2} \right].$$

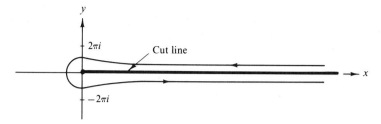

FIG. 7.16   Riemann zeta function contour

7.3.4   The product z times the gamma function, $z\Gamma(z)$ has simple poles at $z = -1, -2, -3, \ldots,$ $-n, \ldots$. Develop an infinite product representation of the reciprocal of the gamma function. *Hint*. You will encounter the Euler-Mascheroni constant.

7.3.5   (a) The function $g(z)$ is analytic in the entire finite complex plane and has simple zeros at $z = z_k$. Further, $g'(z)/z\,g(z)$ vanishes as $|z| \to \infty$. If, finally, $g(z)$ is an even function of z, show that

$$g(z) = g(0) \prod_{k=1}^{\infty} \left(1 - \frac{z^2}{z_k^2}\right),$$

where only one of the two zeros z_i and $-z_i$ is included in the infinite product.
(b) If $g(0) = 1$, show that

$$g''(0) = -2\sum_{k=1}^{\infty} \frac{1}{z_k^2},$$

$$g^{(4)}(0) = 3[g''(0)]^2 - 12\sum_{k=1}^{\infty} \frac{1}{z_k^4}.$$

7.3.6   From the results of Exercise 7.3.5 show that

$$\sum_{n=1}^{\infty} n^{-2} = \frac{\pi^2}{6},$$

$$\sum_{n=1}^{\infty} n^{-4} = \frac{\pi^4}{90},$$

in agreement with Section 5.8. *Hint*. Try $g(z) = (\sin z)/z$.

7.3.7   A simple series RCL circuit (Fig. 7.17) obeys the equation

$$L\ddot{I} + R\dot{I} + C^{-1}I = 0$$

for $t > 0$; the switch is closed at $t = 0$. Assume a solution of the form

$$I = I_0 e^{pt}.$$

Show that if
(a) $R = 0$, then p is on the imaginary axis (steady oscillation),
(b) $0 < \dfrac{R}{2L} < \dfrac{1}{\sqrt{LC}}$, then p is in the left half of the complex plane (damped oscillations),
(c) $\dfrac{R}{2L} = \dfrac{1}{\sqrt{LC}}$, then p is on the negative real axis, double root (critical damping),
(d) $\dfrac{R}{2L} > \dfrac{1}{\sqrt{LC}}$, then p is on the negative real axis (overdamping).

FIG. 7.17   RCL Circuit

Note that if R is made negative in these last three cases p goes into the right half of the complex plane and we have instability.

7.3.8 (a) Rederive the differential expressions for series coefficients b_i (Eqs. 7.52 and 7.54) for the case

$$w = \sum_{n=1}^{\infty} a_n(z - a)^n.$$

(b) Using the result of part (a), find $z(w)$ when

$$w = \frac{z - a}{\sin z} = a_1(z - a) + a_2(z - a)^2 + \cdots.$$

This is Kepler's equation of astronomy.

$$Ans. \ z = a + w \sin a + w^2 \sin a \cos a + \cdots + \frac{w^n}{n!} \frac{d^{n-1}}{dz^{n-1}} \sin^n z \Big|_{z=a} + \cdots.$$

7.3.9 (Inversion of a power series.) With the behavior of Eq. 7.50 for $n = 0$ ($b_0 = 0$), explain why the series being inverted (Eq. 7.45) was adjusted to have *no constant* term.

7.4 The Method of Steepest Descents

In analyzing problems in mathematical physics it is often desirable to know the behavior of a function for large values of the variable, that is, the asymptotic behavior of the function. Specific examples are furnished by the various Bessel functions (Chapter 11) and by the gamma function (Chapter 10). The method of steepest descents is one of determining such asymptotic behavior when the function can be expressed as an integral of the general form

$$I(s) = \int_C g(z) \, e^{sf(z)} \, dz. \tag{7.86}$$

For the present, let us take s to be real. The contour of integration C is then chosen so that the real part of $f(z)$ approaches minus infinity at both limits and that the integrand will vanish at the limits, or is chosen as a closed contour. It is further assumed that the factor $g(z)$ in the integrand is dominated by the exponential in the region of interest.

If the parameter s is large and positive, the value of the integrand will become large when the real part of $f(z)$ is large and small when the real part of $f(z)$ is small or negative. In particular, as s is permitted to increase indefinitely (leading to the asymptotic dependence), the entire contribution of the integrand to the integral will come from the region in which the real part of $f(z)$ takes on a positive maximum value. Away from this positive maximum the integrand will become negligibly small in comparison. This is seen by expressing $f(z)$ as

$$f(z) = u(x, y) + i \, v(x, y). \tag{7.87}$$

Then the integral may be written

$$I(s) = \int_C g(z) \, e^{su(x,y)} e^{isv(x,y)} \, dz. \tag{7.88}$$

If now, in addition, we impose the condition that the imaginary part of the exponent, $i \, v(x, y)$, be constant in the region in which the real part takes on its maximum value, that is, $v(x, y) = v(x_0, y_0) = v_0$, we may approximate the integral by

$$I(s) \approx e^{isv_0} \int_C g(z) \, e^{su(x,y)} \, dz. \tag{7.89}$$

Away from the maximum of the real part, the imaginary part may be permitted to oscillate as it wishes, for the integrand is negligibly small and the varying phase factor is therefore irrelevant.

The real part of $s f(z)$ is a maximum for a given s when the real part of $f(z)$, $u(x, y)$, is a maximum. This implies that

$$\frac{\partial u}{\partial x} = \frac{\partial u}{\partial y} = 0 \tag{7.90}$$

and therefore, by use of the Cauchy Riemann conditions of Section 6.1, that

$$\frac{d f(z)}{dz} = 0. \tag{7.91}$$

We proceed to search for such zeros of the derivative.

It is essential to note that the maximum value of $u(x, y)$ is the maximum only along a given contour. In the finite plane neither the real nor the imaginary part of our analytic function possesses an absolute maximum. This may be seen by recalling that both u and v satisfy Laplace's equation

$$\frac{\partial^2 u}{\partial x^2} + \frac{\partial^2 u}{\partial y^2} = 0. \tag{7.92}$$

From this, if the second derivative with respect to x is positive, the second derivative with respect to y must be negative, and therefore neither u nor v can possess an absolute maximum or minimum. Since the function $f(z)$ was taken to be analytic, singular points are clearly excluded. The vanishing of the derivative (Eq. 7.91) then implies that we have a saddle point, a stationary value, which may be a maximum of $u(x, y)$ for one contour and a minimum for another.

Our problem, then, is to choose the contour of integration to satisfy two conditions. (a) The contour must be chosen so that $u(x, y)$ has a maximum at the saddle point. (b) The contour must pass through the saddle in such a way that the imaginary part, $v(x, y)$, is a constant. This second condition leads to the path of steepest descent and gives the method its name. From Section 6.1, especially Exercise 6.1.3, and Section 6.6 we know that the curves corresponding to $u = $ constant and $v = $ constant form an orthogonal system. This means that a curve $v = c_i$, constant, is everywhere tangential to the gradient of u, ∇u. Hence the curve $v = $ constant is the curve that gives the line of steepest descent from the saddle point.[1]

At the saddle point the function $f(z)$ can be expanded in a Taylor series to give

$$f(z) = f(z_0) + \tfrac{1}{2}(z - z_0)^2 f''(z_0) + \cdots. \tag{7.93}$$

The first derivative is absent, since obviously Eq. 7.91 is satisfied. The first correction

---

[1] The line of steepest ascent is also characterized by constant v. The saddle point must be inspected carefully to distinguish the line of steepest descent from the line of steepest ascent. This is discussed later in two examples.

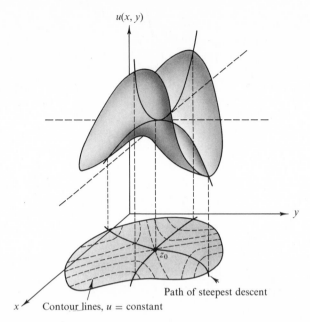

FIG. 7.18 A saddle point

term, $\frac{1}{2}(z - z_0)^2 f''(z_0)$, is real and negative. It is real, for we have specified that the imaginary part shall be constant along our contour and negative because we are moving down from the saddle point or mountain pass. Then, assuming that $f''(z_0) \neq 0$,

$$f(z) - f(z_0) \approx \tfrac{1}{2}(z - z_0)^2 f''(z_0) = -\tfrac{1}{2s} t^2, \tag{7.94}$$

which serves to define a new function t. If $(z - z_0)$ is written in polar form

$$(z - z_0) = \delta e^{i\alpha}, \tag{7.95}$$

(with the phase α held constant), we have

$$t^2 = -s f''(z_0)\, \delta^2 e^{2i\alpha}. \tag{7.96}$$

Since t is real,[1] it may be written

$$t = \pm \delta |s f''(z_0)|^{1/2}. \tag{7.97}$$

Substituting into Eq. 7.86, we obtain

$$I(s) \approx g(z_0)\, e^{sf(z_0)} \int_{-\infty}^{\infty} e^{-t^2/2}\, \frac{dz}{dt}\, dt. \tag{7.98}$$

Since

$$\frac{dz}{dt} = \left(\frac{dt}{dz}\right)^{-1} = \left(\frac{dt}{d\delta}\frac{d\delta}{dz}\right)^{-1} = |s f''(z_0)|^{-1/2} e^{i\alpha}, \tag{7.99}$$

Eq. 7.98 becomes

$$I(s) \approx \frac{g(z_0)\, e^{sf(z_0)} e^{i\alpha}}{|s f''(z_0)|^{1/2}} \int_{-\infty}^{\infty} e^{-t^2/2}\, dt. \tag{7.100}$$

[1] The phase of the contour (specified by α) at the saddle point is chosen so that I.P.$[f(z) - f(z_0)] = 0$, that is, $\frac{1}{2}(z - z_0)^2 f''(z_0)$ must be real.

It will be noted that the limits have been set as minus infinity to plus infinity. This is permissible, for the integrand is essentially zero when t departs appreciably from the origin. Noting that the remaining integral is just a Gauss error integral, we finally obtain

$$I(s) \approx \frac{\sqrt{2\pi}\, g(z_0)\, e^{sf(z_0)} e^{i\alpha}}{|s f''(z_0)|^{1/2}}. \tag{7.101}$$

The phase α was introduced in Eq. 7.95 as the phase of the contour as it passed through the saddle point. It is chosen so that the two conditions given [$\alpha = $ constant; R.P. $f(z) = $ maximum] are satisfied. It sometimes happens that the contour passes through two or more saddle points in succession. If this is the case, we need only add the contribution made by Eq. 7.101 from each of the saddle points in order to get an approximation for the total integral.

One note of warning: we assumed that the only significant contribution to the integral came from the immediate vicinity of the saddle point(s) $z = z_0$, that is,

$$\text{R.P.}[f(z)] = u(x, y) \ll u(x_0, y_0)$$

over the entire contour away from $z_0 = x_0 + iy_0$. This condition must be checked for each new problem.

EXAMPLE 7.4.1

In Section 11.3 it is shown that the Hankel functions, which satisfy Bessel's equation, may be defined by

$$H_\nu^{(1)}(s) = \frac{1}{\pi i} \int_{0C_1}^{-\infty} e^{(s/2)(z - 1/z)} \frac{dz}{z^{\nu+1}} \tag{7.102a}$$

$$H_\nu^{(2)}(s) = \frac{1}{\pi i} \int_{-\infty C_2}^{0} e^{(s/2)(z - 1/z)} \frac{dz}{z^{\nu+1}}. \tag{7.102b}$$

The contour C_1 is the curve in the upper half plane of Fig. 7.19. The contour C_2 is

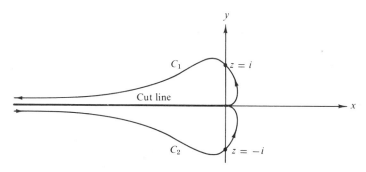

FIG. 7.19 Hankel function contours

in the lower half plane. We apply the method of steepest descents to the first Hankel function, $H_\nu^{(1)}(s)$, which is conveniently in the form specified by Eq. 7.86, with $f(z)$ given by

$$f(z) = \frac{1}{2}\left(z - \frac{1}{z}\right). \tag{7.103}$$

By differentiating we obtain

$$f'(z) = \frac{1}{2} + \frac{1}{2z^2}. \tag{7.104}$$

Setting $f'(z) = 0$ in accordance with Eq. 7.91,

$$z = i, -i. \tag{7.105}$$

Hence there are saddle points at $z = +i$ and $z = -i$. The integral for $H_\nu^{(1)}(s)$ is chosen so that it starts at the origin, moves out tangentially to the positive real axis, then around through the saddle point at $z = +i$, and on out to minus infinity, asymptotic with the negative real axis. We must choose the contour through the point $z = +i$ so that the real part of $(z - 1/z)$ will be a maximum and the phase will be constant in the vicinity of the saddle point.

In the vicinity of the saddle point at $z_0 = +i$ we have

$$z - i = \delta e^{i\alpha}, \tag{7.106}$$

where δ is a small number. Then

$$2f(z) = z - \frac{1}{z} = \delta e^{i\alpha} + i - \frac{1}{\delta e^{i\alpha} + i}$$

$$= \delta \cos \alpha + i(\delta \sin \alpha + 1) - \frac{1}{\delta \cos \alpha + i(\delta \sin \alpha + 1)}$$

$$= \delta \cos \alpha + i(\delta \sin \alpha + 1) - \frac{\delta \cos \alpha - i(\delta \sin \alpha + 1)}{1 + 2\delta \sin \alpha + \delta^2}. \tag{7.107}$$

Therefore our real part becomes

$$\text{R.P.}\left(z - \frac{1}{z}\right) = \delta \cos \alpha - \delta \cos \alpha (1 + 2\delta \sin \alpha + \delta^2)^{-1}. \tag{7.108}$$

Recalling that δ is small, we expand by the binomial theorem and neglect terms of order δ^3 and higher.

$$\text{R.P.}\left(z - \frac{1}{z}\right) = 2\delta^2 \cos \alpha \sin \alpha + O(\delta^3) \approx \delta^2 \sin 2\alpha. \tag{7.109}$$

We see that the real part of $(z - 1/z)$ will take on an extreme value if $\sin 2\alpha$ is an extremum, that is, if 2α is $\pi/2$ or $3\pi/2$. Hence the phase of the contour α should be chosen to be $\pi/4$ or $3\pi/4$. One choice will represent the path of steepest descent we want. The other choice will represent a path of steepest ascent that we must avoid. We distinguish the two possibilities by substituting in the specific values of α. For $\alpha = \pi/4$

$$\text{R.P.}\left(z - \frac{1}{z}\right) = \delta^2, \tag{7.110}$$

whereas for $\alpha = 3\,\pi/4$

$$\text{R.P.}\left(z - \frac{1}{z}\right) = -\delta^2. \tag{7.111}$$

Clearly the first choice leads to a minimum value at the saddle point ($\delta = 0$), whereas the second choice leads to a maximum value. The second choice, then, $\alpha = 3\pi/4$, defines the contour through the saddle point that follows the path of steepest descent.

Direct substitution into Eq. 7.101 now yields

$$H_\nu^{(1)}(s) = \frac{1}{\pi i}\,\frac{\sqrt{2\pi}\,i^{-\nu-1}e^{(s/2)(i-1/i)}e^{i(3\pi/4)}}{|(s/2)(-2/i^3)|^{1/2}}$$

$$= \sqrt{\frac{2}{\pi s}}\,e^{(i\pi/2)(-\nu-2)}e^{is}e^{i(3\pi/4)}. \tag{7.112}$$

By combining terms we finally obtain

$$H_\nu^{(1)}(s) \approx \sqrt{\frac{2}{\pi s}}\,e^{i(s-\nu(\pi/2)-\pi/4)} \tag{7.113}$$

as the leading term of the asymptotic expansion of the Hankel function $H_\nu^{(1)}(s)$. Additional terms, if desired, may be picked up by the Stokes method, described in Section 11.5.

EXAMPLE 7.4.2

In many physical problems, particularly in the field of statistical mechanics, it is desirable to have an accurate approximation of the gamma or factorial function of very large numbers. As developed in Section 10.1, the factorial function may be defined by the integral

$$s! = \int_0^\infty \rho^s e^{-\rho}\,d\rho = s^{s+1}\int_{0C}^\infty e^{s(\ln z - z)}\,dz. \tag{7.114}$$

Here we have made the substitution $\rho = zs$ in order to throw the integral into the form required by Eq. 7.86. As before, we assume that s is real and positive, from which it follows that the integrand vanishes at the limits 0 and ∞. By differentiating the z-dependence appearing in the exponent, we obtain

$$\frac{df(z)}{dz} = \frac{d}{dz}(\ln z - z) = \frac{1}{z} - 1, \tag{7.115}$$

which shows that the point $z = 1$ is a saddle point. We let

$$z - 1 = \delta e^{i\alpha}, \tag{7.116}$$

with δ small to describe the contour in the vicinity of the saddle point. Substituting into $f(z)$, we develop a series expansion

$$f(z) = \ln(1 + \delta e^{i\alpha}) - (1 + \delta e^{i\alpha})$$
$$= \delta e^{i\alpha} - \tfrac{1}{2}\delta^2 e^{2i\alpha} + \cdots - 1 - \delta e^{i\alpha}$$
$$= -1 - \tfrac{1}{2}\delta^2 e^{2i\alpha}. \tag{7.117}$$

From this we see that the integrand takes on a maximum value (e^{-s}) at the saddle point if we choose our contour C to follow the real axis, a conclusion that the reader may well have reached more or less intuitively.

Direct substitution into Eq. 7.101 with $\alpha = 0$ now gives

$$s! \approx \frac{\sqrt{2\pi s^{s+1}e^{-s}}}{|s(-1^{-2})|^{1/2}} \tag{7.118}$$

Thus the first term in the asymptotic expansion of the factorial function is

$$s! \approx \sqrt{2\pi s}\, s^s e^{-s}. \tag{7.119}$$

Additional terms in the asymptotic series are developed in Section 10.3. Equation 7.119 is Stirling's formula.

In the foregoing example the calculation was carried out by assuming s to be real. This assumption is not necessary. The student may show (Exercise 7.4.4) that Eq. 7.119 also holds when s is replaced by the complex variable w, provided only that the real part of w is required to be large and positive.

EXERCISES

7.4.1   Using the method of steepest descents, evaluate the second Hankel function given by

$$H_\nu^{(2)}(s) = \frac{1}{\pi i}\int_{-\infty C_2}^{0} e^{(s/2)(z-1/z)}\frac{dz}{z^{\nu+1}},$$

with contour C_2 as shown in Fig. 7.19.   *Ans.* $H_\nu^{(2)}(s) \approx \sqrt{\dfrac{2}{\pi s}}\, e^{-i(s-\pi/4-\nu\pi/2)}.$

7.4.2   Determine the asymptotic dependence of the modified Bessel functions $I_\nu(x)$, given

$$I_\nu(x) = \frac{1}{2\pi i}\int_C e^{(x/2)(t+1/t)}\frac{dt}{t^{\nu+1}}.$$

The contour starts and ends at $t = -\infty$, encircling the origin in a positive sense and passing through *two* saddle points.

Ans. $I_\nu(x) \approx \dfrac{e^x}{\sqrt{2\pi x}}.$

7.4.3   Determine the asymptotic dependence of the modified Bessel function of the second kind, $K_\nu(x)$, by using

$$K_\nu(x) = \frac{1}{2}\int_0^{\infty} e^{(-x/2)(s+1/s)}\frac{ds}{s^{1-\nu}}.$$

Ans. $K_\nu(x) \approx \sqrt{\dfrac{\pi}{2x}}\, e^{-x}.$

7.4.4   Show that Stirling's formula

$$s! \approx \sqrt{2\pi s}\, s^s e^{-s}$$

holds for complex values of s (with the real part of s large and positive). *Hint.* This involves assigning a phase to s and then demanding that the imaginary part $[sf(z)] = \text{constant}$ in the vicinity of the saddle point.

7.4.5 (a) In applying the method of steepest descent to the Hankel function $H_\nu^{(1)}(s)$, show that

$$\text{R.P.}[f(z)] < \text{R.P.}[f(z_0)] = 0$$

for z on the contour C_1 but away from the point $z = z_0 = i$.

(b) Show that $f(z) \geqslant 0$ for $z = re^{i\theta}$; $0 \leqslant r \leqslant 1$, $\pi \leqslant \theta \leqslant 3\pi/2$.

This is why C, may *not* be deformed to pass through the second saddle point $z = -i$.

$$\frac{1}{\sqrt{a\pi}}\, e^{-x^2/a} \qquad\qquad \frac{1}{\pi}\frac{a}{a^2+x^2}$$

a   c

CHAPTER 8

SECOND-ORDER DIFFERENTIAL EQUATIONS

8.1 Partial Differential Equations of Theoretical Physics

Almost all of the elementary and a great many of the advanced parts of theoretical physics are formulated in terms of differential equations, often partial differential equations. Among the most frequently encountered are the following:

1. Laplace's equation, $\nabla^2\psi = 0$.
    This very common and very important equation occurs in studies of
    a. electromagnetic phenomena including electrostatics, dielectrics, steady currents, and magnetostatics,
    b. hydrodynamics (irrotational flow of perfect fluid and surface waves),
    c. heat flow,
    d. gravitation.

2. Poisson's equation, $\nabla^2\psi = -\rho/\varepsilon_0$.

3. The wave (Helmholtz) and time-independent diffusion equations, $\nabla^2\psi \pm k^2\psi = 0$.
    These equations appear in such diverse phenomena as
    a. elastic waves in solids including vibrating strings, bars, membranes,
    b. sound or acoustics,
    c. electromagnetic waves,
    d. nuclear reactors.

4. The time-dependent diffusion equation

$$\nabla^2\psi = \frac{1}{a^2}\frac{\partial\psi}{\partial t}$$

and the corresponding four-dimensional forms involving the d'Alembertian, a four-dimensional analogue of the Laplacian in Minkowski space,

$$\Box^2 = \nabla^2 + \frac{\partial^2}{\partial x_4^2} = \frac{\partial^2}{\partial x^2} + \frac{\partial^2}{\partial y^2} + \frac{\partial^2}{\partial z^2} + \frac{\partial^2}{(ic)^2\partial t^2}.$$

5. The time-dependent wave equation, $\Box^2\psi = 0$.

6. The scalar potential equation, $\Box^2\psi = -\rho/\varepsilon_0$.

7. The Klein-Gordon equation, $\Box^2\psi = \mu^2\psi$, and the corresponding vector equations in which the scalar function ψ is replaced by a vector function.

Other more complicated forms are common.

8. The Schrödinger wave equation,

$$-\frac{\hbar^2}{2m}\,\mathbf{V}^2\psi + V\psi = i\hbar\,\frac{\partial\psi}{\partial t}$$

and

$$-\frac{\hbar^2}{2m}\,\mathbf{V}^2\psi + V\psi = E\psi$$

for the time-independent case.

9. The equations for elastic waves and for viscous fluids and the telegraphy equation.

10. Maxwell's coupled partial differential equations for electric and magnetic fields and those of Dirac for relativistic electron wave functions.

All of these equations can be written in the form

$$H\psi = F,$$

in which H is a differential operator,

$$H\!\left(\frac{\partial}{\partial x},\frac{\partial}{\partial y},\frac{\partial}{\partial z},\frac{\partial}{\partial t},\,x,\,y,\,z\right),$$

F is a known function, and ψ is the unknown scalar (or vector) function.

Two characteristics are particularly important:

1. All of these equations are linear[1] in the unknown function ψ. As the easier physical and mathematical problems are being solved, nonlinear differential equations such as those describing shock wave phenomena are receiving more and more attention. However, both the nonlinear differential equations themselves and the numerical techniques that we often resort to for determining solutions are beyond the scope of this book.

2. These equations are all second-order differential equations. [Maxwell's and Dirac's equations are first-order but involve two unknown functions. Eliminating one unknown yields a second-order differential equation for the other (cf. Section 1.9).]

Occasionally we do encounter equations of higher order. In both the theory of the slow motion of a viscous fluid and the theory of an elastic body we find the equation

$$(\mathbf{V}^2)^2\psi = \left(\frac{\partial^4}{\partial x^4} + 2\frac{\partial^4}{\partial x^2\,\partial y^2} + \frac{\partial^4}{\partial y^4}\right)\psi = 0.$$

[1] Cf. Section 2.5 for definition of linearity.

Fortunately for introductory treatments such as this one, these higher-order differential equations are relatively rare.

Some general techniques for solving the partial differential equations are discussed in this section.

1. Separation of variables. This technique was introduced in Section 2.5 and is discussed further in Section 8.2. It does not always work, but when it does it is often the simplest method.

2. Integral solutions employing a Green's function. An introduction to the Green's function technique is given in Section 8.6. A more detailed treatment appears in Chapter 16.

3. Other analytical methods such as the use of integral transforms. Some of the techniques in this class are developed and applied in Chapter 15.

4. Numerical calculations. The development of modern high-speed calculating machines has opened up a wealth of possibilities based on the calculus of finite differences. For details of these methods the reader could start with R. W. Hamming's *Numerical Methods for Scientists and Engineers* (McGraw-Hill, 1962) and proceed to specialized references.

8.2   Separation of Variables—Ordinary Differential Equations

The equations of mathematical physics listed in Section 8.1 are all partial differential equations. Our first technique for their solution splits the partial differential equation of n variables into n ordinary differential equations. Each separation introduces an arbitrary constant of separation. If we have n variables, we shall have to introduce $n - 1$ constants, determined by the conditions imposed in the problem being solved.

In Section 2.5 the technique of separation of variables was illustrated for the wave equation in cartesian and spherical polar coordinates. In the spherical polar coordinate system the wave equation

$$\nabla^2 \psi + k^2 \psi = 0 \tag{8.1}$$

led to an azimuthal equation

$$\frac{d^2\Phi(\varphi)}{d\varphi^2} + m^2\,\Phi(\varphi) = 0, \tag{8.2}$$

in which $-m^2$ is a separation constant. As an illustration of how the constant is restricted, we note that φ in spherical polar coordinates is an azimuth angle. If this is a classical problem, we shall certainly require that the azimuthal solution $\Phi(\varphi)$ be single-valued, that is,

$$\Phi(\varphi + 2\pi) = \Phi(\varphi). \tag{8.3}$$

This is equivalent to requiring the azimuthal solution to have a period of 2π or some integral multiple of it.[1] Therefore m must be an integer. Which integer it is depends on the details of the problem. This is taken up in Chapter 9.

The coordinate systems described in Chapter 2 were selected from the infinitely

---

[1] This also applies in most quantum mechanical problems, but the argument is much more involved.

many possible orthogonal coordinate systems, because in these systems[1] the wave and Helmholtz equations would separate into ordinary differential equations. Going through the fourteen coordinate systems one by one, the separated ordinary differential equations show considerable duplication. Whenever a coordinate corresponds to an axis of translation or to an azimuth angle, the separated equation always has the form

$$\frac{d^2\Phi(\varphi)}{d\varphi^2} = -m^2\,\Phi(\varphi)$$

for φ, the azimuth angle, and

$$\frac{d^2Z(z)}{dz^2} = \pm a^2\,Z(z) \tag{8.4}$$

for z, an axis of translation in one of the cylindrical coordinate systems. The solutions, of course, are $\sin az$ and $\cos az$ for $-a^2$ and the corresponding hyperbolic function (or exponentials) $\sinh az$ and $\cosh az$ for $+a^2$.

The Legendre equation,

$$\frac{1}{\sin\theta}\frac{d}{d\theta}\left(\sin\theta\frac{d\Theta}{d\theta}\right) + l(l+1)\Theta = 0,$$

$$(1-x^2)\frac{d^2y}{dx^2} - 2x\frac{dy}{dx} + l(l+1)y = 0, \tag{8.5}$$

and the associated Legendre equation

$$\frac{1}{\sin\theta}\frac{d}{d\theta}\left(\sin\theta\frac{d\Theta}{d\theta}\right) + l(l+1)\Theta - \frac{m^2}{\sin^2\theta}\Theta = 0.$$

$$(1-x^2)\frac{d^2y}{dx^2} - 2x\frac{dy}{dx} + l(l+1)y - \frac{m^2}{1-x^2}y = 0, \quad{}^2 \tag{8.6}$$

also appear frequently. As noted in Section 2.5 these equations appear when ∇^2 is used in spherical polar coordinates. Prolate and oblate spheroidal coordinates also give rise to the Legendre and associated Legendre equations.

A third equation frequently encountered is Bessel's differential equation,

$$x^2\frac{d^2y}{dx^2} + x\frac{dy}{dx} + (x^2 - n^2)y = 0. \tag{8.7}$$

In Sections 2.5 and 2.6 spherical polar and circular cylindrical coordinates yielded varieties of Bessel's equation. The separation of variables of Laplace's equation in parabolic coordinates also gives rise to Bessel's equation. It may be noted that the Bessel equation is notorious for the variety of disguises it may assume. For an

---

[1] Bipolar and its rotational forms, toroidal and bispherical coordinates, are exceptions. They were included to illustrate how special coordinate systems can be used to advantage in special problems.

[2] These are equivalent algebraic forms in which $x = \cos\theta$.

extensive tabulation of possible forms, the reader is referred to *Tables of Functions* by Jahnke and Emde.[1]

Other occasionally encountered ordinary differential equations include the Laguerre and associated Laguerre equations from the supremely important hydrogen atom problem in quantum mechanics:

$$x \frac{dy^2}{dx^2} + (1 - x) \frac{dy}{dx} + \alpha y = 0, \tag{8.8}$$

$$x \frac{d^2 y}{dx^2} + (1 + k - x) \frac{dy}{dx} + \alpha y = 0. \tag{8.9}$$

From the quantum mechanical theory of the linear oscillator we have Hermite's equation,

$$\frac{d^2 y}{dx^2} - 2x \frac{dy}{dx} + 2\alpha y = 0. \tag{8.10}$$

Finally, from time to time we find the Chebyshev differential equation

$$(1 - x^2) \frac{d^2 y}{dx^2} - x \frac{dy}{dx} + n^2 y = 0. \tag{8.11}$$

These ordinary differential equations and two generalizations of them will be examined and systematized in the next section. General properties following from the form of the differential equations are taken up in Chapter 9. The individual solutions are developed and applied in Chapters 10 to 13.

The practicing physicist may and probably will meet other second-order ordinary differential equations, some of which may possibly be transformed into the examples studied here. Some he may have to solve by the techniques of Sections 8.4 and 8.5. Others may drive him to a calculating machine for a numerical solution.

EXERCISES

8.2.1 Show that when Laplace's equation is separated in prolate spheroidal coordinates (Section 2.10) the equations for the u- and v-dependence are Legendre's equation.

8.2.2 Show that when Laplace's equation is separated in oblate spheroidal coordinates (Section 2.11) the equation for v-dependence is Legendre's equation and the equation for u-dependence is the Legendre equation of imaginary argument. *Note.* $\cosh ix = \cos x$, $\sinh ix = i \sin x$.

[1] Fourth revised edition. New York: Dover (1945), p. 146.

8.2.3 Show that when Laplace's equation is separated in parabolic coordinates (Section 2.12) the equation for ξ-dependence is Bessel's equation and the equation for η-dependence is Bessel's equation for imaginary argument. (The η equation is identified in Section 11.4 as the modified Bessel equation.)

8.2.4 The one-dimensional Schrödinger wave equation for a particle in a potential field $V = \frac{1}{2}kx^2$ is

$$-\frac{\hbar^2}{2m}\frac{d^2\psi}{dx^2} + \frac{1}{2}kx^2\psi = E\psi(k).$$

(a) Using $\xi = ax$ and a constant λ,

$$a = \left(\frac{mk}{\hbar^2}\right)^{1/4}$$

$$\lambda = \frac{2E}{\hbar}\left(\frac{m}{k}\right)^{1/2}$$

show that

$$\frac{d^2\psi(\xi)}{d\xi^2} + (\lambda - \xi^2)\,\psi(\xi) = 0.$$

(b) Substituting

$$\psi(\xi) = y(\xi)\,e^{-\xi^2/2}$$

show that $y(\xi)$ satisfies the Hermite differential equation.

8.2.5 Show that Laplace's equation, $\nabla^2\psi = 0$, in plane polar coordinates (two dimensions) has a solution of the form

$$\psi(\rho,\varphi) = \sum_{n=0}^{\infty} (a_n\rho^n + b_n\rho^{-n})e^{\pm in\varphi},$$

in which a_n and b_n are constants.

8.2.6 Show that the one-dimensional diffusion equation

$$\frac{\partial^2\psi(x,t)}{\partial x^2} = \frac{1}{a^2}\frac{\partial\psi(x,t)}{\partial t}$$

has a solution of the form

$$\psi(x,t) = \sum_{n=0}^{\infty} c_n\cos(nx + \varphi_n)\,e^{-a^2n^2t}$$

where c_n and φ_n are constants.

8.3 Singular Points

In this section the concept of singular point or singularity (as applied to a differential equation) is introduced. The interest in this concept stems from its usefulness in classifying differential equations and in investigating the feasibility of a series solution (Section 8.4). First, a definition.

All of the ordinary differential equations listed in Section 8.2 may be solved for d^2y/dx^2. Using the notation $d^2y/dx^2 = y''$, we have

$$y'' = f(x, y, y'). \tag{8.12}$$

Now, if in Eq. 8.12 y and y' can take on all finite values at $x = x_0$ and y'' remains finite, point $x = x_0$ is an ordinary point. On the other hand, if y'' becomes infinite for *any* finite choice of y and y', point $x = x_0$ is labeled a singular point. Another way of presenting this definition of singular point is to write our differential equation as

$$y'' + P(x)y' + Q(x)y = 0. \tag{8.13}$$

Now, if the functions $P(x)$ and $Q(x)$ remain finite at $x = x_0$, point $x = x_0$ is an ordinary point. However, if either $P(x)$ or $Q(x)$ (or both) diverges as $x \to x_0$, point x_0 is a singular point.

Using Eq. 8.13, we may distinguish between two kinds of singular points.

1. If either $P(x)$ or $Q(x)$ diverges as $x \to x_0$ but $(x - x_0) P(x)$ and $(x - x_0)^2 Q(x)$ remain finite as $x \to x_0$, then $x = x_0$ is called a regular or nonessential singular point.

2. If $P(x)$ diverges faster than $1/(x - x_0)$, so that $(x - x_0) P(x)$ goes to infinity as $x \to x_0$, or $Q(x)$ diverges faster than $1/(x - x_0)^2$ so that $(x - x_0)^2 Q(x)$ goes to infinity as $x \to x_0$, then point $x = x_0$ is labeled an irregular or essential singularity.

These definitions hold for all finite values of x_0. The analysis of point $x \to \infty$ is similar to the treatment of functions of a complex variable (Section 6.5). We set $x = 1/z$, substitute into the differential equation, and then let $z \to 0$. By changing variables in the derivatives, we have,

$$\frac{dy(x)}{dx} = \frac{dy(z^{-1})}{dz}\frac{dz}{dx} = -\frac{1}{x^2}\frac{dy(z^{-1})}{dz} = -z^2 \frac{dy(z^{-1})}{dz} \tag{8.14}$$

$$\frac{d^2y(x)}{dx^2} = \frac{d}{dz}\left[\frac{dy(x)}{dx}\right]\frac{dz}{dx} = (-z^2)\left[-2z\frac{dy(z^{-1})}{dz} - z^2\frac{d^2y(z^{-1})}{dz^2}\right]$$

$$= 2z^3 \frac{dy(z^{-1})}{dz} + z^4 \frac{d^2y(z^{-1})}{dz^2}. \tag{8.15}$$

Using these results, we transform Eq. 8.13 into

$$z^4 \frac{d^2y}{dz^2} + [2z^3 - z^2 P(z^{-1})]\frac{dy}{dz} + Q(z^{-1})y = 0. \tag{8.16}$$

The behavior at $x = \infty$ $(z = 0)$ then depends on the behavior of the new coefficients

$$\frac{2z^3 - z^2 P(z^{-1})}{z^4} \quad \text{and} \quad \frac{Q(z^{-1})}{z^4}$$

as $z \to 0$. If these two expressions remain finite, point $x = \infty$ is an ordinary point. If they diverge no more rapidly than $1/z$ and $1/z^2$, respectively, point $x = \infty$ is a regular singular point, otherwise an irregular singular point (an essential singularity).

EXAMPLE 8.3.1

Bessel's equation

$$x^2 y'' + xy' + (x^2 - n^2)y = 0. \tag{8.17}$$

Comparing it with Eq. 8.13, we have

$$P(x) = \frac{1}{x}, \qquad Q(x) = 1 - \frac{n^2}{x^2},$$

which shows that point $x = 0$ is a regular singularity. By inspection we see that there are no other singular points in the finite range. As $x \to \infty$ ($z \to 0$), from Eq. 8.16 we have the coefficients

$$\frac{2z^3 - z^2 \cdot z}{z^4} \quad \text{and} \quad \frac{1 - n^2 z^2}{z^4}.$$

Since the latter expression diverges as z^4, point $x = \infty$ is an irregular or essential singularity.

The ordinary differential equations of Section 8.2, plus two others, the hypergeometric and the confluent hypergeometric, have singular points, as shown in Table 8.1.

TABLE 8.1

Equation	Regular singularity $x=$	Irregular singularity $x=$
1. Hypergeometric $x(x-1)y'' + [(1 + a + b)x - c]y' + aby = 0.$	0, 1, ∞	—
2. Legendre[a] $(1 - x^2)y'' - 2xy' + l(l+1)y = 0.$	-1, 1, ∞	—
3. Chebyshev $(1 - x^2)y'' - xy' + n^2y = 0.$	-1, 1, ∞	—
4. Confluent hypergeometric $xy'' + (c - x)y' - ay = 0.$	0	∞
5. Bessel $x^2y'' + xy' + (x^2 - n^2)y = 0.$	0	∞
6. Laguerre[a] $xy'' + (1 - x)y' + ay = 0.$	0	∞
7. Simple harmonic oscillator $y'' + \omega^2 y = 0.$	—	∞
8. Hermite $y'' - 2xy' + 2\alpha y = 0.$	—	∞

[a] The associated equations have the same singular points.

It will be seen that the first three equations in the preceding tabulation, hypergeometric, Legendre, and Chebyshev, all have three regular singular points. The hypergeometric equation with regular singularities at 0, 1, and ∞ is taken as the standard, the canonical form. The solutions of the other two may then be expressed in terms of its solutions, the hypergeometric functions. This is done in Chapter 13.

In a similar manner the confluent hypergeometric equation is taken as the canonical form of a linear second-order differential equation with one regular and one irregular singular point.

In a sense the confluent hypergeometric equation can be "derived" from the hypergeometric equation:

$$x(x - 1)y'' + [(1 + a + b)x - c]y' + aby = 0. \qquad (8.18)$$

If we let $bx = z$, we obtain

$$\frac{z}{b}\left(\frac{z}{b} - 1\right)b^2 \frac{d^2 y}{dz^2} + \left[(1 + a + b)\frac{z}{b} - c\right]b \frac{dy}{dz} + aby = 0.$$

Dividing by b,

$$z\left(\frac{z}{b} - 1\right)\frac{d^2 y}{dz^2} + \left[\frac{(1 + a)z}{b} + z - c\right]\frac{dy}{dz} + ay = 0.$$

Finally by letting $b \to \infty$, our equation becomes

$$-z^2 \frac{d^2 y}{dz^2} - (c - z)\frac{dy}{dz} + ay = 0, \qquad (8.19)$$

which, within a common factor of -1, is just the confluent hypergeometric equation. Our transformation has the effect of merging (confluence) the two regular singularities at $x = 0$ and 1 into one regular singularity at $z = 0$ and converting the singularity at infinity from a regular to an irregular singularity.

EXERCISES

8.3.1 Show that Legendre's equation has regular singularities at $x = -1$, 1, and ∞.

8.3.2 Show that Laguerre's equation, like the Bessel equation, has a regular singularity at $x = 0$ and an irregular singularity at $x = \infty$.

8.3.3 Show that the substitution

$$x \to \frac{1 - x}{2}, \quad a = -l, \quad b = l + 1, \quad c = 1$$

converts the hypergeometric equation into Legendre's equation.

8.3.4 The quantum mechanical angular momentum operator is given by $\mathbf{L} = -i(\mathbf{r} \times \nabla)$. Show that

$$\mathbf{L} \cdot \mathbf{L}\psi = l(l + 1)\psi$$

leads to the associated Legendre equation.

8.4 Series Solutions—Frobenius' Method

A linear, second-order differential equation may be put in the form

$$\frac{d^2 y}{dx^2} + P(x)\frac{dy}{dx} + Q(x)y = F(x). \qquad (8.20)$$

The function on the right, $F(x)$, represents a source (such as electrostatic charge) or a driving force (as in a driven oscillator). With $F(x) \neq 0$, Eq. 8.20 is inhomogeneous. Solutions of the inhomogeneous equation will be examined in Sections 8.6 and 15.10, Chapter 16, and elsewhere, as they occur. For the present we assume that $F(x) = 0$, that is, that our differential equation is homogeneous.

We shall attempt to develop a solution of our linear, second-order, homogeneous, differential equation by substituting in a power series with undetermined coefficients. Also available as a parameter is the power of the lowest nonvanishing term of the series. To illustrate, we apply the method to two important differential equations. First the linear oscillator equation

$$\frac{d^2 y}{dx^2} + \omega^2 y = 0, \tag{8.21}$$

with known solutions $y = \sin \omega x, \cos \omega x$.

We try

$$y(x) = x^k (a_0 + a_1 x + a_2 x^2 + a_3 x^3 + \cdots)$$

$$= \sum_{\lambda=0}^{\infty} a_\lambda x^{k+\lambda}, \qquad a_0 \neq 0, \tag{8.22}$$

with the exponent k and all the coefficients a_λ still undetermined. By differentiating twice, we obtain

$$\frac{dy}{dx} = \sum_{\lambda=0}^{\infty} a_\lambda (k + \lambda) x^{k+\lambda-1},$$

$$\frac{d^2 y}{dx^2} = \sum_{\lambda=0}^{\infty} a_\lambda (k + \lambda)(k + \lambda - 1) x^{k-\lambda-2}.$$

By substituting into Eq. 8.21, we have

$$\sum_{\lambda=0}^{\infty} a_\lambda (k + \lambda)(k + \lambda - 1) x^{k+\lambda-2} + \omega^2 \sum_{\lambda=0}^{\infty} a_\lambda x^{k+\lambda} = 0. \tag{8.23}$$

From our analysis of the uniqueness of power series (Chapter 5) the coefficients of each power of x on the left-hand side of Eq. 8.23 must vanish individually.

The lowest power of x appearing in Eq. 8.23 is x^{k-2}, for $\lambda = 0$ in the first summation. The requirement that the coefficient vanish[1] yields

$$a_0 k(k - 1) = 0.$$

We had chosen a_0 as the coefficient of the lowest nonvanishing terms of the series (Eq. 8.22), hence, by definition, $a_0 \neq 0$. Therefore we have

$$k(k - 1) = 0. \tag{8.24}$$

This equation, coming from the coefficient of the lowest power of x, we call the *indicial equation*. The indicial equation and its roots are of critical importance to our analysis. Clearly, in this example we must require either that $k = 0$ or $k = 1$.

Before considering these two possibilities for k, we return to Eq. 8.23 and demand that the remaining net coefficients, say the coefficient of x^{k+j} ($j \geqslant 0$), vanish.

---

[1] Uniqueness of power series, Section 5.7.

We set $\lambda = j + 2$ in the first summation and $\lambda = j$ in the second. (They are independent summations and λ is a dummy index.) This results in

$$a_{j+2}(k + j + 2)(k + j + 1) + \omega^2 a_j = 0$$

or

$$a_{j+2} = -a_j \frac{\omega^2}{(k + j + 2)(k + j + 1)}. \tag{8.25}$$

This is a two-term *recurrence relation*. Given a_j, we may compute a_{j+2} and then a_{j+4}, a_{j+6}, and so on up as far as desired. The reader will note that for this example, if we start with a_0, Eq. 8.25 leads to the even coefficients a_2, a_4, etc., and ignores a_1, a_3, a_5, etc. Since a_1 is arbitrary, let us set it equal to zero and then by Eq. 8.25

$$a_3 = a_5 = a_7 = \cdots = 0$$

and all the odd power coefficients vanish. Do not worry about the lost odd powers; the object here is to get a solution.

Returning to Eq. 8.24, our indicial equation, we first try the solution $k = 0$. The recurrence relation (Eq. 8.25) becomes

$$a_{j+2} = -a_j \frac{\omega^2}{(j + 2)(j + 1)}, \tag{8.26}$$

which leads to

$$a_2 = -a_0 \frac{\omega^2}{1 \cdot 2} = -\frac{\omega^2}{2!} a_0,$$

$$a_4 = -a_2 \frac{\omega^2}{3 \cdot 4} = +\frac{\omega^4}{4!} a_0,$$

$$a_6 = -a_4 \frac{\omega^2}{5 \cdot 6} = -\frac{\omega^6}{6!} a_0, \text{ etc.}$$

By inspection (and mathematical induction)

$$a_{2n} = (-1)^n \frac{\omega^{2n}}{(2n)!} a_0, \tag{8.27}$$

and our solution is

$$y(x)_{k=0} = a_0 \left[1 - \frac{(\omega x)^2}{2!} + \frac{(\omega x)^4}{4!} - \frac{(\omega x)^6}{6!} + \cdots \right]$$

$$= a_0 \cos \omega x. \tag{8.28}$$

If we choose the indicial equation root $k = 1$ (Eq. 8.25) the recurrence relation becomes

$$a_{j+2} = -a_j \frac{\omega^2}{(j + 3)(j + 2)}. \tag{8.29}$$

Substituting in $j = 0, 2, 4$, successively, we obtain

$$a_2 = -a_0 \frac{\omega^2}{2 \cdot 3} = -\frac{\omega^2}{3!} a_0,$$

$$a_4 = -a_2 \frac{\omega^2}{4 \cdot 5} = +\frac{\omega^4}{5!} a_0,$$

$$a_6 = -a_4 \frac{\omega^2}{6 \cdot 7} = -\frac{\omega^6}{7!} a_0, \text{ etc.}$$

Again, by inspection and mathematical induction,

$$a_{2n} = (-1)^n \frac{\omega^{2n}}{(2n+1)!} a_0 \qquad (8.30)$$

For this choice, $k = 1$, we obtain

$$y(x)_{k=1} = a_0 x \left[1 - \frac{(\omega x)^2}{3!} + \frac{(\omega x)^4}{5!} - \frac{(\omega x)^6}{7!} + \cdots \right]$$

$$= \frac{a_0}{\omega} \left[(\omega x) - \frac{(\omega x)^3}{3!} + \frac{(\omega x)^5}{5!} - \frac{(\omega x)^7}{7!} + \cdots \right]$$

$$= \frac{a_0}{\omega} \sin \omega x. \qquad (8.31)$$

This series substitution, known as Frobenius' method, has given us two series solutions of the linear oscillator equation. However, there are two points about such series solutions that must be strongly emphasized:

1. The series solution should always be substituted back into the differential equation, to see if it works, as a precaution against algebraic and logical errors. Conversely, if it works, it is a solution.

2. The acceptability of a series solution depends on its convergence (including asymptotic convergence). It is quite possible for Frobenius' method to give a series solution which satisfies the original differential equation when substituted in but which does *not* converge over the region of interest. Legendre's differential equation illustrates this situation.

The alert reader will note that we obtained one solution of even symmetry, $y_1(x) = y_1(-x)$, and one of odd symmetry, $y_2(x) = -y_2(-x)$. This is not just an accident but a direct consequence of the form of the differential equation. Writing a general differential equation as

$$\mathscr{L}(x) \, y(x) = 0, \qquad (8.32)$$

in which $\mathscr{L}(x)$ is the differential operator, we see that for the linear oscillator equation (Eq. 8.21) $\mathscr{L}(x)$ is even, that is,

$$\mathscr{L}(x) = \mathscr{L}(-x). \qquad (8.33)$$

Often this is described as even parity.

Whenever the differential operator has a specific parity or symmetry, either even or odd, we may interchange $+x$ and $-x$, and Eq. 8.32 becomes

$$\pm \mathcal{L}(x)\, y(-x) = 0, \tag{8.34}$$

$+$ if $\mathcal{L}(x)$ is even, $-$ if $\mathcal{L}(x)$ is odd. Clearly, if $y(x)$ is a solution of the differential equaion, $y(-x)$ is also a solution. Then any solution may be resolved into even and odd parts,

$$y(x) = \tfrac{1}{2}[y(x) + y(-x)] + \tfrac{1}{2}[y(x) - y(-x)]. \tag{8.35}$$

the first bracket on the right giving an even solution, the second an odd solution.

If we refer back to Section 8.3, we can see that Legendre, Chebyshev, Bessel, simple harmonic oscillator, and Hermite equations (or differential operators) all exhibit this even parity. Solutions of all of them may be presented as series of even powers of x and separate series of odd powers of x. The Laguerre differential operator has neither even nor odd symmetry; hence its solutions cannot be expected to exhibit even or odd parity.

This attack on the linear oscillator equation was perhaps a bit too easy. By substituting the power series (Eq. 8.22) into the differential equation (Eq. 8.21) we obtained two independent solutions with no trouble at all.

To get some idea of what can happen we try to solve Bessel's equation,

$$x^2 y'' + x y' + (x^2 - n^2)y = 0 \tag{8.36}$$

using y' for dy/dx and y'' for $d^2 y/dx^2$. Again assuming a solution of the form

$$y(x) = \sum_{\lambda=0}^{\infty} a_\lambda x^{k+\lambda},$$

we differentiate and substitute into Eq. 8.36. The result is

$$\sum_{\lambda=0}^{\infty} a_\lambda(k+\lambda)(k+\lambda-1)x^{k+\lambda} + \sum_{\lambda=0}^{\infty} a_\lambda(k+\lambda)x^{k+\lambda}$$
$$+ \sum_{\lambda=0}^{\infty} a_\lambda x^{k+\lambda+2} - \sum_{\lambda=0}^{\infty} a_\lambda n^2 x^{k+\lambda} = 0. \tag{8.37}$$

By setting $\lambda = 0$, the coefficient of x^k, the lowest power of x appearing on the left-hand side, is

$$a_0[k(k-1) + k - n^2] = 0, \tag{8.38}$$

and again $a_0 \neq 0$ by definition. Equation 8.38 therefore yields the *indicial equation*

$$k^2 - n^2 = 0 \tag{8.39}$$

with solutions $k = \pm n$.

It is of some interest to examine the coefficient of x^{k+1} also. Here we obtain

$$a_1[(k+1)k + k + 1 - n^2] = 0$$

or

$$a_1(k+1-n)(k+1+n) = 0. \tag{8.40}$$

For $k = \pm n$ neither $k + 1 - n$ nor $k + 1 + n$ vanishes and we *must* require $a_1 = 0$.[1]

[1] $k = \pm n = -\tfrac{1}{2}$ are exceptions.

Proceeding to the coefficient of x^{k+j} for $k = n$, we set $\lambda = j$ in the first, second, and fourth terms of Eq. 8.37 and $\lambda = j - 2$ in the third term. By requiring the resultant coefficient of x^{k+j} to vanish we obtain

$$a_j[(n+j)(n+j-1) + (n+j) - n^2] + a_{j-2} = 0.$$

When j is replaced by $j + 2$, this can be rewritten

$$a_{j+2} = -a_j \frac{1}{(j+2)(2n+j+2)}, \tag{8.41}$$

which is the desired recurrence relation. Repeated application of this recurrence relation leads to

$$a_2 = -a_0 \frac{1}{2(2n+2)} = -\frac{a_0 n!}{2^2 1!(n+1)!},$$

$$a_4 = -a_2 \frac{1}{4(2n+4)} = +\frac{a_0 n!}{2^4 2!(n+2)!},$$

$$a_6 = -a_4 \frac{1}{6(2n+6)} = -\frac{a_0 n!}{2^6 3!(n+3)!}, \quad \text{etc.,}$$

and in general

$$a_p = (-1)^{p/2} \frac{a_0 n!}{2^p (p/2)!(n+p/2)!} \quad (p \text{ even}). \tag{8.42}$$

Inserting these coefficients in our assumed series solution, we have

$$y(x) = a_0 x^n \left[1 - \frac{n! x^2}{2^2 1!(n+1)!} + \frac{n! x^4}{2^4 2!(n+2)!} - \cdots \right]. \tag{8.43}$$

If we use $2j = p$, the solution may be written

$$y(x) = a_0 \sum_{j=0}^{\infty} (-1)^j \frac{n! x^{n+2j}}{2^{2j} j!(n+j)!}$$

$$= a_0 2^n \sum_{j=0}^{\infty} (-1)^j \frac{n!}{j!(n+j)!} \left(\frac{x}{2} \right)^{n+2j} \tag{8.44}$$

In Chapter 11 the final summation is identified as the Bessel function $J_n(x)$. Notice that this solution $J_n(x)$ has either even or odd symmetry[1] as might be expected from the form of Bessel's equation.

When $k = -n$ and n is not an integer, we may generate a second distinct series to be labeled $J_{-n}(x)$. However, when $-n$ is a negative integer, trouble develops. The recurrence relation for the coefficients a_j is still given by Eq. 8.41, but with $2n$ replaced by $-2n$. Then, when $j + 2 = 2n$ or $j = 2(n-1)$, the coefficient a_{j+2} blows up and we have no series solution. This catastrophe can be remedied in Eq. 8.44, as it is done in Chapter 11, with the result that

$$J_{-n}(x) = (-1)^n J_n(x), \quad n \text{ an integer.} \tag{8.45}$$

---

[1] $J_n(x)$ is an even function if n is an even integer, an odd function if n is an odd integer. For nonintegral n the x^n has no such simple symmetry.

The second solution simply reproduces the first. We have failed to construct a second independent solution for Bessel's equation by this series technique when n is an integer.

By substituting in an infinite series, we have obtained two solutions for the linear oscillator equation and one for Bessel's equation (two if n is not an integer). To the questions "Can we always do this? Will this method always work?", the answer is no, we cannot always do this. This method of series solution will not always work.

The success of the series substitution method depends on the roots of the indicial equation and the degree of singularity of the coefficients in the differential equation. To understand better the effect of the equation coefficients on this naïve series substitution approach consider four simple equations

$$y'' - \frac{6}{x^2} = 0, \tag{8.46a}$$

$$y'' - \frac{6}{x^3} y = 0, \tag{8.46b}$$

$$y'' + \frac{1}{x} y' - \frac{a^2}{x^2} y = 0, \tag{8.46c}$$

$$y'' + \frac{1}{x^2} y' - \frac{a^2}{x^2} y = 0. \tag{8.46d}$$

The reader may show easily that for Eq. 8.46a the indicial equation is

$$k^2 - k - 6 = 0,$$

giving $k = 3, -2$. Since the equation is homogeneous in x (counting d^2/dx^2 as x^{-2}), there is no recurrence relation; $a_i = 0$ for $i > 0$. However, we are left with two perfectly good solutions, x^3 and x^{-2}.

Equation 8.46b differs from 8.46a by only one power of x, but this sends the indicial equation to

$$-6a_0 = 0,$$

with no solution at all, for we have agreed that $a_0 \neq 0$. Our series substitution worked for Eq. 8.46a, which had only a regular singularity, but broke down at Eq. 8.46b, which has an irregular singular point at the origin.

Continuing with Eq. 8.46c, we have added a term y'/x. The indicial equation is

$$k^2 - a^2 = 0,$$

but again there is no recurrence relation. The solutions are $y = x^a$, x^{-a}, both perfectly acceptable one term series.

When we change the power of x in the coefficient of y' from -1 to -2, Eq. 8.46d, there is a drastic change in the solution. The indicial equation (with only the y' term contributing) becomes

$$k = 0.$$

There is a recurrence relation

$$a_{j+1} = -a_j \frac{a^2 - j(j-1)}{j+1},$$

Unless the parameter a is selected to make the series terminate, we have

$$\lim_{j \to \infty} \left| \frac{a_{j+1}}{a_j} \right| = \lim_{j \to \infty} \frac{j(j-1)}{j+1}$$

$$= \lim_{j \to \infty} \frac{j^2}{j} = \infty.$$

Hence our series solution diverges. Again our method worked for Eq. 8.46c with a regular singularity but failed when we had the irregular singularity of 8.46d.

Fuchs's theorem.   The answer to the basic question when the method of series substitution can be expected to work is given by Fuchs's theorem, which asserts that we can always obtain at least one power series solution, provided we are expanding about a point that is an ordinary point or at worst a regular singular point. If we attempt an expansion about an irregular or essential singularity, our method may fail as it did for Eqs. 8.46b and 8.46d. Fortunately, the more important equations of mathematical physics listed in Section 8.3 have no irregular singularities in the finite plane.

Summary.   If we are expanding about an ordinary point or at worst about a regular singularity, the series substitution approach will yield at least one solution (Fuchs's theorem).

Whether we get one or two distinct solutions depends on the roots of the indicial equation.

1. If the two roots of the indicial equation are equal, we can obtain only one solution by this series substitution method.

2. If the two roots differ by a nonintegral number, two independent solutions may be obtained.

3. If the two roots differ by an integer, the larger of the two will yield a solution. The smaller may or may not give a solution, depending on the behavior of the coefficients. In the linear oscillator equation we obtain two solutions; for Bessel's equation, only one solution.

EXERCISES

8.4.1   Solve the Legendre equation

$$(1 - x^2)y'' - 2xy' + n(n+1)y = 0$$

by direct series substitution.
(a) Verify that the indicial equation is

$$k(k-1) = 0.$$

(b) Using $k = 0$, obtain a series of even powers of x, $(a_1 = 0)$.

$$y_{\text{even}} = a_0\left[1 - \frac{n(n+1)}{2!}x^2 + \frac{n(n-2)(n+1)(n+3)}{4!}x^4 + \cdots\right]$$

where

$$a_{j+2} = \frac{j(j+1) - n(n+1)}{(j+1)(j+2)}a_j.$$

(c) Using $k = 1$ develop a series of odd powers of x $(a_1 = 0)$.

$$y_{\text{odd}} = a_0\left[x - \frac{(n-1)(n+2)}{3!}x^3 + \frac{(n-1)(n-3)(n+2)(n+4)}{5!}x^5 + \cdots\right]$$

where

$$a_{j+2} = \frac{(j+1)(j+2) - n(n+1)}{(j+2)(j+3)}a_j.$$

(d) Show that both solutions, y_{even} and y_{odd}, diverge for $x = \pm 1$ *if the series continue to infinity.*

(e) Finally, show that by an appropriate choice of n, one series at a time may be converted into a polynomial, thereby avoiding the divergence catastrophe.

8.4.2 Obtain a series solution of the hypergeometric equation

$$x(x - 1)y'' + [(1 + a + b)x - c]y' + aby = 0.$$

Test your solution for convergence.

8.4.3 Obtain two series solutions of the confluent hypergeometric equation

$$xy'' + (c - x)y' - ay = 0.$$

Test your solutions for convergence.

8.4.4 Develop series solutions for Hermite's differential equation

$$y'' - 2xy' + 2\alpha y = 0.$$

Ans. $k(k - 1) = 0$, indicial equation.

For $k = 0$

$$a_{j+2} = 2a_j\frac{j - \alpha}{(j+1)(j+2)}, \qquad (j\text{ even}),$$

$$y_{\text{even}} = a_0\left[1 + \frac{2(-\alpha)x^2}{2!} + \frac{2^2(-\alpha)(2 - \alpha)x^4}{4!} + \cdots\right].$$

For $k = 1$

$$a_{j+2} = 2a_j\frac{j + 1 - \alpha}{(j+2)(j+3)}, \qquad (j\text{ even}),$$

$$y_{\text{odd}} = a_0\left[x + \frac{2(1 - \alpha)x^3}{3!} + \frac{2^2(1 - \alpha)(3 - \alpha)x^5}{5!} + \cdots\right].$$

(b) Show that both series solutions are convergent, the series behaving like the series expansion of e^{x^2}.

(c) Show that by appropriate choice of α the series solutions may be cut off and converted to finite polynomials. (These polynomials, properly normalized, become the Hermite polynomials in Section 13.1.)

8.4.5 A quantum mechanical analysis of the Stark effect (parabolic coordinates) leads to the differential equation

$$\frac{d}{d\xi}\left(\xi\frac{du}{d\xi}\right) + \left(\frac{1}{2}E\xi + \alpha - \frac{m^2}{4\xi} - \frac{1}{4}F\xi^2\right)u = 0.$$

Here α is a separation constant, E is the total energy, and F is a constant where Fz is the potential energy added to the system by the introduction of an electric field.

Using the larger root of the indicial equation, develop a power series solution about $\xi = 0$. Evaluate the first three coefficients in terms of a_0.

$$\text{Indicial equation} \qquad k^2 - \frac{m^2}{4} = 0,$$

$$u(\xi) = a_0 \xi^{m/2} \left\{ 1 - \frac{\alpha}{m+1} \xi + \left[\frac{\alpha^2}{2(m+1)(m+2)} - \frac{E}{4(m+2)} \right] \xi^2 + \cdots \right\}$$

Note that the perturbation F does not appear until a_3 is included.

8.4.6 For the special case of no azimuthal dependence, the quantum mechanical analysis of the hydrogen molecular ion leads to the equation (Section 2.10)

$$\frac{d}{d\eta} \left[(1 - \eta^2) \frac{du}{d\eta} \right] + \alpha u + \beta \eta^2 u = 0.$$

Develop a power-series solution for $u(\eta)$. Evaluate the first three nonvanishing coefficients in terms of a_0.

$$\text{Indicial equation} \qquad k(k-1) = 0,$$

$$u_{k=1} = a_0 \eta \left\{ 1 + \frac{2-\alpha}{6} \eta^2 + \left[\frac{(2-\alpha)(12-\alpha)}{120} - \frac{\beta}{20} \right] \eta^4 + \cdots \right\}.$$

8.4.7 To a good approximation, the interaction of two nucleons may be described by a meson potential

$$V = \frac{Ae^{-ax}}{x},$$

attractive for A negative. Develop a series solution of the resultant Schrödinger wave equation

$$\frac{\hbar^2}{2m} \frac{d^2\psi}{dx^2} + (E - V)\psi = 0,$$

through the first three nonvanishing coefficients.

$$\psi_{k=1} = a_0 \{ x + \tfrac{1}{2} A'x^2 + \tfrac{1}{6} [\tfrac{1}{2} A'^2 - E' - \alpha A'] x^3 + \cdots \},$$

where the prime indicates multiplication by $2m/\hbar^2$.

8.4.8 Near the nucleus of a complex atom the potential energy of one electron is given by

$$V = \frac{Ze^2}{r} (1 + b_1 r + b_2 r^2),$$

where the coefficients b_1 and b_2 arise from screening effects. For the case of zero angular momentum show that the first three terms of the solution of the Schrödinger equation have the same form as those of Exercise 8.4.7. By appropriate translation of coefficients or parameters, write out the first three terms in a series expansion of the wave function.

8.4.9 Solve

$$(1 - x^2)U_n''(x) - 3x\, U_n'(x) + n(n + 2)\, U_n(x) = 0,$$

choosing the root of the indicial equation to obtain a series of *odd* powers of x. Since the series will diverge for $x = 1$, choose n to convert it into a polynomial.

$$k(k-1) = 0.$$

For $k = 1$

$$a_{j+2} = \frac{(j+1)(j+3) - n(n+2)}{(j+2)(j+3)} a_j.$$

8.4.10 In the development of a series solution of the simple harmonic oscillator equation the second series coefficient a_1 was neglected except to set it equal to zero. From the coefficient of the next to the lowest power of x, x^{k-1}, develop a second indicial type equation.
   (a) (SHO equation with $k = 0$). Show that a_1 may be assigned any finite value (including zero).
   (b) (SHO equation with $k = 1$). Show that a_1 *must* be set equal to zero.

8.4.11   Laguerre's differential equation is
$$x L_n''(x) + (1 - x) L_n'(x) + n L_n(x) = 0.$$
Develop a series solution selecting the parameter n to make your series a polynomial.

8.4.12   Solve the Chebyshev equation
$$(1 - x^2) T_n'' - x T_n' + n^2 T_n = 0,$$
by series substitution. What restrictions are imposed on n if you demand that the series solution converge for $x = \pm 1$?

8.5   A Second Solution

In Section 8.4 a solution of a second-order homogeneous differential equation was developed by substituting in a power series. By Fuchs's theorem this is possible, provided the power series is an expansion about an ordinary point or a nonessential singularity.[1] There is no guarantee that this approach will yield the two independent solutions we expect from a linear second-order differential equation. Indeed, the technique gave only one solution for Bessel's equation (n an integer). In this section we develop two methods of obtaining a second independent solution: an integral method and a power series containing a logarithmic term. First, however, we consider the question of independence of a set of functions.

Linear independence of solutions.   Given a set of functions, φ_λ, the criterion for linear *dependence* is the existence of a relation of the form

$$\sum k_\lambda \varphi_\lambda = 0, \tag{8.47}$$

in which not all of the coefficients k_λ are zero. On the other hand, if the only solution of Eq. 8.47 is $k_\lambda = 0$ for all λ, the set of functions φ_λ is said to be linearly *independent*.

Let us assume that the functions φ_λ are differentiable as needed. Then, differentiating Eq. 8.47 repeatedly, we generate a set of equations

$$\sum_\lambda k_\lambda \varphi_\lambda' = 0 \tag{8.48}$$

$$\sum_\lambda k_\lambda \varphi_\lambda'' = 0, \text{ etc.} \tag{8.49}$$

This gives us a set of homogeneous linear equations in which k_λ are the unknown quantities. By Section 4.1 there is a solution $k_\lambda \neq 0$ only if the determinant of the coefficients of the k_λ's vanishes. This means

$$\begin{vmatrix} \varphi_1 & \varphi_2 & \cdots & \varphi_n \\ \varphi_1' & \varphi_2' & \cdots & \varphi_n' \\ \cdots & \cdots & \cdots & \cdots \\ \varphi_1^{(n-1)} & \varphi_2^{(n-1)} & \cdots & \varphi_n^{(n-1)} \end{vmatrix} = 0. \tag{8.50}$$

This determinant is called the Wronskian.

_____
[1] This is why the classification of singularities in Section 8.3 is of vital importance to us.

1. If the Wronskian is not equal to zero, then Eq. 8.47 has no solution other than $k_\lambda = 0$. The set of functions φ_λ is therefore independent.

2. If the Wronskian vanishes at isolated values of the argument, this does not necessarily prove linear dependence. However, if the Wronskian is zero over the entire range of the variable, the functions φ_λ are linearly dependent over this range[1] (cf. Exercise 8.5.1 for the simple case of two functions).

EXAMPLE 8.5.1

The solutions of the linear oscillator equation 8.21 are $\varphi_1 = \sin \omega x$, $\varphi_2 = \cos \omega x$. The Wronskian becomes

$$\begin{vmatrix} \sin \omega x & \cos \omega x \\ \omega \cos \omega x & -\omega \sin \omega x \end{vmatrix} = -\omega \neq 0.$$

These two solutions, φ_1 and φ_2, are therefore linearly independent. For just two functions this means that one is not a multiple of the other, which is obviously true in this case.

EXAMPLE 8.5.2

For an illustration of linear dependence, consider the solutions of the one-dimensional diffusion equation. We have $\varphi_1 = e^x$, $\varphi_2 = e^{-x}$, and we add $\varphi_3 = \cosh x$, also a solution. The Wronskian is

$$\begin{vmatrix} e^x & e^{-x} & \cosh x \\ e^x & -e^{-x} & \sinh x \\ e^x & e^{-x} & \cosh x \end{vmatrix} = 0.$$

The determinant vanishes for all x, because the first and third rows are identical. Hence e^x, e^{-x}, and $\cosh x$ are linearly dependent, and indeed we have a relation of the form of Eq. 8.47:

$$e^x + e^{-x} - 2 \cosh x = 0.$$

Returning to our linear, second-order, homogeneous, differential equation of the general form

$$y'' + P(x)y' + Q(x)y = 0, \tag{8.51}$$

let y_1 and y_2 be two independent solutions. Then the Wronskian, by definition, is

$$W = y_1 y_2' - y_1' y_2 \tag{8.52}$$

By differentiating the Wronskian, we obtain

$$W' = y_1' y_2' + y_1 y_2'' - y_1'' y_2 - y_1' y_2'$$
$$= y_1[-P(x)y_2' - Q(x)y_2] - y_2[-P(x)y_1' - Q(x)y_1]$$
$$= -P(x)(y_1 y_2' - y_1' y_2). \tag{8.53}$$

[1] Cf. p. 187 of H. LASS, *Elements of Pure and Applied Mathematics*. New York: McGraw-Hill (1957) for proof of this assertion.

The expression in parentheses is just W, the Wronskian, and we have

$$W' = -P(x)W. \tag{8.54}$$

If $P(x) = 0$, that is,

$$y'' + Q(x)y = 0, \tag{8.55}$$

the Wronskian

$$W = y_1 y_2' - y_1' y_2 = \text{constant}. \tag{8.56}$$

Since our original differential equation is homogeneous, we may multiply the solutions y_1 and y_2 by whatever constants we wish and arrange to have the Wronskian equal to unity (or -1). This case, $P(x) = 0$, appears more frequently than might be expected. The reader will recall that ∇^2 in cartesian coordinates contains no first derivative. Similarly the radial dependence of $\nabla^2(r\psi)$ in spherical polar coordinates lacks a first derivative. Finally, every linear second-order differential equation can be transformed into an equation of the form of Eq. 8.55 (cf. Exercise 8.5.4).

Let us now assume that we have one solution of Eq. 8.51 by a series substitution (or by guessing). We now proceed to develop a second, independent solution. Rewriting Eq. 8.54 as

$$\frac{dW}{W} = -P \, dx_1,$$

we integrate, from $x_1 = a$ to $x_1 = x$ to obtain

$$\ln \frac{W(x)}{W(a)} = -\int_a^x P(x_1) \, dx_1,$$

or

$$W(x) = W(a) \exp[-\int_a^x P(x_1) \, dx_1]. \tag{8.57}$$

But

$$W(x) = y_1 y_2' - y_1' y_2$$

$$= y_1^2 \frac{d}{dx}\left(\frac{y_2}{y_1}\right). \tag{8.58}$$

By combining Eqs. 8.57 and 8.58, we have

$$\frac{d}{dx}\left(\frac{y_2}{y_1}\right) = W(a) \frac{\exp[-\int_a^x P(x_1) \, dx_1]}{y_1^2} \tag{8.59}$$

Finally, by integrating Eq. 8.59 from $x_2 = b$ to $x_2 = x$ we get

$$y_2(x) = y_1(x) W(a) \int_a^x \frac{\exp[-\int_a^{x_2} P(x_1) \, dx_1]}{[y_1(x_2)]^2} \, dx_2. \tag{8.60}$$

Here a and b are arbitrary constants and a term $y_1(x) y_2(b)/y_1(b)$ has been dropped, for it leads to nothing new. Since $W(a)$, the Wronskian evaluated at $x = a$, is a constant and our solutions for the homogeneous differential equation always contain an unknown normalizing factor, we set $W(a) = 1$ and write

$$y_2(x) = y_1(x) \int^x \frac{\exp[-\int^{x_2} P(x_1) \, dx_1]}{[y_1(x_2)]^2} \, dx_2. \tag{8.61}$$

Note that the lower limits $x_1 = a$ and $x_2 = b$ have been omitted. If they are retained, they simply make a contribution equal to a constant times the known first solution, $y_1(x)$, hence add nothing new.

If we have the important special case of $P(x) = 0$, Eq. 8.61 reduces to

$$y_2(x) = y_1(x) \int^x \frac{dx_2}{[y_1(x_2)]^2}. \tag{8.62}$$

This means that by using either Eq. 8.61 or 8.62 we can take one known solution and by integrating can generate a second independent solution of Eq. 8.51. This technique is used in Section 12.9 to generate a second solution of Legendre's differential equation.

EXAMPLE 8.5.3

From Eq. 8.21 with $P(x) = 0$, let one solution be $y_1 = \sin x$. By applying Eq. 8.62 we obtain

$$y_2(x) = \sin x \int^x \frac{dx_2}{\sin^2 x_2}$$

$$= \sin x(-\cot x) = -\cos x,$$

which is clearly independent (not a linear multiple) of $\sin x$.

Further insight into the nature of the second solution of our differential equation may be obtained by the following sequence of operations:

1. Express $P(x)$ and $Q(x)$ in Eq. 8.51 as

$$P(x) = \sum_{i=-1}^{\infty} p_i x^i, \qquad Q(x) = \sum_{j=-2}^{\infty} q_j x^j. \tag{8.63}$$

The lower limits of the summations are selected to just satisfy Fuchs's theorem and because of this we may gain a better understanding of it.

2. Develop the first few terms of a power-series solution, as in Section 8.4.

3. Using this solution as y_1, obtain a second series type solution, y_2, with Eq. 8.61, integrating term by term.

Proceeding with Step 1, we have

$$y'' + (p_{-1}x^{-1} + p_0 + p_1 x + \cdots)y' + (q_{-2}x^{-2} + q_{-1}x^{-1} + \cdots)y = 0, \tag{8.64}$$

in which point $x = 0$ is at worst a regular singular point. If $p_{-1} = q_{-1} = q_{-2} = 0$, it reduces to an ordinary point. Substituting

$$y = \sum_{\lambda=0}^{\infty} a_\lambda x^{k+\lambda}$$

(Step 2), we obtain

$$\sum_{\lambda=0}^{\infty} (k+\lambda)(k+\lambda-1)a_\lambda x^{k+\lambda-2} + \sum_{i=-1}^{\infty} p_i x^i \sum_{\lambda=0}^{\infty} (k+\lambda)a_\lambda x^{k+\lambda-1}$$

$$+ \sum_{j=-2}^{\infty} q_j x^j \sum_{\lambda=0}^{\infty} a_\lambda x^{k+\lambda} = 0. \tag{8.65}$$

Assuming that $p_{-1} \neq 0$, $q_{-2} \neq 0$, our indicial equation is

$$k(k-1) + p_{-1}k + q_{-2} = 0,$$

which sets the net coefficient of x^{k-2} equal to zero. This reduces to

$$k^2 + (p_{-1} - 1)k + q_{-2} = 0. \tag{8.66}$$

We denote the two roots of this indicial equation by $k = \alpha$ and $k = \alpha - n$ where n is zero or a positive integer. (If n is not an integer, we expect two independent series solutions by the methods of Section 8.4 and there is no problem.) Then

$$(k - \alpha)(k - \alpha + n) = 0, \tag{8.67}$$

and, equating coefficients of k in Eqs. 8.66 and 8.67,

$$p_{-1} - 1 = n - 2\alpha. \tag{8.68}$$

The series solution corresponding to $k = \alpha$ may be written

$$y_1 = x^\alpha \sum_{\lambda=0}^{\infty} a_\lambda x^\lambda.$$

Substituting this series solution into Eq. 8.61 (Step 3), we are faced with

$$y_2(x) = y_1(x) \int^x \frac{\exp(-\int_a^{x_2} \sum_{i=-1}^{\infty} p_i x_1^i \, dx_1)}{x_2^{2\alpha}(\sum_{\lambda=0}^{\infty} a_\lambda x_2^\lambda)^2} \, dx_2, \tag{8.69}$$

where the solutions y_1 and y_2 have been normalized so that the Wronskian, $W(a) = 1$. Tackling the exponential factor first,

$$\int_a^{x_2} \sum_{i=-1}^{\infty} p_i x_1^i \, dx_1 = p_{-1} \ln x_2 + \sum_{k=0}^{\infty} \frac{p_k}{k+1} x_2^{k+1} + f(a) \tag{8.70}$$

Hence

$$\exp\left(-\int_a^{x_2} \sum_i p_i x_1^i \, dx_1\right) = \exp[-f(a)] x_2^{-p_{-1}} \exp\left(-\sum_{k=0}^{\infty} \frac{p_k}{k+1} x_2^{k+1}\right)$$

$$= \exp[-f(a)] x_2^{-p_{-1}}\left[1 - \sum_{k=0}^{\infty} \frac{p_k}{k+1} x_2^{k+1} + \frac{1}{2!}\left(\sum_{k=0}^{\infty} \frac{p_k}{k+1} x_2^{k+1}\right)^2 + \cdots\right] \tag{8.71}$$

This final series expansion of the exponential is certainly convergent if the original expansion of the coefficient $P(x)$ was convergent.

The denominator in Eq. 8.69 may be handled by writing

$$\left[x_2^{2\alpha}\left(\sum_{\lambda=0}^{\infty} a_\lambda x_2^\lambda\right)^2\right]^{-1} = x_2^{-2\alpha}\left(\sum_{\lambda=0}^{\infty} a_\lambda x_2^\lambda\right)^{-2}$$

$$= x_2^{-2\alpha} \sum_{\lambda=0}^{\infty} b_\lambda x_2^\lambda. \tag{8.72}$$

Neglecting constant factors that will be picked up anyway by the requirement that $W(a) = 1$, we obtain

$$y_2(x) = y_1(x) \int^x x_2^{-p-1-2\alpha}\left(\sum_{\lambda=0}^{\infty} c_\lambda x_2^\lambda\right) dx_2 \tag{8.73}$$

By Eq. 8.68

$$x_2^{-p-1-2\alpha} = x_2^{-n-1}, \tag{8.74}$$

and we have assumed here that n is an integer. Therefore the integration indicated in Eq. 8.73 leads to a coefficient of $y_1(x)$ consisting of two parts:

1. A power series starting with x^{-n}.
2. A logarithmic term from the integration of x^{-1} (when $\lambda = n$). This term always appears when n is an integer *unless* c_n fortuitously happens to vanish.

The second solution of Eq. 8.51, $y_2(x)$, may therefore be written

$$y_2(x) = y_1(x) \ln x + \sum_{j=-n}^{\infty} d_j x^{j+\alpha}, \tag{8.75}$$

the first solution times $\ln x$ and another power series, this one starting with $x^{\alpha-n}$, which means that we may look for a logarithmic term when the indicial equation of Section 8.4 gives only one series solution.

Finally, with the form of the second solution specified by Eq. 8.75, we can substitute Eq. 8.75 into the original differential equation and determine the coefficients d_λ exactly as in Section 8.4.

The second solution will usually diverge at the origin because of the logarithmic factor and the negative powers of x in the series. For this reason $y_2(x)$ is often referred to as the irregular solution. The first series solution, $y_1(x)$, which usually converges at the origin, is called the regular solution. The question of behavior at the origin is discussed in more detail in Chapters 11 and 12 in which we take up Bessel functions, modified Bessel functions, and Legendre functions.

EXERCISES

8.5.1 If the Wronskian of two functions y_1 and y_2 is identically zero, show by direct integration that

$$y_1 = cy_2,$$

that is, that y_1 and y_2 are dependent.

8.5.2 By direct differentiation and substitution show that

$$y_2(x) = y_1(x) \int^x \frac{\exp[-\int^s P(t)dt]}{[y_1(s)]^2} ds$$

satisfies

$$y_2''(x) + P(x)\, y_2'(x) + Q(x)\, y_2(x) = 0.$$

8.5.3 Show, by means of the Wronskian, that a linear, second-order, homogeneous, differential equation of the form

$$y''(x) + P(x)\, y'(x) + Q(x)\, y(x) = 0$$

cannot have three independent solutions. (Assume a third solution and show that the Wronskian vanishes for all x.)

8.5.4 Transform our linear, second-order, differential equation
$$y'' + P(x)y' + Q(x)y = 0$$
by the substitution
$$y = z \exp[- \tfrac{1}{2}\textstyle\int^x P(t)dt$$
and show that the resulting differential equation for z is
$$z'' + q(x)z = 0,$$
where
$$q(x) = Q(x) - \tfrac{1}{2}P'(x) - \tfrac{1}{4}P^2(x).$$

8.5.5 Use the result of Exercise 8.5.4 to show that the replacement of $\psi(r)$ by $r\,\psi(r)$ may be expected to eliminate the first derivative from the Laplacian in spherical polar coordinates.

8.5.6 Given that one solution of
$$R'' + \frac{1}{r}R' - \frac{m^2}{r^2}R = 0$$
is $R = r^m$, show that Eq. 8.61 predicts a second solution, $R = r^{-m}$.

8.5.7 Using $y_1(x) = \sum_{n\ \text{odd}}(-1)^{n+1}(x^n/n!)$ as a solution of the linear oscillator equation, follow the analysis culminating in Eq. 8.75 and show that $c_0 = 0$ so that the second solution does not, in this case, contain a logarithmic term.

8.5.8 Show that when n is *not* an integer the second solution of Bessel's equation, obtained from Eq. 8.61, does *not* contain a logarithmic term.

8.5.9 (a) One solution of Hermite's differential equation
$$y'' - 2xy' + 2\alpha y = 0$$
for $\alpha = 0$ is $y_1(x) = 1$. Find a second solution $y_2(x)$, using Eq. 8.61. Show that your second solution is equivalent to y_{odd} (Exercise 8.4.4).
(b) Find a second solution for $\alpha = 1$, where $y_1(x) = x$, using Eq. 8.61. Show that your second solution is equivalent to y_{even} (Exercise 8.4.4).

8.5.10 Show that if a second solution, y_2, is assumed to have the form $y_2(x) = y_1(x)f(x)$ substitution back into the original equation
$$y_2'' + P(x)y_2' + Q(x)y_2 = 0$$
leads to
$$f(x) = \int^x \frac{\exp[-\int^s P(t)dt]}{[y_1(s)]^2}\,ds$$
in agreement with Eq. 8.61.

8.5.11 Legendre's differential equation
$$(1 - x^2)y'' - 2xy' + n(n+1)y = 0$$
has a regular solution $P_n(x)$ and an irregular solution $Q_n(x)$. Show that the Wronskian of P_n and Q_n is given by
$$P_n(x)\,Q_n'(x) - P_n'(x)\,Q_n(x) = \frac{A_n}{1 - x^2}$$
with A_n *independent* of x.

8.5.12 In the equation
$$y_2(x) = y_1(x)\int^x \frac{\exp[- \int^s P(t)dt]}{[y_1(s)]^2}\,ds$$
$y_1(x)$ satisfies
$$y_1'' + P(x)y_1' + Q(x)y_1 = 0.$$
The function $y_2(x)$ is a linearly *independent* second-solution of the same equation. Show that the inclusion of lower limits on the two integrals leads to nothing new; that is, it throws in only over-all factors and/or a multiple of the known solution $y_1(x)$.

8.5.13   One solution of Laguerre's differential equation

$$xy'' + (1 - x)y' + ny = 0$$

for $n = 0$ is $y_1(x) = 1$. Using Eq. 8.61, develop a second, linearly independent solution. Exhibit the logarithmic term explicitly.

8.6   Green's Function—Electrostatic Analog

For a brief introduction to Green's function method, as applied to the solution of a nonhomogeneous partial differential equation, it is helpful to use the electrostatic analog. In the presence of charges the electrostatic potential ψ satisfies Poisson's nonhomogeneous equation (cf. Section 1.14)

$$\nabla^2 \psi = \frac{-\rho}{\varepsilon_0} \qquad \text{(mks units)} \tag{8.76}$$

and Laplace's homogeneous equation,

$$\nabla^2 \psi = 0, \tag{8.77}$$

in the absence of electric charge ($\rho = 0$). If the charges are point charges q_i, we know that the solution is

$$\psi = \frac{1}{4\pi\varepsilon_0} \sum_i \frac{q_i}{r_i}, \tag{8.78}$$

a superposition of single-point charge solutions obtained from Coulomb's law for the force between two point charges q_1 and q_2,

$$\mathbf{F} = \frac{q_1 q_2 \mathbf{r}_0}{4\pi\varepsilon_0 r^2}. \tag{8.79}$$

By replacement of the discrete point charges with a smeared out distributed charge, charge density ρ, Eq. 8.78 becomes

$$\psi(r = 0) = \frac{1}{4\pi\varepsilon_0} \int \frac{\rho(\mathbf{r})}{r} \, d\mathbf{r} \tag{8.80}$$

or, for the potential at $\mathbf{r} = \mathbf{r}_1$ away from the origin and the charge at $\mathbf{r} = \mathbf{r}_2$,

$$\psi(\mathbf{r}_1) = \frac{1}{4\pi\varepsilon_0} \int \frac{\rho(\mathbf{r}_2)}{|\mathbf{r}_1 - \mathbf{r}_2|} \, d\mathbf{r}_2 \tag{8.81}$$

Dirac delta function.   A formal derivation and generalization of this result is facilitated by using $\delta(x)$, the Dirac delta function, as in Section 1.15. For the one-dimensional case the Dirac delta function may be defined by the following properties:

$$\delta(x) = 0, \qquad x \neq 0, \tag{8.82}$$

$$\int_{-\infty}^{\infty} \delta(x) \, dx = 1, \tag{8.83}$$

and

$$\int_{-\infty}^{\infty} f(x) \, \delta(x) \, dx = f(0). \tag{8.84}$$

This Dirac delta function, $\delta(x)$, is not analytic, but it can be obtained as a limiting case of either analytic continuous or piecewise continuous functions. Among the many possible representations are

$$\delta(x) = \lim_{a \to 0} \frac{1}{\sqrt{a\pi}} e^{-x^2/a}, \tag{8.85a}$$

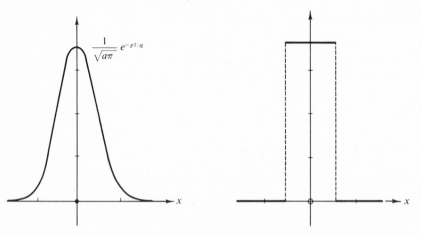

FIG. 8.1a Dirac delta function representation   **FIG. 8.1b** Dirac delta function representation

$$\delta(x) = \lim_{a \to 0} \begin{cases} 0, & x < -\dfrac{a}{2}, \\[2mm] \dfrac{1}{a}, & -\dfrac{a}{2} < x < \dfrac{a}{2}, \\[2mm] 0, & \dfrac{a}{2} < x. \end{cases} \tag{8.85b}$$

$$\delta(x) = \lim_{a \to \infty} \frac{1}{\pi} \frac{a}{a^2 + x^2}, \tag{8.85c}$$

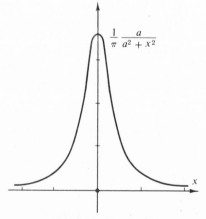

FIG. 8.1c Dirac delta function representation

$$\delta(x) = \lim_{a \to \infty} \frac{\sin ax}{\pi x}$$

$$= \lim_{a \to \infty} \frac{1}{2\pi} \int_{-a}^{a} e^{ixt} \, dt. \qquad (8.85d)$$

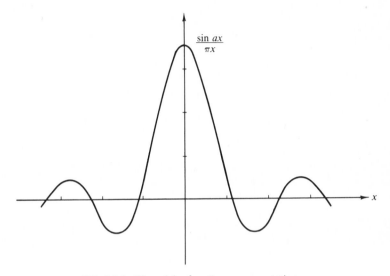

FIG. 8.1d   Dirac delta function representation

Among the foregoing representations (a), (b), and (c) are useful primarily for giving the reader a picture of what the delta function looks like. Form (b) is also useful in providing a simple derivation of the integral properties used to define the Dirac delta function (cf. Exercise 8.6.1). The final form (d) will be particularly useful when we take up Fourier analysis and its applications in quantum mechanics.

The Dirac delta function is pathological; indeed, it is really not a function at all. It is essentially a shorthand notation for the functional properties of the defining equations, (8.82), (8.83), and (8.84). It should be understood that the Dirac delta function has significance only as part of an integrand and never as an end result.

Shifting our singularity to the point $x = x'$, the Dirac delta function is written $\delta(x - x')$. Equation 8.84 becomes

$$\int_{-\infty}^{\infty} f(x) \, \delta(x - x') \, dx = f(x'). \qquad (8.86)$$

As a description of a singularity at $x = x'$, the Dirac delta function may be written as $\delta(x - x')$ or as $\delta(x' - x)$. Going to three dimensions and using spherical polar coordinates, we obtain

$$\int_{0}^{2\pi} \int_{0}^{\pi} \int_{0}^{\infty} \delta(\mathbf{r}) r^2 \, dr \sin \theta \, d\theta \, d\varphi = \int \int \int_{r-\infty}^{\infty} \delta(x) \, \delta(y) \delta(z) \, dx \, dy \, dz = 1. \qquad (8.87)$$

This corresponds to a singularity (or source) at the origin. Again, if our source is at

$\mathbf{r} = \mathbf{r}_1$, Eq. 8.87 becomes

$$\int \int \int \delta(\mathbf{r}_2 - \mathbf{r}_1) r_2^2 \, dr_2 \sin \theta_2 \, d\theta_2 \, d\varphi_2 = 1. \qquad (8.88)$$

As already mentioned,

$$\delta(\mathbf{r}_2 - \mathbf{r}_1) = \delta(\mathbf{r}_1 - \mathbf{r}_2). \qquad (8.89)$$

Returning to our electrostatic problem, we use ψ as the potential corresponding to the given distribution of charge and therefore satisfying Poisson's equation

$$\nabla^2 \psi = -\frac{\rho}{\varepsilon_0}, \qquad (8.90)$$

whereas a function φ, which we label a Green's function, is required to satisfy Poisson's equation with a point source at the point defined by $\mathbf{r}_2$:

$$\nabla^2 \varphi = -\delta(\mathbf{r}_1 - \mathbf{r}_2). \qquad (8.91)$$

Physically, then, φ is the potential at $\mathbf{r}_1$ corresponding to a unit source (ε_0) at $\mathbf{r}_2$. By Green's theorem (Section 1.11)

$$\int (\psi \, \nabla^2 \varphi - \varphi \, \nabla^2 \psi) \, d\tau_2 = \quad (\psi \, \nabla\varphi - \varphi \, \nabla\psi) \cdot d\boldsymbol{\sigma}. \qquad (8.92)$$

Assuming that the integrand falls off faster than r^{-2}, we may simplify our problem by taking the volume so large that the surface integral vanishes, leaving

$$\int \psi \, \nabla^2 \varphi \, d\tau_2 = \int \varphi \, \nabla^2 \psi \, d\tau_2 \qquad (8.93)$$

or by substituting in Eqs. 8.90 and 8.91,

$$-\int \psi(\mathbf{r}_2) \, \delta(\mathbf{r}_1 - \mathbf{r}_2) \, d\tau_2 = -\int \frac{\varphi(\mathbf{r}_1, \mathbf{r}_2) \, \rho(\mathbf{r}_2)}{\varepsilon_0} \, d\tau_2. \qquad (8.94)$$

Integration by employing the defining property of the Dirac delta function (Eq. 8.84), produces

$$\psi(\mathbf{r}_1) = \frac{1}{\varepsilon_0} \int \varphi(\mathbf{r}_1, \mathbf{r}_2) \, \rho(\mathbf{r}_1) \, d\tau_2. \qquad (8.95)$$

Note that we have used Eq. 8.91 to eliminate $\nabla^2 \varphi$ but that the function φ itself is still unknown. In Section 1.13, Gauss's law, we found that

$$\int \nabla^2 \left(\frac{1}{r}\right) d\tau = \begin{cases} 0, \\ -4\pi, \end{cases} \qquad (8.96)$$

0 if the volume did not include the origin and -4π if the origin were included. This result from Section 1.13 may be rewritten as

$$\nabla^2 \left(\frac{1}{4\pi r}\right) = -\delta(r)$$

or

$$\qquad (8.97)$$

$$\nabla^2 \left(\frac{1}{4\pi r_{12}}\right) = -\delta(\mathbf{r}_1 - \mathbf{r}_2),$$

corresponding to a shift of the electrostatic charge from the origin to the position $\mathbf{r} = \mathbf{r}_2$. Here $r_{12} = |\mathbf{r}_1 - \mathbf{r}_2|$, and the Dirac delta function $\delta(\mathbf{r}_1 - \mathbf{r}_2)$ vanishes unless $\mathbf{r}_1 = \mathbf{r}_2$. Therefore, in a comparison of Eqs. 8.91 and 8.97 the function φ (Green's function) is given by

$$\varphi(\mathbf{r}_1, \mathbf{r}_2) = \frac{1}{4\pi|\mathbf{r}_1 - \mathbf{r}_2|}. \tag{8.98}$$

The solution of our differential equation (Poisson's equation) is

$$\psi(\mathbf{r}_1) = \frac{1}{4\pi\varepsilon_0} \int \frac{\rho(\mathbf{r}_2)}{|\mathbf{r}_1 - \mathbf{r}_2|} \, d\mathbf{r}_2 \tag{8.99}$$

in complete agreement with Eq. 8.81.

In summary, Green's function, $\varphi(\mathbf{r}_1, \mathbf{r}_2)$, often written $G(\mathbf{r}_1, \mathbf{r}_2)$ as a reminder of the name, is a solution of Eq. 8.91. It enters in an integral solution of our differential equation, as in Eq. 8.81. For the simple, but important electrostatic case we obtain Green's function $G(\mathbf{r}_1, \mathbf{r}_2)$ by Gauss's law, comparing Eqs. 8.91 and 8.97. Finally, from the final solution (Eq. 8.99), it is possible to develop a physical interpretation of Green's function. It occurs as a weighting function or influence function which enhances or reduces the effect of the charge element $\rho(\mathbf{r}_2) \, d\mathbf{r}_2$ according to its distance from the field point $\mathbf{r}_1$. Green's function, $G(\mathbf{r}_1, \mathbf{r}_2)$, gives the effect of a unit point source at $\mathbf{r}_2$ in producing a potential at $\mathbf{r}_1$. This is how it was introduced in Eq. 8.91; this is how it appears in Eq. 8.99.

An important property of Green's function is the symmetry of its two variables, that is,

$$G(\mathbf{r}_1, \mathbf{r}_2) = G(\mathbf{r}_2, \mathbf{r}_1). \tag{8.100}$$

Although this is obvious in the electrostatic case just considered, it can be proved under much more general conditions. In place of Eq. 8.91, let us require that $G(\mathbf{r}, \mathbf{r}_1)$ satisfy

$$\nabla \cdot [p(\mathbf{r}) \nabla G(\mathbf{r}, \mathbf{r}_1)] + \lambda q(\mathbf{r}) \, G(\mathbf{r}, \mathbf{r}_1) = -\delta(\mathbf{r} - \mathbf{r}_1), \tag{8.101}$$

corresponding to a mathematical point source at $\mathbf{r} = \mathbf{r}_1$. Here the functions $p(\mathbf{r})$ and $q(\mathbf{r})$ are well-behaved but otherwise arbitrary functions of $\mathbf{r}$. Green's function, $G(\mathbf{r}, \mathbf{r}_2)$, satisfies the same equation but the subscript 1 is replaced by subscript 2.

$$\nabla \cdot [p(\mathbf{r}) \nabla G(\mathbf{r}, \mathbf{r}_2)] + \lambda \, q(\mathbf{r}) \, G(\mathbf{r}, \mathbf{r}_2) = -\delta(\mathbf{r} - \mathbf{r}_2). \tag{8.102}$$

Then $G(\mathbf{r}, \mathbf{r}_2)$ is a sort of potential at $\mathbf{r}$, created by a unit point source at $\mathbf{r}_2$. We multiply the equation for $G(\mathbf{r}, \mathbf{r}_1)$ by $G(\mathbf{r}, \mathbf{r}_2)$ and the equation for $G(\mathbf{r}, \mathbf{r}_2)$ by $G(\mathbf{r}, \mathbf{r}_1)$ and then subtract the two:

$$G(\mathbf{r}, \mathbf{r}_2)\nabla \cdot [p(\mathbf{r}) \nabla G(\mathbf{r}, \mathbf{r}_1)] - G(\mathbf{r}, \mathbf{r}_1) \nabla \cdot [p(\mathbf{r}) \nabla G(\mathbf{r}, \mathbf{r}_2)]$$
$$= - G(\mathbf{r}, \mathbf{r}_2) \, \delta(\mathbf{r} - \mathbf{r}_1) + G(\mathbf{r}, \mathbf{r}_1) \, \delta(\mathbf{r} - \mathbf{r}_2). \tag{8.103}$$

By integrating over whatever volume is involved, we obtain a surface integral by Green's theorem:

$$\int_S [G(\mathbf{r}, \mathbf{r}_2) \, p(\mathbf{r}) \nabla G(\mathbf{r}, \mathbf{r}_1) - G(\mathbf{r}, \mathbf{r}_1) \, p(\mathbf{r}) \nabla G(\mathbf{r}, \mathbf{r}_2)] \cdot d\boldsymbol{\sigma}$$
$$= - G(\mathbf{r}_1, \mathbf{r}_2) + G(\mathbf{r}_2, \mathbf{r}_1). \tag{8.104}$$

The terms on the right-hand side appear when we use the Dirac delta functions and carry out the volume integration. Under the requirement that Green's functions, $G(\mathbf{r}, \mathbf{r}_1)$ and $G(\mathbf{r}, \mathbf{r}_2)$, have the same values over the surface S and that their normal derivatives have the same values over the surface S, or that either they or their normal gradients vanish over the surface S, the surface integral vanishes and

$$G(\mathbf{r}_1, \mathbf{r}_2) = G(\mathbf{r}_2, \mathbf{r}_1), \qquad (8.105)$$

which shows that Green's function is symmetric. Note that this symmetry property holds for Green's function in every equation in the form of (8.101). In Chapter 9 we shall call equations in this form self-adjoint. The symmetry is the basis of various reciprocity theorems; the effect of a charge at $\mathbf{r}_2$ on the potential at $\mathbf{r}_1$ is the same as the effect of a charge at $\mathbf{r}_1$ on the potential at $\mathbf{r}_2$.

This use of Green's functions is a powerful technique for solving many of the more difficult problems of mathematical physics. We shall return to it when we take up integral equations in Chapter 16.

EXERCISES

8.6.1 Let $\delta_a(x) = \begin{cases} 0, & x < -\dfrac{a}{2}, \\ \dfrac{1}{a}, & -\dfrac{a}{2} < x < \dfrac{a}{2}, \\ 0, & \dfrac{a}{2} < x. \end{cases}$

Show that

$$\lim_{a \to 0} \int_{-\infty}^{\infty} f(x)\, \delta_a(x)\, dx = f(0),$$

assuming that $f(x)$ is continuous at $x = 0$.

8.6.2 Show that

$$G(\mathbf{r}_1, \mathbf{r}_2) = \frac{e^{ik|\mathbf{r}_1 - \mathbf{r}_2|}}{4\pi|\mathbf{r}_1 - \mathbf{r}_2|}$$

is a Green's function satisfying the differential equation

$$(\nabla_1^2 + k^2)\, G(\mathbf{r}_1, \mathbf{r}_2) = -\delta(\mathbf{r}_1 - \mathbf{r}_2).$$

This involves two parts:
(a) Show that $G(\mathbf{r}_1, \mathbf{r}_2)$ satisfies the homogeneous differential equation away from $\mathbf{r}_1 = \mathbf{r}_2$
(b) Show that for $|\mathbf{r}_1 - \mathbf{r}_2|$ small enough

$$\int (\nabla_1^2 + k^2)\, G(\mathbf{r}_1, \mathbf{r}_2)\, d\mathbf{r}_1 = \begin{cases} 0, & \mathbf{r}_2 \neq \mathbf{r}_1, \\ -1, & \mathbf{r}_2 = \mathbf{r}_1. \end{cases}$$

8.6.3 Prove that

$$\delta(f(x)) = \left|\frac{df(x)}{dx}\right|^{-1} \delta(x - x_0),$$

where x_0 is chosen so that $f(x_0) = 0$. *Hint.* Note that $\delta(f)\, df = \delta(x)\, dx$.

8.6.4 Show that in spherical polar coordinates $(r, \cos \theta, \varphi)$ the delta function $\delta(\mathbf{r}_1 - \mathbf{r}_2)$ becomes

$$\frac{1}{r_1^2} \delta(r_1 - r_2)\, \delta(\cos \theta_1 - \cos \theta_2)\, \delta(\varphi_1 - \varphi_2).$$

Generalize this to the curvilinear coordinates (q_1, q_2, q_3) of Section 2.1 with scale factors h_1, h_2, and h_3.

8.6.5 Using the Gauss error curve representation of the Dirac delta function show that

$$x \frac{d}{dx} \delta(x) = -\delta(x).$$

This and other results for the Dirac delta function can be proved more rigorously (and possibly more obscurely) by the use of the mathematical theory of distributions.

REFERENCES

BATEMAN, H., *Partial Differential Equations of Mathematical Physics*. New York: Dover (1944; first edition, 1932). A wealth of applications of various partial differential equations in classical physics. Excellent examples of the use of different coordinate systems—ellipsoidal, paraboloidal, toroidal coordinates, and so on.

INCE, E. L., *Ordinary Differential Equations*. New York: Dover (1926). The classic work in the theory of ordinary differential equations.

MURPHY, G. M., *Ordinary Differential Equations and Their Solutions*. Princeton, New Jersey: Van Nostrand (1960). A thorough, relatively readable treatment of ordinary differential equations, both linear and nonlinear.

$$\mathscr{L}u = \mathscr{L}u = \frac{d}{dx}\left[p(x)\frac{du(x)}{dx}\right] + q(x)\,u(x)$$

$$\mathscr{L}u(x) + \lambda\,w(x)\,u(x) = 0.$$

CHAPTER 9

STURM-LIOUVILLE
THEORY—ORTHOGONAL FUNCTIONS

9.1 Self-Adjoint Differential Equations

In Chapter 8 we studied, classified, and solved linear, second-order, differential equations corresponding to linear, second-order, differential operators of the general form

$$\mathscr{L}\,u(x) = p_0(x)\frac{d^2}{dx^2}\,u(x) + p_1(x)\frac{d}{dx}\,u(x) + p_2(x)\,u(x). \qquad (9.1)$$

The *functions* $p_0(x)$, $p_1(x)$, and $p_2(x)$ are not to be confused with the constants p_i of Section 8.5. Reference to Eq. 8.51 shows that $P(x) = p_1(x)/p_0(x)$ and $Q(x) = p_2(x)/p_0(x)$.

These coefficients, $p_0(x)$, $p_1(x)$, and $p_2(x)$ are real functions of x and over the region of interest, $a \le x \le b$, the first $2 - i$ derivatives of $p_i(x)$ are continuous. Further, $p_0(x)$ does not vanish for $a < x < b$. Now, the zeros of $p_0(x)$ are singular points (Section 8.3) and the preceding statement simply means that we choose our interval $[a, b]$ so that there are no singular points in the interior of the interval. There may be and often are singular points on the boundaries.

It is convenient in the mathematical theory of differential equations to define an *adjoint*[1] operator $\bar{\mathscr{L}}$ by

$$\bar{\mathscr{L}}u = \frac{d^2}{dx^2}\,[p_0 u] - \frac{d}{dx}\,[p_1 u] + p_2 u$$

$$= p_0\frac{d^2 u}{dx^2} + (2p_0' - p_1)\frac{du}{dx} + (p_0'' - p_1' + p_2)u. \qquad (9.2)$$

---

[1] The *adjoint* operator bears a somewhat forced relationship to the *adjoint* matrix. A better justification for the nomenclature is found in a comparison of the *self-adjoint* operator (plus appropriate boundary conditions) with the *self-adjoint* matrix. The significant properties are developed in Section 9.2.

In a comparison of Eqs. 9.1 and 9.2 the necessary and sufficient condition that $\mathscr{L} = \bar{\mathscr{L}}$ is that

$$p_0'(x) = \frac{dp_0(x)}{dx} = p_1(x). \tag{9.3}$$

When this condition is satisfied,

$$\bar{\mathscr{L}}u = \mathscr{L}u = \frac{d}{dx}\left[p(x)\frac{du(x)}{dx}\right] + q(x)\,u(x) \tag{9.4}$$

and the operator $\mathscr{L}$ is said to be *self-adjoint*. Here, for the self-adjoint case, $p_0(x)$ is replaced by $p(x)$ and $p_2(x)$ by $q(x)$ to avoid unnecessary subscripts.

In a survey of the differential equations introduced in Section 8.2, Legendre's equation and the linear oscillator equation are self-adjoint, but others, such as the Laguerre and Hermite equations, are not. However, the theory of linear, second-order, self-adjoint differential equations is perfectly general because we can *always* transform the non-self-adjoint operator into the required self-adjoint form. Consider Eq. 9.1 with $p_0' \neq p_1$. If we multiply $\mathscr{L}$ by[1]

$$\frac{1}{p_0(x)}\exp\left[\int^x \frac{p_1(t)}{p_0(t)}\,dt\right]$$

we obtain

$$\frac{1}{p_0(x)}\exp\left[\int^x \frac{p_1(t)}{p_0(t)}\,dt\right]\mathscr{L}\,u(x) = \frac{d}{dx}\left\{\exp\left[\int^x \frac{p_1(t)}{p_0(t)}\,dt\right]\frac{du(x)}{dx}\right\}$$

$$+ \frac{p_2(x)}{p_0(x)}\cdot\exp\left[\int^x \frac{p_1(t)}{p_0(t)}\,dt\right]u, \tag{9.5}$$

which is clearly self-adjoint. Notice the $p_0(x)$ in the denominator. This is why we require $p_0(x) \neq 0$, $a < x < b$. In the following development we assume that $\mathscr{L}$ has been put in self-adjoint form.

Eigenfunctions, eigenvalues.   Let us form the differential equation

$$\mathscr{L}u(x) + \lambda\,w(x)\,u(x) = 0. \tag{9.6}$$

Here λ is a constant and $w(x)$ is a known function of x, called a density or weighting function. The significance of these labels will appear in subsequent sections. We require that $w(x) > 0$ except, possibly, at isolated points at which $w(x) = 0$. For a given choice of the parameter λ, a function $u_\lambda(x)$, which satisfies Eq. 9.6 *and the imposed boundary conditions*, is called an *eigenfunction* corresponding to λ. The constant λ is then called an *eigenvalue*. There is no guarantee that an eigenfunction

[1] If we multiply $\mathscr{L}$ by $f(x)/h_0(x)$ and then demand that

$$f'(x) = \frac{fp_1}{p_0},$$

so that the new operator will be self-adjoint, we obtain

$$f(x) = \exp\left[\int^x \frac{p_1(t)}{p_0(t)}\,dt\right]$$

$u_\lambda(x)$ will exist for any arbitrary choice of eigenvalue λ. Indeed, the requirement that there be an eigenfunction often restricts the acceptable values of λ to a discrete set. Here we have one mathematical approach to the process of quantization in quantum mechanics.

EXAMPLE 9.1.1

Legendre's equation is given by

$$(1 - x^2)y'' - 2xy' + n(n + 1)y = 0. \tag{9.7}$$

From Eqs. 9.1 and 9.6

$$p_0(x) = 1 - x^2 = p \qquad w(x) = 1,$$

$$p_1(x) = -2x = p' \qquad \lambda = n(n + 1), \tag{9.8}$$

$$p_2(x) = 0 = q.$$

The reader will recall that our series solutions of Legendre's equation (Section 8.4)[1] diverged unless n was restricted to one of the integers. This represents a quantization of the eigenvalue λ.

When the equations of Chapter 8 are transformed into self-adjoint form, we find the following values of the coefficients and parameters (Table 9.1).

TABLE 9.1

Equation	$p(x)$	$q(x)$	λ	$w(x)$
Legendre	$1 - x^2$	0	$l(l + 1)$	1
Associated Legendre	$1 - x^2$	$-m^2/(1 - x^2)$	$l(l + 1)$	1
Chebyshev I	$(1 - x^2)^{1/2}$	0	n^2	$(1 - x^2)^{-1/2}$
Chebyshev II	$(1 - x^2)^{3/2}$	0	$n(n + 2)$	$(1 - x^2)^{1/2}$
Bessel	x	$-\dfrac{n^2}{x}$	a^2	x
Laguerre	xe^{-x}	0	α	e^{-x}
Associated Laguerre	$x^{k+1}e^{-x}$	0	$\alpha - k$	$x^k e^{-x}$
Hermite	e^{-x^2}	0	2α	e^{-x^2}
Simple harmonic oscillator[a]	1	0	ω^2	1

[a] This will form the basis for Chapter 14, Fourier series.

In the foregoing definition of eigenfunction it was noted that the eigenfunction $u_\lambda(x)$ was required to satisfy certain imposed boundary conditions. These boundary conditions may take three forms:

[1] Cf. also Section 12.9.

1. Cauchy boundary conditions. The value of a function and normal derivative specified on the boundary. In electrostatics this would mean φ, the potential, and E_n the normal components of the electric field.

2. Dirichlet boundary conditions. The value of a function specified on the boundary.

3. Neumann boundary conditions. The normal derivative (normal gradient) of a function specified on the boundary. In the electrostatic case this would be E_n and therefore σ, the surface charge density.

A summary of the relation of these three types of boundary condition to the three types of two-dimensional partial differential equation is given in Table 9.2. For extended discussions of these partial differential equations the reader may consult Sommerfeld, Chapter 2, or Morse and Feshbach, Chapter 6.

TABLE 9.2

Boundary conditions	Type of partial differential equation		
	Elliptic	Hyperbolic	Parabolic
	Laplace, Poisson in (x, y)	Wave equation in (x, t)	Diffusion equation in (x, t)
Cauchy			
Open surface	Unphysical results (instability)	*Unique, stable solution*	Too restrictive
Closed surface	Too restrictive	Too restrictive	Too restrictive
Dirichlet			
Open surface	Insufficient	Insufficient	*Unique, stable solution in* one direction
Closed surface	*Unique, stable solution*	Solution not unique	Too restrictive
Neumann			
Open surface	Insufficient	Insufficient	*Unique, stable solution* in one direction
Closed surface	*Unique, stable solution*	Solution not unique	Too restrictive

The term boundary conditions includes as a special case the concept of initial conditions. For instance, specifying the initial position x_0 and the initial velocity v_0 in some dynamical problem would correspond to the Cauchy boundary conditions. The only difference in the present usage of boundary conditions in these one-dimensional problems is that we are going to apply the conditions on *both* ends of the allowed range of the variable.

Usually the boundary conditions in one of the three forms will guarantee that at the ends of our interval (that is, at the boundary) the following products will vanish:

$$p(x)\, u(x)\, \frac{du(x)}{dx}\bigg|_{x=a} = 0$$

and   (9.9)

$$p(x)\, u(x)\, \frac{du(x)}{dx}\bigg|_{x=b} = 0.$$

Here $u(x)$ is a solution of the particular differential equation (9.6) being considered. We can however, work with a somewhat less restrictive set of boundary conditions,

$$vpu'|_{x=a} = vpu'|_{x=b},\tag{9.10}$$

in which $u(x)$ and $v(x)$ are solutions of the differential equation corresponding to the same or to different eigenvalues.

In anticipation of applications in quantum mechanics let us consider the possibility that Eq. 9.6 may have complex solutions, $u(x)$ and $v(x)$. We replace Eq. 9.10 with the complex boundary condition

$$v^*pu'|_{x=a} = v^*pu'|_{x=b},\tag{9.11}$$

in which v^* is the complex conjugate of $v(x)$. Clearly, if $v(x)$ is real, $v = v^*$ and Eq. 9.11 will reduce to Eq. 9.10. Because we take the coefficient $p_0(x)$ to be real, the boundary condition may equally well be written as the complex conjugate of Eq. 9.11,

$$vpu^{*\prime}|_{x=a} = vpu^{*\prime}|_{x=b}.\tag{9.12a}$$

Finally, since $u(x)$ and $v(x)$ are to be any two solutions, we may interchange u and v to obtain

$$v^{*\prime}pu|_{x=a} = v^{*\prime}pu|_{x=b}\tag{9.12b}$$

and its complex conjugate.

Hermitian operators.   We now prove an important property of the combination self-adjoint, second-order differential operator (Eq. 9.6), plus solutions that satisfy boundary conditions given by Eqs. 9.11 and 9.12. By integrating over the range $a \leqslant x \leqslant b$ we obtain

$$\int_a^b v^* \mathscr{L}u\, dx = \int_a^b v^*(pu')'\, dx + \int_a^b v^*qu\, dx\tag{9.13}$$

using Eq. 9.4. Integrating by parts, we have

$$\int_a^b v^*(p_0u')'\, dx = v^*pu' \bigg|_a^b - \int_a^b v^{*\prime}pu'\, dx.\tag{9.14}$$

The integrated part vanishes on application of the boundary conditions (Eq. 9.11). Integrating the remaining integral by parts a second time, we have

$$-\int_a^b v^{*\prime}pu'\, dx = -v^{*\prime}pu \bigg|_a^b + \int_a^b u(pv^{*\prime})'\, dx.\tag{9.15}$$

Again the integrated part vanishes in an application of Eq. 9.12. A combination of Eqs. 9.13, 9.14, and 9.15 gives us

$$\int_a^b v^* \mathcal{L} u \, dx = \int_a^b u \mathcal{L} v^* \, dx. \tag{9.16}$$

This property, given by Eq. 9.16, is expressed by saying that the operator $\mathcal{L}$ is Hermitian with respect to the functions $u(x)$ and $v(x)$ which satisfy the boundary conditions specified by Eq. 9.11.

EXAMPLE 9.1.2

Choice of interval $[a, b]$. For $\mathcal{L} = d^2/dx^2$ a possible eigenvalue equation is

$$\frac{d^2}{dx^2} y(x) + n^2 y(x) = 0,$$

with eigenfunctions

$$u_n = \cos nx$$

$$v_m = \sin mx.$$

Equation 9.10 becomes

$$-n \sin mx \sin nx \mid_a^b = 0$$

or

$$m \cos mx \cos nx \mid_a^b = 0,$$

interchanging u_n and v_n. Since $\sin mx$ and $\cos nx$ are periodic with period 2π (for n and m integral), Eq. 9.10 is clearly satisfied if $a = x_0$ and $b = x_0 + 2\pi$.

EXERCISES

9.1.1 Show that Laguerre's equation may be put into self-adjoint form by multiplying by e^{-x} and that $w(x) = e^{-x}$ is the weighting function.

9.1.2 Show that the Hermite equation may be put into self-adjoint form by multiplying by e^{-x^2} and that this gives $w(x) = e^{-x^2}$ as the appropriate density function.

9.1.3 Show that the Chebyshev equation (type I) may be put into self-adjoint form by multiplying by $(1 - x^2)^{-1/2}$ and that this gives $w(x) = (1 - x^2)^{-1/2}$ as the appropriate density function.

9.1.4 Show that the self-adjoint equation

$$z\frac{d^2 y}{dz^2} + \frac{dy}{dz} - \frac{n^2 y}{z} + a^2 z y = 0, \qquad \text{with } z = \frac{x}{a}$$

can be obtained from Bessel's equation. Identify the density function.

9.1.5 From the results of Exercise 9.1.4 show that

$$\int_a^b Z_m(z) \, Z_n(z) \, \frac{dz}{z} = 0$$

is an orthogonality integral for the solutions, Z_n, of the Bessel equation. Disregard normalization. For details of setting $a = 0$, $b = \infty$, and the condition $m + n > 0$, see Chapter 11. Another possibility, which uses [0, 1] as an interval, is developed in Section 11.1.

9.1.6 Show the following when the linear second-order differential equation is expressed in self-adjoint form:

(a) The Wronskian is equal to a constant divided by the intitial coefficient p.

$$W = \frac{C}{p}$$

(b) A second solution is given by

$$y_2(x) = C \, y_1(x) \int^x \frac{dt}{p[y_1(t)]^2} \, .$$

9.1.7 Given the differential equation

$$y'' + \left(\frac{1}{x} - 2x\right) y' + 4ny = 0.$$

(a) Transform this equation into Sturm-Liouville (self-adjoint) form.

(b) Show that the transformation $z = x^2$ leads to Laguerre's equation.

9.1.8 $U_n(x)$, the Chebyshev polynomial (type II) satisfies the differential equation

$$(1 - x^2) \, U_n''(x) - 3x \, U_n'(x) + n(n + 2) \, U_n(x) = 0.$$

(a) Locate the singular points that appear in the *finite* plane and show whether they are regular or irregular.

(b) Put this equation in self-adjoint form.

(c) Identify the complete eigenvalue.

(d) Identify the weighting function.

(e) Write out an orthogonality integral for $U_n(x)$ and $U_m(x)$, $n \neq m$.

9.1.9 For the very special case $\lambda = 0$ and $q(x) = 0$ the self-adjoint eigenvalue equation becomes

$$\frac{d}{dx}\left[p(x) \frac{du(x)}{dx}\right] = 0,$$

satisfied by

$$\frac{du}{dx} = \frac{1}{p(x)} \, .$$

Use this to obtain a second solution of the following:

(a) Legendre's equation,

(b) Laguerre's equation,

(c) Hermite's equation.

$$Ans. \ (a) \ u_2(x) = \frac{1}{2} \ln \frac{1 + x}{1 - x},$$

$$(b) \ u_2(x) - u_2(x_0) = \int_{x_0}^x e^t \frac{dt}{t},$$

$$(c) \ u_2(x) = \int_0^x e^{t^2} \, dt.$$

These second solutions illustrate the divergent behavior usually found in a second solution.

9.1.10 Given that $\mathscr{L}u = 0$ and $g\mathscr{L}u$ is self-adjoint, show that for the adjoint operator $\overline{\mathscr{L}}$, $\overline{\mathscr{L}}(gu) = 0$.

9.2 Hermitian (Self-Adjoint) Operators

Hermitian or self-adjoint operators have three properties that are of extreme importance in physics, both classical and quantum.

1. The eigenvalues of an Hermitian operator are real.
2. The eigenfunctions of an Hermitian operator are orthogonal.
3. The eigenfunctions of an Hermitian operator from a complete set.[1]

Real eigenvalues.　We proceed to prove the first two of these three properties. Let

$$\mathcal{L}u_i + \lambda_i w u_i = 0, \tag{9.17}$$

$$\mathcal{L}u_j + \lambda_j w u_j = 0, \tag{9.18a}$$

$$\mathcal{L}u_j^* + \lambda_j^* w u_j^* = 0. \tag{9.18b}$$

Here $\mathcal{L}$ is a real operator (p and q are real functions of x) and $w(x)$ is a real function. But we permit λ_k, the eigenvalues, and u_k, the eigenfunctions, to be complex. Multiplying Eq. 9.17 by u_j^* and Eq. 9.18b by u_i and then subtracting, we have

$$u_j^* \mathcal{L}u_i - u_i \mathcal{L}u_j^* = (\lambda_j^* - \lambda_i) w u_i u_j^* \tag{9.19}$$

We integrate over the range $a \leqslant x \leqslant b$,

$$\int_a^b u_j^* \mathcal{L}u_i \, dx - \int_a^b u_i \mathcal{L}u_j^* \, dx = (\lambda_j^* - \lambda_i) \int_a^b u_i u_j^* w \, dx. \tag{9.20}$$

Since $\mathcal{L}$ is Hermitian, the left-hand side vanishes by Eq. 9.16 and

$$(\lambda_j^* - \lambda_i) \int_a^b u_i u_j^* w \, dx = 0. \tag{9.21}$$

If $i = j$, the integral cannot vanish [$w(x) > 0$, apart from isolated points], except in the trivial case $u_i = 0$. Hence the coefficient $(\lambda_i^* - \lambda_i)$ must be zero,

$$\lambda_i^* = \lambda_i, \tag{9.22}$$

which is a mathematical statement that the eigenvalue is real. Since λ_i can represent any one of the eigenvalues, this proves the first property. This is an exact analog of the nature of the eigenvalues of real symmetric (and of Hermitian) matrices (cf. Section 4.5).

This reality of the eigenvalues of Hermitian operators has a fundamental significance in quantum mechanics. In quantum mechanics the eigenvalues correspond to precisely measurable quantities, such as energy and angular momentum. With the theory formulated in terms of Hermitian operators, this proof of the reality of the eigenvalues guarantees that the theory will predict real numbers for these measurable physical quantities.

Orthogonal eigenfunctions.　If we now take $i \neq j$ and if $\lambda_i \neq \lambda_j$, the integral

[1] This third property is not universal. It *does* hold for our linear, second-order differential operators in Sturm-Liouville (self-adjoint) form.

of the product of the two different eigenfunctions must vanish.

$$\int_a^b u_i u_j^* w \, dx = 0. \tag{9.23}$$

This condition, called orthogonality, is the continuum analog of the vanishing of a scalar product of two vectors. We say that the eigenfunctions $u_i(x)$ and $u_j(x)$ are orthogonal with respect to the weighting function $w(x)$ over the interval $[a, b]$. Equation 9.23 constitutes a partial proof of the second property of our Hermitian operators. Again the precise analogy with matrix analysis should be noted. Indeed, we can establish a one-to-one correspondence between this Sturm-Liouville theory of differential equations and the treatment of Hermitian matrices. Historically, this correspondence has been significant in establishing the mathematical equivalence of matrix mechanics developed by Heisenberg and wave mechanics developed by Schrödinger. Today, the two diverse approaches are merged into the theory of quantum mechanics and the mathematical formulation which is more convenient for a particular problem is used for that problem. Actually, the mathematical alternatives do not end here. Integral equations, Chapter 16, form a third equivalent and sometimes more convenient or more powerful approach.

This proof of orthogonality is not quite complete. There is a loophole, because we may have $i \neq j$ but still have $\lambda_i = \lambda_j$. Such a case is labeled degenerate. If $\lambda_i = \lambda_j$, the integral in Eq. 9.21 need not vanish. This means that linearly independent eigenfunctions corresponding to the same eigenvalue are not automatically orthogonal and that some other method must be sought to obtain an orthogonal set. Although the eigenfunctions in this degenerate case may not be orthogonal, they can always be made orthogonal. One method is developed in the next section.

It will be seen in succeeding chapters that it is just as desirable to have a given set of functions orthogonal as it is to have an orthogonal coordinate system. We can work with nonorthogonal functions, but they are likely to prove as messy as an oblique coordinate system.

The third property, completeness, is defined and discussed in Section 9.4. The formal proof, which involves the calculus of variations (cf. Chapter 17), is not given here. For details the reader is referred to Courant and Hilbert, Vol. I, or to Titchmarsh.

EXAMPLE 9.2.1.   FOURIER SERIES: ORTHOGONALITY

Continuing Example 9.1.2, the eigenvalue equation

$$\frac{d^2}{dx^2} y(x) + n^2 \, y(x) = 0,$$

perhaps describes a quantum mechanical particle in a box, perhaps a vibrating violin string with (degenerate) eigenfunctions—$\cos nx$, $\sin nx$.

With n real (here taken to be integral), the orthogonality integrals become

(a) $$\int_{x_0}^{x_0 + 2\pi} \sin mx \sin nx \, dx = C_n \, \delta_{nm},$$

(b)
$$\int_{x_0}^{x_0 + 2\pi} \cos mx \cos nx \, dx = D_n \delta_{nm},$$

(c)
$$\int_{x_0}^{x_0 + 2\pi} \sin mx \cos nx \, dx = 0.$$

For an interval of 2π the preceding analysis guarantees the Kronecker delta in (a) and (b) but not the zero in (c) because (c) involves degenerate eigenfunctions. However, inspection shows that (c) always vanishes for all integral m and n.

Our Sturm-Liouville theory says nothing about the values of C_n and D_n. Actual calculation yields

$$C_n = \begin{cases} \pi, & n \neq 0, \\ 0, & n = 0, \end{cases}$$

$$D = \begin{cases} \pi, & n \neq 0, \\ 2\pi, & n = 0. \end{cases}$$

These orthogonality integrals from the basis of the Fourier series developed in Chapter 14.

EXAMPLE 9.2.2.   EXPANSION IN ORTHOGONAL EIGENFUNCTIONS: SQUARE WAVE

The property of completeness means that certain classes of function (that is, sectionally or piecewise continuous) may be represented by a series of orthogonal eigenfunctions to any desired degree of accuracy. Consider the square wave

$$f(x) = \begin{cases} \dfrac{h}{2}, & 0 < x < \pi, \\[2mm] -\dfrac{h}{2}, & -\pi < x < 0. \end{cases}$$

The eigenfunction series is conveniently (and conventionally) written

$$f(x) = \frac{a_0}{2} + \sum_{n=1}^{\infty} (a_n \cos nx + b_n \sin nx).$$

From the orthogonality integrals of Example 9.2.1 the coefficients are given by

$$a_n = \frac{1}{\pi} \int_{-\pi}^{\pi} f(t) \cos nt \, dt,$$

$$b_n = \frac{1}{\pi} \int_{-\pi}^{\pi} f(t) \sin nt \, dt, \qquad n = 0, 1, 2, \ldots .$$

Direct substitution of $\pm h/2$ for $f(x)$ yields

$$a_n = 0,$$

which is expected here because of the antisymmetry, and

$$b_n = \frac{h}{n\pi}(1 - \cos n\pi) = \begin{cases} 0, & n \text{ even}, \\[2mm] \dfrac{2h}{n\pi}, & n \text{ odd}. \end{cases}$$

Hence the eigenfunction (Fourier) expansion of the square wave is

$$f(x) = \frac{2h}{\pi} \sum_{n=0}^{\infty} \frac{\sin(2n+1)x}{(2n+1)}.$$

Additional examples, using other eigenfunctions, appear in Chapters 11 and 12.

EXERCISES

9.2.1 The functions $u_1(x)$ and $u_2(x)$ are eigenfunctions of the same Hermitian operator but for distinct eigenvalues λ_1 and λ_2. Prove that $u_1(x)$ and $u_2(x)$ are linearly independent.

9.2.2 With $\mathscr{L}$ *not* self-adjoint,

$$\mathscr{L}u_i + \lambda_i w u_i = 0$$

and

$$\overline{\mathscr{L}}v_j + \lambda_j w v_j = 0.$$

(a) Show that

$$\int_a^b v_j \mathscr{L}u_i \, dx = \int_a^b u_i \overline{\mathscr{L}}v_j \, dx$$

provided

$$u_i p_0 v_j \Big|_a^b = v_j p_0 u_i' \Big|_a^b$$

and

$$u_i(p_1 - p_0')v_j \Big|_a^b = 0.$$

(b) Show that the orthogonality integral for the eigenfunctions u_i and v_j becomes

$$\int_a^b u_i v_j w \, dx = 0 \qquad (\lambda_i \neq \lambda_j).$$

9.3 Schmidt Orthogonalization

This is a method of taking a nonorthogonal set of linearly independent functions[1] and literally constructing an orthogonal set over an arbitrary interval and with respect to an arbitrary weight or density factor. Here, for convenience, the functions are assumed to be real. The generalization to the complex case should offer little difficulty.

So far no normalization has been specified. This means that

$$\int_a^b \varphi_i^2 w \, dx = N_i^2,$$

---

[1] Such a set of functions might well arise from the solutions of a (partial) differential equation in which the eigenvalue was independent of one or more of the constants of separation. As an example, we have the hydrogen atom problem (Section 13.2). The eigenvalue (energy) is independent of both the electron orbital angular momentum and its projection on the z-axis, m. The student should note, however, that the origin of the set of functions is irrelevant to the Schmidt orthogonalization procedure.

but no attention has been paid to the value of N_i. Since our basic equation, (9.6), is linear and homogeneous, we may multiply our solution by any constant and it will still be a solution. We now demand that each solution $\varphi_i(x)$ be multiplied by N_i^{-1} so that the new (normalized) φ_i will satisfy

$$\int_a^b \varphi_i^2(x)\, w(x)\, dx = 1 \tag{9.24}$$

or

$$\int_a^b \varphi_i(x)\, \varphi_j(x)\, w(x)\, dx = \delta_{ij}. \tag{9.25}$$

Equation 9.24 says that we have normalized to unity. Including the property of orthogonality, we have Eq. 9.25. Functions satisfying this equation are said to be orthonormal (orthogonal plus unit normalization). It should be emphasized that other normalizations are possible, and indeed, by historical convention, each of the special functions of mathematical physics treated in Chapters 12 and 13 will be normalized differently!

Suppose our linearly independent but nonorthogonal, unnormalized set of functions is $u_n(x)$, $n = 0, 1, 2, \cdots$. Let

$$\varphi_0(x) = \frac{u_0(x)}{\left(\int u_0^2 w\, dx\right)^{1/2}}, \tag{9.26}$$

that is, $\varphi_0(x)$ is here normalized to unity.

We then put

$$\psi_1(x)\,(\text{unnormalized}) = a_{10}\, \varphi_0(x) + u_1(x), \tag{9.27}$$

where a_{10} is an undetermined constant. We require that $\psi_1(x)$ satisfy these conditions:

1. Orthogonality with respect to $\varphi_0(x)$.
2. Unit normalization.

For orthogonality

$$\int \psi_1 \varphi_0 w\, dx = a_{10} \int \varphi_0^2 w\, dx + \int u_1 \varphi_0 w\, dx$$

$$= 0. \tag{9.28}$$

Since φ_0 is normalized to unity (Eq. 9.26), we have

$$a_{10} = -\int u_1 \varphi_0 w\, dx, \tag{9.29}$$

fixing the value of a_{10}. Normalizing, we define

$$\varphi_1(x) = \frac{\psi_1(x)}{\left(\int \psi_1^2 w\, dx\right)^{1/2}}. \tag{9.30}$$

Generalizing, we have

$$\varphi_i(x) = \frac{\psi_i(x)}{\left(\int \psi_i^2(x)\, w(x)\, dx\right)^{1/2}} \tag{9.31}$$

where

$$\psi_i(x) = a_{i0}\varphi_0 + a_{i,1}\varphi_1 + \cdots + a_{i,i-1}\varphi_{i-1} + u_i. \tag{9.32}$$

The coefficients a_{ij} are given by

$$a_{ij} = -\int u_i\varphi_j w \, dx. \tag{9.33}$$

It will be noticed that although this is one possible way of constructing an orthogonal or orthonormal set the functions $\varphi_i(x)$ are not unique. There is an infinite number of possible orthonormal sets for a given interval and a given density function. As an illustration of the freedom involved, consider two (nonparallel) vectors $\mathbf{A}$ and $\mathbf{B}$ in the xy-plane. We may normalize $\mathbf{A}$ to unit magnitude and then form $\mathbf{B}' = a\mathbf{A} + \mathbf{B}$ so that $\mathbf{B}'$ is perpendicular to $\mathbf{A}$. By normalizing $\mathbf{B}'$ we have completed the Schmidt orthogonalization for two vectors. But any two perpendicular unit vectors such as $\mathbf{i}$ and $\mathbf{j}$ could have been chosen as our orthonormal set. Again, with an infinite number of possible rotations of $\mathbf{i}$ and $\mathbf{j}$ about the z-axis, we have an infinite number of possible orthonormal sets.

EXAMPLE 9.3.1

Form an orthonormal set from the set of functions $u_n(x) = x^n$, $n = 0, 1, 2, \cdots$. The interval is $-1 \leqslant x \leqslant 1$ and the density function is $w(x) = 1$.

In accordance with the Schmidt orthogonalization process described,

$$u_0 = 1 \quad \text{and} \quad \varphi_0 = \frac{1}{\sqrt{2}}. \tag{9.34}$$

Then

$$\psi_1(x) = a_{10}\frac{1}{\sqrt{2}} + x \tag{9.35}$$

and

$$a_{10} = -\int_{-1}^{1} \frac{x}{\sqrt{2}} dx = 0 \tag{9.36}$$

by symmetry. Normalizing, we obtain

$$\varphi_1(x) = \sqrt{\frac{3}{2}}\, x. \tag{9.37}$$

Continuing the Schmidt process, we define

$$\psi_2(x) = a_{20}\frac{1}{\sqrt{2}} + a_{21}\sqrt{\frac{3}{2}}\, x + x^2, \tag{9.38}$$

where

$$a_{20} = -\int_{-1}^{1} \frac{x_2}{\sqrt{2}} dx = -\frac{\sqrt{2}}{3}, \tag{9.39}$$

$$a_{21} = -\int_{-1}^{1} \sqrt{\frac{3}{2}}\, x^3 \, dx = 0, \tag{9.40}$$

again by symmetry. Therefore

$$\psi_2(x) = x^2 - \tfrac{1}{3},$$
(9.41)

and, on normalizing to unity,

$$\varphi_2(x) = \sqrt{\tfrac{5}{2}} \cdot \tfrac{1}{2}(3x^2 - 1).$$
(9.42)

The next function $\varphi_3(x)$ is

$$\varphi_3(x) = \sqrt{\tfrac{7}{2}} \cdot \tfrac{1}{2}(5x^3 - 3x).$$
(9.43)

Reference to Chapter 12 will show that

$$\varphi_n(x) = \sqrt{\frac{2n+1}{2}}\, P_n(x),$$
(9.44)

where $P_n(x)$ is the nth-order Legendre polynomial. Our Schmidt process provides a possible but very cumbersome method of generating the Legendre polynomials.

Orthogonal polynomials.   This particular example has been chosen strictly to illustrate the Schmidt procedure. Although it has the advantage of introducing the Legendre polynomials, the initial functions $u_n = x^n$ are not degenerate eigenfunctions and they are not solutions of Legendre's equation. They are simply a set of functions which we have here rearranged to create an orthonormal set for the given interval and given weighting function. That we obtained the Legendre polynomials is not quite black magic but a direct consequence of the choice of interval and weighting function. The use of $u_n(x) = x^n$ but with other choices of interval and weighting function leads to other sets of orthogonal polynomials as shown in Table 9.3. We consider these polynomials in detail in Chapters 12 and 13 as solutions of particular differential equations.

TABLE 9.3

Orthogonal Polynomials Generated by Schmidt Orthogonalization of $u_n(x)=x^n$, $n = 0, 1, 2, \ldots$

Polynomials	Interval	Weighting function $w(x)$	Standard normalization
Legendre	$-1 \leqslant x \leqslant 1$	1	$\displaystyle\int_{-1}^{1} [P_n(x)]^2\, dx = \frac{2}{2n+1}$
Chebyshev I	$-1 \leqslant x \leqslant 1$	$(1-x^2)^{-1/2}$	$\displaystyle\int_{-1}^{1} [T_n(x)]^2(1-x^2)^{-1/2}\, dx = \begin{cases} \pi/2, & n \neq 0 \\ \pi, & n = 0 \end{cases}$
Chebyshev II	$-1 \leqslant x \leqslant 1$	$(1-x^2)^{1/2}$	$\displaystyle\int_{-1}^{1} [U_n(x)]^2(1-x^2)^{1/2}\, dx = \frac{\pi}{2}$
Laguerre	$0 \leqslant x < \infty$	e^{-x}	$\displaystyle\int_{0}^{\infty} [L_n(x)]^2 e^{-x}\, dx = 1$
Associated Laguerre	$0 \leqslant x < \infty$	$x^k e^{-x}$	$\displaystyle\int_{0}^{\infty} [L_n^k(x)]^2 x^k e^{-x}\, dx = \frac{(n+k)!}{n!}$
Hermite	$-\infty < x < \infty$	e^{-x^2}	$\displaystyle\int_{-\infty}^{\infty} [H_n(x)]^2 e^{-x^2}\, dx = 2^n \pi^{1/2} n!$

An examination of this orthogonalization process will reveal two arbitrary features. First, as emphasized before, it is not necessary to normalize the functions to unity. In the example just given we could have required

$$\int_{-1}^{1} \varphi_n(x)\, \varphi_m(x)\, dx = \frac{2}{2n + 1}\, \delta_{nm}, \tag{9.45}$$

and the resulting set would have been the actual Legendre polynomials. Second, the sign of φ_n is always indeterminant. In the example we chose the sign by requiring the coefficient of the highest power of x in the polynomial to be positive. For the Laguerre polynomials, on the other hand, we would require the coefficient of the highest power to be $(-1)^n/n!$

EXERCISES

9.3.1 Apply the Schmidt procedure to form the first three Laguerre polynomials

$$u_n(x) = x^n, \qquad n = 0, 1, 2, \ldots,$$
$$0 \leqslant x < \infty,$$
$$w(x) = e^{-x}.$$

The conventional normalization is

$$\int_0^\infty L_m(x)\, L_n(x)\, e^{-x}\, dx = \delta_{mn}$$

Ans. $L_0 = 1,$
$L_1 = 1 - x,$
$L_2 = \dfrac{(2 - 4x + x^2)}{2}.$

9.3.2 Using the Schmidt orthogonalization procedure, construct the lowest three Hermite polynomials:

$$u_n(x) = x^n, \qquad n = 0, 1, 2, \cdots \qquad -\infty < x < \infty, \qquad w(x) = e^{-x^2}.$$

For this set of polynomials the usual normalization is

$$\int_{-\infty}^\infty H_m(x)\, H_n(x)\, w(x)\, dx = \delta_{mn} 2^m m!\, \pi^{1/2}.$$

Ans. $H_0 = 1,$
$H_1 = 2x,$
$H_2 = 4x^2 - 2.$

9.3.3 Use the Schmidt orthogonalization scheme to construct the first three Chebyshev polynomials (type I).

$$u_n(x) = x^n, \qquad n = 0, 1, 2, \cdots \qquad -1 \leqslant x \leqslant 1, \qquad w(x) = (1 - x^2)^{-1/2}.$$

Take the normalization

$$\int_{-1}^{1} T_m(x)\, T_n(x)\, w(x)\, dx = \delta_{mn}\begin{cases} \pi, & m = n = 0 \\ \dfrac{\pi}{2}, & m = n \geqslant 1. \end{cases}$$

Ans. $T_0 = 1,$
$T_1 = x,$
$T_2 = 2x^2 - 1,$
$(T_3 = 4x^3 - 3x).$

9.3.4 Use the Schmidt orthogonalization scheme to construct the first three Chebyshev polynomials (type II).

$$u_n(x) = x^n, \qquad n = 0, 1, 2, \cdots \qquad -1 \leqslant x \leqslant 1, \qquad w(x) = (1 - x^2)^{+1/2}.$$

Take the normalization to be

$$\int_{-1}^{1} U(x) \, U_m(x) \, w(x) \, dx = \delta_{mn} \frac{\pi}{2}.$$

Hint.

$$\int_{-1}^{1} (1 - x^2)^{1/2} x^{2n} \, dx = \frac{\pi}{2} \times \frac{1 \cdot 3 \cdot 5 \cdots (2n - 1)}{4 \cdot 6 \cdot 8 \cdots (2n + 2)}, \qquad n = 1, 2, 3 \cdots$$

$$= \frac{\pi}{2}, \qquad n = 0.$$

Ans. $U_0 = 1, \qquad U_1 = 2x, \qquad U_2 = 4x^2 - 1.$

9.3.5 Form an orthogonal set over the interval $0 \leqslant x < \infty$, using $u_n(x) = e^{-nx}$, $n = 1, 2, 3, \ldots$. Take the weighting factor, $w(x)$, to be unity. These functions are solutions of $u_n'' - n^2 u_n = 0$, which is clearly already in Sturm-Liouville (self-adjoint) form. Why doesn't the Sturm-Liouville theory guarantee the orthogonality of these functions?

9.4 Completeness of Eigenfunctions

The third important property of an Hermitian operator is that its eigenfunctions form a complete set. This completeness means that any well-behaved (at least piecewise continuous) function $F(x)$ can be approximated by a series

$$F(x) = \sum_{n=0}^{\infty} a_n \, \varphi_n(x) \tag{9.46}$$

to any desired degree of accuracy.[1] More precisely, the set $\varphi_n(x)$ is called complete[2] if the limit of the mean square error vanishes;

$$\lim_{m \to \infty} \int_{a}^{b} \left[F(x) - \sum_{n=0}^{m} a_n \, \varphi_n(x) \right]^2 w(x) \, dx = 0. \tag{9.47}$$

Proof that this can indeed be done with the Hermitian operator eigenfunctions is given by Titchmarsh and by Courant and Hilbert (Vol. I). It is worth noting that our Hermitian operators here are linear, second-order differential operators in self-adjoint form.

In Eq. 9.46 the expansion coefficients a_m may be determined by

$$a_m = \int_{a}^{b} F(x) \, \varphi_m(x) \, w(x) \, dx. \tag{9.48}$$

This follows from multiplying Eq. 9.46 by $\varphi_m(x) \, w(x)$ and integrating. From the orthogonality of the eigenfunctions, $\varphi_n(x)$, only the mth term survives. Here we see the value of orthogonality.

If the set of functions $\varphi_n(x)$ does not form a complete set, possibly because we simply have not included the required infinite number of members of an infinite

---

[1] If we have a finite set, as with vectors, the summation is over the number of linearly independent members of the set.

[2] Many authors use the term closed here.

set, we are led to Bessel's inequality. First, consider the finite case. Let $\mathbf{A}$ be an n component vector,

$$\mathbf{A} = \mathbf{e}_1 a_1 + \mathbf{e}_2 a_2 + \cdots + \mathbf{e}_n a_n, \qquad (9.49)$$

in which $\mathbf{e}_i$ is a unit vector and a_i is the corresponding component (projection) of $\mathbf{A}$, that is,

$$a_i = \mathbf{A} \cdot \mathbf{e}_i. \qquad (9.50)$$

Then

$$\left(\mathbf{A} - \sum_i \mathbf{e}_i a_i \right)^2 \geqslant 0. \qquad (9.51)$$

Bessel's inequality.   If we sum over all n components, clearly the summation equals $\mathbf{A}$ by Eq. 9.49 and the equality holds. If, however, the summation does not include all n components, the inequality results. By expanding Eq. 9.51 and remembering that the unit vectors satisfy an orthogonality relation,

$$\mathbf{e}_i \cdot \mathbf{e}_j = \delta_{ij}, \qquad (9.52)$$

we have

$$A^2 \geqslant \sum_i a_i^2. \qquad (9.53)$$

This is Bessel's inequality.

For functions we consider the integral

$$\int_a^b \left[f(x) - \sum_i a_i \, \varphi_i(x) \right]^2 w(x) \, dx \geqslant 0. \qquad (9.54)$$

This is the continuum analog of Eq. 9.51, letting $n \to \infty$ and replacing the summation by an integration. Again, with the weighting factor $w(x) > 0$ the integrand is nonnegative. The integral vanishes by Eq. 9.46 if we have a complete set. Otherwise, it is positive. Expanding the squared term, we obtain

$$\int_a^b [f(x)]^2 \, w(x) \, dx - 2 \sum_i a_i \int_a^b f(x) \, \varphi_i(x) \, w(x) \, dx + \sum_i a_i^2 \geqslant 0. \qquad (9.55)$$

Applying Eq. 9.48, we have

$$\int_a^b [f(x)]^2 \, w(x) \, dx \geqslant \sum_i a_i^2. \qquad (9.56)$$

Hence the sum of the squares of the expansion coefficients a_i is less than or equal to the weighted integral of $[f(x)]^2$, the equality holding if and only if the expansion is exact, that is, if the set of functions $\varphi_n(x)$ is a complete set.

Schwarz inequality.   The frequently used Schwarz inequality is similar to the Bessel inequality. Consider the quadratic equation

$$\sum_{i=1}^n (a_i x + b_i)^2 = 0. \qquad (9.57)$$

Since every term is greater than or equal to 0 for real x, we conclude that the solution of this quadratic may be real only if b_i/a_i equals a constant. If b_i/a_i does not equal a constant, then x must be complex. Expanding, we find that

$$x^2 \sum_i^n a_i^2 + 2x \sum_i^n a_i b_i + \sum_i^n b_i^2 = 0, \tag{9.58}$$

and since x is complex (or $= -b_i/a_i$) the quadratic formula for x^1 leads to

$$\left(\sum_{i=1}^n a_i b_i \right)^2 \leqslant \left(\sum_{i=1}^n a_i^2 \right) \left(\sum_{i=1}^n b_i^2 \right), \tag{9.59}$$

the equality holding when b_i/a_i equals a constant.

Once more, in terms of vectors, we have

$$(\mathbf{a} \cdot \mathbf{b})^2 = a^2 b^2 \cos^2 \theta \leqslant a^2 b^2, \tag{9.60}$$

where θ is the included angle.

The Schwarz inequality for functions has the form

$$\left[\int_a^b f(x) \, g(x) \, dx \right]^2 \leqslant \int_a^b [f(x)]^2 \, dx \int_a^b [g(x)]^2 \, dx, \tag{9.61}$$

the equality holding if and only if $g(x) = \alpha f(x)$, α being a constant. Equation 9.61 may be derived by considering the equation

$$\int [\lambda f(x) + g(x)]^2 \, dx = 0 \tag{9.62}$$

and proceeding as in Eq. 9.57 for an n-component vector.

If $g(x)$ is a normalized eigenfunction, $\varphi_i(x)$, Eq. 9.61 yields [here $w(x) = 1$]

$$a_i^2 \leqslant \int_a^b [f(x)]^2 \, dx, \tag{9.63}$$

a result that also follows from Eq. 9.56.

Dirac delta function.   Our orthonormal set of eigenfunctions, $\varphi_n(x)$, provides another interesting representation of the Dirac delta function. Consider the sum

$$K(x, t) = K(t, x) = \sum_{n=0}^{\infty} \varphi_n(x) \, \varphi_n(t). \tag{9.64}$$

(For convenience we assume that $\varphi_n(x)$ has been redefined to include $[w(x)]^{1/2}$ if $w(x) \neq 1$.) This series in Eq. 9.64 is assuredly not uniformly convergent, but it may be used as part of an integrand in which the ensuing integration will make it convergent (cf. Section 5.5).

Suppose we form the integral

$$\int F(t) \, K(x, t) \, dt,$$

---

[1] With discriminant complex (or zero).

where it is assumed that $F(t)$ can be expanded in a series of eigenfunctions, $\varphi_p(t)$. We obtain

$$\int F(t) K(x, t)\, dt = \int \sum_{p=0}^{\infty} a_p\, \varphi_p(t) \sum_{n=0}^{\infty} \varphi_n(x)\, \varphi_n(t)\, dt$$

$$= \sum_{p=0}^{\infty} a_p\, \varphi_p(x) = F(x), \qquad (9.65)$$

the cross products $\varphi_p \varphi_n$ $(n \neq p)$ vanishing by orthogonality (Eq. 9.25). Referring back to the definition of the Dirac delta function (Sections 1.15 and 8.6) the result of Eq. 9.65 means that

$$K(x, t) = \delta(x - t). \qquad (9.66)$$

We may easily show that

$$\int K(x, t)\, dt = 1 \qquad (9.67)$$

by letting $F(t) = \varphi_0$, a constant. Confirmation of the behavior at $x = t$ may be found by using the Bessel inequality. We have

$$K(t, t) = \sum_{n=0}^{\infty} [\varphi_n(t)]^2. \qquad (9.68)$$

Using Eq. 9.56, we obtain

$$\int [K(t, t)]^2\, dt \geqslant \sum_{n=0}^{\infty} a_n^2 = \sum_{n=0}^{\infty} 1 = \infty. \qquad (9.69)$$

Hence, $K(x, t)$ diverges for $x = t$, as expected.

Green's function.   A series somewhat similar to that representing $K(x, t)$ results when we expand Green's function in the eigenfunctions of the corresponding homogeneous equation. In the inhomogeneous Helmholtz equation we have

$$\nabla^2 \psi(\mathbf{r}) + k^2 \psi(\mathbf{r}) = -\rho(\mathbf{r}). \qquad (9.70)$$

The homogeneous Helmholtz equation is satisfied by its eigenfunctions φ_n.

$$\nabla^2 \varphi_n(\mathbf{r}) + k_n^2\, \varphi_n(\mathbf{r}) = 0. \qquad (9.71)$$

As outlined in Section 8.6, Green's function $G(\mathbf{r}_1, \mathbf{r}_2)$ satisfies the point source equation

$$\nabla^2 G(\mathbf{r}_1, \mathbf{r}_2) + k^2\, G(\mathbf{r}_1, \mathbf{r}_2) = -\delta(\mathbf{r}_1 - \mathbf{r}_2). \qquad (9.72)$$

We expand Green's function in a series of eigenfunctions of the homogeneous equation (9.71), that is,

$$G(\mathbf{r}_1, \mathbf{r}_2) = \sum_{n=0}^{\infty} a_n(\mathbf{r}_2)\, \varphi_n(\mathbf{r}_1), \qquad (9.73)$$

and by substituting into Eq. 9.72 obtain

$$-\sum_{n=0}^{\infty} a_n(\mathbf{r}_2)\, k_n^2\, \varphi_n(\mathbf{r}_1) + k^2 \sum_{n=0}^{\infty} a_n(\mathbf{r}_2)\, \varphi_n(\mathbf{r}_1) = -\sum_{n=0}^{\infty} \varphi_n(\mathbf{r}_1)\, \varphi_n(\mathbf{r}_2). \qquad (9.74)$$

Here $\delta(\mathbf{r}_1 - \mathbf{r}_2)$ has been replaced by its eigenfunction expansion, (Eqs. 9.64 and 9.66). When we employ the orthogonality of $\varphi_n(\mathbf{r}_1)$ to isolate a_n and then substitute into Eq. 9.73, Green's function becomes

$$G(\mathbf{r}_1, \mathbf{r}_2) = \sum_{n=0}^{\infty} \frac{\varphi_n(\mathbf{r}_1) \, \varphi_n(\mathbf{r}_2)}{k_n^2 - k^2}, \qquad (9.75)$$

a bilinear expansion, symmetric with respect to $\mathbf{r}_1$ and $\mathbf{r}_2$ as expected. Finally $\psi(\mathbf{r}_1)$, the desired solution of the inhomogeneous equation, is given by

$$\psi(\mathbf{r}_1) = \int G(\mathbf{r}_1, \mathbf{r}_2) \, \rho(\mathbf{r}_2) \, d\mathbf{r}_2 \qquad (9.76)$$

If we generalize our inhomogeneous differential equation to

$$\mathcal{L}\psi + \lambda\psi = -\rho, \qquad (9.77)$$

where $\mathcal{L}$ is an Hermitian operator, we find that

$$G(\mathbf{r}_1, \mathbf{r}_2) = \sum_{n=0}^{\infty} \frac{\varphi_n(\mathbf{r}_1) \, \varphi_n(\mathbf{r}_2)}{\lambda_n - \lambda}, \qquad (9.78)$$

where λ_n is the nth eigenvalue and φ_n, the corresponding orthonormal eigenfunction of the homogeneous differential equation

$$\mathcal{L}\psi + \lambda\psi = 0. \qquad (9.79)$$

Green's function will be encountered again in Section 16.5, in which we investigate it in more detail and relate it to integral equations.

EXERCISES

9.4.1 In place of the expansion of a function $F(x)$ given by

$$F(x) = \sum_{n=0}^{\infty} a_n \, \varphi_n(x)$$

with

$$a_n = \int_a^b F(x) \, \varphi_n(x) \, w(x) \, dx,$$

take the *finite* series approximation

$$F(x) \approx \sum_{n=0}^{m} c_n \, \varphi_n(x).$$

Show that the mean square error

$$\int_a^b \left[F(x) - \sum_{n=0}^{m} c_n \, \varphi_n(x) \right]^2 w(x) \, dx$$

is minimized by taking $c_n = a_n$.

9.4.2 Derive the Schwarz inequality from the identity

$$\left[\int_a^b f(x)\,g(x)\,dx\right]^2 = \int_a^b [f(x)]^2\,dx \int_a^b [g(x)]^2\,dx - \frac{1}{2}\int_a^b \int_a^b [f(x)\,g(y) - f(y)\,g(x)]^2\,dx\,dy.$$

9.4.3 Substitute Eq. 9.75, the eigenfunction expansion of Green's function, into Eq. 9.76 and then show that Eq. 9.76 is indeed a solution of the nonhomogeneous Helmholtz equation (9.70).

9.4.4 The Dirac delta function representation given by Eqs. 9.64 and 9.66,

$$\delta(x - t) = \sum_{n=0}^{\infty} \varphi_n(x)\,\varphi_n(t)$$

is often called the *closure relation*. For an orthonormal set of functions, φ_n, show that closure implies completeness, that is, that Eq. 9.46 follows from Eqs. 9.64 and 9.66. *Hint*. One can take

$$F(x) = \int F(t)\,\delta(x - t)\,dt.$$

9.4.5 The operator H is Hermitian and positive definite, that is,

$$\int_a^b f^*Hf\,dx > 0.$$

Prove the generalized Schwarz inequality:

$$\left| \int_a^b f^*Hg\,dx \right|^2 \leq \int_a^b f^*Hf\,dx \int_a^b g^*Hg\,dx.$$

REFERENCES

MILLER, K. S., *Linear Differential Equations in the Real Domain*. New York: Norton (1963).

TITCHMARSH, E. C., *Eigenfunction Expansions Associated with Second Order Differential Equations*. London: Oxford University Press, Vol. I, Second Edition (1962), Vol. II (1958).

CHAPTER 10

THE GAMMA FUNCTION
(FACTORIAL FUNCTION)

The Gamma Function (Factorial Function)

The gamma function appears occasionally in physical problems such as the normalization of Coulomb wave functions and the computation of probabilities in statistical mechanics. In general, however, it has less direct physical application and interpretation than, say, the Legendre and Bessel functions of Chapters 11 and 12. Rather its importance stems from its usefulness in developing other functions which have direct physical application. The gamma function, therefore, is included here.

10.1 Definitions, Simple Properties

At least three different, convenient definitions of the gamma function are in common use. Our first task is to state these definitions, to develop some simple, direct consequences, and to show the equivalence of the three forms.

Infinite limit (Euler).   The first definition, named after Euler is

$$\Gamma(z) \equiv \lim_{n \to \infty} \frac{1 \cdot 2 \cdot 3 \cdots n}{z(z+1)(z+2) \cdots (z+n)} n^z. \tag{10.1}$$

Here and elsewhere in this chapter z may be either real or complex. Replacing z with $z + 1$, we have

$$\Gamma(z+1) = \lim_{n \to \infty} \frac{1 \cdot 2 \cdot 3 \cdots n}{(z+1)(z+2)(z+3) \cdots (z+n+1)} n^{z+1}$$

$$= \lim_{n \to \infty} \frac{nz}{z+n+1} \cdot \frac{1 \cdot 2 \cdot 3 \cdots n}{z(z+1)(z+2) \cdots (z+n)} n^z$$

$$= z\,\Gamma(z). \tag{10.2}$$

351

This is the basic functional relation for the gamma function. It should be noted that it is a *difference* equation. It has been shown that the gamma function is one of a general class of functions which do not satisfy any differential equation with rational coefficients. Also from the definition

$$\Gamma(1) = \lim_{n \to \infty} \frac{1 \cdot 2 \cdot 3 \cdots n}{1 \cdot 2 \cdot 3 \cdots n(n+1)} \, n$$

$$= 1. \tag{10.3}$$

Now, application of Eq. 10.2 gives

$$\Gamma(2) = 1,$$

$$\Gamma(3) = 2 \, \Gamma(2) = 2, \tag{10.4}$$

$$\Gamma(n) = 1 \cdot 2 \cdot 3 \cdots (n-1)! = (n-1)!$$

Definite integral (Euler). A second definition, also frequently called Euler's form, is

$$\Gamma(z) \equiv \int_0^\infty e^{-t} t^{z-1} \, dt, \qquad \text{R.P.}(z) > 0. \tag{10.5}$$

The restriction on z is necessary to avoid divergence of the integral. When the gamma function does appear in physical problems, it is often in this form or some variation such as

$$\Gamma(z) = 2 \int_0^\infty e^{-t^2} t^{2z-1} \, dt, \qquad \text{R.P.}(z) > 0, \tag{10.6}$$

$$\Gamma(z) = \int_0^1 \left[\ln\left(\frac{1}{t}\right) \right]^{z-1} \, dt, \qquad \text{R.P.}(z) > 0. \tag{10.7}$$

When $z = \tfrac{1}{2}$, Eq. 10.6 is just the Gauss error function, and we have the interesting result

$$\Gamma(\tfrac{1}{2}) = \sqrt{\pi}. \tag{10.8}$$

To show the equivalence of these two definitions, Eqs. 10.1 and 10.5, consider the function of two variables

$$F(z, n) = \int_0^n \left(1 - \frac{t}{n} \right)^n t^{z-1} \, dt, \qquad \text{R.P.}(z) > 0 \tag{10.9}$$

with n a positive integer.[1] Since

$$\lim_{n \to \infty} \left(1 - \frac{t}{n} \right)^n \equiv e^{-t}, \tag{10.10}$$

from the definition of the exponential,

$$\lim_{n \to \infty} F(n, z) = F(z, \infty) = \int_0^\infty e^{-t} t^{z-1} \, dt$$

$$\equiv \Gamma(z) \tag{10.11}$$

by Eq. 10.5.

---

[1] The form of $F(z, n)$ is suggested by the beta function (cf. Eq. 10.60).

Returning to $F(z, n)$, we evaluate it in successive integrations by parts. For convenience let $u = t/n$. Then

$$F(z, n) = n^z \int_0^1 (1 - u)^n u^{z-1} \, du. \tag{10.12}$$

Integrating by parts,

$$\frac{F(z, n)}{n^z} = (1 - u)^n \left. \frac{u^z}{z} \right|_0^1 + \frac{n}{z} \int_0^1 (1 - u)^{n-1} u^z \, du. \tag{10.13}$$

Repeating this with the integrated part vanishing at both end points each time, we finally get

$$F(z, n) = n^z \frac{n(n - 1) \cdots 1}{z(z + 1) \cdots (z + n - 1)} \int_0^1 u^{z+n-1} \, du$$

$$= \frac{1 \cdot 2 \cdot 3 \cdots n}{z(z + 1)(z + 2) \cdots (z + n)} n^z \tag{10.14}$$

This is identical with the expression on the right side of Eq. 10.1. Hence

$$\lim_{n \to \infty} F(z, n) = F(z, \infty) \equiv \Gamma(z), \tag{10.15}$$

by Eq. 10.1, completing the proof.

Infinite product (Weierstrass).   The third definition (Weierstrass' form) is

$$\frac{1}{\Gamma(z)} \equiv z e^{Cz} \prod_{n=1}^{\infty} \left(1 + \frac{z}{n} \right) e^{-z/n}, \tag{10.16}$$

where C is the usual Euler-Mascheroni constant,

$$C = 0.577\ 216 \cdots. \tag{10.17}$$

This form can be derived from the original definition (Eq. 10.1) by rewriting it as

$$\Gamma(z) = \lim_{n \to \infty} \frac{1 \cdot 2 \cdot 3 \cdots n}{z(z + 1) \cdots (z + n)} n^z$$

$$= \lim_{n \to \infty} \frac{1}{z} \prod_{m=1}^{n} \left(1 + \frac{z}{m} \right)^{-1} n^z. \tag{10.18}$$

Inverting and using

$$n^{-z} = e^{(-\ln n)z}, \tag{10.19}$$

we obtain

$$\frac{1}{\Gamma(z)} + z \lim_{n \to \infty} e^{(-\ln n)z} \prod_{m=1}^{n} \left(1 + \frac{z}{m} \right). \tag{10.20}$$

Multiplying and dividing by

$$\exp\left[\left(1 + \frac{1}{2} + \frac{1}{3} + \cdots + \frac{1}{n} \right) z \right] = \prod_{m=1}^{n} e^{z/m}, \tag{10.21}$$

$$\frac{1}{\Gamma(z)} = z \left\{ \lim_{n \to \infty} \exp\left[\left(1 + \frac{1}{2} + \frac{1}{3} + \cdots + \frac{1}{n} - \ln n \right) z \right] \right\}$$

$$\times \left[\lim_{n \to \infty} \prod_{m=1}^{n} \left(1 + \frac{z}{m} \right) e^{-z/m} \right]. \tag{10.22}$$

As shown in Section 5.2, the infinite series in the exponent converges and defines C, the Euler-Mascheroni constant. Hence Eq. 10.16 follows.

It was also shown in Section 5.9 that the Weierstrass infinite product definition of $\Gamma(z)$ led directly to an important identity,

$$\Gamma(z)\,\Gamma(1-z) = \frac{\pi}{\sin \pi z}. \tag{10.23}$$

Again, letting $z = \frac{1}{2}$, we obtain

$$\Gamma(\tfrac{1}{2}) = \sqrt{\pi} \tag{10.24}$$

(taking the positive square root) in agreement with Eq. 10.8.

The Weierstrass definition shows immediately that $\Gamma(z)$ has simple poles at $z = 0, -1, -2, -3 \cdots$ and that $[\Gamma(z)]^{-1}$ has no poles in the finite complex plane, which means that $\Gamma(z)$ has no zeros. This behavior may also be seen in Eq. 10.23, in which we note that $\pi/(\sin \pi z)$ is never equal to zero.

Factorial notation.   So far this discussion has been presented in terms of the classical notation. As pointed out by Jeffreys and others, the -1 of the $z - 1$ exponent in our second definition (Eq. 10.5) is a continual nuisance. Accordingly, Eq. 10.5 is rewritten as

$$\int_0^\infty e^{-t}t^z \, dt \equiv z!, \qquad \text{R.P.}(z) > -1, \tag{10.25}$$

to *define* a factorial function $z!$. Occasionally we may still encounter Gauss's notation, $\Pi(z)$, for the factorial function

$$\prod (z) = z!. \tag{10.26}$$

The Γ notation is due to Legendre. The factorial function of Eq. 10.25 is, of course, related to the gamma function by

$$\Gamma(z) = (z - 1)!$$

or

$$\Gamma(z + 1) = z! \tag{10.27}$$

If $z = n$, a positive integer (Eq. 10.4) shows that

$$z! = n! = 1 \cdot 2 \cdot 3 \cdots n, \tag{10.28}$$

the familiar factorial. However, it should be noted carefully that since $z!$ is now defined by Eq. 10.25 (or equivalently by Eq. 10.27) *the factorial function is no longer limited to positive integral values of the argument.* The difference relation (Eq. 10.2) becomes

$$(z - 1)! = \frac{z!}{z}. \tag{10.29}$$

This shows immediately that

$$0! = 1 \tag{10.30}$$

and

$$n! = \pm\infty \quad \text{for} \quad n, \text{ a } \textit{negative} \text{ integer.} \tag{10.31}$$

In terms of the factorial function (Eq. 10.23) becomes

$$z!(-z)! = \frac{\pi z}{\sin \pi z} .$$ (10.32)

By restricting ourselves to the real values of the argument $x!$ defines the curve shown in Fig. 10.1. The minimum of the curve is

$$x! = (0.461{,}63 \cdots)! = 0.885{,}60 \cdots .$$ (10.33)

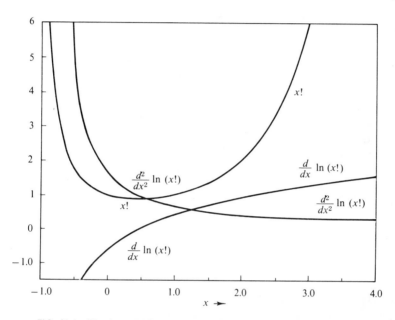

FIG. 10.1   The factorial function and the first two derivatives of $\ln(x!)$

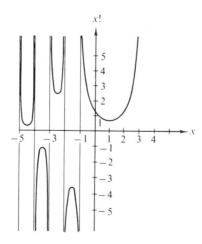

FIG. 10.2   The factorial function—extension to negative arguments

Integral representation.   An integral representation that is useful in developing asymptotic series for the Bessel functions is

$$\int_C e^{-z} z^v \, dz = (e^{2\pi i v} - 1) v! \tag{10.34}$$

where C is the contour shown in Figure 10.3. This contour integral representation is particularly useful when v is not an integer, $z = 0$ then being a *branch point*.

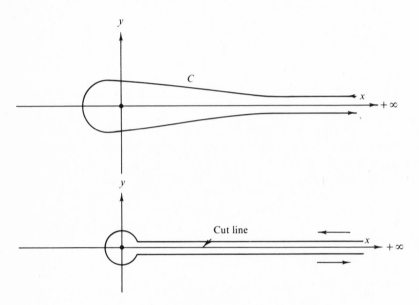

FIG. 10.3   (*Top*) Factorial function contour
FIG. 10.4   (*Bottom*) The contour of Fig. 10.3 deformed

Equation 10.34 may be readily verified for $v > -1$ by deforming the contour as shown in Fig. 10.3. The integral from ∞ into the origin yields $-(v!)$, placing the phase of z at 0. The integral out to ∞ (in the fourth quadrant) then yields $e^{2\pi i v} v!$, the phase of z having increased to 2π. Since the circle around the origin contributes nothing when $v > -1$, Eq. 10.34 follows.

It is often convenient to throw this result into a more symmetrical form

$$\int_C e^{-z}(-z)^v \, dv = 2i \sin v\pi \, v! \tag{10.35}$$

This corresponds to choosing the phase of z to have a range of $-\pi$ to $+\pi$ in Eq. 10.34.

This analysis establishes Eqs. 10.34 and 10.35 for $v > -1$. It is relatively simple to extend the range to include all nonintegral v. First, we note that the integral exists for $v < -1$ as long as we stay away from the origin. Second, integrating by parts we find that Eq. 10.35 yields the familiar difference relation (Eq. 10.29). If we take the difference relation to define the factorial function of $v < -1$, then Eqs. 10.34 and 10.35 are verified for all v (except negative integers).

EXERCISES

10.1.1 Derive the recurrence relations

$$\Gamma(z + 1) = z\,\Gamma(z)$$

from the Euler integral form (Eq. 10.5),

$$\Gamma(z) = \int_0^\infty e^{-t}t^{z-1}\,dt.$$

10.1.2 The asymptotic series (Section 5.10) for the error function is given by

$$\int_x^\infty e^{-t^2}\,dt = \frac{e^{-x^2}}{x}\left(1 - \frac{1}{2x^2} + \frac{1\cdot 3}{2^2 x^4} - \cdots(-1)^n\frac{1\cdot 3\cdot 5\cdots(2n-1)}{2^n x^{2n}} + \cdots\right).$$

Express the series as a summation over n, describing the coefficient of the nth term by factorials (and powers of 2).

10.1.3 By transforming the integral into a gamma function show that

$$-\int_0^1 x^k \ln x\,dx = \frac{1}{(k+1)^2}\qquad k > -1.$$

10.1.4 In statistical mechanics we encounter the integral

$$\int_{-\infty}^\infty x^{2n}\,e^{-ax^2}\,dx.$$

Show that

$$\int_{-\infty}^\infty x^{2n}e^{-ax^2}\,dx = \frac{1\cdot 3\cdot 5\cdots(2n-1)}{2^n}\left(\frac{\pi}{a^{2n+1}}\right)^{1/2}.$$

Rewrite the right-hand side of this equation in a general form that will yield $(\pi/a)^{1/2}$ when $n = 0$.

10.1.5 Show that $\Gamma(z)$ may be written

$$\Gamma(z) = 2\int_0^\infty e^{-t^2}t^{2z-1}\,dt,\qquad \text{R.P.}(z) > 0,$$

$$\Gamma(z) = \int_0^1 \left[\ln\left(\frac{1}{t}\right)\right]^{z-1}dt,\qquad \text{R.P.}(z) > 0.$$

10.1.6 Show that

$$\int_0^\infty e^{-x^4}\,dx = (\tfrac{1}{4})!$$

10.1.7 Verify

(a) $\displaystyle\int_0^\infty e^{-r}\ln r\,dr = -C.$

(b) $\displaystyle\int_0^\infty re^{-r}\ln r\,dr = 1 - C.$

(c) $\displaystyle\int_0^\infty r^n e^{-r}\ln r\,dr = (n-1)! + n\int_0^\infty r^{n-1}e^{-r}\ln r\,dr,\quad n = 1, 2, 3, \dots.$

Hint. These may be verified by integration by parts, three parts, or differentiating the integral form of $n!$ with respect to n.

10.1.8 Locate the poles of $\Gamma(z)$. Show that they are simple poles and determine the residues.

10.1.9 Show that the equation $x! = k$, $k \neq 0$, has an infinite number of real roots.

10.1.10 Show that

$$|(ix)!|^2 = \frac{\pi x}{\sinh \pi x} .$$

10.1.11 Prove that

$$|\Gamma(\alpha + i\beta)| = \frac{\Gamma(1 + \alpha)}{\alpha} \prod_{n=0}^{\infty} \left[1 + \frac{\beta^2}{(\alpha + n)^2}\right]^{-1/2}.$$

This equation has been useful in calculations in the theory of beta decay.

10.1.12 Show that

$$|(n + ib)!| = \left(\frac{\pi b}{\sinh \pi b}\right)^{1/2} \prod_{s=1}^{n} (s^2 + b^2)^{1/2}$$

for n, a positive integer.

10.1.13 In many problems in electromagnetic theory we encounter the products

$$2n(2n - 2) \cdots 6.4.2 \equiv (2n)!!$$
$$(2n + 1)(2n - 1) \cdots 5.3.1 \equiv (2n + 1)!!$$

Show that

$$(2n)!! = 2^n n!$$
$$(2n + 1)!! = \frac{(2n + 1)!}{2^n n!} .$$

10.1.14 In a power series solution for the Legendre functions of the second kind we encounter the expression

$$\frac{(n + 1)(n + 2)(n + 3) \cdots (n + 2s - 1)(n + 2s)}{2 \cdot 4 \cdot 6 \cdot 8 \cdots (2s - 2)(2s) \cdot (2s + 3)(2s + 5)(2s + 7) \cdots (2s + 2n + 1)},$$

in which s is a positive integer. Rewrite this expression in terms of factorials.

10.2 Digamma and Polygamma Functions

Digamma functions. As may be noted from the three definitions in Section 10.1, it is inconvenient to deal with the derivatives of the gamma or factorial function directly. Instead, it is customary to take the natural logarithm of the factorial function, (Eq. 10.1), convert the product to a sum, and then differentiate, that is,

$$z! = \lim_{n \to \infty} \frac{n!}{(z + 1)(z + 2) \cdots (z + n)} n^z \qquad (10.36)$$

and

$$\ln(z!) = \lim_{n \to \infty} [\ln(n!) + z \ln n - \ln(z + 1)$$
$$- \ln(z + 2) - \cdots - \ln(z + n)], \qquad (10.37)$$

in which the logarithm of the limit is equal to the limit of the logarithm. Differentiating with respect to z, we obtain

$$\frac{d}{dz} \ln(z!) \equiv F(z) = \lim_{n \to \infty} \left(\ln n - \frac{1}{z + 1} - \frac{1}{z + 2} - \cdots - \frac{1}{z + n}\right), \qquad (10.38)$$

which defines $F(z)$, the digamma function. From the definition of the Euler-Mascheroni constant[1] Eq. 10.38 may be rewritten

$$F(z) = -C - \sum_{n=1}^{\infty} \left(\frac{1}{z+n} - \frac{1}{n} \right). \tag{10.39}$$

One application of Eq. 10.39 is in the derivation of the series form of the Neumann function (Section 11.2). Clearly

$$F(0) = -C = -0.577\ 215\ 664\ 901\ \dots\ [2] \tag{10.40}$$

Polygamma function.   Another, perhaps more useful expression for $F(z)$ is derived in Section 10.3.

The digamma function may be differentiated repeatedly, giving rise to the polygamma function:

$$F^{(m)}(z) \equiv \frac{d^{m+1}}{dz^{m+1}} \ln(z!)$$

$$= (-1)^{m+1} m! \sum_{n=1}^{\infty} \frac{1}{(z+n)^{m+1}}, \qquad m = 1, 2, 3, \dots. \tag{10.41}$$

A plot of $F(x)$ and $F'(x)$ is included in Fig. 10.1. Since the series in Eq. 10.41 defines the Riemann zeta function[3] (with $z = 0$),

$$\zeta(m) \equiv \sum_{n=1}^{\infty} \frac{1}{n^m}, \tag{10.42}$$

we have

$$F^{(m)}(0) = (-1)^{m+1} m!\ \zeta(m+1). \tag{10.43}$$

Riemann zeta function.   For convenience the Riemann zeta function is given in Table 10.1. The general behavior is described in Fig. 5.7.

TABLE 10.1

Riemann Zeta Function

s	$\zeta(s)$
2	1.64493 40668
3	1.20205 69032
4	1.08232 32337
5	1.03692 77551
6	1.01734 30620
7	1.00834 92774
8	1.00407 73562
9	1.00200 83928
10	1.00099 45751

[1] Cf. Sections 5.2 and 5.6.

[2] C has been computed to 1271 places by D. E. Knuth, *Math. Comp.* **16**, 275 (1962) and to 3566 decimal places by D. W. Sweeney, *Math. Comp.* **17**, 170 (1963). It may be of interest that the fraction 228/395 gives C accurate to six places.

[3] Section 5.8. For $z \neq 0$ this series may be used to define a generalized zeta function.

It is now possible to write a Maclaurin expansion for $\ln (z!)$.

$$\ln (z!) = - Cz + \frac{z^2}{2} \zeta(2) - \frac{z^3}{3} \zeta(3) + \cdots + (-1)^n \frac{z^n}{n} \zeta(n) + \cdots, \quad (10.44)$$

convergent for $|z| < 1$; for $z = x$ the range is $-1 < x \leqslant 1$. This is a possible means of computing $z!$ for real or complex z, but Stirling's series (Section 10.3) is usually better, and, in addition, an excellent table of values of the gamma function for complex arguments based on the use of Stirling's series and the recurrence relation (Eq. 10.29) is now available.[1]

EXERCISES

10.2.1 Verify that the following two forms of the digamma function,

$$F(x) = \sum_{r=1}^{x} \frac{1}{r} - C$$

and

$$F(x) = \sum_{r=1}^{\infty} \frac{x}{r(r + x)} - C,$$

are equal to each other (for x a positive integer).

10.2.2 Jeffreys and Jeffreys[2] list the Neumann function as

$$N_n(x) = \frac{2}{\pi} J_n(x) \ln \frac{x}{2}$$

$$- \frac{1}{\pi} \sum_{r=0}^{\infty} (-1)^r \frac{[F(r) + F(n + r)]}{r! \ (n + r)!} \left(\frac{x}{2}\right)^{n+2r}$$

$$- \frac{1}{\pi} \sum_{r=0}^{n-1} \frac{(n - r - 1)!}{r!} \left(\frac{x}{2}\right)^{-n+2r}.$$

Morse and Feshbach have

$$N_n(x) = \frac{1}{\pi} \left[2 \ln\left(\frac{x}{2}\right) + C - \psi(n + 1)\right] J_n(x)$$

$$- \frac{1}{\pi} \sum_{r=0}^{\infty} (-1)^r \frac{\sum_{p=1}^{r}[1/p + 1/(p + n)]}{r!(n + r)!} \left(\frac{x}{2}\right)^{n+2r}$$

$$- \frac{1}{\pi} \sum_{r=0}^{n-1} \frac{(n - r - 1)!}{r!} \left(\frac{x}{2}\right)^{-n+2r}.$$

Here $\psi(z) = d/dz \ln \Gamma(z)$. Using the series representations, reconcile these two diverse forms of the Neumann function.

10.2.3 Derive the difference relation for the polygamma function

$$F^{(m)}(z + 1) = F^{(m)}(z) + (-1)^m \frac{m!}{(z + 1)^{m+1}}, \qquad m = 0, 1, 2, \ldots.$$

[1] *Table of the Gamma Function for Complex Arguments*, National Bureau of Standards, Applied Mathematics Series No. 34.

[2] Jeffreys, H. and B. S. Jeffreys, *Methods of Mathematical Physics*, Second Edition, Cambridge University Press (1950).

10.2.4   From Eq. 10.39 show that

(a) $\dfrac{\Gamma'(z)}{\Gamma(z)} = -C - \dfrac{1}{z} - \displaystyle\sum_{n=1}^{\infty}\left(\dfrac{1}{z+n} - \dfrac{1}{n}\right),$

(b) $\dfrac{2\Gamma'(2z)}{\Gamma(2z)} - \dfrac{\Gamma'(z)}{\Gamma(z)} - \dfrac{\Gamma'(z+\frac{1}{2})}{\Gamma(z+\frac{1}{2})} = 2\ln 2.$

Integrating the last result provides another derivation of Legendre's duplication formula (Section 10.4). *Hint.* Be careful *not* to rearrange the terms of a conditionally convergent series.

10.2.5   Prove that

$$\frac{d}{dz}\ln(z!) = \int_0^{\infty}\left(\frac{e^{-t}}{t} - \frac{e^{-(z+1)t}}{1-e^{-t}}\right)dt$$

and therefore that the Euler-Mascheroni constant

$$C = \int_0^{\infty} e^{-t}\left(\frac{1}{1-e^{-t}} - \frac{1}{t}\right)dt.$$

10.2.6   Show that if

$$\Gamma(x+iy) = u + iv$$

then

$$\Gamma(x-iy) = u - iv.$$

10.2.7   The total energy radiated by a black body is given by

$$u = \frac{8\pi k^4 T^4}{c^3 h^3}\int_0^{\infty}\frac{x^3}{e^x - 1}\,dx.$$

Show that the integral in this expression is equal to $3!\;\zeta(4)$. $[\zeta(4) = \pi^4/90 = 1.0823\ldots.]$ The final result is the Stefan-Boltzmann law.

10.2.8   As a generalization of the result in Exercise 10.2.7, show that

$$\int_0^{\infty}\frac{x^s\,dx}{e^x - 1} = s!\;\zeta(s+1), \qquad \text{R.P.}(s) > 0.$$

10.2.9   Prove that

$$\int_0^{\infty}\frac{x^s\,ds}{e^x + 1} = s!(1 - 2^{-s})\,\zeta(s+1), \qquad \text{R.P.}(s) > 0.$$

Exercises 10.2.8 and 10.2.9 actually constitute Mellin integral transforms (cf. Section 15.1).

10.2.10   Dirac relativistic wave functions for hydrogen involve factors such as $[2(1-\alpha^2 Z^2)^{1/2}]!$ where α, the fine structure constant, is $\frac{1}{137}$ and Z is the atomic number. Expand $[2(1-\alpha^2 Z^2)^{1/2}]!$ in a series of powers of $\alpha^2 Z^2$.

10.2.11   The quantum mechanical description of a particle in a coulomb field requires a knowledge of the phase of the complex factorial function. Determine the phase of $(1+ib)!$ for small b.

10.3   Stirling's Series

For computation of $\ln(z!)$ for very large z (statistical mechanics) and for numerical computations at nonintegral values of z a series expansion of $\ln(z!)$ in negative powers of z is desirable. Perhaps the most elegant way of deriving such an expansion is by the method of steepest descents (Section 7.4). The following method, starting with a numerical integration formula, does not require knowledge of contour integration and is particularly direct.

Derivation from Euler-Maclaurin integration formula.   The Euler-Maclaurin formula for evaluating a definite integral[1] is

$$\int_0^n f(x)\,dx = \tfrac{1}{2}f(0) + f(1) + f(2) + \cdots + \tfrac{1}{2}f(n)$$

$$- b_2[f'(n) - f'(0)] - b_4[f'''(n) - f'''(0)] - \cdots, \quad (10.45)$$

in which the b_{2n} are related to the Bernoulli numbers B_{2n} (cf., Section 5.8) by

$$(2n)!\,b_{2n} = B_{2n}, \quad (10.46)$$

$$B_0 = 1, \qquad B_6 = \tfrac{1}{42},$$

$$B_2 = \tfrac{1}{6}, \qquad B_8 = -\tfrac{1}{30}, \quad (10.47)$$

$$B_4 = -\tfrac{1}{30}, \qquad B_{10} = \tfrac{5}{66}, \text{ etc.}$$

By applying Eq. 10.45 to the definite integral

$$\int_0^\infty \frac{dx}{(z+x)^2} = \frac{1}{z} \quad (10.48)$$

(for z not on the negative real axis) we obtain

$$\frac{1}{z} = \frac{1}{2z^2} + F'(z) - \frac{2!\,b_2}{z^3} - \frac{4!\,b_4}{z^5} - \cdots. \quad (10.49)$$

Using Eq. 10.46 and solving for $F'(z)$, we have

$$F'(z) = \frac{1}{z} - \frac{1}{2z^2} + \frac{B_2}{z^3} + \frac{B_4}{z^5} + \cdots$$

$$= \frac{1}{z} - \frac{1}{2z^2} + \sum_{n=1}^{\infty} \frac{B_{2n}}{z^{2n+1}}, \quad (10.50)$$

Since the Bernoulli numbers diverge strongly, this series does not converge! It is a semiconvergent or asymptotic series, useful for computation despite its divergence (cf. Section 5.10).

Integrating once, we get the digamma function

$$F'(z) = C_1 + \ln z + \frac{1}{2z} - \frac{B_2}{2z^2} - \frac{B_4}{4z^4} - \cdots$$

$$= C_1 + \ln z + \frac{1}{2z} - \sum_{n=1}^{\infty} \frac{B_{2n}}{2nz^{2n}}. \quad (10.51)$$

Integrating Eq. 10.51 with respect to z from $z-1$ to z and then letting z approach infinity, C_1, the constant of integration may be shown to vanish. This gives us a second expression for the digamma function, often more useful than Eq. 10.38.

[1] Obtained by repeated integration by parts.

Stirling's series. The indefinite integral of the digamma function (Eq. 10.51) is

$$\ln(z!) = C_2 + \left(z + \frac{1}{2}\right) \ln z - z + \frac{B_2}{2z} + \cdots + \frac{B_{2n}}{2n(2n-1)z^{2n-1}} + \cdots, \quad (10.52)$$

in which C_2 is another constant of integration. To fix C_2 it is convenient to use the doubling or Legendre duplication formula derived in Section 10.4,

$$z!(z - \tfrac{1}{2})! = 2^{-2z}\pi^{1/2}(2z)! \quad (10.53)$$

This may be proved directly when z is a positive integer by writing $(2z)!$ as a product of even terms times a product of odd terms and extracting a factor of two from each term (Exercise 10.3.5). Substituting Eq. 10.53 into the logarithm of the doubling formula, we find that C_2 is

$$C_2 = \tfrac{1}{2} \ln 2\pi, \quad (10.54)$$

giving

$$\ln(z!) = \frac{1}{2}\ln 2\pi + \left(z + \frac{1}{2}\right)\ln z - z + \frac{1}{12z} - \frac{1}{360z^3} + \frac{1}{1260z^5} - \cdots. \quad (10.55)$$

This is Stirling's series, an asymptotic expansion. The absolute value of the error is less than the absolute value of the first term neglected.

The constants of integration C_1 and C_2 may also be evaluated by comparison with the first term of the series expansion obtained by the method of "steepest descent". This is carried out in Section 7.4.

To help convey a feeling of the remarkable precision of Stirling's series for $s!$ the ratio of the first term of Stirling's approximation to $s!$ is plotted in Fig. 10.5.

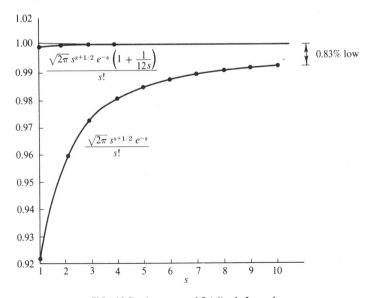

FIG. 10.5 Accuracy of Stirling's formula

A tabulation gives the ratio of the first term in the expansion to $s!$ and the ratio of the first two terms in the expansion to $s!$. The derivation of these forms is Exercise 10.3.1.

TABLE 10.2

s	$\dfrac{\sqrt{2\pi}\, s^{s+1/2}e^{-s}}{s!}$	$\dfrac{\sqrt{2\pi}\, s^{s+1/2}e^{-s}[1+\frac{1}{12s}]}{s!}$
1	0.92213	0.99898
2	0.95950	0.99949
3	0.97270	0.99972
4	0.97942	0.99983
5	0.98349	0.99988
6	0.98621	0.99992
7	0.98817	0.99994
8	0.98964	0.99995
9	0.99078	0.99996
10	0.99170	0.99998

EXERCISES

10.3.1 Rewrite Stirling's series to give $z!$ instead of $\ln(z!)$.

$$Ans: z! = \sqrt{2\pi}\, z^{z+1/2}e^{-z}\left(1 + \frac{1}{12z} + \frac{1}{288z^3} - \frac{139}{51,840z^5} + \cdots\right).$$

10.3.2 Find the relative accuracy of Stirling's series for $\ln(z!)$ for $z = 4$ using (a) one term, (b) two terms, (c) three terms, and (d) four terms.

10.3.3 By integrating Eq. 10.51 from $z - 1$ to z and then letting $z \to \infty$, evaluate the constant C_1 in the asymptotic series for the digamma function $F(z)$.

10.3.4 Show that the constant C_2 in Stirling's formula equals $\frac{1}{2}\ln 2\pi$ by using the logarithm of the doubling formula.

10.3.5 By direct expansion verify the doubling formula for $z = n + \frac{1}{2}$; n is an integer.

10.3.6 Without using Stirling's series show that

(a) $\ln(n!) < \displaystyle\int_1^{n+1} \ln x\, dx$,

(b) $\ln(n!) > \displaystyle\int_1^{n} \ln x\, dx$; n is an integer $\geqslant 2$.

Notice that the arithmetic mean of these two integrals gives a good approximation for Stirling's series.

10.3.7 Calculate $(0.100)! = \Gamma(1.100)$. *Hint.* This may be done easily by using Stirling's formula or Maclaurin's series and the digamma functions.

10.3.8 Test for convergence

$$\sum_{p=0}^{\infty} \left[\frac{(p - \frac{1}{2})!}{p!} \right]^2 \times \frac{2p + 1}{2p + 2}.$$

This series arises in an attempt to describe the magnetic field created by and enclosed by a current loop.

10.3.9 Use Stirling's formula to estimate 52!, the number of possible rearrangements of cards in a standard deck of playing cards.

10.4 The Beta Function

Using the integral definition (Eq. 10.25), we write the product of two factorials as the product of two integrals. To facilitate a change in variables, the integrals are taken over a finite range.

$$m!n! = \lim_{a^2 \to \infty} \int_0^{a^2} e^{-u} u^m \, du \int_0^{a^2} e^{-v} v^n \, dv, \qquad \begin{matrix} \text{R.P.}(m) > -1, \\ \text{R.P.}(n) > -1. \end{matrix} \qquad (10.56)$$

Replacing u with x^2 and v with y^2, we obtain

$$m!n! = \lim_{a \to \infty} 4 \int_0^{a} e^{-x^2} x^{2m+1} \, dx \int_0^{a} e^{-y^2} y^{2n+1} \, dy. \qquad (10.57)$$

Transforming to polar coordinates gives us

$$m!n! = \lim_{a \to \infty} 4 \int_0^{a} e^{-r^2} r^{2m+2n+3} \, dr \int_0^{\pi/2} \cos^{2m+1} \theta \sin^{2n+1} \theta \, d\theta$$

$$= (m + n + 1)! \, 2 \int_0^{\pi/2} \cos^{2m+1} \theta \sin^{2n+1} \theta \, d\theta. \qquad (10.58)$$

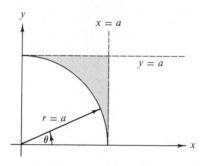

FIG. 10.6 Transformation from cartesian to polar coordinates

The definite integral, together with the factor 2, has been named the beta function

$$B(m + 1, n + 1) \equiv 2 \int_0^{\pi/2} \cos^{2m+1} \theta \sin^{2n+1} \theta \, d\theta$$

$$= \frac{m!n!}{(m + n + 1)!} = B(n + 1, m + 1). \qquad (10.59)$$

The only reason for choosing $m + 1$ and $n + 1$, rather than m and n, as the arguments of B is to be in agreement with the conventional, historical beta function. Clearly the extra 1's are about as useful as the human appendix.

In this manipulation the transformation from cartesian to polar coordinates needs some justification. As seen in Fig. 10.6 the shaded area is being neglected. However, the maximum value of the integrand in this region is $e^{-a^2}a^{2m+2n+3}$ which vanishes so strongly as a approaches infinity that the integral over the neglected region vanishes.

Definite integrals, alternate forms.   One immediate application of the beta function is in the evaluation of a wide variety of definite integrals having the form of Eq. 10.59. The substitution $t = \cos^2 \theta$ converts the beta function to

$$B(m + 1, n + 1) = \int_0^1 t^m(1 - t)^n \, dt, \tag{10.60}$$

which is almost identical to the integral in Eq. 10.9. The further substitution $t = u/(1 + u)$ yields still another useful form,

$$B(m + 1, n + 1) = \int_0^\infty \frac{u^m}{(1 + u)^{m+n+2}} \, du. \tag{10.61}$$

Verification of $\pi a/\sin \pi a$ relation.   If we take $m = a, n = -a, -1 < a < 1$, then

$$\int_0^\infty \frac{u^a}{(1 + u)^2} \, du = a!(-a)! \tag{10.62}$$

By contour integration this integral may be shown to be equal to $\pi a/\sin \pi a$ (Chapter 7), thus providing another method of obtaining Eq. 10.32.

Derivation of Legendre duplication formula.   The form of Eq. 10.59 suggests that the beta function may be useful in deriving the doubling formula used in the preceding section. For R.P.$(z) > -1$,

$$\frac{z!z!}{(2z + 1)!} = \int_0^1 t^z(1 - t)^z \, dt, \tag{10.63}$$

and by substituting $t = (1 + s)/2$

$$\frac{z!z!}{(2z + 1)!} = 2^{-2z-1} \int_{-1}^1 (1 - s^2)^z \, ds$$

$$= 2^{-2z} \int_0^1 (1 - s^2)^z \, ds; \tag{10.64}$$

the last equality holds because the integrand is even. To throw this integral back into the form of Eq. 10.60 we substitute $u = s^2$ and

$$\frac{z!z!}{(2z + 1)!} = 2^{-2z-1} \int_0^1 (1 - u)^z u^{-1/2} \, du$$

$$= 2^{-2z-1} \frac{z!(-\tfrac{1}{2})!}{(z + \tfrac{1}{2})!}. \tag{10.65}$$

Rearranging terms and recalling that $(-\frac{1}{2})! = \pi^{1/2}$, we quickly reduce these equations to one form of the Legendre duplication formula,

$$z!(z + \tfrac{1}{2})! = 2^{-2z-1}\pi^{1/2}(2z + 1)! \tag{10.66}$$

Dividing by $(z + \frac{1}{2})$, we obtain an alternate form of the duplication formula.

$$z!(z - \tfrac{1}{2})! = 2^{-2z}\pi^{1/2}(2z)! \tag{10.67}$$

Although the integrals used in this derivation are defined only for R.P.$(z) > -1$, the results (Eq. 10.66 and 10.67) hold for all z by analytic continuation.[1]

EXERCISES

10.4.1 Evaluate (using the beta function)

(a) $\displaystyle\int_0^{\pi/2} (\cot\theta)^{1/2}\, d\theta = \frac{\pi}{\sqrt{2}}$,

(b) $\displaystyle\int_0^{\pi/2} \cos^{4/3}\theta \, \sin^{5/3}\theta \, d\theta = \frac{2(\frac{1}{6})!(\frac{1}{3})!}{3\sqrt{\pi}}$,

(c) $\displaystyle\int_0^{\pi/2} \cos^{1/2}\theta \, d\theta = \frac{(2\pi)^{3/2}}{16[(\frac{1}{4})!]^2}$,

(d) $\displaystyle\int_0^{\pi/2} \cos^n\theta \, d\theta = \int_0^{\pi/2} \sin^n\theta \, d\theta = \frac{\sqrt{\pi}[(n-1)/2]!}{2(n/2)!}$.

10.4.2 Verify the following beta function identities:

(a) $B(a, b) = B(a + 1, b) + B(a, b + 1)$,

(b) $B(a, b) = \dfrac{a + b}{b} B(a, b + 1)$,

(c) $B(a, b) = \dfrac{b - 1}{a} B(a + 1, b - 1)$,

(d) $B(a, b)\, B(a + b, c) = B(b, c)\, B(a, b + c)$.

10.4.3 Evaluate $\displaystyle\int_{-1}^{1} (1 + x)^a (1 - x)^b \, dx$ in terms of the beta function.

Ans. $2^{a+b+1}\, B(a + 1, b + 1)$.

10.4.4 Show that

$$B(p, p)\, B\left(p + \frac{1}{2}, p + \frac{1}{2}\right) = \frac{\pi}{2^{4p-1}p} \cdot$$

Hint. Use Legendre duplication formula.

10.4.5 Show, by means of beta function, that

$$\int_t^z \frac{dx}{(z - x)^{1-\alpha}\,(x - t)^\alpha} = \frac{\pi}{\sin\pi\alpha}, \qquad 0 < \alpha < 1.$$

This result is used in Section 16.2 to solve Abel's generalized integral equation.

[1] If $2z$ is a negative integer, we get the valid but unilluminating result $\infty = \infty$.

10.4.6   Show that the Dirichlet integral

$$\iint x^p y^q \, dA = \frac{p!q!}{(p+q+2)!} = \frac{B(p+1, q+1)}{p+q+2},$$

where the range of integration is the triangle bounded by the positive x- and y-axes and the line $x + y = 1$.

10.4.7   Derive the doubling formula for the factorial function by integrating $(\sin 2\theta)^{2n+1} = (2 \sin \theta \cos \theta)^{2n+1}$ (and using the beta function).

10.4.8   Indicate how a complete table of the factorial function could be constructed for $x = 0$, 0.1, 0.2, 0.3, etc., using
(a) known values of $(0.1)! \, (0.2)! \, (0.5)!$ and (b) trigonometric tables.

10.4.9   From

$$J_\nu(z) = \sum_{s=0}^{\infty} (-1)^s \frac{1}{s!(s+\nu)!} \left(\frac{z}{2}\right)^{2s+\nu}$$

and

$$B(m+1, n+1) = 2 \int_0^{\pi/2} \sin^{2m+1} \theta \cos^{2n+1} \theta \, d\theta,$$

show that

$$J_\nu(z) = \frac{2}{\pi^{1/2}(\nu - \tfrac{1}{2})!} \left(\frac{z}{2}\right)^\nu \int_0^{\pi/2} \sin^{2\nu} \theta \cos(z \cos \theta) \, d\theta, \qquad \text{R.P.}(\nu) > -\tfrac{1}{2}.$$

Since $J_\nu(z)$ is a Bessel function (Section 11.1), a useful integral representation of the Bessel function is established.

10.5   The Incomplete Gamma Functions and Related Functions

Generalizing the Euler definition of the gamma function (Eq. 10.5), we define the incomplete gamma functions by the *variable* limit integrals

$$\gamma(a, x) = \int_0^x e^{-t} t^{a-1} \, dt, \qquad \text{R.P.}(a) > 0$$

and

$$\Gamma(a, x) = \int_x^\infty e^{-t} t^{a-1} \, dt. \tag{10.68}$$

Clearly, the two functions are related, for

$$\gamma(a, x) + \Gamma(a, x) = \Gamma(a). \tag{10.69}$$

The choice of employing $\gamma(a, x)$ or $\Gamma(a, x)$ is purely a matter of convenience. If the parameter a is a positive integer, Eqs. 10.68 may be integrated completely to yield

$$\gamma(n, x) = (n-1)! \left(1 - e^{-x} \sum_{s=0}^{n-1} \frac{x^s}{s!}\right)$$

$$\Gamma(n, x) = (n-1)! \, e^{-x} \sum_{s=0}^{n-1} \frac{x^s}{s!}. \tag{10.70}$$

For nonintegral a a power series expansion of $\gamma(a, x)$ for small x and an asymptotic expansion of $\Gamma(a, x)$ are developed in Sections 5.6 and 5.10.

$$\gamma(a, x) = x^a \sum_{n=0}^{\infty} (-1)^n \frac{x^n}{n!(a + n)},$$

$$\Gamma(a, x) = \frac{e^{-x}}{x^{a-1}} \sum_{n=0}^{\infty} \frac{(a - 1)!}{(a - 1 - n)!} \cdot \frac{1}{x^n}$$

$$= \frac{e^{-x}}{x^{a-1}} \sum_{n=0}^{\infty} (-1)^n \frac{(n - a)!}{(-a)!} \cdot \frac{1}{x^n}. \tag{10.71}$$

These incomplete gamma functions may also be expressed quite elegantly in terms of confluence hypergeometric functions (cf. Section 13.5).

Exponential integral. Although the incomplete gamma function $\Gamma(a, x)$ in its general form (Eq. 10.68) is only infrequently encountered in physical problems, a special case is quite common and very useful. We define the exponential integral by[1]

$$-Ei(-x) \equiv \int_{x}^{\infty} \frac{e^{-t}}{t} dt = E_1(x). \tag{10.72}$$

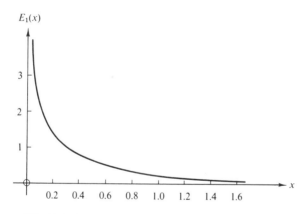

FIG. 10.7 The exponential integral, $E_1(x) = -Ei(-x)$

Then

$$E_1(x) = \Gamma(0, x)$$

$$= \lim_{a \to 0} [\Gamma(a) - \gamma(a, x)]. \tag{10.73}$$

Caution is needed here, for the integral in Eq. 10.72 diverges logarithmically as $x \to 0$. If we split off the divergent term in the series expansion for $\gamma(a, x)$,

$$E_1(x) = \lim_{a \to 0} \left[\frac{a\Gamma(a) - x^a}{a} \right] - \sum_{n=1}^{\infty} \frac{(-1)^n x^n}{n \cdot n!}, \tag{10.74}$$

[1] The appearance of the two minus signs in $-Ei(-x)$ is an historical monstrosity. AMS-55 denotes this integral as $E_1(x)$.

and with the aid of l'Hospital's rule and the digamma function (cf. Eq. 10.40)

$$E_1(x) = -C - \ln x - \sum_{n=1}^{\infty} \frac{(-1)^n x^n}{n \cdot n!}, \tag{10.75}$$

useful for small x. An asymptotic expansion is given in Section 5.10.

Further special forms related to the exponential integral are the sine integral, cosine integral, and logarithmic integral defined by

$$si(x) = -\int_x^{\infty} \frac{\sin t}{t}\, dt$$

$$Ci(x) = -\int_x^{\infty} \frac{\cos t}{t}\, dt \tag{10.76}$$

$$li(x) = \int_0^x \frac{du}{\ln u} = Ei(\ln u).$$

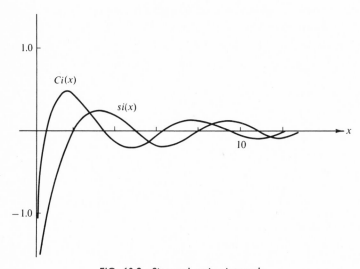

FIG. 10.8   Sine and cosine integrals

By transforming from real to imaginary argument, we can show that

$$si(x) = \frac{1}{2i} [Ei(ix) - Ei(-ix)], \tag{10.77}$$

whereas

$$Ci(x) = \tfrac{1}{2}[Ei(ix) + Ei(-ix)]. \tag{10.78}$$

Adding these two relations, we obtain

$$Ei(ix) = Ci(x) + i\, si(x), \tag{10.79}$$

to show that the relation among these integrals is exactly analogous to that among e^{ix}, $\cos x$, and $\sin x$.

Power series expansions about the origin and asymptotic expansions for $si(x)$, $Ci(x)$, and $li(x)$ may be obtained from those for the exponential integral, $-Ei(-x)$.

EXERCISES

10.5.1 Prove that the exponential integral

$$\int_x^\infty \frac{e^{-t}}{t}\, dt = -C - \ln x - \sum_{n=1}^\infty \frac{(-1)^n x^n}{n \cdot n!} .$$

C is the Euler-Mascheroni constant.

10.5.2 With $\gamma(a, x)$ and $\Gamma(a, x)$, the incomplete gamma functions defined in Section 10.5, show that

(a) $\gamma(a, x) = x^{a/2} \int_0^\infty e^{-t} t^{(a/2-1)}\, J_a[2(xt)^{1/2}]\, dt, \qquad \text{R.P.}(a) > 0,$

(b) $\Gamma(a, x) = \dfrac{2x^{a/2} e^{-x}}{\Gamma(1-a)} \int_0^\infty e^{-t} t^{-a/2}\, K_a[2(xt)^{1/2}]\, dt, \qquad \text{R.P.}(a) < 1.$

Hint. 1. Use the power series expansion of $J_a[2(xt)^{1/2}]$ (Section 11.1).

2. Express K_a in terms of I_a and use the power series expansion (Section 11.4).

10.5.3 Show that

(a) $\dfrac{d^m}{dx^m}\, [x^{-a}\, \gamma(a, x)] = (-1)^m\, x^{-a-m}\, \gamma(a + m, x),$

(b) $\dfrac{d^m}{dx^m}\, [e^x\, \gamma(a, x)] = e^x\, \dfrac{\Gamma(a)}{\Gamma(a-m)}\, \gamma(a - m, \gamma).$

10.5.4 Show that $\gamma(a, x)$ and $\Gamma(a, x)$ satisfy the recurrence relations

(a) $\gamma(a + 1, x) = a\, \gamma(a, x) - x^a e^{-x},$

(b) $\Gamma(a + 1, x) = a\, \Gamma(a, x) + x^a e^{-x}.$

10.5.5 Show that

$$\gamma(a, x) = e^{-x} \sum_{n=0}^\infty \frac{(a-1)!}{(a+n)!}\, x^{a+n}.$$

(a) By repeatedly integrating by parts.

(b) Demonstrate this relation by transforming it into Eq. 10.71.

10.5.6 Related to the exponential integral (Eq. 10.72) by a simple change of variable is the function

$$E_n(x) = \int_1^\infty \frac{e^{-xt}}{t^n}\, dt.$$

Show that $E_n(x)$ satisfies the recurrence relation

$$E_{n+1}(x) = \frac{1}{n}e^{-x} - \frac{x}{n}E_n(x), \qquad n = 1, 2, 3, \dots .$$

REFERENCES

ARTIN, Emil, *The Gamma Function*. (Translated by Michael Butler). New York: Holt, Rinehart and Winston (1964). Demonstrates that if a function $f(x)$ is smooth (log convex) and equal to $(n - 1)!$ when $x = n$, it is the gamma function.

CHAPTER 11

BESSEL FUNCTIONS

11.1 Bessel Functions of the First Kind, $J_\nu(x)$

Generating function, integral order, $J_n(x)$.   Although Bessel functions are of interest primarily as solutions of a differential equation, it is instructive and convenient to develop them from a completely different approach, that of the generating function. This approach also has the advantage of focusing attention on the functions themselves rather than on the differential equations they happen to satisfy. Let us introduce a function of two variables,

$$g(x, t) = e^{(x/2)(t - 1/t)}. \tag{11.1}$$

Series form.   Expanding this generating function in a Laurent series (Section 6.4), we obtain

$$e^{(x/2)(t - 1/t)} = \sum_{n=-\infty}^{\infty} J_n(x) t^n, \tag{11.2}$$

and $J_n(x)$, which is the coefficient of t^n, is labeled a Bessel function of the first kind of integral order n.

Expanding the exponential, we have

$$e^{xt/2} \cdot e^{-x/2t} = \sum_{r=0}^{\infty} \left(\frac{x}{2}\right)^r \frac{t^r}{r!} \sum_{s=0}^{\infty} (-1)^s \left(\frac{x}{2}\right)^s \frac{t^{-s}}{s!}. \tag{11.3}$$

For a given s we get t^n ($n \geqslant 0$) from

$$\left(\frac{x}{2}\right)^{n+s} \frac{t^{n+s}}{(n+s)!} (-1)^s \left(\frac{x}{2}\right)^s \frac{t^{-s}}{s!} \tag{11.4}$$

The coefficient of t^n is then[1]

$$J_n(x) = \sum_{s=0}^{\infty} \frac{(-1)^s}{s!(n+s)!} \left(\frac{x}{2}\right)^{n+2s} \tag{11.5}$$

[1] From the steps leading to this series and from its convergence characteristics it should be clear that this series may be used with x replaced by z and with z any point in the finite complex plane.

This expression actually holds for $n \leqslant 0$, also giving

$$J_{-n}(x) = \sum_{s=0}^{\infty} \frac{(-1)^s}{s!(s-n)!}\left(\frac{x}{2}\right)^{2s-n}, \tag{11.6}$$

which amounts to replacing n by $-n$ in Eq. 11.5. Since n is an integer (here),

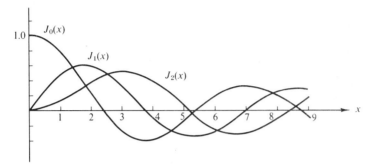

FIG. 11.1   Bessel functions, $J_0(x)$, $J_1(x)$, and $J_2(x)$

$(s-n)! \to \infty$ for $s = 0, ..., (n-1)$. Hence the series may be considered to start with $s = n$. Replacing s by $s + n$, we obtain

$$J_{-n}(x) = \sum_{s=0}^{\infty} \frac{(-1)^{s+n}}{s!(n+s)!}\left(\frac{x}{2}\right)^{n+2s}, \tag{11.7}$$

showing immediately that $J_n(x)$ and $J_{-n}(x)$ are not independent but are related by

$$J_{-n}(x) = (-1)^n J_n(x), \qquad \text{(integral } n\text{).} \tag{11.8}$$

These series expressions (Eqs. 11.5 and 11.6) may be used with n not an integer to *define* $J_n(x)$ and $J_{-n}(x)$ for nonintegral n (cf. Exercise 11.1.1).

Recurrence relations.   The recurrence relations for $J_n(x)$ and its derivatives may all be derived by operating on the series (Eq. 11.5), but it is convenient to obtain them from the generating function, $g(x, t)$. Differentiating Eq. 11.1 partially with respect to t, we find that

$$\frac{\partial}{\partial t} g(x, t) = \frac{1}{2} x \left(1 + \frac{1}{t^2}\right) e^{(x/2)(t-1/t)} \tag{11.9}$$

$$= \sum_{n=-\infty}^{\infty} n J_n(x) t^{n-1}.$$

and substituting Eq. 11.1 for the exponential and equating the coefficients of like powers of t^1 we obtain

$$J_{n-1}(x) + J_{n+1}(x) = \frac{2n}{x} J_n(x). \tag{11.10}$$

This is a three-term recurrence relation. Given J_0 and J_1, for example, J_2 (and any other integral order J_n) may be computed.

---

[1] This depends on the fact that the power series representation is unique (Sections 5.7, 6.4).

Differentiating Eq. 11.1 partially with respect to x, we have

$$\frac{\partial}{\partial x} g(x, t) = \frac{1}{2}\left(t - \frac{1}{t}\right) e^{(x/2)(t - 1/t)}$$

$$= \sum_{n=-\infty}^{\infty} J_n'(x)t^n. \tag{11.11}$$

Again, substituting in Eq. 11.1 and equating the coefficients of like powers of t, we obtain the result

$$J_{n-1}(x) - J_{n+1}(x) = 2J_n'(x). \tag{11.12}$$

As a special case of this general recurrence relation,

$$J_0'(x) = -J_1(x). \tag{11.13}$$

Adding Eqs. 11.10 and 11.12 and dividing by 2, we have

$$J_{n-1}(x) = \frac{n}{x} J_n(x) + J_n'(x). \tag{11.14}$$

Multiplying by x^n and rearranging terms produces

$$\frac{d}{dx}\left[x^n J_n(x)\right] = x^n J_{n-1}(x). \tag{11.15}$$

Subtracting Eq. 11.12 from 11.10 and dividing by 2 leads to

$$J_{n+1}(x) = \frac{n}{x} J_n(x) - J_n'(x). \tag{11.16}$$

Multiplying by x^{-n} and rearranging terms, we obtain

$$\frac{d}{dx}\left[x^{-n} J_n(x)\right] = -x^{-n} J_{n+1}(x). \tag{11.17}$$

Bessel's differential equation.   Suppose we consider a set of functions $Z_\nu(x)$ which satisfies the basic recurrence relations (Eqs. 11.10 and 11.12), but with ν not necessarily an integer and Z_ν not necessarily given by the series (Eq. 11.5). Equation 11.14 may be rewritten $(n \to \nu)$

$$x Z_\nu'(x) = x Z_{\nu-1}(x) - \nu Z_\nu(x). \tag{11.18}$$

On differentiating with respect to x, we have

$$x Z_\nu''(x) + (\nu + 1)Z_\nu' - x Z_{\nu-1}' - Z_{\nu-1} = 0. \tag{11.19}$$

Multiplying by x and then subtracting Eq. 11.18 mutliplied by ν gives us

$$x^2 Z_\nu'' + x Z_\nu' - \nu^2 Z_\nu + (\nu - 1)x Z_{\nu-1} - x^2 Z_{\nu-1}' = 0. \tag{11.20}$$

Now we rewrite Eq. 11.16 and replace n by $\nu - 1$.

$$x Z_{\nu-1}' = (\nu - 1)Z_{\nu-1} - x Z_\nu. \tag{11.21}$$

Using this to eliminate $Z_{\nu-1}$ and $Z'_{\nu-1}$ from Eq. 11.20, we finally get

$$x^2 Z''_\nu + x Z'_\nu + (x^2 - \nu^2)Z_\nu = 0. \tag{11.22}$$

This is just Bessel's equation. Hence *any* functions, $Z_\nu(x)$, that satisfy the recurrence relations (Eqs. 11.10 and 11.12, 11.14 and 11.16, or 11.15 and 11.17) satisfy Bessel's equation; that is, the unknown Z_ν are Bessel functions. In particular, we have shown that the functions $J_n(x)$, defined by our generating function, satisfy Bessel's equation.

Integral representation. A particularly useful and powerful way of treating Bessel functions employs integral representations. If we return to the generating function (Eq. 11.1), and substitute $t = e^{i\theta}$,

$$e^{ix\sin\theta} = J_0(x) + 2(J_2(x)\cos 2\theta + J_4(x)\cos 4\theta + \cdots)$$

$$+ 2i(J_1(x)\sin\theta + J_3(x)\sin 3\theta + \cdots), \tag{11.23}$$

in which we have used the relations

$$J_1(x)e^{i\theta} + J_1(x)e^{-i\theta} = J_1(x)(e^{i\theta} - e^{-i\theta})$$

$$= 2iJ_1(x)\sin\theta, \tag{11.24}$$

$$J_2(x)e^{2i\theta} + J_2(x)e^{-2i\theta} = 2J_2(x)\cos 2\theta,$$

and so on.

In summation notation,

$$\cos(x\sin\theta) = J_0(x) + 2\sum_{n=1}^{\infty} J_{2n}(x)\cos(2n\theta),$$

$$\sin(x\sin\theta) = 2\sum_{n=1}^{\infty} J_{2n-1}(x)\sin[(2n-1)\theta], \tag{11.25}$$

equating real and imaginary parts, respectively. By employing the orthogonality properties of cosine and sine,[1]

$$\int_0^\pi \cos n\theta \cos m\theta \, d\theta = \frac{\pi}{2}\delta_{nm}$$

$$\int_0^\pi \sin n\theta \sin m\theta \, d\theta = \frac{\pi}{2}\delta_{nm}, \tag{11.26}$$

in which n and m are *positive* integers (zero is excluded),[2] we obtain

$$\frac{1}{\pi}\int_0^\pi \cos(x\sin\theta)\cos n\theta \, d\theta = \begin{cases} J_n(x), & n \text{ even,} \\ 0, & n \text{ odd,} \end{cases} \tag{11.27}$$

$$\frac{1}{\pi}\int_0^\pi \sin(x\sin\theta)\sin n\theta \, d\theta = \begin{cases} 0, & n \text{ even,} \\ J_n(x), & n \text{ odd.} \end{cases} \tag{11.28}$$

---

[1] They are eigenfunctions of a self-adjoint equation (linear oscillator equation) and satisfy appropriate boundary conditions cf. Sections 9.2 and 14.1).

[2] Equation 11.26 holds for either $n = 0$ or $m = 0$ but not for both equal to zero.

If these two equations are added together,

$$J_n(x) = \frac{1}{\pi} \int_0^\pi [\cos(x \sin \theta) \cos n\theta + \sin(x \sin \theta) \sin n\theta] \, d\theta$$

$$= \frac{1}{\pi} \int_0^\pi \cos(n\theta - x \sin \theta) \, d\theta, \qquad n = 0, 1, 2, 3, \ldots. \tag{11.29}$$

As a special case

$$J_0(x) = \frac{1}{\pi} \int_0^\pi \cos(x \sin \theta) \, d\theta. \tag{11.30}$$

This integral representation (Eq. 11.29) may be obtained somewhat more directly by employing contour integration (cf. Exercise 11.1.13). Many other integral representations exist (cf. Exercise 11.1.22). Still another integral form is developed in Section 11.5 for use with the method of steepest descents in the derivation of asymptotic forms of the various Bessel functions.

EXAMPLE 11.1.1.   FRAUNHOFER DIFFRACTION, CIRCULAR APERTURE

In the theory of diffraction through a circular aperture we encounter the integral

$$\Phi \sim \int_0^a \int_0^{2\pi} e^{ibr\sin\theta} \, d\theta r \, dr \tag{11.31}$$

for Φ, the amplitude of the diffracted wave. Here θ is an azimuth angle in the plane

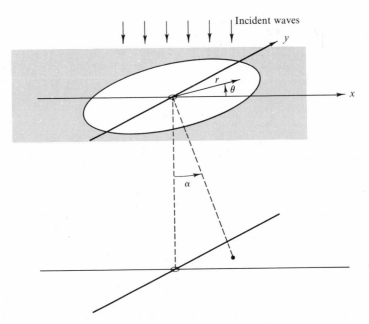

FIG. 11.2 Fraunhofer diffraction—circular aperture

of the circular aperture and α is the angle defined by a point on a screen below the circular aperture relative to the normal through the center point. The parameter b is given by

$$b = \frac{2\pi}{\lambda} \sin \alpha, \tag{11.32}$$

with λ the wavelength of the incident wave. The other symbols are defined by Fig. 11.2. Expressing the exponential in trigonometric form and using Eq. 11.30, we obtain

$$\Phi \sim 2\pi \int_0^a J_0(br)r \, dr. \tag{11.33}$$

Equation 11.15 enables us to integrate Eq. 11.33 immediately to obtain

$$\Phi \sim \frac{2\pi ab}{b^2} J_1(ab)$$

$$\sim \frac{\lambda a}{\sin \alpha} J_1\left(\frac{2\pi a}{\lambda} \sin \alpha\right). \tag{11.34}$$

The intensity of the light in the diffraction pattern is proportional to Φ^2 and

$$\Phi^2 \sim \left\{\frac{J_1[(2\pi a/\lambda) \sin \alpha]}{\sin \alpha}\right\}^2. \tag{11.35}$$

From Table 11.1, which lists the zeros of the Bessel functions and their first derivatives, this will have a zero at

$$\frac{2\pi a}{\lambda} \sin \alpha = 3.8317 \cdots \tag{11.36}$$

or

$$\sin \alpha = \frac{3.8317\lambda}{2\pi a}. \tag{11.37}$$

For green light $\lambda = 5.5 \times 10^{-5}$ cm. Hence, if $a = 0.5$ cm,

$$\alpha \approx \sin \alpha = 6.7 \times 10^{-5} \text{ (radian)}$$

$$\approx 14 \text{ seconds of arc}, \tag{11.38}$$

which shows that the bending or spreading of the light ray is extremely small. Had this analysis been known in the seventeenth century, the arguments against the wave theory of light would have collapsed.

In mid-twentieth century this same diffraction pattern appears in the scattering of nuclear particles by atomic nuclei—a striking demonstration of the wave properties of the nuclear particles.

Additional roots of the Bessel functions and their first derivatives may be found in C. L. Beattie, "Table of First 700 Zeros of Bessel Functions," *Bell Tech. J.* **37**, 689 (1958) and Bell Monograph 3055. *Note.* $J_0'(x) = -J_1(x)$.

TABLE 11.1

Zeros of the Bessel Functions and Their First Derivatives

Number of zero	$J_0(x)$	$J_1(x)$	$J_2(x)$	$J_3(x)$	$J_4(x)$	$J_5(x)$
1	2.4048	3.8317	5.1356	6.3802	7.5883	8.7715
2	5.5201	7.0156	8.4172	9.7610	11.0647	12.3386
3	8.6537	10.1735	11.6198	13.0152	14.3725	15.7002
4	11.7915	13.3237	14.7960	16.2235	17.6160	18.9801
5	14.9309	16.4706	17.9598	19.4094	20.8269	22.2178
	$J_0'(x)$	$J_1'(x)$	$J_2'(x)$	$J_3'(x)$		
1	3.8317	1.8412	3.0542	4.2012		
2	7.0156	5.3314	6.7061	8.0152		
3	10.1735	8.5363	9.9695	11.3459		

As noted earlier, Bessel's equation is likely to occur whenever we use cylindrical coordinates or polar coordinates for the two-dimensional case. A familiar physical example of the two-dimensional case is provided by a circular membrane or drum.

EXAMPLE 11.1.2.   VIBRATIONS OF A CIRCULAR MEMBRANE

The amplitude U of the circular membrane expressed as a function of space (r, θ) and time (t) must satisfy the wave equation

$$\nabla^2 U - \frac{1}{v^2}\frac{\partial^2 U}{\partial t^2} = 0. \tag{11.39}$$

Here v is the (phase) velocity of the wave fixed by the elastic constants of the membrane and whatever damping is imposed. Our partial differential equation may be solved by separation of variables, $U = S(r, \theta)\,T(t)$ or by assuming a periodic time dependence

$$T = e^{\pm i\omega t} \tag{11.40}$$

of angular frequency ω.

The space-dependent part of the amplitude S must satisfy the time-independent wave equation

$$\nabla^2 S + k^2 S = 0. \tag{11.41}$$

with

$$k^2 = \frac{w^2}{v^2}. \tag{11.42}$$

In terms of wavelength λ and frequency v,

$$k = \frac{2\pi v}{v} = \frac{2\pi}{\lambda} \tag{11.43}$$

and is usually called the wave number.

By separating variables in polar coordinates, as discussed in Sections 2.6 and 8.2, we assume

$$S(r, \theta) = R(r)\,\Theta(\theta) \tag{11.44}$$

and obtain

$$\frac{r^2}{R}\frac{d^2R}{dr^2} + \frac{r}{R}\frac{dR}{dr} + \frac{1}{\Theta}\frac{d^2\Theta}{d\theta^2} + r^2k^2 = 0. \tag{11.45}$$

We set

$$\frac{1}{\Theta}\frac{d^2\Theta}{d\theta^2} = -m^2, \tag{11.46}$$

which is satisfied by

$$\Theta = e^{\pm im\theta}. \tag{11.47}$$

The constant of separation was chosen as $-m^2$ as a matter of convenience. It must be negative to avoid blowing up as θ becomes infinitely large and, indeed, since the membrane displacement must be a single-valued function of azimuth, we further require m to be an integer.

The radial equation becomes

$$r^2\frac{d^2R}{dr^2} + r\frac{dR}{dr} + (k^2r^2 - m^2)R = 0, \tag{11.48}$$

which is just Bessel's equation, satisfied by

$$R(r) = J_m(kr). \tag{11.49}$$

The complete solution[1] is

$$U(r, \theta, t) = J_m(kr)(a_1 e^{im\theta} + a_2 e^{-im\theta})(b_1 e^{i\omega t} + b_2 e^{-i\omega t}). \tag{11.50}$$

The constants a_1, a_2, b_1, and b_2 are fixed by the initial conditions for the vibration. On the other hand, the wave number k enters as an eigenvalue and is *quantized* by the requirement that

$$U(a, \theta, t) = 0, \tag{11.51}$$

taking a as the radius of the membrane. Therefore

$$J_m(ka) = 0 \quad \text{and} \quad ka = \frac{2\pi a}{\lambda} \tag{11.52}$$

is a root of J_m. By Eq. 11.43 this means that the allowable frequencies v (or ω) are also quantized.

Orthogonality.   We consider two Bessel functions of the first kind, order n,

$$u = J_n(ax),$$
$$v = J_n(bx), \tag{11.53}$$

---

[1] There are other Bessel functions besides J_m, but they all diverge at $r = 0$. This is shown explicitly in Section 11.2. The divergent behavior is actually implicit in Eq. 11.6.

which satisfy

$$xu'' + u' + x\left(a^2 - \frac{n^2}{x^2}\right)u = 0, \tag{11.54a}$$

$$xv'' + v' + x\left(b^2 - \frac{n^2}{x^2}\right)v = 0, \tag{11.54b}$$

with

$$u' = \frac{d}{dx} J_n(ax), \text{ etc.} \tag{11.55}$$

Equations 11.54 are self-adjoint and therefore, by the Sturm-Liouville theory [Chapter 9 $(\lambda = a^2, b^2; \; w = x)$] we expect u and v to be orthogonal, subject to satisfying certain boundary conditions. Repeating part of the general theory of Chapter 9, we multiply Eq. 11.54a by v and Eq. 11.54b by u, integrate from 0 to 1, and then subtract to get

$$(a^2 - b^2) \int_0^1 uvx \, dx = x(uv' - u'v)\Big|_0^1. \tag{11.56}$$

Since the $J_n(0)$ are all finite,[1] the right-hand side vanishes at $x = 0$. It will also vanish at $x = 1$ *if we choose the parameters a and b to be roots of $J_n(x)$*,

$$J_n(a) = J_n(b) = 0. \tag{11.57}$$

Then for $a \neq b$

$$\int_0^1 J_n(ax) \, J_n(bx)x \, dx = 0. \tag{11.58}$$

Note the presence of x as a weighting factor. If $a = b$, we have the normalization integral

$$\int_0^1 [J_n(ax)]x \, dx = \frac{1}{2}\left[\frac{d}{d(ax)} J_n(ax)\Big|_{x=1}\right]^2. \tag{11.59}$$

The proof of Eq. 11.59 is left as an exercise.

Bessel functions of nonintegral order.   The reader will probably have noticed that the generating function defined only Bessel functions of integral order, J_0, J_1, J_2, etc. This is a great limitation of the generating function approach. However, the Bessel function of the first kind $J_\nu(x)$, may easily be defined for nonintegral ν by using the series (Eq. 11.6) as a new definition.

The recurrence relations may be verified by substituting in the series form of $J_\nu(x)$ (Exercise 11.1.1). From these relations Bessel's equation follows. In fact, if ν is not an integer, there is actually an important simplification. It is found that J_ν and $J_{-\nu}$ are independent, for no relation of the form of Eq. 11.8 exists. On the other hand, for $\nu = n$, an integer, we will need another solution. The development of this second solution and an investigation of its properties form the subject of Section 11.2.

---

[1] This is easily seen from the series form (Eq. 11.5).

EXERCISES

11.1.1 Show, by direct differentiation, that
$$J_\nu(x) = \sum_{s=0}^{\infty} \frac{(-1)^s}{s!(s+\nu)!} \left(\frac{x}{2}\right)^{\nu+2s}$$
satisfies the two recurrence relations
$$J_{\nu-1}(x) + J_{\nu+1}(x) = \frac{2\nu}{x} J_\nu(x),$$
$$J_{\nu-1}(x) - J_{\nu+1}(x) = 2J_\nu'(x),$$
and Bessel's differential equation
$$x^2 J_\nu''(x) + x J_\nu'(x) + (x^2 - \nu^2) J_\nu(x) = 0.$$

11.1.2 From the product of the generating functions $g(x, t) \cdot g(-x, t)$ show that
$$1 = [J_0(x)]^2 + 2[J_1(x)]^2 + 2[J_2(x)]^2 + \cdots$$
and therefore that $|J_0(x)| \leq 1$ and $|J_n(x)| \leq 1/\sqrt{2}$, $n = 1, 2, 3, \ldots$.

11.1.3 Using a generating function $g(x, t) = g(u + v, t) = g(u, t) \cdot g(v, t)$, show that

(a) $J_n(u + v) = \sum_{s=-\infty}^{\infty} J_s(u) \cdot J_{n-s}(v),$

(b) $J_0(u + v) = J_0(u) J_0(v) + 2 \sum_{s=1}^{\infty} J_s(u) J_{-s}(v).$

These are addition theorems for the Bessel functions.

11.1.4 Using only the generating function
$$e^{(x/2)(t-1/t)} = \sum_{n=-\infty}^{\infty} J_n(x) t^n$$
and not the explicit series form of $J_n(x)$, show that $J_n(x)$ has odd or even parity according to whether n is odd or even, that is,
$$J_n(x) = (-1)^n J_n(-x).$$

11.1.5 Derive
$$\frac{d}{dx}[x^n J_n(x)] = x^n J_{n-1}(x)$$
$$\frac{d}{dx}[x^{-n} J_n(x)] = -x^{-n} J_{n+1}(x)$$
by multiplying the series representation of $J_n(x)$ by x^n, x^{-n} and differentiating.

11.1.6 Show that between any two consecutive zeros of $J_n(x)$ there is one and only one zero of $J_{n+1}(x)$. *Hint.* Eqs. 11.15 and 11.17 may be useful.

11.1.7 Evaluate

(a) $\int_0^\infty J_1(x) \, dx.$ *Ans.* 1.

(b) $\int_0^\infty J_2(x) x^{-1} \, dx.$ *Ans.* $\frac{1}{2}$.

(c) $\int_0^\infty J_{n+1}(x) x^{-n} \, dx.$ *Ans.* $\dfrac{1}{2^n n!}$.

Assume that $J_n(x)$ vanishes as $x^{-1/2}$ as $x \to \infty$ (Section 11.5).

11.1.8   Prove that
$$\int_0^\infty J_n(x)\,dx = \int_0^\infty J_{n+2}(x)\,dx, \qquad n = 0, 1, 2, \dots .$$

11.1.9   Show that the following differential equations are forms of Bessel's equations and obtain solutions.

(a) $y'' + xy = 0$,

(b) $y'' + 2n^2 xy = 0$,

(c) $xy'' + (2n+1)y' + xy = 0$.

11.1.10   A set of functions $C_n(x)$ satisfies the recurrence relations
$$C_{n-1}(x) - C_{n+1}(x) = \frac{2n}{x}\,C_n(x),$$
$$C_{n-1}(x) + C_{n+1}(x) = 2C_n'(x).$$

(a) What linear second-order differential equation do the $C_n(x)$ satisfy?

(b) By a change of variable transform your differential equation into Bessel's equation. This suggests that $C_n(x)$ may be expressed in terms of Bessel functions of transformed argument.

11.1.11   Prove that

(a) $\dfrac{\sin x}{x} = \displaystyle\int_0^{\pi/2} J_0(x\cos\theta)\cos\theta\,d\theta$,

(b) $\dfrac{1 - \cos x}{x} = \displaystyle\int_0^{\pi/2} J_1(x\cos\theta)\,d\theta$.

Hint. The definite integral
$$\int_0^{\pi/2} \cos^{2s+1}\theta\,d\theta = \frac{2\cdot 4\cdot 6\cdots(2s)}{1\cdot 3\cdot 5\cdots(2s+1)}$$
may be useful.

11.1.12   Show that

(a) $J_0(x) = \dfrac{2}{\pi}\displaystyle\int_0^1 \frac{\cos xt}{\sqrt{1 - t^2}}\,dt$,

(b) $J_0(x) = \dfrac{2}{\pi}\displaystyle\int_1^\infty \frac{\sin xt}{\sqrt{t^2 - 1}}\,dt$.

11.1.13   (a) Show by direct differentiation and substitution that
$$J_\nu(x) = \frac{1}{2\pi i}\oint_C e^{(x/2)(t - 1/t)}t^{-\nu-1}\,dt$$
or that the equivalent equation
$$J_\nu(x) = \frac{1}{2\pi i}\left(\frac{x}{2}\right)^\nu \oint e^{s - x^2/4s}s^{-\nu-1}\,ds$$
satisfies Bessel's equation. C is the contour shown in Fig. 11.3. The negative real axis is a cut line.

(b) Show that the first integral may be transformed into
$$J_n(x) = \frac{1}{2\pi}\int_0^{2\pi} e^{i(x\sin\theta - n\theta)}\,d\theta$$
$$= \frac{i^{-n}}{2\pi}\int_0^{2\pi} e^{i(x\cos\theta + n\theta)}\,d\theta.$$

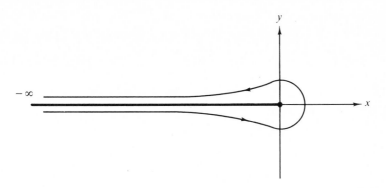

FIG. 11.3   Bessel function contour

11.1.14   The contour C in Exercise 11.1.13 is deformed to the path $-\infty$ to -1, unit circle $e^{-i\pi}$ to $e^{i\pi}$, and finally -1 to $-\infty$. Show that

$$J_\nu(x) = \frac{1}{\pi} \int_0^\pi \cos(\nu\theta - x\sin\theta)\, d\theta$$

$$- \frac{\sin\nu\pi}{\pi} \int_0^\infty e^{(-\nu\theta - x\sinh\theta)}\, d\theta.$$

This is Bessel's integral. *Hint.* The negative values of the variable of integration u may be handled by using

$$u = t e^{\pm i\pi}.$$

11.1.15   Using trigonometric forms, verify that

$$J_0(br) = \frac{1}{2\pi} \int_0^{2\pi} e^{i\,br\sin\theta}\, d\theta.$$

11.1.16   Plot the intensity (Φ^2 of Eq. 11.35) as a function of $(\sin\alpha/\lambda)$ along a diameter of the circular diffraction pattern. Locate the first two minima.

11.1.17   Show that the recurrence relation
$$J_n'(x) = \tfrac{1}{2}[J_{n-1}(x) - J_{n+1}(x)]$$

follows directly from differentiation of

$$J_n(x) = \frac{1}{\pi} \int_0^\pi \cos(n\theta - x\sin\theta)\, d\theta.$$

11.1.18   Show that

$$J_0(R) = \sum_{n=-\infty}^{\infty} J_n(r_1)\, J_n(r_2) e^{in\varphi},$$

where
$$R^2 = r_1^2 + r_2^2 - 2r_1 r_2 \cos\varphi.$$

Hint. (1) Represent $J_0(R)$ by the integral of Exercise 11.1.13b with cosine argument $(\theta - \alpha)$.
(2) Eliminate $R\sin\alpha$, $R\cos\alpha$.
(3) Use Eq. 11.23 for $e^{ir_1\sin\theta}$.
(4) Evaluate the integral by Exercise 11.1.13a.
This result may be generalized to

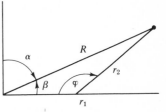

FIG. 11.4

$$J_m(R)e^{im\beta} = \sum_{n=-\infty}^{\infty} J_n(r_1)\, J_{n+m}(r_2) e^{in\varphi}$$

$$H_m^{(1)}(R)e^{im\beta} = \sum_{n=-\infty}^{\infty} J_n(r_1)\, H_{n+m}^{(1)}(r_2) e^{in\varphi} \qquad |r_2| > |r_1\cos\varphi|.$$

11.1.19   (a) By changing the upper limit of the integral in Eq. 11.56 from 1 to P show that

$$(a^2 - b^2) \int_0^P J_n(ax) \, J_n(bx) x \, dx = P[b \, J_n(aP) \, J_n'(bP) - a \, J_n'(aP) \, J_n(bP)]$$

with

$$J_n'(aP) = \frac{d}{d(ax)} J_n(ax) \big|_{x=P} .$$

(b) Replace b with $a + \varepsilon$ ($\varepsilon \to 0$) and show that

$$\int_0^P [J_n(ax)]^2 x \, dx = \frac{P^2}{2} \left\{ [J_n'(aP)]^2 + \left(1 - \frac{n^2}{a^2 P^2} \right) [J_n(aP)]^2 \right\} .$$

The two integrals are usually called the first and second Lommel integrals.

11.1.20   A particle (mass m) is contained in a right circular cylinder (pillbox) of radius R and height H. The particle is described by a wave function satisfying the Schrödinger wave equation

$$-\frac{\hbar^2}{2m} \nabla^2 \psi(\rho, \varphi, z) = E \psi(\rho, \varphi, z)$$

and the condition that the wave function go to zero over the surface of the pillbox. Find the lowest (zero point) permitted energy.

$$Ans. \ E = \frac{\hbar^2}{2m} \left[\left(\frac{z_{pq}}{R} \right)^2 + \left(\frac{n\pi}{H} \right)^2 \right],$$

where z_{pq} is the qth zero of J_p, the index p fixed by the azimuthal dependence.

$$E_{min} = \frac{\hbar^2}{2m} \left[\left(\frac{2.405}{R} \right)^2 + \left(\frac{\pi}{H} \right)^2 \right] .$$

11.1.21   An analysis of antenna radiation patterns for a system with a circular aperture involves the equation

$$g(u) = \int_0^1 f(r) J_0(ur) r \, dr.$$

If $f(r) = 1 - r^2$, show that

$$g(u) = \frac{2}{u^2} J_2(u).$$

11.1.22   (a) Show that

$$J_\nu(x) = \frac{2}{\pi^{1/2}(\nu - \frac{1}{2})!} \left(\frac{x}{2} \right)^\nu \int_0^{\pi/2} \cos(x \sin \theta) \cos^{2\nu} \theta \, d\theta,$$

where $\nu > -\frac{1}{2}$. *Hint.* Here is a chance to use series expansion and term-by-term integration. The formulas of Section 10.4 will prove useful.

(b) Transform the integral in part (a) into

$$J_\nu(x) = \frac{1}{\pi^{1/2}(\nu - \frac{1}{2})!} \left(\frac{x}{2} \right)^\nu \int_0^\pi \cos(x \cos \theta) \sin^{2\nu} \theta \, d\theta$$

$$= \frac{1}{\pi^{1/2}(\nu - \frac{1}{2})!} \left(\frac{x}{2} \right)^\nu \int_0^\pi e^{\pm ix \cos \theta} \sin^{2\nu} \theta \, d\theta$$

$$= \frac{1}{\pi^{1/2}(\nu - \frac{1}{2})!} \left(\frac{x}{2} \right)^\nu \int_{-1}^1 e^{\pm ipx} (1 - p^2)^{\nu - 1/2} \, dp.$$

These are alternate integral representations of $J_\nu(x)$.

11.1.23   (a) From

$$J_\nu(x) = \frac{1}{2\pi i} \left(\frac{x}{2} \right)^\nu \int t^{-\nu-1} e^{t - x^2/4t} \, dt$$

derive the recurrence relation

$$J_\nu'(x) = \frac{\nu}{x} J_\nu(x) - J_{\nu+1}(x).$$

(b) From

$$J_\nu(x) = \frac{1}{2\pi i} \int t^{-\nu-1} e^{(x/2)(t-1/t)} \, dt$$

derive the recurrence relation

$$J'_\nu(x) = \tfrac{1}{2} J_{\nu-1}(x) - \tfrac{1}{2} J_{\nu+1}(x).$$

11.1.24   Derive the addition theorem for Bessel functions,

$$J_0(\sqrt{a^2 + 2ab \cos\theta + b^2}) = J_0(a) J_0(b) + 2 \sum_{n=1}^{\infty} J_n(a) J_n(b) \cos n\theta.$$

11.1.25   Evaluate

$$\int_0^1 [J_n(ax)]^2 \, dx,$$

where a is a root of J_n; that is, $J_n(a) = 0$.

11.1.26   Derive

$$J_n(x) = (-1)^n \, x^n \left(\frac{d}{x\,dx}\right)^n J_0(x).$$

11.1.27   A thin conducting disk of radius a carries a charge q. Show that the potential is described by

$$\varphi(r, z) = \frac{q}{4\pi\varepsilon_0 a} \int_0^\infty e^{-k|z|} J_0(kr) \frac{\sin ka}{k} \, dk,$$

where J_0 is the usual Bessel function and r and z are the familiar cylindrical coordinates.

11.1.28.   Derive the Jacobi-Anger expansion

$$e^{iz \cos\theta} = \sum_{m=-\infty}^{\infty} i^m J_m(z) e^{im\theta}.$$

This is an expansion of a plane wave in a series of cylindrical waves.

11.2   Neumann Functions, Bessel Functions of the Second Kind, $N_\nu(x)$

From the theory of differential equations it is known that Bessel's equation has two independent solutions. Indeed, for nonintegral order ν we have already found two solutions and labeled them $J_\nu(x)$ and $J_{-\nu}(x)$, using the infinite series (Eq. 11.5). The trouble is that when ν is integral Eq. 11.8 holds and we have but one independent solution. A second solution may be developed by the methods of Section 8.5. This yields a perfectly good second solution of Bessel's equation, but it is not the usual standard form.

Definition.   As an alternate approach we take the particular linear combination of $J_\nu(x)$ and $J_{-\nu}(x)$

$$N_\nu(x) = \frac{\cos \nu\pi \, J_\nu(x) - J_{-\nu}(x)}{\sin \nu\pi}. \tag{11.60}$$

This is the Neumann function.[1] For nonintegral ν, $N_\nu(x)$ clearly satisfies Bessel's equation, for it is a linear combination of known solutions, $J_\nu(x)$ and $J_{-\nu}(x)$. However, for integral ν, $\nu = n$, Eq. 11.8 applies and Eq. 11.60 becomes indeterminate. The definition of $N_\nu(x)$ was chosen deliberately for this indeterminate

---

[1] This is often labeled $Y_\nu(x)$.

property. Evaluating $N_n(x)$ by L'Hospital's rule for indeterminate forms, we obtain

$$
N_n(x) = \frac{(d/dv)[\cos v\pi J_v(x) - J_{-v}(x)]}{(d/dv)\sin v\pi}
$$

$$
= \frac{-\pi \sin n\pi J_n(x) + [\cos n\pi(\partial J_v/\partial v - \partial J_{-v}/\partial v)]}{\pi \cos n\pi}\bigg|_{v=n}
$$

$$
= \frac{1}{\pi}\left[\frac{\partial J_v(x)}{\partial v} - (-1)^n \frac{\partial J_{-v}(x)}{\partial v}\right]\bigg|_{v=n}. \tag{11.61}
$$

Series form.   A series expansion[1] gives the horrible result

$$
N_n(x) = \frac{2}{\pi} J_n(x) \ln\left(\frac{x}{2}\right)
$$

$$
- \frac{1}{\pi} \sum_{r=0}^{\infty} (-1)^r \frac{1}{r!(n+r)!}\left(\frac{x}{2}\right)^{n+2r} [F(r) + F(n+r)] \tag{11.62}
$$

$$
- \frac{1}{\pi} \sum_{r=0}^{n-1} \frac{(n-r-1)!}{r!}\left(\frac{x}{2}\right)^{-n+2r},
$$

which exhibits the logarithmic dependence that was to be expected. This, of course, verifies the independence of J_n and N_n. $F(r)$ is the digamma function which arises from differentiating the factorials in the denominator of $J_v(x)$ (cf. Section 10.2 and especially Eq. 10.39). Using the properties of the digamma function (cf. Exercise 10.2.2), we rewrite Eq. 11.62 in the only slightly less horrible form

$$
N_n(x) = \frac{2}{\pi}\left[\ln\left(\frac{x}{2}\right) + C - \frac{1}{2}\sum_{p=1}^{n} p^{-1}\right] J_n(x)
$$

$$
- \frac{1}{\pi} \sum_{r=0}^{\infty} (-1)^r \frac{(x/2)^{n+2r}}{r!(n+r)!} \sum_{p=1}^{r}\left[\frac{1}{p} + \frac{1}{p+n}\right] \tag{11.63}
$$

$$
- \frac{1}{\pi} \sum_{r=0}^{n-1} \frac{(n-r-1)!}{r!}\left(\frac{x}{2}\right)^{-n+2r}.
$$

For $n = 0$ we have the limiting value

$$
N_0(x) = \frac{2}{\pi}(\ln x + C - \ln 2) + O(x^2) \tag{11.64}
$$

and for $v > 0$

$$
N_v(x) = -\frac{(v-1)!}{\pi}\left(\frac{2}{x}\right)^v + \cdots. [2] \tag{11.65}
$$

To verify that $N_v(x)$, our Neumann function or Bessel function of the second kind, actually does satisfy Bessel's equation for integral n, we may proceed as follows. Differentiating Bessel's equation for $J_{\pm v}(x)$ with respect to v, we have

$$
x^2 \frac{d^2}{dx^2}\left(\frac{\partial J_{\pm v}}{\partial v}\right) + x \frac{d}{dx}\left(\frac{\partial J_{\pm v}}{\partial v}\right) + (x^2 - v^2)\frac{\partial J_{\pm v}}{\partial v} = 2v J_{\pm v}. \tag{11.66}
$$

---

[1] Using $(d/dv)x^v = x^v \ln x$.

[2] Note that this limiting form applies to *both* integral and nonintegral values of the index v.

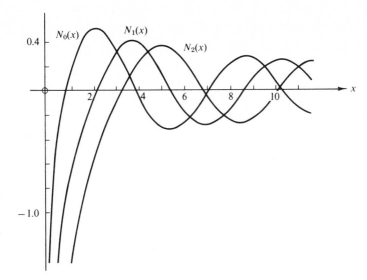

FIG. 11.5   Neumann functions, $N_0(x)$, $N_1(x)$, and $N_2(x)$

Multiplying the equation for J_{-v} by $(-1)^v$, subtracting from the equation for J_v (as suggested by Eq. 11.61), and taking the limit $v \to n$, we obtain

$$x^2 \frac{d^2}{dx^2} N_n + x \frac{d}{dx} N_n + (x^2 - n^2)N_n = \frac{2n}{\pi} [J_n - (-1)^n J_{-n}]. \qquad (11.67)$$

For $v = n$, an integer, the right-hand side vanishes by Eq. 11.8 and $N_n(x)$ is seen to be a solution of Bessel's equation. The most general solution for any v can therefore be written

$$y(x) = A J_v(x) + B N_v(x). \qquad (11.68)$$

It is seen from Eq. 11.62 that N_n diverges at least logarithmically. Any boundary condition that requires the solution to be finite at the origin [as in our vibrating circular membrane (section 11.1)] automatically excludes $N_n(x)$. Conversely, in the absence of such a requirement $N_n(x)$ must be considered.

Recurrence relations.   Substituting Eq. 11.60 for $N_v(x)$ (nonintegral v) or Eq. 11.61 (integral v) into the recurrence relations (Eqs. 11.10 and 11.12) for $J_n(x)$, we see immediately that $N_v(x)$ satisfies these same recurrence relations. This actually constitutes another proof that N_v is a solution. Note carefully that the converse is not necessarily true. All solutions need not satisfy the same recurrence relations. An example of this sort of trouble appears in Section 11.4.

Wronskian formulas.   From Section 8.5 we have the Wronskian formula for solutions of the Bessel equation

$$u_v(x)\, v_v'(x) - u_v'(x)\, v_v(x) = \frac{A_v}{x}, \qquad (11.69)$$

in which A_v is a parameter that depends on the particular Bessel functions $u_v(x)$

and $v_\nu(x)$ being considered. It is a constant in the sense that it is independent of x. Consider the special case

$$u_\nu(x) = J_\nu(x), \qquad v_\nu(x) = J_{-\nu}(x), \tag{11.70}$$

$$J_\nu J'_{-\nu} - J'_\nu J_{-\nu} = \frac{A_\nu}{x}. \tag{11.71}$$

Since A_ν is a constant, it may be identified at any convenient point such as $x = 0$. Using the first terms in the series expansions (Eqs. 11.5 and 11.6), we obtain

$$
\begin{aligned}
J_\nu &\to \frac{x^\nu}{2^\nu \nu!}, & J_{-\nu} &\to \frac{2^\nu x^{-\nu}}{(-\nu)!}, \\
J'_\nu &\to \frac{\nu x^{\nu-1}}{2^\nu \nu!}, & J'_{-\nu} &\to \frac{-\nu 2^\nu x^{-\nu-1}}{(-\nu)!}.
\end{aligned}
\tag{11.72}
$$

Substitution into Eq. 11.69 yields

$$J_\nu(x) J'_{-\nu}(x) - J'_\nu(x) J_{-\nu}(x) = \frac{-2\nu}{x\nu!(-\nu)!}$$

$$= -\frac{2 \sin \nu\pi}{\pi x} \tag{11.73}$$

using Eq. 10.32

$$\nu!(-\nu)! = \frac{\pi\nu}{\sin \pi\nu}.$$

Note that A_ν vanishes for integral ν, as it must, since the nonvanishing of the Wronskian is a test of the independence of the two solutions. By Eq. 11.73 J_n and J_{-n} are clearly linearly dependent.

Using our recurrence relations, we may readily develop a large number of alternate forms, among which are

$$J_\nu J_{-\nu+1} + J_{-\nu} J_{\nu-1} = \frac{2 \sin \nu\pi}{\pi x}, \tag{11.74}$$

$$J_\nu J_{-\nu-1} + J_{-\nu} J_{\nu+1} = -\frac{2 \sin \nu\pi}{\pi x}, \tag{11.75}$$

$$J_\nu N'_\nu - J'_\nu N_\nu = \frac{2}{\pi x}, \tag{11.76}$$

$$J_\nu N_{\nu+1} - J_{\nu+1} N_\nu = -\frac{2}{\pi x}. \tag{11.77}$$

Many more will be found in the references given.

The reader will recall that in Chapter 8 Wronskians were of great value in two respects: (1) in establishing the linear independence or linear dependence of solutions of differential equations and (2) in developing an integral form of a second solution. Here, the specific forms of the Wronskians and Wronskian-derived combinations of Bessel functions are useful primarily to illustrate the general behavior of the various Bessel functions.

EXAMPLE 11.2.1. CYLINDRICAL WAVEGUIDES

One application of Bessel and Neumann functions is in the propagation of electromagnetic waves in circular waveguides. Here the electromagnetic wave equations

$$\nabla^2 \mathbf{E} - \frac{1}{c^2}\frac{\partial^2 \mathbf{E}}{\partial t^2} = 0, \qquad \nabla^2 \mathbf{H} - \frac{1}{c^2}\frac{\partial^2 \mathbf{H}}{\partial t^2} = 0, \qquad (11.78)$$

which follow from Maxwell's equations, must be satisfied. Note the *vector* Laplacians. Using circular cylindrical coordinates because of the symmetry of our wave guide, we assume a solution of the form

$$E_z = u(r, \theta)e^{i[\omega t - 2\pi z/\lambda_g]}$$
$$H_z = 0, \qquad \text{TM, transverse magnetic wave.} \qquad (11.79)$$

Here we take the axis of the waveguide as the axis of cylindrical coordinates. The parameter λ_g is an effective wavelength along the guide which includes the effect of the waves' zig-zag path.

Substituting into the wave equation (Eq. 11.78), we obtain

$$r\frac{\partial}{\partial r}\left(r\frac{\partial u}{\partial r}\right) + \frac{\partial^2 u}{\partial \theta^2} + r^2\left(\frac{2\pi}{\lambda_c}\right)^2 u = 0. \qquad (11.80)$$

Here λ_c, another effective wavelength, is related to λ_0 (free space) and λ_g by

$$\frac{1}{\lambda_c^2} + \frac{1}{\lambda_g^2} = \frac{1}{\lambda_0^2},$$

$$\lambda_0 = \frac{2\pi c}{\omega}. \qquad (11.81)$$

Separating variables, we let

$$u(r, \theta) = R(r)\,\Theta(\theta) \qquad (11.82)$$

and find that $R(r)$ must satisfy

$$\frac{1}{r}\frac{d}{dr}\left(r\frac{dR}{dr}\right) + \left[\left(\frac{2\pi}{\lambda_c}\right)^2 - \frac{n^2}{r^2}\right]R = 0, \qquad (11.83)$$

which is Bessel's equation. The complete solution of Eq. 11.80 is

$$u(r, \theta) = J_n\left(\frac{2\pi r}{\lambda_c}\right)(a_1 \cos n\theta + b_1 \sin n\theta) + N_n\left(\frac{2\pi r}{\lambda_c}\right)(a_2 \cos n\theta + b_2 \sin n\theta). \qquad (11.84)$$

The cosines and sines, of course, come from the equation for $\Theta(\theta)$ with n required to be an integer in order to have $\Theta(\theta)$ single-valued.

The boundary condition for the TM wave is that $u = E_z$ must vanish at the conducting boundaries. This is an example of a Dirichlet boundary condition. We also require that E_z remain finite, which excludes N_n, the Neumann function *if there is no center conductor.* Then

$$E_z(r = r_0) = J_n\left(\frac{2\pi r_0}{\lambda_c}\right)(a_1 \cos n\theta + b_1 \sin n\theta) = 0 \quad \text{for all } \theta. \qquad (11.85)$$

This means that λ_c must be such that $2\pi r_0/\lambda_c$ is a root of J_n.

If we had investigated a TE (transverse electric) wave, we would have had

$$E_z = 0$$

and

$$H_z = u(r, \theta)e^{i[\omega t - 2\pi z/\lambda_g]}$$

$$\left.\frac{\partial u}{\partial r}\right|_{r=r_1} = \left.\frac{\partial u}{\partial r}\right|_{r=r_2} = 0, \tag{11.86}$$

a Neumann boundary condition.

If there is a center conductor (coaxial line), the Neumann function cannot be excluded and, in general, must be retained to satisfy the boundary conditions at both inner ($r = r_1$) and outer ($r = r_2$) surfaces. We have

$$J_n\left(\frac{2\pi r_1}{\lambda_c}\right)(a_1 \cos n\theta + b_1 \sin n\theta) + N_n\left(\frac{2\pi r_1}{\lambda_c}\right)(a_2 \cos n\theta + b_2 \sin n\theta) = 0, \tag{11.87}$$

again for all values of θ. This means that we must have $a_1/b_1 = a_2/b_2$, and the boundary condition on the inner surface ($r = r_1$) becomes

$$a_1 J_n\left(\frac{2\pi r_1}{\lambda_c}\right) + a_2 N_n\left(\frac{2\pi r_1}{\lambda_c}\right) = 0. \tag{11.88}$$

Similarly at the outer surface ($r = r_2$)

$$a_1 J_n\left(\frac{2\pi r_2}{\lambda_c}\right) + a_2 N_n\left(\frac{2\pi r_2}{\lambda_c}\right) = 0. \tag{11.89}$$

Equations 11.88 and 11.89 must be solved for λ_c and the ratio a_1/a_2.

To conclude this discussion of Neumann functions, the Neumann function, $N_\nu(x)$, is introduced for the following reasons:

1. It is a second, independent solution of Bessel's equation, which completes the general solution.

2. It is required for specific physical problems such as electromagnetic waves in coaxial cables.

3. It leads to Green's function for the Bessel equation (Section 11.4).

4. It leads directly to the two Hankel functions (Section 11.3).

EXERCISES

11.2.1 Verify the expansions (leading term only)

$$N_0(x) \to \frac{2}{\pi} (\ln x + C - \ln 2)$$

$$N_\nu(x) \to -\frac{(\nu - 1)!}{\pi}\left(\frac{2}{x}\right)^\nu, \qquad \nu > 0$$

$$x \ll 1.$$

by direct differentiation of the definition of the Neumann function as indicated in Eq. 11.68.

11.2.2 Prove that the Neumann functions N_n (with n an integer) satisfy the recurrence relations

$$N_{n-1}(x) + N_{n+1}(x) = \frac{2n}{x} N_n(x)$$

$$N_{n-1}(x) - N_{n+1}(x) = 2N_n'(x).$$

Hint. These relations may be proved by differentiating the recurrence relations for J_ν or by using the limit form of N_ν but *not* dividing everything by zero.

11.2.3 If Y and Z are any two solutions of Bessel's equation, show that

$$Y_\nu(x) Z_\nu'(x) - Y_\nu'(x) Z_\nu(x) = \frac{A_\nu}{x},$$

in which A_ν may depend on ν but is independent of x.

11.2.4 Verify the Wronskian formulas

$$J_\nu(x) J_{-\nu+1}(x) + J_{-\nu}(x) J_{\nu-1}(x) = \frac{2 \sin \nu\pi}{\pi x},$$

$$J_\nu(x) N_\nu'(x) - J_\nu'(x) N_\nu(x) = \frac{2}{\pi x}.$$

11.2.5 A cylindrical waveguide has radius r_0. Find the nonvanishing components of the electric and magnetic fields for
(a) TM_{01}, transverse magnetic wave ($H_z = H_r = E_\theta = 0$),
(b) TE_{01}, transverse electric wave ($E_z = E_r = H_\theta = 0$).
The subscripts 01 indicate that the longitudinal component (E_z or H_z) involves J_0 and the boundary condition is satisfied by the *first* zero of J_0 or J_0'.

11.2.6 For a given mode of oscillation the *minimum* frequency that will be passed by a circular cylindrical wave guide is

$$\nu_{\min} = \frac{c}{\lambda_c},$$

in which λ_c is fixed by the boundary condition

$$J_n\left(\frac{2\pi r_0}{\lambda_c}\right) = 0 \quad \text{for } TM_{nm} \text{ mode},$$

$$J_n'\left(\frac{2\pi r_0}{\lambda_c}\right) = 0 \quad \text{for } TE_{nm} \text{ mode}.$$

The subscript n denotes the order of the Bessel function and m indicates the zero used. Find this cut-off wavelength, λ_c for the three TM and three TE modes with the longest cut-off wavelengths. Explain your results in terms of the graph of J_0, J_1, and J_2, (Fig. 11.1).

11.2.7 Derive or verify the integral representation

$$N_0(z) = -\frac{2}{\pi} \int_0^\infty \cos\left(z \cosh t\right) dt$$

for the zero-order Neumann function.

11.2.8 An annular membrane has an outer radius r_1 and an inner radius r_2. Show that the lowest vibrational frequency is given by the smallest root of the equation

$$J_0(kr_1) N_0(kr_2) - J_0(kr_2) N_0(kr_1) = 0.$$

(From Section 11.1, $k = \omega/v = 2\pi/\lambda$.)

11.2.9 Show that

$$N_{-n}(x) = (-1)^n N_n(x).$$

11.2.10 Show that

(a) $\dfrac{\partial J_\nu(x)}{\partial \nu}\bigg|_{\nu=0} = \dfrac{\pi}{2}\, N_0(x),$

(b) $\dfrac{\partial N_\nu(x)}{\partial \nu}\bigg|_{\nu=0} = -\dfrac{\pi}{2}\, J_0(x).$

11.3 Hankel Functions

Many authors prefer to introduce the Hankel functions by means of integral representations and then use them to define the Neumann function, $N(z)$. An outline of this approach is given at the end of this section.

Definitions. As we have already obtained the Neumann function by more elementary (and less powerful) techniques, we may use it to define the Hankel functions, $H_\nu^{(1)}(x)$ and $H_\nu^{(2)}(x)$:

$$H_\nu^{(1)}(x) = J_\nu(x) + i\, N_\nu(x) \tag{11.90}$$

and

$$H_\nu^{(2)}(x) = J_\nu(x) - i\, N_\nu(x). \tag{11.91}$$

This is exactly analogous to taking

$$e^{\pm i\theta} = \cos\theta \pm i\sin\theta. \tag{11.92}$$

The extent of the analogy will be seen even better when the asymptotic forms are considered (Section 11.5). Indeed, it is their asymptotic behavior that makes the Hankel functions useful.

Series expansion of $H_\nu^{(1)}(x)$ and $H_\nu^{(2)}(x)$ may be obtained by combining Eqs. 11.5 and 11.63. Often only the first term is of interest; it is given by

$$H_0^{(1)}(x) = i\,\frac{2}{\pi}\ln x + 1 + i\,\frac{2}{\pi}(C - \ln 2) + \cdots,$$

$$H_\nu^{(1)}(x) = -i\,\frac{(\nu-1)!}{\pi}\left(\frac{2}{x}\right)^{\nu} + \cdots, \qquad \nu > 0, \tag{11.93}$$

$$H_0^{(2)}(x) = -i\,\frac{2}{\pi}\ln x + 1 - i\,\frac{2}{\pi}(C - \ln 2) + \cdots,$$

$$H_\nu^{(2)}(x) = i\,\frac{(\nu-1)!}{\pi}\left(\frac{2}{x}\right)^{\nu} + \cdots, \qquad \nu > 0. \tag{11.94}$$

Since the Hankel functions are linear combinations (with constant coefficients) of J_ν and N_ν, they satisfy the same recurrence relations (Eqs. 11.10 and 11.12).

$$H_{\nu-1}(x) + H_{\nu+1}(x) = \frac{2\nu}{x}\, H_\nu(x), \tag{11.95}$$

$$H_{\nu-1}(x) - H_{\nu+1}(x) = 2H_\nu'(x), \tag{11.96}$$

for both $H_\nu^{(1)}(x)$ and $H_\nu^{(2)}(x)$.

A variety of Wronskian formulas can be developed:

$$H_\nu^{(2)}H_{\nu+1}^{(1)} - H_\nu^{(1)}H_{\nu+1}^{(2)} = \frac{4}{i\pi x},$$

(11.97)

$$J_{\nu-1}H_\nu^{(1)} - J_\nu H_{\nu-1}^{(1)} = \frac{2}{i\pi x},$$

(11.98)

$$J_\nu H_{\nu-1}^{(2)} - J_{\nu-1}H_\nu^{(2)} = \frac{2}{i\pi x}.$$

(11.99)

EXAMPLE 11.3.1. CYLINDRICAL TRAVELING WAVES

As an illustration of the use of Hankel functions, consider a two-dimensional wave problem similar to the vibrating circular membrane of Section 11.1. Now imagine that the waves are generated at $r = 0$ and move outward to infinity. We replace our standing waves by traveling ones. The differential equation (Eq. 11.53) remains the same, but the boundary conditions change. We now demand that for large r the solution behave like

$$U \to e^{i(kr - \omega t)}$$

(11.100)

to describe an outgoing wave. As before, k is the wave number. This assumes, for simplicity, that there is no azimuthal dependence, that is, no angular momentum, or $m = 0$. In Section 11.5 $H_0^{(1)}(kr)$ has the asymptotic behavior

$$H_0^{(1)}(kr) \to e^{ikr}.$$

(11.101)

This boundary condition at infinity then determines our wave solution as

$$U(r, t) = H_0^{(1)}(kr)\, e^{-i\omega t}.$$

(11.102)

This solution diverges as $r \to 0$, which is just the behavior to be expected with a source at the origin.

The choice of a *two*-dimensional wave problem to illustrate the Hankel function $H_0^{(1)}(z)$ is not accidental. Bessel functions may appear in a variety of ways, such as in the separation of conical coordinates. However, they enter most commonly from the radial equations from the separation of variables in the Helmholtz equation in cylindrical and in spherical polar coordinates. We have taken a degenerate form of cylindrical coordinates for this illustration. Had we used spherical polar coordinates (spherical waves) we should have encountered index $\nu = n + \frac{1}{2}$, n an integer. These special values yield the spherical Bessel functions to be discussed in Section 11.6.

Contour integral representation of the Hankel functions. The integral representation (Schlaefi integral)

$$J_\nu(x) = \frac{1}{2\pi i} \oint e^{(x/2)(t - 1/t)} \frac{dt}{t^{\nu+1}}$$

(11.103)

may easily be established for $v = n$, an integer [recognizing that the numerator is the generating function (Eq. 11.1) and integrating around the origin]. If v is not an integer, the integrand is not single-valued and a cut line is needed in our complex plane. Choosing the negative real axis as the cut line and using the contour shown in Fig. 11.6, Eq. 11.103 can be extended to nonintegral v. Substituting Eq. 11.103

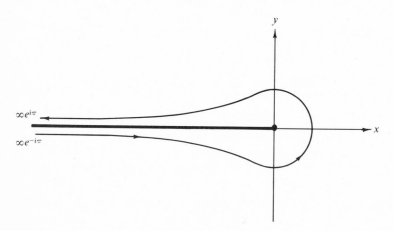

FIG. 11.6   Bessel function contour

into Bessel's differential equation, the combined integrand can be represented by an exact differential which vanishes as $t \to \infty\, e^{\pm i\pi}$.

We now deform the contour so that it approaches the origin along the positive real axis, as shown in Fig. 11.7. This particular approach guarantees that the exact

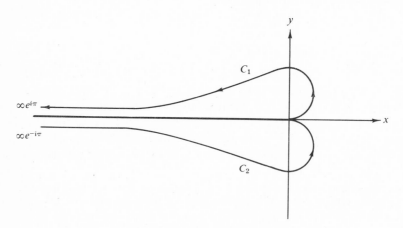

FIG. 11.7   Hankel function contours

differential mentioned will vanish as $t \to 0$ because of the $e^{-x/2t}$ factor. Hence each of the separate portions $\infty\, e^{-i\pi}$ to 0 and 0 to $\infty\, e^{i\pi}$ is a solution of Bessel's equation. We define

$$H_\nu^{(1)}(x) = \frac{1}{\pi i} \int_0^{\infty e^{i\pi}} e^{(x/2)(t-1/t)} \frac{dt}{t^{\nu+1}}$$

$$H_\nu^{(2)}(x) = \frac{1}{\pi i} \int_{\infty e^{-i\pi}}^0 e^{(x/2)(t-1/t)} \frac{dt}{t^{\nu+1}}.$$

(11.104)

These expressions are particularly convenient because they may be handled by the method of steepest descents (Section 7.4). $H_\nu^{(1)}(x)$ has a saddle point at $t = +i$, whereas $H_\nu^{(2)}(x)$ has a saddle point at $t = -i$.

The problem of relating Eqs. 11.104 to our earlier definition of the Hankel function (Eqs. 11.90 and 11.91), remains. Since Eqs. 11.103 and 11.104 combined yield

$$J_\nu(x) = \tfrac{1}{2}[H_\nu^{(1)}(x) + H_\nu^{(2)}(x)]$$

(11.105)

by inspection, we need only show that

$$N_\nu(x) = \frac{1}{2i}[H_\nu^{(1)}(x) - H_\nu^{(2)}(x)]$$

(11.106)

This may be accomplished by the substitutions, $t = e^{i\pi}/s$ for $H^{(1)}$ and $t = e^{-i\pi}/s$ for $H^{(2)}$. It follows that

$$H_\nu^{(1)}(x) = e^{-i\nu\pi}H_{-\nu}^{(1)}(x),$$

$$H_\nu^{(2)}(x) = e^{i\nu\pi}H_{-\nu}^{(2)}(x).$$

(11.107)

Finally, by writing $J_{-\nu}(x)$ in terms of $H_\nu^{(1)}(x)$ and $H_\nu^{(2)}(x)$ we may express the right-hand side of Eq. 11.106 in terms of $J_\nu(x)$ and $J_{-\nu}(x)$. When this is done, Eq. 11.106 reduces to Eq. 11.60, and our original definition of the Neumann function verifies that the two contour integrals (Eqs. 11.104) are indeed the Hankel functions. The details are left as Exercises 11.3.2 and 11.3.3.

In conclusion, the Hankel functions are introduced here for the following reasons:

1. As analogs of $e^{\pm ix}$ they are useful for describing traveling waves.
2. They offer an alternate (contour integral) and a rather elegant definition of Bessel functions.
3. $H_\nu^{(1)}$ is used to define the modified Bessel function K_ν of Section 11.4.

EXERCISES

11.3.1 Verify the Wronskian formulas

(a) $J_\nu(x) H_\nu^{(1)\prime}(x) - J_\nu'(x) H_\nu^{(1)}(x) = \dfrac{i2}{\pi x}$,

(b) $J_\nu(x) H_\nu^{(2)\prime}(x) - J_\nu'(x) H_\nu^{(2)}(x) = \dfrac{-i2}{\pi x}$,

(c) $N_\nu(x) H_\nu^{(1)\prime}(x) - N_\nu'(x) H_\nu^{(1)}(x) = \dfrac{-2}{\pi x}$,

(d) $N_\nu(x) H_\nu^{(2)\prime}(x) - N_\nu'(x) H_\nu^{(2)}(x) = \dfrac{-2}{\pi x}$,

(e) $H_\nu^{(1)}(x) H_\nu^{(2)\prime}(x) - H_\nu^{(1)\prime}(x) H_\nu^{(2)}(x) = \dfrac{-i4}{\pi x}$,

(f) $H_\nu^{(2)}(x) H_{\nu+1}^{(1)}(x) - H_\nu^{(1)}(x) H_{\nu+1}^{(2)}(x) = \dfrac{4}{i\pi x}$,

(g) $J_{\nu-1}(x) H_\nu^{(1)}(x) - J_\nu(x) H_{\nu-1}^{(1)}(x) = \dfrac{2}{i\pi x}$.

11.3.2 Show that the integral forms

(a) $\dfrac{1}{i\pi} \displaystyle\int_{0 C_1}^{\infty e^{i\pi}} e^{(x/2)(t-1/t)} \dfrac{dt}{t^{\nu+1}} = H_\nu^{(1)}(x)$,

(b) $\dfrac{1}{i\pi} \displaystyle\int_{\infty e^{-i\pi} C_2}^{0} e^{(x/2)(t-1/t)} \dfrac{dt}{t^{\nu+1}} = H_\nu^{(2)}(x)$,

satisfy Bessel's differential equation. The contours C_1 and C_2 are shown in Fig. 11.7.

11.3.3 Using the integrals and contours given in problem 11.3.2, show that

$$\frac{1}{2i} [H_\nu^{(1)}(x) - H_\nu^{(2)}(x)] = N_\nu(x).$$

11.3.4 Show that the integrals in Exercise 11.3.2 may be transformed to yield

(a) $H_\nu^{(1)}(x) = \dfrac{1}{\pi i} \displaystyle\int_{C_3} e^{x \sinh \gamma - \nu\gamma} \, d\gamma$,   (b) $H_\nu^{(2)}(x) = \dfrac{1}{\pi i} \displaystyle\int_{C_4} e^{x \sinh \gamma - \nu\gamma} \, d\gamma$.

FIG. 11.8 Hankel function contours

11.4 Modified Bessel Functions, $I_\nu(x)$ and $K_\nu(x)$

Frequently in physical problems the equation

$$x^2 \frac{d^2}{dx^2} y(x) + x \frac{d}{dx} y(x) - (x^2 + \nu^2)\, y(x) = 0 \qquad (11.108)$$

occurs. This is not quite Bessel's equation, but it may be put in the form of Bessel's equation by replacing x by $-it$

$$x \frac{d}{dx} \to t \frac{d}{dt},$$

$$x^2 \frac{d^2}{dx^2} \to t^2 \frac{d^2}{dt^2}.$$

Then

$$t^2 \frac{d^2}{dt^2} y(-it) + t \frac{d}{dt} y(-it) + (t^2 - v^2) y(-it) = 0, \qquad (11.109)$$

or $y(-it)$ is a Bessel function. It is customary (and convenient) to choose the normalization so that

$$y(x) = I_v(x) = i^{-v} J_v(ix). \qquad (11.110)$$

Often this is written

$$I_v(x) = e^{-v\pi i/2} J_v(xe^{i\pi/2}). \qquad (11.111)$$

Series form.   In terms of infinite series, this is equivalent to removing the $(-1)^s$ sign in Eq. 11.5 and writing

$$I_v(x) = \sum_{s=0}^{\infty} \frac{1}{s!(s+v)!} \left(\frac{x}{2}\right)^{2s+v},$$

$$\qquad (11.112)$$

$$I_{-v}(x) = \sum_{s=0}^{\infty} \frac{1}{s!(s-v)!} \left(\frac{x}{2}\right)^{2s-v}.$$

For the integral v this yields

$$I_n(x) = I_{-n}(x). \qquad (11.113)$$

Recurrence relations.   The recurrence relations satisfied by $I_v(x)$ may be developed from the series expansions, but it is perhaps easier to work from the existing recurrence relations for $J_v(x)$. Let us replace x by $-ix$ and rewrite Eq. 11.110 as

$$J_v(x) = i^v I_v(-ix). \qquad (11.114)$$

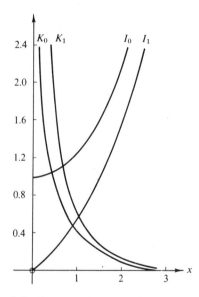

FIG. 11.9   Modified Bessel functions

Then Eq. 11.10 becomes

$$i^{v-1} I_{v-1}(-ix) + i^{v+1} I_{v+1}(-ix) = \frac{2v}{x} i^v I_v(-ix).$$

Replacing x by ix, we have a recurrence relation for $I_v(x)$,

$$I_{v-1}(x) - I_{v+1}(x) = \frac{2v}{x} I_v(x). \qquad (11.115)$$

Equation 11.12 transforms to

$$I_{v-1}(x) + I_{v+1}(x) = 2I_v'(x). \qquad (11.116)$$

These are the recurrence relations used in Exercise 11.1.10

From Eq. 11.113 it is seen that we have but one independent solution when v is an integer, exactly as in the Bessel functions J_v. The choice of a second, independent solution of Eq. 11.108 is essentially a matter of convenience. The second solution given here is selected on the basis of its asymptotic behavior—as shown in the next section. The confusion of choice and notation for this solution is perhaps greater than anywhere else in this field.[1] Many authors[2] choose to define a second solution in terms of the Hankel function $H_v^{(1)}(x)$ by

$$K_v(x) \equiv \frac{\pi}{2} i^{v+1} H_v^{(1)}(ix)$$

$$= \frac{\pi}{2} i^{v+1}[J_v(ix) + i N_v(ix)].$$

(11.117)

Using Eqs. 11.60 and 11.110 we may transform Eq. 11.117 to[3]

$$K_v(x) = \frac{\pi}{2} \frac{I_{-v}(x) - I_v(x)}{\sin v\pi},$$

(11.118)

analogous to Eq. 11.60 for $N_v(x)$. The choice of Eq. 11.117 as a definition is somewhat unfortunate in that the function $K_v(x)$ does *not* satisfy the same recurrence relations as $I_v(x)$ (cf. Exercise 11.4.4). To avoid this annoyance other authors[4] have included an additional factor of cosine $n\pi$. This permits K_v to satisfy the same recurrence relations as I_v, but it has the disadvantage of making $K_v = 0$ for $v = \frac{1}{2}$, $\frac{3}{2}, \frac{5}{2}, \ldots$.

The series expansion of $K_v(x)$ follows directly from the series form of $H_v^{(1)}(ix)$. The lowest order terms are

$$K_0(x) = -\ln x - C + \ln 2 + \cdots,$$

$$K_v(x) = 2^{v-1}(v-1)! x^{-v} + \cdots.$$

(11.119)

Because the modified Bessel function I_v is related to the Bessel function J_v, much as sinh is related to sine, I_v and the second solution K_v are sometimes referred to as hyperbolic Bessel functions.

EXAMPLE 11.4.1.   NEUTRON DIFFUSION THEORY

An illustration of the occurrence of modified Bessel functions is provided by the theory of diffusion of thermal neutrons. In the steady state the continuity equation is

$$D \, \nabla^2 \varphi - \sum_a \varphi + S = 0,$$

(11.120)

the first term representing diffusion, the second term giving the absorption losses,

[1] A discussion and comparison of notations will be found in MTOAC **1**, 207–308 (1944).
[2] Watson, Morse and Feshbach, Jeffreys and Jeffreys (without the $\pi/2$).
[3] For integral index n we take the limit as $v \to n$.
[4] Whittaker and Watson.

and the third representing the source strength. The parameter D is given by

$$D = \frac{\lambda_s}{3(1 - 2/3A)}$$

in which λ_s is the mean free path between scattering collisions. A is the atomic number of the scattering nucleus and enters here as a correction for the anisotropy of scattering in the laboratory system. The neutron flux φ is the product of neutron density times average velocity. $\sum_a$ is the macroscopic absorption cross section, the product of absorption probability per atom (σ_a) and the number of atoms per unit volume. It is assumed that the absorption is small compared to the scattering.

In this illustration let us consider the neutron source as an infinitely long line source embedded in an infinite diffusing medium. This line source is the z-axis. For the emission of S_0 neutrons per unit length per unit time

$$S = S_0\, \delta(\mathbf{r}),$$

in which $\delta(\mathbf{r})$ is a cylindrical Dirac delta function. The symmetry of the problem demands cylindrical coordinates. Because there is no dependence on z or θ the diffusion equation quickly reduces to

$$r^2 \frac{d^2\varphi}{dr^2} + r \frac{d\varphi}{dr} - r^2 \frac{\sum_a}{D} \varphi = 0 \qquad (11.121)$$

away from the line source ($r \neq 0$). Using

$$k^2 = \frac{\sum_a}{D},$$

where k^{-1} is called "diffusion length,"

$$\varphi = a_1 I_0(kr) + a_2 K_0(kr). \qquad (11.122)$$

Since $I_0(kr)$ increases exponentially for large kr [cf., the series expansion (Eq. 11.112) and Section 11.5], its coefficient a_1 must be set equal to zero; then

$$\varphi = a_2 K_0(kr). \qquad (11.123)$$

The net flow of neutrons through an area $d\boldsymbol{\sigma}$ is given by

$$-D\, \nabla\varphi \cdot d\boldsymbol{\sigma}.$$

The constant of integration a_2 may be determined by requiring that D times the integral of the negative gradient of the neutron flux around the edge of a small pillbox of unit height be equal to the production within the pillbox S_0. The box is small ($r \to 0$) to eliminate absorption and gives

$$S_0 = \lim_{r \to 0} Da_2 \int -\nabla K_0(kr) \cdot \mathbf{r}_0\, r\, d\theta, \qquad (11.124)$$

which is actually a two-dimensional form of Gauss's law (Section 1.14). Using the series form of $K_0(kr)$ this becomes

$$S_0 = Da_2 \lim_{r \to 0} \frac{2\pi r}{r} \qquad (11.125)$$

or

$$a_2 = \frac{S_0}{2\pi D}.$$

By substituting into Eq. 11.123, we have

$$\varphi = \frac{S_0}{2\pi D} K_0(kr) \tag{11.126}$$

for the complete solution of this diffusion problem.

Green's function.　A comparison with Section 8.6 will show that we have, in effect, determined a Green's function for the diffusion equation (11.120). This may be readily verified by rewriting Eq. 11.120 as

$$D \nabla^2 G(kr) - Dk^2 G(kr) = -\delta(\mathbf{r}), \tag{11.127}$$

for a unit line source (per unit length) along the z-axis. Integrating over the pillbox volume, we have

$$\int \nabla^2 G(kr)\, dv - k^2 \int G(kr)\, dv = -\frac{1}{D} \int \delta(\mathbf{r})\, dv$$

$$= -\frac{1}{D}.$$

The second integral on the left vanishes as $r \to 0$. The evaluation of the first integral on the left may be carried out by Gauss's theorem and corresponds exactly to our previous solution. The result is

$$G(kr) = \frac{1}{2\pi D} K_0(kr). \tag{11.128}$$

This is the Green's function.

If our source is now generalized to be a continuous distribution of parallel line sources described by the radial vector $\boldsymbol{\rho}$, we find the Green's function is

$$G(\mathbf{r}, \boldsymbol{\rho}) = \frac{1}{2\pi D} K_0(k|\mathbf{r} - \boldsymbol{\rho}|). \tag{11.129}$$

The resulting neutron flux is

$$\varphi(\mathbf{r}) = \int G(\mathbf{r}, \boldsymbol{\rho}) S(\boldsymbol{\rho})\, d\boldsymbol{\rho}$$

$$= \frac{1}{2\pi D} \int K_0(k|\mathbf{r} - \boldsymbol{\rho}|) S(\boldsymbol{\rho})\, d\boldsymbol{\rho}, \tag{11.130}$$

where the integration is over the plane perpendicular to the line sources and $S(\boldsymbol{\rho})$ is the source strength (per unit volume per second).

To put the modified Bessel functions $I_\nu(x)$ and $K_\nu(x)$ in proper perspective, they are introduced here.

1. These functions are solutions of the frequently encountered modified Bessel equation.

2. They are needed for specific physical problems such as diffusion problems.

3. $K_\nu(x)$ provides a Green's function.

4. $K_\nu(x)$ leads to a convenient determination of asymptotic behavior (Section 11.5).

EXERCISES

11.4.1 Show that Laplace's equation in parabolic coordinates separates into the following:
(a) A simple harmonic oscillator equation.
(b) A Bessel equation.
(c) A modified Bessel equation.

11.4.2 Show that

$$e^{(x/2)(t+1/t)} = \sum_{n=-\infty}^{\infty} I_n(x)t^n,$$

thus generating modified Bessel functions, $I_n(x)$.

11.4.3 For $\nu > -\frac{1}{2}$ show that $I_\nu(z)$ may be represented by

$$I_\nu(z) = \frac{1}{\pi^{1/2}(\nu - \frac{1}{2})!} \left(\frac{z}{2}\right)^\nu \int_0^\pi e^{\pm z\cos\theta} \sin^{2\nu}\theta \, d\theta$$

$$= \frac{1}{\pi^{1/2}(\nu - \frac{1}{2})!} \left(\frac{z}{2}\right)^\nu \int_{-1}^1 e^{\pm zp}(1 - p^2)^{\nu-1/2} \, dp$$

$$= \frac{2}{\pi^{1/2}(\nu - \frac{1}{2})!} \left(\frac{z}{2}\right)^\nu \int_0^{\pi/2} \cosh(z\cos\theta) \sin^{2\nu}\theta \, d\theta.$$

11.4.4 Show that $K_\nu(x)$ satisfies the recurrence relations

$$K_{\nu-1}(x) - K_{\nu+1}(x) = -\frac{2\nu}{x} K_\nu(x),$$

$$K_{\nu-1}(x) + K_{\nu+1}(x) = -2K_\nu'(x).$$

11.4.5 Verify that $K(x)$ is given by

$$K_\nu(x) = \frac{\pi}{2} \frac{I_{-\nu}(x) - I_\nu(x)}{\sin\nu\pi}$$

and from this show that

$$K_\nu(x) = K_{-\nu}(x).$$

11.4.6 Show that $I_\nu(x)$ and $K_\nu(x)$ satisfy the Wronskian relation

$$I_\nu(x) K_\nu'(x) - I_\nu'(x) K_\nu(x) = -\frac{1}{x}.$$

11.4.7 For $\nu > -\frac{1}{2}$ show that $K_\nu(z)$ may be represented by

$$K_\nu(z) = \frac{\pi^{1/2}}{(\nu - \frac{1}{2})!} \left(\frac{z}{2}\right)^\nu \int_0^\infty e^{-z\cosh t} \sinh^{2\nu} t \, dt \qquad -\frac{\pi}{2} < \arg z < \frac{\pi}{2}$$

$$= \frac{\pi^{1/2}}{(\nu - \frac{1}{2})!} \left(\frac{z}{2}\right)^\nu \int_1^\infty e^{-zp}(p^2 - 1)^{\nu-1/2} \, dp.$$

11.4.8 If $r = (x^2 + y^2)^{1/2}$, prove that

$$\frac{1}{r} = \frac{2}{\pi} \int_0^\infty \cos{(xt)}\, K_0(yt)\, dt.$$

11.4.9 Show that $J_\nu(x)$, $N_\nu(x)$, $I_\nu(x)$, and $K_\nu(x)$ all satisfy the fourth-order differential equation

$$\frac{d^4}{dx^4} y + \frac{2}{x} \frac{d^3}{dx^3} y - \frac{2\nu^2 + 1}{x^2} \frac{d^2}{dx^2} y + \frac{2\nu^2 + 1}{x^3} \frac{d}{dx} y + \left(\frac{\nu^4 - 4\nu^2}{x^4} - 1 \right) y = 0.$$

11.4.10 Show that $-\tfrac{1}{4} N_0(kr)$ is a possible Green's function for the Helmholtz equation in circular cylindrical coordinates

$$\nabla^2 \psi + k^2 \psi = 0$$

(no axial or azimuthal dependence).

11.4.11 The Green's functions satisfying

$$(\nabla^2 - k^2)\, G(\mathbf{r}) = -\,\delta(\mathbf{r})$$

are

$$G_1(x) = \frac{1}{2k}\, e^{-kx},$$

$$G_2(\rho) = \frac{1}{2\pi}\, K_0(k\rho),$$

$$G_3(r) = \frac{k}{4\pi}\, \frac{e^{-kr}}{kr},$$

corresponding to a plane source, a line source, and a point source respectively.

(a) By integrating the point source to form a line source show that

$$\int_\rho^\infty \frac{e^{-kr}}{(r^2 - \rho^2)^{1/2}}\, dr = K_0(k\rho)$$

or

$$\int_1^\infty \frac{e^{-\alpha u}}{(u^2 - 1)^{1/2}}\, du = \int_0^\infty e^{-\alpha \cosh t}\, dt = K_0(\alpha).$$

(b) By integrating the line source to form a plane source show that

$$\int_x^\infty \frac{K_0(k\rho)\rho\, d\rho}{(\rho^2 - x^2)^{1/2}} = \frac{\pi}{2} \frac{e^{-kx}}{k}.$$

or

$$\int_1^\infty \frac{K_0(\alpha u)u\, du}{(u^2 - 1)^{1/2}} = \frac{\pi}{2} \frac{e^{-\alpha}}{\alpha}.$$

11.4.12 Show that

$$\left(\frac{z}{2} \right)^{-n} \sum_{r=0}^\infty (-1)^r \left(\frac{z}{2} \right)^r \frac{(n - r - 1)!}{r!} = \frac{\pi}{\sin \pi n} I_{-n}(z).$$

11.4.13 Show that

(a) $\left. \dfrac{\partial I_\nu(x)}{\partial \nu} \right|_{\nu=0} = -K_0(x),$

(b) $\left. \dfrac{\partial K_\nu(x)}{\partial \nu} \right|_{\nu=0} = 0.$

11.5 Asymptotic Expansions

Stokes's method.   If $Z_\nu(x)$, a solution of Bessel's equation is replaced by $x^{-1/2}\, y(x)$, then $y(x)$ satisfies the equation

$$y'' + \left(1 - \frac{\nu^2 - \tfrac{1}{4}}{x^2} \right) y = 0. \tag{11.131}$$

For large values of $x(x \gg v)$, this becomes

$$y_1'' + y_1 = 0, \tag{11.132}$$

with the familiar solutions

$$y_1 = a_0 \sin x + b_0 \cos x. \tag{11.133}$$

We may improve the approximation (still for large x) by replacing the constants a_0 and b_0 by a series of negative powers of x,

$$a_0 \to \sum_{n=0}^{\infty} a_n x^{-n},$$

$$b_0 \to \sum_{n=0}^{\infty} b_n x^{-n}.$$

This means that we must look for a solution of the form

$$y(x) = \sum_{n=0}^{\infty} a_n x^{-n} \sin x + \sum_{n=0}^{\infty} b_n x^{-n} \cos x. \tag{11.134}$$

By substituting Eq. 11.134 into the original differential equation (11.131), we may obtain

$$y(x) = \left[a_0 - \frac{v^2 - \frac{1}{4}}{2x} b_0 - \frac{(v^2 - \frac{1}{4})(v^2 - \frac{9}{4})}{2 \cdot (2x)^2} a_0 + \cdots \right] \sin x$$

$$+ \left[b_0 + \frac{v^2 - \frac{1}{4}}{2x} a_0 - \frac{(v^2 - \frac{1}{4})(v^2 - \frac{9}{4})}{2 \cdot (2x)^2} b_0 + \cdots \right] \cos x. \tag{11.135}$$

This process may be continued as far as desired. It is worth noting that this form terminates and yields an exact result for $v = \pm\frac{1}{2}, \pm\frac{3}{2}, \pm\frac{5}{2}, \ldots$, etc. These exact results are the spherical Bessel functions of Section 11.6.

With the two constants a_0 and b_0 Stokes's method yields a general solution for Bessel's equation for large values of the variable x. However, the usefulness of this solution is limited in that it has not yet been related or joined to the standard solutions $J_v(x)$ and $N_v(x)$. In particular, the relative contributions of $\sin x$ and $\cos x$ are undetermined. This joining or determination of the phase may be carried out by using the method of steepest descent (Section 7.4) to determine the leading terms in the asymptotic expansions of $J_v(x)$ and $N_v(x)$.

Expansion of an integral representation, $K_v(z)$. As an alternate and direct approach, consider the integral representation (Exercise 11.4.7)

$$K_v(z) = \frac{\pi^{1/2}}{(v - \frac{1}{2})!} \left(\frac{z}{2} \right)^v \int_1^{\infty} e^{-zx}(x^2 - 1)^{v - 1/2} dx, \qquad v > -\frac{1}{2}. \tag{11.136}$$

For the present let us take z to be real, although Eq. 11.136 may be established for $-\pi/2 < \arg z < \pi/2$. We have two problems: first, to show that K, as given in Eq. 11.136, actually satisfies the modified Bessel equation (11.108); second, to show that it has the proper normalization.

1. That Eq. 11.136 is a solution of the modified Bessel equation may be verified by direct substitution. We obtain

$$z^{v+1} \int_1^\infty \frac{d}{dx} \left[e^{-zx}(x^2 - 1)^{v+1/2} \right] dx = 0,$$

which transforms the combined integrand into the derivative of a function that vanishes at both end points. The rejection of the possibility that this solution contains I_v constitutes Exercise 11.5.2.

2. The normalization may be verified by substituting $x = 1 + t/z$.

$$\frac{\pi^{1/2}}{(v - \frac{1}{2})!} \left(\frac{z}{2}\right)^v \int_1^\infty e^{-zx}(x^2 - 1)^{v-1/2} dx$$

$$= \frac{\pi^{1/2}}{(v - \frac{1}{2})!} \left(\frac{z}{2}\right)^v e^{-z} \int_0^\infty e^{-t} \left(\frac{t^2}{z^2} + \frac{2t}{z}\right)^{v-1/2} \frac{dt}{z}$$

$$= \frac{\pi^{1/2}}{(v - \frac{1}{2})!} \frac{e^{-z}}{2^v z^v} \int_0^\infty e^{-t} t^{2v-1} \left(1 + \frac{2z}{t}\right)^{v-1/2} dt. \qquad (11.137)$$

This substitution has changed the limits of integration to a more convenient range and has isolated the negative exponential dependence, e^{-z}. The last integral in Eq. 11.137 may be evaluated for $z = 0$ to yielding $(2v - 1)!$ Then, using the duplication formula (Section 10.4),

$$\lim_{z \to 0} K_v(z) = \frac{(v - 1)! 2^{v-1}}{z^v}, \qquad v > 0, \qquad (11.138)$$

in agreement with Eq. 11.119, thus checking the normalization.[1]

Now to develop an asymptotic series for $K(z)$. Equation 11.136 may be rewritten (for large z) as

$$K_v(z) = \sqrt{\frac{\pi}{2z}} \frac{e^{-z}}{(v - \frac{1}{2})!} \int_0^\infty e^{-t} t^{v-1/2} \left(1 + \frac{t}{2z}\right)^{v-1/2} dt.$$

We expand $(1 + t/2z)^{v-1/2}$ by the binomial theorem to obtain

$$K_v(z) = \sqrt{\frac{\pi}{2z}} \frac{e^{-z}}{(v - \frac{1}{2})!} \sum_{r=0}^\infty \frac{(v - \frac{1}{2})!}{r!(v - r - \frac{1}{2})!} (2z)^{-r} \int_0^\infty e^{-t} t^{v+r-1/2} dt. \qquad (11.139)$$

Term-by-term integration (valid for asymptotic series) yields the desired asymptotic expansion of $K_v(z)$.

$$K_v(z) = \sqrt{\frac{\pi}{2z}} e^{-z} \left[1 + \frac{(4v^2 - 1)}{1!8z} + \frac{(4v^2 - 1)(4v^2 - 3^2)}{2!(8z)^2} + \cdots \right]. \qquad (11.140)$$

Although the integral of Eq. 11.136, integrating along the real axis, was convergent only for $-\pi/2 < \arg z < \pi/2$, Eq. 11.140 may be extended to $-\pi < \arg z < \pi$. Considered as an infinite series, Eq. 11.140 is actually divergent. However, this series is asymptotic in the sense that for large enough z, $K_v(z)$ may be approximated

---

[1] For $v = 0$ the integral diverges logarithmically in agreement with the logarithmic divergence of $K_0(z)$ (Section 11.4).

to any fixed degree of accuracy. (Cf. Section 5.10 for a definition and discussion of asymptotic series.)

With the asymptotic expansion of $K_\nu(z)$ developed, we can obtain expansions for all the other Bessel and hyperbolic Bessel functions by the defining relations:

1. From

$$\frac{\pi}{2} i^{\nu+1} H_\nu^{(1)}(iz) = K_\nu(z) \tag{11.141}$$

we have

$$H_\nu^{(1)}(z) = \sqrt{\frac{2}{\pi z}}\, e^{-i(\pi/2)(\nu+1/2)} e^{iz}\left[1 + i\frac{(4\nu^2 - 1^2)}{8z}\right.$$
$$\left. - \frac{(4\nu^2 - 1^2)(4\nu^2 - 3^2)}{2!(8z)^2} - \cdots\right], \qquad -\frac{\pi}{2} < \arg z < \frac{\pi}{2}. \tag{11.142}$$

2. The second Hankel function is just the complex conjugate of the first.

$$H_\nu^{(2)}(z) = \sqrt{\frac{2}{\pi z}}\, e^{i(\pi/2)(\nu+1/2)} e^{-iz}$$
$$\times\left[1 - i\frac{4\nu^2 - 1^2}{8z} - \frac{(4\nu^2 - 1^2)(4\nu^2 - 3^2)}{2!(8z)^2} - \cdots\right]. \tag{11.143}$$

An alternate derivation of the asymptotic behavior of the Hankel functions appears in Section 7.4 as an application of the method of steepest descents.

3. Since $J_\nu(z)$ is the real part of $H_\nu^{(1)}(z)$,

$$J_\nu(z) = \sqrt{\frac{2}{\pi z}}\left\{\cos\left[z - \left(\nu + \frac{1}{2}\right)\frac{\pi}{2}\right]\left[1 - \frac{(4\nu^2 - 1^2)(4\nu^2 - 3^2)}{2!(8z)^2} + \cdots\right]\right.$$
$$\left. + \sin\left[z - \left(\nu + \frac{1}{2}\right)\frac{\pi}{2}\right]\left(-\frac{4\nu^2 - 1^2}{8z} + \cdots\right)\right\}. \tag{11.144}$$

4. The Neumann function is the imaginary part of $H^{(1)}(z)$, or

$$N_\nu(z) = \sqrt{\frac{2}{\pi z}}\left\{\sin\left[z - \left(\nu + \frac{1}{2}\right)\frac{\pi}{2}\right]\left[1 - \frac{(4\nu^2 - 1^2)(4\nu^2 - 3^2)}{2!(8z)^2} + \cdots\right]\right.$$
$$\left. + \cos\left[z - \left(\nu + \frac{1}{2}\right)\frac{\pi}{2}\right]\left(\frac{4\nu^2 - 1^2}{8z} - \cdots\right)\right\}. \tag{11.145}$$

5. Finally, the regular hyperbolic or modified Bessel function $I_\nu(z)$ is given by

$$I_\nu(z) = i^{-\nu} J_\nu(iz) \tag{11.146}$$

or

$$I_\nu(z) = \frac{e^z}{\sqrt{2\pi z}}\left[1 - \frac{4\nu^2 - 1^2}{1!(8z)} + \frac{(4\nu^2 - 1^2)(4\nu^2 - 3^2)}{2!(8z)^2} - \cdots\right]. \tag{11.147}$$

This completes our determination of the asymptotic expansions. However, it is perhaps worth noting the primary characteristics. Apart from the ubiquitous

$z^{-1/2}$, J_ν and N_ν behave as cosine and sine, respectively. The zeros are *almost* evenly spaced at intervals of π; the spacing becomes exactly π in the limit as $z \to \infty$. The Hankel functions have been defined to behave like the imaginary exponentials, and the modified Bessel functions, I_ν and K_ν, go into the positive and negative exponentials. This asymptotic behavior may be sufficient to eliminate immediately one of these functions as a solution for a physical problem. Indeed, in Section 11.4 this was the basis for eliminating I_0 as a solution in the infinite medium neutron diffusion problem.

As pointed out in Section 11.2, the asymptotic forms may be used to evaluate the various Wronskian formulas (cf. Exercise 11.5.4).

EXERCISES

11.5.1 Show that the Stokes's method leads to a series solution of Bessel's equation that is asymptotic in the sense of Section 5.10.

11.5.2 In checking the normalization of the integral representation of $K_\nu(z)$ (Eq. 11.136), we assumed that $I_\nu(z)$ was not present. How do we know that the integral representation (Eq. 11.136) does not yield $K_\nu(z) + \varepsilon\, I_\nu(z)$ with $\varepsilon \neq 0$?

11.5.3 (a) Show that

$$y(z) = z^\nu \int e^{-zt}(t^2 - 1)^{\nu - 1/2}\, dt$$

satisfies the modified Bessel equation, provided the contour is chosen so that

$$e^{-zt}(t^2 - 1)^{\nu + 1/2}$$

has the same value at the initial and final points of the contour.

(b) Verify that the contours shown in Fig. 11.10 are suitable for this problem.

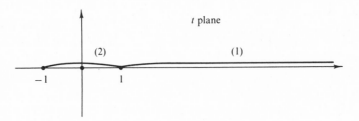

FIG. 11.10   Modified Bessel function contours

11.5.4 Use the asymptotic expansions to verify the following Wronskian formulas:

(a) $J_\nu(x)\, J_{-\nu-1}(x) + J_{-\nu}(x)\, J_{\nu+1}(x) = -\dfrac{2 \sin \nu\pi}{\pi x}$,

(b) $J_\nu(x)\, N_{\nu+1}(x) - J_{\nu+1}(x)\, N_\nu(x) = -\dfrac{2}{\pi x}$,

(c) $J_\nu(x)\, H^{(2)}_{\nu-1}(x) - J_{\nu-1}(x)\, H^{(2)}_\nu(x) = \dfrac{2}{i\pi x}$,

(d) $I_\nu(x)\, K'_\nu(x) - I'_\nu(x)\, K_\nu(x) = -\dfrac{1}{x}$,

(e) $I_\nu(x)\, K_{\nu+1}(x) + I_{\nu+1}(x)\, K_\nu(x) = \dfrac{1}{x}$.

11.5.5 In Exercise 11.5.4e the verification that the constant is unity does not depend on ν. Does this mean that

$$I_\nu(x)\, K_{\nu+2}(x) + I_{\nu+2}(x)\, K_\nu(x) = \frac{1}{x}\ ?$$

Check this by the asymptotic behavior. What has gone wrong?

11.6 Spherical Bessel Functions

When the Helmholtz equation in spherical polar (or conical) coordinates is separated, the radial equation has the form

$$r^2\,\frac{d^2 R}{dr^2} + 2r\,\frac{dR}{dr} + [k^2 r^2 - n(n+1)]R = 0; \tag{11.148}$$

k enters from the Helmhotz equation and the integer n is a separation constant which often has the physical interpretation of angular momentum. Clearly, this is *not* Bessel's equation, but if we substitute

$$R(kr) = \frac{Z(kr)}{(kr)^{1/2}}$$

Eq. 11.148 becomes

$$r^2\,\frac{d^2 Z}{dr^2} + r\,\frac{dZ}{dr} + \left[k^2 r^2 - \left(n+\frac{1}{2}\right)^2\right]Z = 0, \tag{11.149}$$

which *is* Bessel's equation. Z is a Bessel function of order $n + \frac{1}{2}$ (n and integer). Because of the importance of spherical coordinates this combination,

$$\frac{Z_{n+1/2}(kr)}{(kr)^{1/2}},$$

occurs quite often.

Definitions.   It is convenient to label these functions spherical Bessel functions with the following defining equations:

$$j_n(x) = \sqrt{\frac{\pi}{2x}}\, J_{n+1/2}(x),$$

$$n_n(x) = \sqrt{\frac{\pi}{2x}}\, N_{n+1/2}(x) = (-1)^{n+1}\sqrt{\frac{\pi}{2x}}\, J_{-n-1/2}(x),\quad [1]$$

$$h^{(1)}_n(x) = \sqrt{\frac{\pi}{2x}}\, H^{(1)}_{n+1/2}(x) = j_n(x) + i\,n_n(x), \tag{11.150}$$

$$h^{(2)}_n(x) = \sqrt{\frac{\pi}{2x}}\, H^{(2)}_{n+1/2}(x) = j_n(x) - i\,n_n(x).$$

[1] This is possible because $\cos(n+\tfrac{1}{2})\pi = 0$.

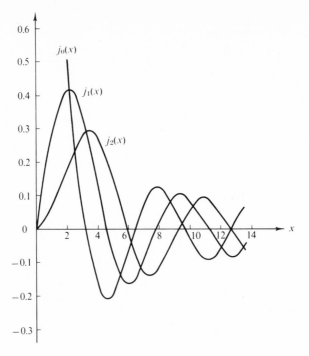

FIG. 11.11   Spherical Bessel functions

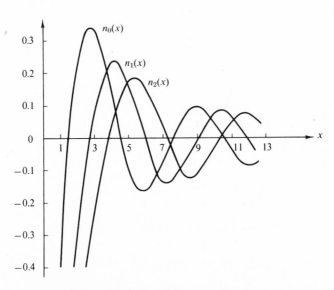

FIG. 11.12   Spherical Neumann functions

These spherical Bessel functions can be expressed in series form by using the series (Eq. 11.5) for J_n, replacing n with $n + \frac{1}{2}$.

$$J_{n+1/2}(x) = \sum_{s=0}^{\infty} \frac{(-1)^s}{s!(s + n + \frac{1}{2})!} \left(\frac{x}{2}\right)^{2s+n+1/2} \tag{11.151}$$

Using the Legendre duplication formula,

$$z!(z + \tfrac{1}{2})! = 2^{-2z-1}\pi^{1/2}(2z + 1)!, \tag{11.152}$$

we have

$$j_n(x) = \sqrt{\frac{\pi}{2x}} \sum_{s=0}^{\infty} \frac{(-1)^s 2^{2s+2n+1}(s + n)!}{\pi^{1/2}(2s + 2n + 1)!s!} \left(\frac{x}{2}\right)^{2s+n+1/2}$$

$$= 2^n x^n \sum_{s=0}^{\infty} \frac{(-1)^s(s + n)!}{s!(2s + 2n + 1)!} x^{2s}. \tag{11.153}$$

Now $N_{n+1/2}(x) = (-1)^{n+1} J_{-n-1/2}(x)$ and from Eq. 11.5 we find that

$$J_{-n-1/2}(x) = \sum_{s=0}^{\infty} \frac{(-1)^s}{s!(s - n - \frac{1}{2})!} \left(\frac{x}{2}\right)^{2s-n-1/2} \tag{11.154}$$

This yields

$$n_n(x) = (-1)^{n+1} \frac{2^n \pi^{1/2}}{x^{n+1}} \sum_{s=0}^{\infty} \frac{(-1)^s}{s!(s - n - \frac{1}{2})!} \left(\frac{x}{2}\right)^{2s} \tag{11.155}$$

The Legendre duplication formula can be used again to give

$$n_n(x) = \frac{(-1)^{n+1}}{2^n x^{n+1}} \sum_{s=0}^{\infty} \frac{(-1)^s(s - n)!}{s!(2s - 2n)!} x^{2s}. \tag{11.156}$$

However, this is awkward to handle for n, a positive integer, because of the factorials in both numerator and denominator. These spherical Bessel functions are closely related to the trigonometric functions, as may be seen by considering the special case, $n = 0$. We find

$$j_0(x) = \sum_{s=0}^{\infty} \frac{(-1)^s}{(2s + 1)!} x^{2s}$$

$$= \frac{\sin x}{x}, \tag{11.157}$$

whereas for n_0 Eq. 11.156 yields

$$n_0(x) = -\frac{\cos x}{x}. \tag{11.158}$$

From the definition of the spherical Hankel functions (Eq. 11.150),

$$h_0^{(1)}(x) = \frac{1}{x}(\sin x - i \cos x) = -\frac{i}{x} e^{ix}$$

$$h_0^{(2)}(x) = \frac{1}{x}(\sin x + i \cos x) = \frac{i}{x} e^{-ix}. \tag{11.159}$$

The relationship to the trigonometric functions may perhaps best be seen by considering the asymptotic series of Section 11.5. For $v = \pm\frac{1}{2}, \pm\frac{3}{2}, \pm\frac{5}{2}$, etc., the asymptotic series terminate, giving finite combinations of trigonometric functions.

Recurrence relations.   The recurrence relations to which we now turn provide a convenient way of developing the higher-order spherical Bessel functions. These recurrence relations may be derived from the series, but as with the modified Bessel functions it is easier to substitute into the known recurrence relations (Eqs. 11.10 and 11.12). This gives

$$f_{n-1}(x) + f_{n+1}(x) = \frac{2n+1}{x} f_n(x), \tag{11.160}$$

$$n f_{n-1}(x) - (n+1) f_{n+1}(x) = (2n+1) f_n'(x). \tag{11.161}$$

Rearranging these relations (or substituting into Eqs. 11.15 and 11.17), we obtain

$$\frac{d}{dx} [x^{n+1} f_n(x)] = x^{n+1} f_{n-1}(x), \tag{11.162}$$

$$\frac{d}{dx} [x^{-n} f_n(x)] = -x^{-n} f_{n+1}(x). \tag{11.163}$$

Here f_n may represent j_n, n_n, $h_n^{(1)}$, or $h_n^{(2)}$.
  Applying Eq. 11.163, we quickly get

$$j_1(x) = \frac{\sin x}{x^2} - \frac{\cos x}{x},$$

$$j_2(x) = \left(\frac{3}{x^3} - \frac{1}{x}\right) \sin x - \frac{3}{x^2} \cos x, \tag{11.164}$$

$$n_1(x) = -\frac{\cos x}{x^2} - \frac{\sin x}{x},$$

$$n_2(x) = -\left(\frac{3}{x^3} - \frac{1}{x}\right) \cos x - \frac{3}{x^2} \sin x, \text{ etc.} \tag{11.165}$$

By mathematical induction we may establish the formulas

$$j_n(x) = (-1)^n x^n \left(\frac{d}{x\,dx}\right)^n \left(\frac{\sin x}{x}\right), \tag{11.166}$$

$$n_n(x) = -(-1)^n x^n \left(\frac{d}{x\,dx}\right)^n \left(\frac{\cos x}{x}\right). \tag{11.167}$$

We note that the spherical Bessel functions $j_n(x)$ and $n_n(x)$ can always be expressed as $\sin x$ and $\cos x$ with coefficients that are polynomials involving negative powers of x. For the spherical Hankel functions

$$h_n^{(1)}(x) = -i(-1)^n x^n \left(\frac{d}{x\,dx}\right)^n \left(\frac{e^{ix}}{x}\right)$$

$$h_n^{(2)}(x) = i(-1)^n x^n \left(\frac{d}{x\,dx}\right)^n \left(\frac{e^{-ix}}{x}\right). \tag{11.168}$$

Orthogonality. We may take the orthogonality integral for the ordinary Bessel functions (Eq. 11.59),

$$\int_0^1 J_\nu(ax) J_\nu(bx) x \, dx = \frac{1}{2} \delta_{ab} \left[\frac{d}{d(ax)} J_\nu(ax) \Big|_{x=1} \right]^2, \tag{11.169}$$

and substitute in the expression for j_n to obtain

$$\int_0^1 j_n(ax) j_n(bx) x^2 \, dx = \frac{1}{2} \delta_{ab} \left\{ \frac{d}{dx} [x^{1/2} j_n(x)]_{x=a} \right\}^2. \tag{11.170}$$

Here a and b are roots of J_ν (or j_n).

This represents orthogonality with respect to the roots of the Bessel functions. An illustration of this sort of orthogonality is provided later in this section by the problem of a particle in a sphere. Equation 11.170 guarantees orthogonality of the wave functions $j_n(r)$ for fixed n. (If n varies, the spherical harmonic will provide orthogonality.) Another form, orthogonality with respect to the indices, may be developed as follows. From Eq. 11.148, with $x = kr$,

$$x^2 j_n'' + 2x j_n' + [x^2 - n(n+1)] j_n = 0,$$
$$x^2 j_m'' + 2x j_m' + [x^2 - m(m+1)] j_m = 0. \tag{11.171}$$

We multiply the first equation by j_m, the second by j_n, and subtract:

$$[n(n+1) - m(m+1)] j_n j_m = x^2 (j_n'' j_m - j_n j_m'') + 2x(j_n' j_m - j_n j_m')$$

$$= \frac{d}{dx} [x^2 (j_n' j_m - j_n j_m')]. \tag{11.172}$$

The last equation is an expression of the Sturm-Liouville form of Eq. 11.148 (cf. Section 9.1). Integrating from zero to infinity, we obtain

$$[n(n+1) - m(m+1)] \int_0^\infty j_m(x) j_n(x) \, dx = \left| x^2 (j_n' j_m - j_n j_m') \right|_0^\infty. \tag{11.173}$$

The right-hand side clearly vanishes for $x = 0$ (m, n are assumed to be non-negative integers).

As $x \to \infty$, it will also vanish provided $(n - m)$ is even, as shown by examination of the asymptotic forms

$$j_n(x) \to \frac{1}{x} \sin\left(x - \frac{n\pi}{2}\right),$$

$$j_n'(x) \to \frac{1}{x} \cos\left(x - \frac{n\pi}{2}\right).$$

We find

$$x^2(j_n' j_m - j_n j_m') \to \cos\left(x - \frac{n\pi}{2}\right) \sin\left(x - \frac{m\pi}{2}\right) - \sin\left(x - \frac{n\pi}{2}\right) \cos\left(x - \frac{m\pi}{2}\right) + O(x^{-1})$$

$$= \sin \frac{\pi}{2}(n - m) + O(x^{-1}).$$

Therefore

$$\int_0^{\infty} j_m(x)\, j_n(x)\, dx = \frac{\sin[(n - m)\pi/2]}{n(n + 1) - m(m + 1)}. \tag{11.174}$$

The right-hand side of Eq. 11.174 vanishes for $(n - m)$ even. If $(n - m)$ is odd, one of the spherical Bessel functions, say j_m, will be odd, whereas the other will be even,

$$j_p(x) = (-1)^p j_p(-x). \tag{11.175}$$

Hence the integral will vanish if we extend the lower limit to $-\infty$. We then have

$$\int_{-\infty}^{\infty} j_m(x)\, j_n(x)\, dx = 0, \qquad m \neq n, \qquad m, n \geqslant 0. \tag{11.176}$$

If $m = n$ (cf. Exercise 11.6.8), we have

$$\int_{-\infty}^{\infty} [j_n(x)]^2\, dx = \frac{\pi}{2n + 1}. \tag{11.177}$$

EXAMPLE 11.6.1. PARTICLE IN A SPHERE

An illustration of the use of the spherical Bessel functions is provided by the problem of a quantum mechanical particle in a sphere of radius a. Quantum theory requires that the wave function ψ, describing our particle, satisfy

$$-\frac{\hbar^2}{2m}\, \nabla^2 \psi = E\psi, \tag{11.178}$$

and the boundary conditions (a) $\psi(r \leqslant a)$ remains finite, (b) $\psi(a) = 0$. This corresponds to a potential $V = 0$, $r \leqslant a$, and $V = \infty$, $r > a$. Here $\hbar$ is Planck's constant (divided by 2π), m, the mass of our particle, and E, its energy. Let us determine the *minimum* value of the energy for which our wave equation has an acceptable solution. Equation 11.178 is just Helmholtz' equation with a radial part (cf. Section 2.5 for separation of variables)

$$\frac{d^2 R}{dr^2} + \frac{2}{r}\frac{dR}{dr} + \left[\frac{2mE}{\hbar^2} - \frac{n(n + 1)}{r^2}\right] R = 0. \tag{11.179}$$

Hence by Eq. 11.148, with $n = 0$,

$$R = A j_0\left(\frac{\sqrt{2mE}}{\hbar}\, r\right) + B n_0\left(\frac{\sqrt{2mE}}{\hbar}\, r\right) \tag{11.180}$$

We choose the index $n = 0$, for any angular dependence would raise the energy. The spherical Neumann function is rejected because of its divergent behavior at the origin. To satisfy the second boundary condition (for all angles) we require

$$\frac{\sqrt{2mE}}{\hbar}\, a = \alpha,$$

where α is a root of j_0, that is, $j_0(\alpha) = 0$. This has the effect of limiting the allowable energies to a certain discrete set or, in other words, application of boundary condition (b) quantizes the energy E. The smallest α is the first zero of j_0,

$$\alpha = \pi$$

and

$$E_{\min} = \frac{\pi^2 h^2}{2ma^2} = \frac{h^2}{8ma^2}, \qquad (11.181)$$

which means that for any finite sphere the particle will have a positive minimum or zero-point energy. This is an illustration of the Heisenberg uncertainty principle.

The spherical Bessel functions will enter again in connection with spherical waves, but further consideration is postponed until the corresponding angular functions, the Legendre functions, have been introduced.

EXERCISES

11.6.1 Show that one of the differential equations resulting from the separation of the Helmholtz equation,

$$\nabla^2 \psi + k^2 \psi = 0,$$

in conical coordinates is the spherical Bessel equation.

11.6.2 (a) Derive the recurrence relations

$$f_{n-1}(x) + f_{n+1}(x) = \frac{2n+1}{x} f_n(x),$$

$$n f_{n-1}(x) - (n+1) f_{n+1}(x) = (2n+1) f_n'(x),$$

satisfied by the spherical Bessel functions, $j_n(x)$, $n_n(x)$, $h_n^{(1)}(x)$, and $h_n^{(2)}(x)$.

(b) Show, from these two recurrence relations, that the spherical Bessel function $f_n(x)$ satisfies the differential equation

$$x^2 f_n''(x) + 2x f_n'(x) + [x^2 - n(n+1)] f_n(x) = 0.$$

11.6.3 Prove by mathematical induction that

$$j_n(x) = (-1)^n x^n \left(\frac{d}{x\,dx}\right)^n \left(\frac{\sin x}{x}\right)$$

for n an arbitrary non-negative integer.

11.6.4 The Fresnel integrals occurring in diffraction theory are given by

$$x(t) = \int_0^t \cos(v^2)\,dv,$$

$$y(t) = \int_0^t \sin(v^2)\,dv.$$

Show that these integrals may be expanded in series of spherical Bessel functions,

$$x(s) = \frac{1}{2} \int_0^s j_{-1}(u) u^{1/2}\,du = s^{1/2} \sum_{n=0}^{\infty} j_{2n}(s),$$

$$y(s) = \frac{1}{2} \int_0^s j_0(u) u^{1/2}\,du = s^{1/2} \sum_{n=0}^{\infty} j_{2n+1}(s).$$

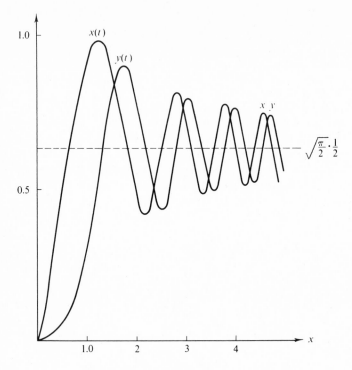

FIG. 11.13 Fresnel integrals

11.6.5 Show that if

$$n_n(x) = \sqrt{\frac{\pi}{2x}}\, N_{n+1/2}(x),$$

it automatically equals

$$(-1)^{n+1} \sqrt{\frac{\pi}{2x}}\, J_{-n-1/2}(x).$$

11.6.6 From the discussion of orthogonality of the spherical Bessel functions, show that a Wronskian relation for $j_n(x)$ and $n_n(x)$ is

$$j_n(x)\, n_n'(x) - j_n'(x)\, n_n(x) = \frac{1}{x^2}.$$

11.6.7 From Eq. 11.173 show that Eq. 11.174 follows and also that

$$\int_0^{\infty} J_\mu(x)\, J_\nu(x)\, \frac{dx}{x} = \frac{2}{\pi} \frac{\sin[(\mu - \nu)\pi/2]}{\mu^2 - \nu^2}, \qquad \mu + \nu > -1.$$

11.6.8 Derive Eq. 11.177.

$$\int_{-\infty}^{\infty} [j_n(x)]^2\, dx = \frac{\pi}{2n+1}.$$

11.6.9 Use the integral representations of $J_\nu(x)$,

$$J_\nu(x) = \frac{1}{\pi^{1/2}(\nu - \tfrac{1}{2})!} \left(\frac{x}{2}\right)^\nu \int_{-1}^{1} e^{\pm ixp}(1 - p^2)^{\nu - 1/2}\, dp,$$

to show that the spherical Bessel functions $j_n(x)$ are expressible in terms of trigonometric functions; that is,

$$j_0(x) = \frac{\sin x}{x},$$

$$j_1(x) = \frac{\sin x}{x^2} - \frac{\cos x}{x}.$$

11.6.10 Defining the spherical modified Bessel functions by

$$i_n(x) = \sqrt{\frac{\pi}{2x}}\, I_{n+1/2}(x),$$

$$k_n(x) = \sqrt{\frac{2}{\pi x}}\, K_{n+1/2}(x),$$

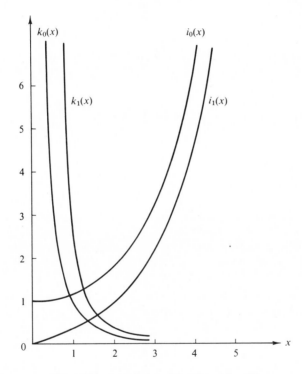

FIG. 11.14 Spherical modified Bessel functions

show that

$$i_0(x) = \frac{\sinh x}{x}$$

$$k_0(x) = \frac{e^{-x}}{x}.$$

11.6.11 Show that the Wronskian of the spherical modified Bessel functions is given by

$$i_n(x)\, k_n'(x) - i_n'(x)\, k_n(x) = -\frac{1}{x^2}.$$

11.6.12 Show that the spherical modified Bessel functions satisfy the following relations:

(a) $i_n(x) = i^{-n} j_n(ix)$,

  $k_n(x) = -i^n h_n^{(1)}(ix)$,

(b) $i_{n+1}(x) = x^n \dfrac{d}{dx}(x^{-n} i_n)$,

  $k_{n+1}(x) = -x^n \dfrac{d}{dx}(x^{-n} k_n)$,

(c) $i_n(x) = x^n \left(\dfrac{d}{x\,dx}\right)^n \dfrac{\sinh x}{x}$,

  $k_n(x) = (-1)^n x^n \left(\dfrac{d}{x\,dx}\right)^n \dfrac{e^{-x}}{x}$.

11.6.13 (a) Show that the parity of $i_n(x)$ is $(-1)^n$.
(b) Show that $k_n(x)$ has no definite parity.

11.6.14 Set up the orthogonality integral for $j_L(kr)$ in a sphere of radius R with the boundary condition

$$j_L(kR) = 0.$$

The result is used in classifying electromagnetic radiation according to its angular momentum.

11.6.15 Verify

$$h_n^{(1)}(x)\,h_n^{(2)\prime}(x) - h_n^{(1)\prime}(x)\,h_n^{(2)}(x) = -\frac{2i}{x^2}.$$

11.6.16 Show that $x^{-1}\cos\sqrt{x^2 - 2xt}$ and $x^{-1}\sin\sqrt{x^2 + 2xt}$ *generate* the spherical Bessel functions according to the relations

(a) $x^{-1}\cos\sqrt{x^2 - 2xt} = \displaystyle\sum_{n=0}^{\infty} \frac{1}{n!} j_{n-1}(x) t^n$

(b) $x^{-1}\sin\sqrt{x^2 + 2xt} = \displaystyle\sum_{n-0}^{\infty} \frac{(-1)^n}{n!} n_{n-1}(x) t^n$, with $|t| < \dfrac{|x|}{2}$.

11.6.17 Show that the modified spherical Bessel functions, $i_n(x)$, are generated by

$$x^{-1}\cosh\sqrt{x^2 + 2ixt} = \sum_{n-0}^{\infty} \frac{i^n}{n!} i_{n-1}(x) t^n, \qquad \text{with } |t| < \frac{|x|}{2}.$$

11.6.18 Verify that, within the factor of $\pi/2x$, j_0, j_1, n_0, and n_1 are given by the asymptotic forms of J_ν and N_ν; $\nu = \frac{1}{2}, \frac{3}{2}$ (Eqs. 11.144 and 11.145).

REFERENCES

WATSON, G. N., *A Treatise on the Theory of Bessel Functions.* 2nd Ed. Cambridge: Cambridge University Press (1952). This is the definitive text on Bessel functions and their properties. Although difficult reading, it is invaluable as the ultimate reference.

RELTON, F. E., *Applied Bessel Functions.* London: Blackie and Son (1946). A very readable short volume. Perhaps the best reference for the beginning student.

See also the references listed at the end of Chapter 13.

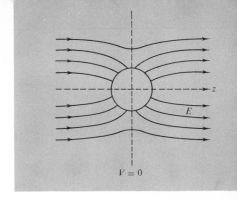

$V = 0$

CHAPTER 12

LEGENDRE FUNCTIONS

12.1 Generating Function

The Legendre differential equation has already been encountered in the separation of variables for Laplace's equation, Helmholtz' equation, and similar differential equations in spherical polar coordinates and also in oblate and prolate spheroidal coordinates. In Section 9.1 the Legendre equation was shown to be self-adjoint, and, as a consequence, the (undetermined) solutions were orthogonal.

The polynomial solutions were actually constructed in Section 9.3 by the Schmidt process. However, it was not proved that this process would generate all of the Legendre polynomials nor that these polynomials were actually solutions of Legendre's equation.

Physical basis—electrostatics. As in Bessel functions, it is convenient to introduce the Legendre polynomials by means of a generating function. However, a direct physical interpretation is possible. Consider an electric charge q placed on the z-axis at $z = a$. As shown in Fig. 12.1, the electrostatic potential of charge q is

$$\varphi = \frac{1}{4\pi\varepsilon_0} \cdot \frac{q}{r_1} \text{ (mks units)} \tag{12.1}$$

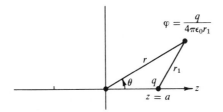

$$\varphi = \frac{q}{4\pi\epsilon_0 r_1}$$

FIG. 12.1 Electrostatic potential. Charge q displaced from origin

417

Our problem is to express the electrostatic potential in terms of the spherical polar coordinates r and θ (the coordinate φ is absent because of symmetry about the z-axis). Using the law of cosines, we obtain

$$\varphi = \frac{q}{4\pi\varepsilon_0}\,(r^2 + a^2 - 2ar\cos\theta)^{-1/2}. \tag{12.2}$$

Legendre polynomials.   Consider the base of $r > a$ or, more precisely, $r^2 > |a^2 - 2ar\cos\theta|$. The radical may be expanded by the binomial series to give

$$\varphi = \frac{q}{4\pi\varepsilon_0 r}\sum_{n=0}^{\infty} P_n(\cos\theta)\left(\frac{a}{r}\right)^n, \tag{12.3}$$

a series of powers of (a/r) with the coefficient of the nth power denoted by $P_n\,(\cos\theta)$. The P_n are the Legendre polynomials (Fig. 12.2) and may be defined by

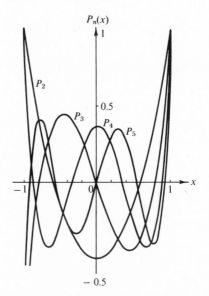

FIG. 12.2   Legendre polynomials, $P_0(x)$, $P_1(x)$, $P_2(x)$ and $P_3(x)$

$$g(t, x) = (1 - 2xt + t^2)^{-1/2} = \sum_{n=0}^{\infty} P_n(x)t^n, \qquad |t| < 1. \tag{12.4}$$

This is our generating function. In the next section it is shown that $|P_n\,(\cos\theta)| \leqslant 1$, which means that the series expansion (Eq. 12.4) is convergent for $|t| < 1$.[1]

Actually since Eq. 12.4 defines the Legendre polynomials, $P_n(x)$, convergence of the series is not necessary. We can still obtain the explicit values of the polynomials and develop useful relations between them even when the series diverges. However, the property of convergence is convenient in order to be able to exploit the properties of power series (Section 5.7).

[1] Note that the series in Eq. 12.3 is convergent for $r > a$ even though the binomial expansion involved is valid only for $r > (a^2 + 2ar)^{1/2}$, $\cos\theta = -1$.

Using the binomial theorem (Section 5.6), we expand the generating function as follows:

$$(1 - 2xt + t^2)^{-1/2} = \sum_{n=0}^{\infty} \frac{(n - \frac{1}{2})!}{n!(-\frac{1}{2})!} (2xt - t^2)^n. \tag{12.5}$$

Binomial expansion of the $(2xt - t^2)^n$ factor yields the double series

$$(1 - 2xt + t^2)^{-1/2} = \sum_{n=0}^{\infty} \frac{(n - \frac{1}{2})!}{n!(-\frac{1}{2})!} t^n \sum_{k=0}^{n} (2x)^{n-k}(-1)^k t^k \frac{n!}{k!(n-k)!}$$

$$= \sum_{n=0}^{\infty} \sum_{k=0}^{n} \frac{(n - \frac{1}{2})!(-1)^k(2x)^{n-k}}{(-\frac{1}{2})!(n-k)!k!} t^{n+k}. \tag{12.6}$$

From the identities in Section 5.4 (rearranging the order of summation) Eq. 12.6 becomes

$$(1 - 2xt + t^2)^{-1/2} = \sum_{n=0}^{\infty} \sum_{k=0}^{[n/2]} \frac{(n - k - \frac{1}{2})!(-1)^k(2x)^{n-2k}}{(-\frac{1}{2})!k!(n-2k)!} t^n, \tag{12.7}$$

with the variable t independent of the index k. Now, equating our two power series term by term, we have

$$P_n(x) = \sum_{k=0}^{[n/2]} (-1)^k \frac{(n - k - \frac{1}{2})!}{(-\frac{1}{2})!k!(n-2k)!} (2x)^{n-2k}$$

$$= \sum_{k=0}^{[n/2]} (-1)^k \frac{(2n - 2k)!}{2^n k!(n-k)!(n-2k)!} x^{n-2k}. \tag{12.8}$$

Returning to the electric charge on the z-axis, we demonstrate the usefulness and power of the generating function by adding a charge $-q$ at $z = -a$, as shown in Fig. 12.3. The potential becomes

$$\varphi = \frac{q}{4\pi\varepsilon_0} \left(\frac{1}{r_1} - \frac{1}{r_2} \right), \tag{12.9}$$

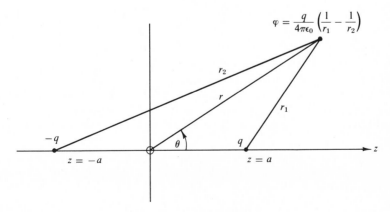

FIG. 12.3 Electric dipole

and by using the law of cosines we have

$$\varphi = \frac{q}{4\pi\varepsilon \cdot r}\left\{\left[1 - 2\left(\frac{a}{r}\right)\cos\theta + \left(\frac{a}{r}\right)^2\right]^{-1/2} - \left[1 + 2\left(\frac{a}{r}\right)\cos\theta + \left(\frac{a}{r}\right)^2\right]^{-1/2}\right\},$$

$$(12.10)$$

$$(r > a)$$

Clearly, the second radical is like the first, except that a has been replaced by $-a$. Then, using Eq. 12.4, we obtain

$$\varphi = \frac{q}{4\pi\varepsilon_0 r}\left[\sum_{n=0}^{\infty} P_n(\cos\theta)\left(\frac{a}{r}\right)^n - \sum_{n=0}^{\infty} P_n(\cos\theta)(-1)^n\left(\frac{a}{r}\right)^n\right]$$

$$= \frac{2q}{4\pi\varepsilon_0 r}\left[P_1(\cos\theta)\left(\frac{a}{r}\right) + P_3(\cos\theta)\left(\frac{a}{r}\right)^3 + \cdots\right].$$

$$(12.11)$$

The first term (and dominant term for $r \gg a$) is

$$\varphi = \frac{2aq}{4\pi\varepsilon_0} \times \frac{P_1(\cos\theta)}{r^2},$$

$$(12.12)$$

which is the usual electric dipole potential. Here $2aq$ is the dipole moment (Fig. 12.3).

Linear electric multipoles.   This analysis may be extended by placing additional charges on the z-axis so that the P_1 term, as well as the P_0 (monopole) term, is cancelled out. For instance, charges of q at $z = a$ and $z = -a$, $-2q$ at $z = 0$ give rise to a potential whose series expansion starts with $P_2(\cos\theta)$. This is a linear electric

FIG. 12.4   Electric quadrupole, electric octupole

quadrupole. Two linear quadrupoles may be placed so that the quadrupole term is cancelled, but the P_3, the octupole term, survives. Other configurations are possible. For instance (Fig. 12.4), alternate positive and negative charges at the vertices of a square (or parallelogram) yield a quadrupole field, alternate charges on the vertices of a cube, an octupole field. Further information about electric multipoles and other methods of treating them can be found in the texts on electromagnetic theory listed in the introduction.

Extension to Gegenbauer polynomials.   The generating function $g(t, x)$ used here is actually a special case of a more general generating function,

$$\frac{2^m}{(1 - 2xt + t^2)^{m+1/2}} = \frac{\pi^{1/2}}{(m - \frac{1}{2})!}\sum_{n=0}^{\infty} T_n^m(x)t^n.$$

$$(12.13)$$

The coefficients $T_n^m(x)$ are often called Gegenbauer polynomials. For $n = 0$ this reduces to Eq. 12.4; that is, $T_n^0(x) = P_n(x)$. The cases $m = \pm\frac{1}{2}$ are considered in Chapter 13 in connection with the Chebyshev polynomials.

Before leaving multipole fields, perhaps two points should be emphasized. First, an electric (or magnetic) multipole has an absolute significance only if all lower-order terms vanish. For instance, the potential of one charge q at $z = a$ was expanded in a series of Legendre polynomials. Although we may refer to the $P_1(\cos \theta)$ term in this expansion as a dipole term, it should be remembered that this term exists only because of our choice of coordinates. We actually have a monopole, $P_0(\cos \theta)$.

Second, in physical systems we do not encounter pure multipoles. As an example, the potential of the finite dipole (q at $z = a$, $-q$ at $z = -a$) contained a $P_3(\cos \theta)$ term. These higher-order terms may be eliminated by shrinking the multipole to a point multipole, in this case keeping the product qa constant ($a \rightarrow 0$, $q \rightarrow \infty$) to maintain the same dipole moment.

EXERCISES

12.1.1 Show that the electrostatic potential produced by a charge q at $z = a$ for $r < a$ is

$$\varphi = \frac{q}{4\pi\varepsilon_0 a} \sum_{n=0}^{\infty} \left(\frac{r}{a}\right)^n P_n(\cos \theta).$$

12.1.2 Using $E = -\nabla\varphi$, determine the components of the electric field corresponding to the (pure) electric dipole potential

$$\varphi = \frac{2aq\, P_1(\cos \theta)}{4\pi\varepsilon_0 r^2}.$$

Here it is assumed that $r \gg a$.

$$E_r = +\frac{4aq \cos \theta}{4\pi\varepsilon_0 r^3},$$

$$E_\theta = +\frac{2aq \sin \theta}{4\pi\varepsilon_0 r^3},$$

$$E_\varphi = 0.$$

12.1.3 Develop the electrostatic potential for the array of charges shown. This is a linear electric quadrupole (Fig. 12.5).

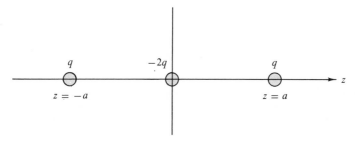

FIG. 12.5 Linear electric quadrupole

12.1.4   Draw a simple one-dimensional array of charges that will have no monopole, dipole, or quadrupole moments but will have an octupole [$P_3(\cos\theta)$] term. Show that your array of charges has these properties.

12.1.5   A point electric dipole of strength $p^{(1)}$ is placed at $z = a$; a second point electric dipole of equal but opposite strength is at the origin. Keeping the product $p^{(1)}a$ constant, let $a \to 0$. Show that this results in a point electric quadrupole.

12.1.6   A conducting ring of radius a in the xy-plane carries a total charge of q. Show that the electrostatic potential is

$$\varphi(\mathbf{r}) = \frac{q}{4\pi\varepsilon_0 r} \sum_{n=0}^{\infty} (-1)^n \frac{(2n)!}{2^{2n}(n!)^2} \left(\frac{a}{r}\right)^{2n} P_{2n}(\cos\theta) \qquad r > a.$$

Hint. 1. Expand $\varphi(\mathbf{r})$ as a series of solutions of Laplace's equation

$$\frac{1}{r} a_n \left(\frac{a}{r}\right)^n P_n(\cos\theta).$$

2. Evaluate a_n by computing $\varphi(r = r, \theta = 0)$, that is, along z-axis, and comparing solutions.

12.1.7   Prove that

$$P_n(\cos\theta) = (-1)^n \frac{r^{n+1}}{n!} \frac{\partial^n}{\partial z^n}\left(\frac{1}{r}\right).$$

Hint. Compare the Legendre polynomial expansion of the generating function with a Taylor series expansion.

12.1.8   Using hypergeometric functions, we can derive

$$e^{xt} J_0(t\sqrt{1-x^2}) = \sum_{n=0}^{\infty} P_n(x)\frac{t^n}{n!}.$$

Verify this for powers of t through t^2.

12.2   Recurrence Relations and Special Properties

Recurrence relations.   The Legendre polynomial generating function provides a convenient way of deriving the recurrence relations[1] and some special properties. If our generating function (Eq. 12.4) is differentiated with respect to t, we obtain

$$\frac{\partial g(t,x)}{\partial t} = \frac{x-t}{(1-2xt+t^2)^{3/2}} = \sum_{n=0}^{\infty} n\, P_n(x)t^{n-1}. \tag{12.14}$$

By substituting Eq. 12.4 into this and rearranging terms, we have

$$(1-2xt+t^2)\sum_{n=0}^{\infty} n\, P_n(x)t^{n-1} + (t-x)\sum_{n=0}^{\infty} P_n(x)t^n = 0. \tag{12.15}$$

The left-hand side is a power series in t. Since this power series vanishes for all values of t, we may put the coefficient of each power of t equal to zero, that is, our power series is unique (Section 5.7). This may be done easily by separating the individual summations and using distinctive summation indices,

[1] We can also apply the explicit series form (Eq. 12.8) directly.

$$\sum_{m=0}^{\infty} m\, P_m(x)t^{m-1} - \sum_{n=0}^{\infty} 2nx\, P_n(x)t^n + \sum_{s=0}^{\infty} s\, P_s(x)t^{s+1}$$

$$+ \sum_{s=0}^{\infty} P_s(x)t^{s+1} - \sum_{n=0}^{\infty} x\, P_n(x)t^n = 0. \tag{12.16}$$

Now letting $m = n + 1$, $s = n - 1$, we find

$$(2n + 1)x\, P_n(x) = (n + 1)\, P_{n+1}(x) + n\, P_{n-1}(x), \qquad n = 1, 2, 3, \ldots \,. \tag{12.17}$$

This is another three-term recurrence relation similar to (but not identical with) the recurrence relation for Bessel functions. With this recurrence relation we may easily construct the higher Legendre polynomials. If we take $n = 1$ and insert the easily found values of $P_0(x)$ and $P_1(x)$ (Exercise 12.1.7 or Eq. 12.8),

$$3x\, P_1(x) = 2P_2(x) + P_0(x) \tag{12.18}$$

or

$$P_2(x) = \tfrac{1}{2}(3x^2 - 1). \tag{12.19}$$

This process may be continued indefinitely. The first few Legendre polynomials are listed in Table 12.1.

TABLE 12.1

Legendre Polynomials

$P_0(x) = 1$

$P_1(x) = x$

$P_2(x) = \tfrac{1}{2}(3x^2 - 1)$

$P_3(x) = \tfrac{1}{2}(5x^3 - 3x)$

$P_4(x) = \tfrac{1}{8}(35x^4 - 30x^2 + 3)$

$P_5(x) = \tfrac{1}{8}(63x^5 - 70x^3 + 15x)$

Differential equations.   More information about the behavior of the Legendre polynomials can be obtained if we now differentiate Eq. 12.4 with respect to x. This gives

$$\frac{\partial g(t, x)}{\partial x} = \frac{t}{(1 - 2xt + t^2)^{3/2}} = \sum_{n=0}^{\infty} P_n'(x)t^n \tag{12.20}$$

or

$$(1 - 2xt + t^2)\sum_{n=0}^{\infty} P_n'(x)t^n - t\sum_{n=0}^{\infty} P_n(x)t^n = 0. \tag{12.21}$$

As before, the coefficient of each power of t is set equal to zero and we obtain

$$P_{n+1}'(x) + P_{n-1}'(x) = 2xP_n'(x) + P_n(x). \tag{12.22}$$

A more useful relation may be found by differentiating Eq. 12.17 with respect to x and multiplying by two. To this we add $(2n + 1)$ times Eq. 12.22, cancelling the P_n' term. The result is

$$P_{n+1}'(x) - P_{n-1}'(x) = (2n + 1)\, P_n(x). \tag{12.23}$$

From Eqs. 12.17 and 12.23 numerous additional equations may be developed, including

$$P'_{n+1}(x) = (n + 1) P_n(x) + x P'_n(x), \tag{12.24}$$

$$P'_{n-1}(x) = -n P_n(x) + x P'_n(x), \tag{12.25}$$

$$(1 - x^2) P'_n(x) = n P_{n-1}(x) - nx P_n(x), \tag{12.26}$$

$$(1 - x^2) P'_n(x) = (n + 1)xP_n(x) - (n + 1)P_{n+1}(x). \tag{12.27}$$

By differentiating Eq. 12.26 and using Eq. 12.25 to eliminate $P'_{n-1}(x)$ we find that $P_n(x)$ satisfies the linear, second-order differential equation

$$(1 - x^2)P''_n(x) - 2x P'_n(x) + n(n + 1) P_n(x) = 0. \tag{12.28}$$

This is Legendre's differential equation. We now see that the polynomials $P_n(x)$ generated by the expansion of $(1 - 2xt + t^2)^{-1/2}$ satisfy Legendre's equation which, of course, is why they are called Legendre polynomials. In Eq. 12.28 differentiation is with respect to x ($x = \cos \theta$). Frequently, we encounter Legendre's equation expressed in terms of differentiation with respect to θ.

$$\frac{1}{\sin \theta} \frac{d}{d\theta} \left(\sin \theta \frac{dP_n(\cos \theta)}{d\theta} \right) + n(n + 1)P_n(\cos \theta) = 0. \tag{12.29}$$

Our generating function provides still more information about the Legendre polynomials. If we set $x = 1$, Eq. 12.4 becomes

$$\frac{1}{(1 - 2t + t^2)^{1/2}} = \frac{1}{1 - t}$$

$$= \sum_{n=0}^{\infty} t^n. \tag{12.30}$$

But

$$\frac{1}{(1 - 2tx + t^2)^{1/2}_{x=1}} = \sum_{n=0}^{\infty} P_n(1) \, t^n.$$

Comparing the two series expansions,

$$P_n(1) = 1. \tag{12.31}$$

If we let $x = -1$, the same sort of analysis shows that

$$P_n(-1) = (-1)^n. \tag{12.32}$$

If we take $x = 0$, using the expansion

$$(1 + t^2)^{-1/2} = 1 - \tfrac{1}{2}t^2 + \tfrac{3}{8}t^4 + \cdots + (-1)^n \frac{1 \cdot 3 \cdots (2n - 1)}{2^n n!} t^{2n} + \cdots, \tag{12.33}$$

we have

$$P_{2n}(0) = (-1)^n \frac{1 \cdot 3 \cdots (2n - 1)}{2^n n!} = (-1)^n \frac{(2n - 1)!!}{(2n)!!} \tag{12.34}$$

$$P_{2n+1}(0) = 0, \quad n = 0, 1, 2, \ldots. \tag{12.35}$$

Parity.   Some of these results are special cases of the parity property of the Legendre polynomials. We refer once more to Eq. 12.4. If we replace x by $-x$ and t by $-t$, the generating function is unchanged. Hence

$$g(t, x) = g(-t, -x)$$

$$= [1 - 2(-t)(-x) + (-t)^2]^{-1/2}$$

$$= \sum_{n=0}^{\infty} P_n(-x)(-t)^n$$

$$= \sum_{n=0}^{\infty} P_n(x)t^n. \qquad (12.36)$$

Comparing these two series, we have

$$P_n(-x) = (-1)^n P_n(x); \qquad (12.37)$$

that is, the polynomial functions are odd or even (with respect to $x = 0$, $\theta = \pi/2$) according to whether the index n is odd or even. This is the parity or reflection property that plays such an important role in quantum mechanics. For central forces the index n is a measure of the orbital angular momentum, thus linking parity and orbital angular momentum.

The reader will see this parity property confirmed by the series solution and for the special values tabulated in Table 12.1. It might also be noted that Eq. 12.37 may be predicted by inspection of Eq. 12.17, the recurrence relation. Specifically, if $P_{n-1}(x)$ and $xP_n(x)$ are even, then $P_{n+1}(x)$ must be even.

Finally, in addition to these results, our generating function enables us to set an upper limit on $|P_n(\cos\theta)|$. We have

$$(1 - 2t\cos\theta + t^2)^{-1/2} = (1 - te^{i\theta})^{-1/2}(1 - te^{-i\theta})^{-1/2}$$

$$= (1 + \tfrac{1}{2}te^{i\theta} + \tfrac{3}{8}t^2e^{2i\theta} + \cdots) \times (1 + \tfrac{1}{2}te^{-i\theta} + \tfrac{3}{8}t^2e^{-2i\theta} + \cdots).$$

$$(12.38)$$

Our Legendre polynomial, $P_n(\cos\theta)$, still the coefficient of t^n, may now be written as a sum of terms of the form $a_m \cos m\theta$ *with all coefficients positive.* This series is clearly a maximum when $\theta = 0$, $\cos m\theta = 1$. But for $x = \cos\theta = 1$, Eq. 12.31 shows that $P_n(1) = 1$. Therefore

$$|P_n(\cos\theta)| \leqslant P_n(1) = 1. \qquad (12.39)$$

EXERCISES

12.2.1   Show in detail that

$$P_n(\cos\theta) \geqslant -1.$$

This lower bound is reached for $P_n(-1)$, n odd.

12.2.2   From Eq. 12.38 write out the coefficient of t^2 in terms of $\cos n\theta$, $n \leqslant 2$. This coefficient is $P_2(\cos\theta)$.

12.2.3   By differentiating the generating function, $g(t, x)$, with respect to t, multiplying by $2t$, and then adding $g(t, x)$, show that

$$\frac{1 - t^2}{(1 - 2tx + t^2)^{3/2}} = \sum_{n=0}^{\infty} (2n + 1)P_n(x)t^n.$$

This result is useful in calculating the charge induced on a grounded metal sphere by a point charge q.

12.2.4   Show that $P_n(\cos\theta) = (-1)^n P_n(-\cos\theta)$ by use of the recurrence relation relating P_n, P_{n+1}, and P_{n-1} and your knowledge of P_0 and P_1.

12.2.5   A point electric octupole may be constructed by placing a point electric quadrupole (pole strength $P^{(2)}$ in the z-direction) at $z = a$ and an equal but opposite point electric quadrupole at $z = 0$ and then letting $a \to 0$, subject to $P^{(2)}a = $ constant. Find the electrostatic potential corresponding to a point electric octupole. Show from the construction of the point electric octupole that the corresponding potential may be obtained by differentiating the point quadrupole potential.

12.2.6   From

$$P_L(\cos\theta) = \frac{1}{L!}\frac{d^L}{dt^L}(1 - 2t\cos\theta + t^2)^{-1/2}\big|_{t=0}$$

show that

$$P_L(1) = 1, \qquad P_L(-1) = (-1)^L.$$

12.2.7   Prove that

$$P_n'(1) = \frac{d}{dx}P_n(x)\big|_{x=1} = \frac{1}{2}n(n + 1).$$

12.2.8   Given the series

$$\alpha_0 + \alpha_2\cos^2\theta + \alpha_4\cos^4\theta + \alpha_6\cos^6\theta = a_0P_0 + a_2P_2 + a_4P_4 + a_6P_6.$$

Express the coefficients α_i as a column vector $\boldsymbol{\alpha}$ and the coefficients a_i as a column vector **a** and determine the matrices **A** and **B** such that

$$\mathbf{A\alpha} = \mathbf{a} \quad \text{and} \quad \mathbf{Ba} = \boldsymbol{\alpha}.$$

Check your computation by showing that $\mathbf{AB} = \mathbf{1}$ (unit matrix). Repeat for the odd case

$$\alpha_1\cos\theta + \alpha_3\cos^3\theta + \alpha_5\cos^5\theta + \alpha_7\cos^7\theta = a_1P_1 + a_3P_3 + a_5P_5 + a_7P_7.$$

12.3   Orthogonality

Legendre's differential equation (12.26) may be written in the form

$$\frac{d}{dx}[(1 - x^2)P_n'(x)] + n(n + 1)P_n(x) = 0, \tag{12.40}$$

showing clearly that it is self-adjoint. Subject to satisfying certain boundary conditions, then, it is known that the solutions $P_n(x)$ will be orthogonal. Repeating the Sturm-Liouville analysis (Section 9.2), we multiply Eq. 12.40 by $P_m(x)$ and subtract the corresponding equation with m and n interchanged. Integrating from -1 to $+1$, we get

$$\int_{-1}^{1} \left\{ P_m(x) \frac{d}{dx} [(1 - x^2) P_n'(x)] - P_n(x) \frac{d}{dx} [(1 - x^2) P_m'(x)] \right\} dx$$

$$= [m(m + 1) - n(n + 1)] \int_{-1}^{1} P_n(x) P_m(x) \, dx. \tag{12.41}$$

Integrating by parts, the integrated part vanishing because of the factor $(1 - x^2)$,[1] we have

$$[m(m + 1) - n(n + 1)] \int_{-1}^{1} P_n(x) P_m(x) \, dx = 0. \tag{12.42}$$

Then for $m \neq n$

$$\int_{-1}^{1} P_n(x) P_m(x) \, dx = 0,$$

$$\int_{0}^{\pi} P_n(\cos \theta) P_m(\cos \theta) \sin \theta \, d\theta = 0, \tag{12.43}$$

showing that $P_n(x)$ and $P_m(x)$ are orthogonal for the interval $[-1, 1]$. This orthogonality may also be demonstrated quite readily by using Rodrigues' definition of $P_n(x)$ (cf. Section 12.4, Exercise 12.4.1).

We still need to evaluate the integral (Eq. 12.42) when $n = m$. Certainly it is no longer zero. From our generating function

$$(1 - 2tx + t^2)^{-1} = \left[\sum_{n=0}^{\infty} P_n(x)t^n \right]^2. \tag{12.44}$$

Integrating from $x = -1$ to $x = +1$, we have

$$\int_{-1}^{1} \frac{dx}{1 - 2tx + t^2} = \sum_{n=0}^{\infty} t^{2n} \int_{-1}^{1} [P_n(x)]^2 \, dx; \tag{12.45}$$

the cross terms in the series vanish by means of Eq. 12.43. Using $y = 1 - 2tx + t^2$, we obtain

$$\int_{-1}^{1} \frac{dx}{1 - 2tx + t^2} = \frac{1}{2t} \int_{(1-t)^2}^{(1+t)^2} \frac{dy}{y}$$

$$= \frac{1}{t} \ln\left(\frac{1 + t}{1 - t}\right). \tag{12.46}$$

Expanding this in a power series (Sections 5.6 and 5.7) gives us

$$\frac{1}{t} \ln\left(\frac{1 + t}{1 - t}\right) = 2 \sum_{n=0}^{\infty} \frac{t^{2n}}{2n + 1}. \tag{12.47}$$

Since our power series representation is known to be unique, we must have

$$\int_{-1}^{1} [P_n(x)]^2 \, dx = \frac{2}{2n + 1}. \tag{12.48}$$

[1] This, of course, is why the limits were chosen as -1 and $+1$.

We shall return to this result in Section 12.6 when we construct the orthonormal spherical harmonics.

Expansion of functions, Legendre series.   In addition to orthogonality, the Sturm-Liouville theory shows that the Legendre polynomials form a complete set. Let us assume, then, that the series

$$\sum_{n=0}^{\infty} a_n P_n(x) = f(x). \tag{12.49}$$

converges uniformly to $f(x)$ in the $[-1, 1]$. This demands that $f(x)$ and $f'(x)$ be at least sectionally continuous in this interval. The coefficients a_n are found by multiplying the series by $P_m(x)$ and integrating term by term. Using the orthogonality property expressed in Eqs. 12.43 and 12.48, we obtain

$$\frac{2}{2m+1} a_m = \int_{-1}^{1} f(x) P_m(x) \, dx \tag{12.50}$$

or

$$f(x) = \sum_{n=0}^{\infty} \frac{2n+1}{2} \int_{-1}^{1} f(t) P_n(t) \, dt \, P_n(x). \tag{12.51}$$

This expansion in a series of Legendre polynomials is usually referred to as a Legendre series. Its properties are quite similar to the more familiar Fourier series (Chapter 14). In particular, we can use the orthogonality property, (Eq. 12.43) to show that the series is unique.

EXAMPLE 12.3.1. EARTH'S GRAVITATIONAL FIELD

An example of a Legendre series is provided by the description of the earth's gravitational potential U (for exterior points), neglecting azimuthal effects. With

$$R = \text{equatorial radius}$$

$$= 6378.1 \pm 0.1 \text{ km}$$

$$\frac{GM}{R} = 62.494 \pm 0.001 \text{ km}^2/\text{sec}^2$$

we write

$$U(r, \theta) = \frac{GM}{R} \left[\frac{R}{r} - \sum_{n=2}^{\infty} a_n \left(\frac{R}{r} \right)^{n+1} P_n(\cos \theta) \right], \tag{12.52}$$

a Legendre series. Artificial satellite motions have shown that

$$a_2 = 1.08279 \pm 0.00015 \, (\times 10^{-3})$$

$$a_3 = -2.4 \pm 0.3 \, (\times 10^{-6}).$$

This is the famous pear-shaped deformation of the earth.

$$a_4 = (-1.4 \pm 0.2) \times 10^{-6}.$$

The higher-order coefficients are approximately zero, within experimental accuracy. The reader might note that P_1 is omitted, since it would represent a displacement and not a deformation.

EXAMPLE 12.3.2.   SPHERE IN A UNIFORM FIELD

An illustration of the use of Legendre polynomials is provided by the problem of a neutral conducting sphere (radius r_0) placed in a (previously) uniform electric field. The problem is to find the new, perturbed, electrostatic potential. Calling the electrostatic potential V [1]

$$\mathbf{V}^2 V = 0,\tag{12.53}$$

Laplace's equation. We select spherical polar coordinates because of the spherical shape of the conductor. (This will simplify the application of the boundary condition at the surface of the conductor.) Separating variables, we obtain

$$V = \sum_{n=0}^{\infty} a_n r^n \, P_n(\cos\theta) + \sum_{n=0}^{\infty} b_n \frac{P_n(\cos\theta)}{r^{n+1}}.\tag{12.54}$$

No φ-dependence appears because of the axial symmetry of our problem. (The center of the conducting sphere is taken as the origin and the z-axis is oriented parallel to the original uniform field.)

Now, our (Dirichlet) boundary conditions come in. If the original unperturbed electrostatic field is E_0, we require

$$V(r \to \infty) = -E_0 z = -E_0 r \cos\theta$$

$$= -E_0 r \, P_1(\cos\theta).\tag{12.55}$$

Since our Legendre series is unique, we may equate coefficients of $P_n(\cos\theta)$ in Eq. 12.54 ($r \to \infty$) and Eq. 12.55 to obtain

$$a_n = 0, \qquad n > 1,$$

$$a_1 = -E_0.\tag{12.56}$$

If $a_n \neq 0$ for $n > 1$, these terms would dominate at large r and the boundary condition (Eq. 12.55) could not be satisfied. We may choose the conducting sphere and the plane $\theta = \pi/2$ to be at zero potential, which means that Eq. 12.54 now becomes

$$V(r = r_0) = a_0 + \frac{b_0}{r_0} + \left(\frac{b_1}{r_0^2} - E_0 r_0\right) P_1(\cos\theta) + \sum_{n=2}^{\infty} b_n \frac{P_n(\cos\theta)}{r_0^{n+1}}$$

$$= 0.\tag{12.57}$$

In order that this may hold for all values of θ, each coefficient of $P_n(\cos\theta)$ must vanish.[2] Hence

[1] It should be emphasized that this is not a presentation of a Legendre series expansion of a known $V(\cos\theta)$. Here we are back to *boundary value* problems.

[2] Again this is equivalent to saying that a series expansion in Legendre polynomials (or any complete orthogonal set) is unique.

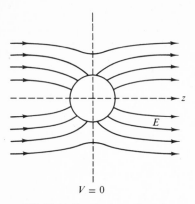

$$a_0 = b_0 = 0,[1]$$
$$b_n = 0, \qquad n \geqslant 2. \qquad (12.58)$$

whereas

$$b_1 = E_0 r_0^3. \qquad (12.59)$$

The electrostatic potential (outside the sphere) is then

$$V = -E_0 r \, P_1(\cos \theta) + \frac{E_0 r_0^3}{r^2} P_1(\cos \theta)$$

$$= -E_0 r \, P_1(\cos \theta)\left(1 - \frac{r_0^3}{r^3}\right). \qquad (12.60)$$

$V = 0$

FIG. 12.6 Conducting sphere in a uniform field

In Section 1.15 it was shown that a solution of Laplace's equation which satisfied the boundary conditions over the entire boundary was unique. The electrostatic potential V, as given by Eq. 12.60, is a solution of Laplace's equation. It satisfies our boundary conditions and is therefore the solution of Laplace's equation for this problem.

It may further be shown that there is an induced surface charge density

$$\sigma = 3\varepsilon_0 E_0 \cos \theta \qquad (12.61)$$

on the surface of the sphere and an induced electric dipole moment

$$P = 4\pi r_0^3 \varepsilon_0 E_0 \qquad (12.62)$$

(Exercise 12.3.1).

EXERCISES

12.3.1 A conducting sphere of radius r_0 is placed in an initially uniform electric field, E_0. Show the following:
(a) The induced surface charge density is

$$\sigma = 3\varepsilon_0 E_0 \cos \theta.$$

(b) The induced electric dipole moment is

$$P = 4\pi r_0^3 \varepsilon_0 E_0.$$

The induced electric dipole moment can be calculated either from the surface charge [part (a)], or by noting that the final electric field E is the result of superimposing a dipole field on the original uniform field.

[1] The coefficient of P_0 is $a_0 + b_0/r_0$. We set $b_0 = 0$ (and therefore $a_0 = 0$ also), since there is **no** net charge on the sphere. If there is a net charge q, then $b_0 \neq 0$.

12.3.2 A charge q is displaced a distance a along the z-axis from the center of a spherical cavity of radius R.
(a) Show that the electric field averaged over the volume $a \leqslant r \leqslant R$ is zero.
(b) Show that the electric field averaged over the volume $0 \leqslant r \leqslant a$ is

$$\mathbf{E} = \mathbf{k}E_z = -\,\mathbf{k}\,\frac{q}{4\pi\varepsilon_0 a^2}, \qquad \text{(mks units)}$$

$$= -\,\mathbf{k}\,\frac{nqa}{3\varepsilon_0},$$

where n is the number of such displaced charges per unit volume. This is a basic calculation in the polarization of a dielectric. *Hint.* $\mathbf{E} = -\nabla\varphi$.

12.3.3 You have constructed a set of orthogonal functions by the Schmidt process (Section 9.3), taking $u_n(x) = x^n$, $n = 0, 1, 2, \ldots$, in increasing order with $w(x) = 1$ and an interval $-1 \leqslant x \leqslant 1$. Prove that the nth such function constructed is proportional to $P_n(x)$. *Hint.* Use mathematical induction.

12.3.4 Expand the Dirac delta function in a series of Legendre polynomials, using the interval $-1 \leqslant x \leqslant 1$.

12.3.5 Prove that

$$\int_{-1}^{1} x(1 - x^2)\,P_n'\,P_m'\,dx = 0, \qquad \text{unless } m = n \pm 1.$$

12.4 Alternate Definitions of Legendre Polynomials

Rodrigues' formula.   The series form the Legendre polynomials (Eq. 12.8) of Section 12.1 may be transformed as follows. From Eq. 12.8

$$P_n(x) = \sum_{r=0}^{[n/2]} (-1)^r \,\frac{(2n - 2r)!}{2^n r!(n - r)!(n - 2r)!}\, x^{n-2r}. \tag{12.63}$$

For n an integer

$$P_n(x) = \sum_{r=0}^{[n/2]} (-1)^r \,\frac{1}{2^n r!(n - r)!}\left(\frac{d}{dx}\right)^n x^{2n-2r}$$

$$= \frac{1}{2^n n!}\left(\frac{d}{dx}\right)^n \sum_{r=0}^{n} \frac{(-1)^r n!}{r!(n - r)!}\, x^{2n-2r}. \tag{12.64}$$

Note the extension of the upper limit. The reader is asked to show in Exercise 12.4.6 that the additional terms $[n/2] + 1$ to n in the summation contribute nothing. However, the effect of these extra terms is to permit the replacement of the new summation by $(x^2 - 1)^n$ (binomial theorem once again) to obtain,

$$P_n(x) = \frac{1}{2^n n!}\left(\frac{d}{dx}\right)^n (x^2 - 1)^n. \tag{12.65}$$

This is Rodrigues' formula. It is useful in proving many of the properties of the Legendre polynomials such as orthogonality. A related application is seen in Exercise 12.4.2.

Schlaefi integral.   Rodrigues' formula provides a means of developing an integral representation of $P_n(z)$. Using Cauchy's integral formula (Section 6.3)

$$f(z) = \frac{1}{2\pi i} \oint \frac{f(t)}{t - z} \, dt \tag{12.66}$$

with

$$f(z) = (z^2 - 1)^n, \tag{12.67}$$

we have

$$(z^2 - 1)^n = \frac{1}{2\pi i} \oint \frac{(t^2 - 1)^n}{t - z} \, dt. \tag{12.68}$$

Differentiating n times with respect to z and multiplying by $1/2^n n!$ gives us

$$P_n(z) = \frac{1}{2^n n!} \frac{d^n}{dz^n} (z^2 - 1)^n$$

$$= \frac{2^{-n}}{2\pi i} \oint \frac{(t^2 - 1)^n}{(t - z)^{n+1}} \, dt \cdot \tag{12.69}$$

with the contour enclosing the point $t = z$.

This is the Schlaefi integral. Margenau and Murphy use this to derive the recurrence relations we obtained from the generating function.

The Schlaefi integral may readily be shown to satisfy Legendre's equation by differentiation and direct substitution. We obtain

$$(1 - z^2) \frac{d^2 P^n}{dz^2} - 2z \frac{dP_n}{dz} + n(n + 1)P_n = \frac{n + 1}{2^n 2\pi i} \oint \frac{d}{dt} \left[\frac{(t^2 - 1)^{n+1}}{(t - z)^{n+2}} \right] dt. \tag{12.70}$$

For integral n our function $(t^2 - 1)^{n+1}/(t - z)^{n+2}$ is single-valued, and the integral around the closed path vanishes. The Schlaefi integral may also be used to define $P_\nu(z)$ for nonintegral ν integrating around the points $t = z$, $t = 1$, but not crossing the cut line -1 to $-\infty$. We could equally well encircle the points $t = z$ and $t = -1$, but this would lead to nothing new. A contour about $t = +1$ and $t = -1$ will lead to a second solution $Q_\nu(z)$ in Section 12.10.

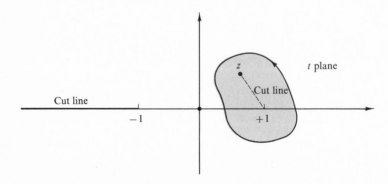

FIG. 12.7   Schlaefi integral contour

A change of variable

$$t = z + \sqrt{z^2 - 1} \, e^{i\varphi} \tag{12.71}$$

with R.P. $(z) > 0$ so that we still enclose the point $t = 1$ and not the point $t = -1$ yields

$$P_n(z) = \frac{1}{2\pi i} \oint \frac{2^n(z^2 - 1)^{n/2} e^{in\varphi}(z + \sqrt{z^2 - 1} \cos \varphi)^n i \sqrt{z^2 - 1} \, e^{i\varphi}}{2^n(\sqrt{z^2 - 1} \, e^{i\varphi})^{n+1}} \, d\varphi$$

$$= \frac{1}{2\pi} \int_0^{2\pi} (z + \sqrt{z^2 - 1} \cos \varphi)^n \, d\varphi. \tag{12.72}$$

This is Laplace's first integral representation. The contour is a circle of radius $\left|\sqrt{z^2 - 1}\right|$ about the point $t = z$. A second representation may be obtained by replacing n by $-n - 1$. The differential equation is invariant to this substitution.

$$P_n(z) = \frac{1}{2\pi} \int_0^{2\pi} (z + \sqrt{z^2 - 1} \cos \varphi)^{-n-1} \, d\varphi. \tag{12.73}$$

The justification for calling this integral $P_n(z)$ rather than $P_{-n-1}(z)$ is the subject of Exercise 12.4.5.

FIG. 12.8 Contour for Laplace's integral representation of the Legendre function

FIG. 12.9 Contour for $P_\nu(z)$, nonintegral ν

In Section 12.1 the generating function, despite its immediate and important physical application, was really pulled out of nowhere. Perhaps it may be made less mysterious by going just a little further. Using the substitution

$$t = z + \sqrt{z^2 - 1} \cos \varphi, \tag{12.74}$$

Eq. 12.73 becomes

$$P_n(z) = \frac{1}{2\pi i} \oint \frac{t^{-n-1}}{[1 - 2tz + t^2]^{1/2}} \, dt, \tag{12.75}$$

our contour enclosing the origin (integral n).[1] By the calculus of residues (Section 7.2) this is simply the coefficient of t^n in the expansion of $(1 - 2tz + t^2)^{-1/2}$, $\left|t^2 - 2tz\right| < 1$. Hence starting with the Schlaefi integral, a solution of Legendre's equation, we have developed a generating function for the Legendre polynomials.

[1] If n is not an integer, $t = 0$ is a branch point and the path of integration is a loop around the singular points $t = z \pm \sqrt{z^2 - 1}$, *clockwise*.

EXERCISES

12.4.1 Using Rodrigues' formula, show that the $P_n(x)$ are orthogonal and that

$$\int_{-1}^{1} [P_n(x)]^2 \, dx = \frac{2}{2n+1}.$$

12.4.2 Show that $\int_{-1}^{1} x^m P_n(x) \, dx = 0$ when $m < n$. *Hint.* Use Rodrigues' formula.

12.4.3 Show that

$$\int_{-1}^{1} x^n P_n(x) \, dx = \frac{2^{n+1} n! \, n!}{(2n+1)!}.$$

12.4.4 By direct evaluation of the Schlaefi integral show that $P_n(1) = 1$.

12.4.5 Using the Laplace integral representations, show that $P_n(z) = P_{-n-1}(z)$. *Hint.* Since $P_{-n-1}(z)$ satisfies Legendre's equation, it must be a linear combination of $P_{+n}(z)$, regular at $z = \pm 1$ and $Q_{+n}(z)$ divergent, at $z = \pm 1$.

$$P_{n-1}(z) = a_1 P_n(z) + a_2 Q_n(z).$$

Show that
(a) $a_2 = 0$ and   (b) $a_1 = 1$.

12.4.6 Show that *each* term in the summation

$$\sum_{r=[n/2]+1}^{n} \left(\frac{d}{dx}\right)^n \frac{(-1)^r \, n!}{r! \, (n-r)!} x^{2n-2r}$$

vanishes (r and n integral).

12.4.7 A plane wave may be expanded in a series of spherical waves by the Rayleigh equation

$$e^{ikr\cos\gamma} = \sum_{n=0}^{\infty} a_n j_n(kr) P_n(\cos \gamma).$$

Show that $a_n = i^n(2n+1)$.

Hint. 1. Use the orthogonality of the P_n to solve for $a_n j_n(kr)$.
2. Differentiate n times with respect to (kr) and set $r = 0$ to eliminate the r-dependence.
3. Evaluate the remaining integral by Exercise 12.4.3.

Note. This problem may also be treated by noting that both sides of the equation satisfy the Helmholtz equation. The equality can be established by showing that the solutions have the same behavior at the origin and also behave alike at large distances.

12.4.8 Show that

$$j_n(kr) = \frac{1}{2i^n} \int_{-1}^{1} e^{ikr\mu} P_n(\mu) \, d\mu.$$

12.5 Associated Legendre Polynomials

Differential equation.   The associated Legendre polynomials which are closely related to ordinary Legendre polynomials reduce to the latter when a particular parameter m goes to zero. To develop the associated Legendre polynomials and the differential equation they satisfy we take Legendre's equation,

$$(1 - x^2)P_n'' - 2xP_n' + n(n + 1)P_n = 0 \tag{12.76}$$

and with the help of Leibnitz' formula[1] differentiate m times. The result is,

$$(1 - x^2)u'' - 2x(m + 1)u' + (n - m)(n + m + 1)u = 0, \tag{12.77}$$

where

$$u \equiv \frac{d^m}{dx^m} P_n(x). \tag{12.78}$$

Now let

$$v(x) = (1 - x^2)^{m/2}u(x) = (1 - x^2)^{m/2} \frac{d^m P_n(x)}{dx^m}. \tag{12.79}$$

Solving for u and differentiating, we obtain

$$u' = \left(v' + \frac{mxv}{1 - x^2}\right)(1 - x^2)^{-m/2}, \tag{12.80}$$

$$u'' = \left[v'' + \frac{2mxv'}{1 - x^2} + \frac{mv}{1 - x^2} + \frac{m(m + 2)x^2v}{(1 - x^2)^2}\right] \cdot (1 - x^2)^{-m/2}. \tag{12.81}$$

Substituting into Eq. 12.77, we find that the new function v satisfies the differential equation

$$(1 - x^2)v'' - 2xv' + \left[n(n + 1) - \frac{m^2}{1 - x^2}\right]v = 0, \tag{12.82}$$

which is the associated Legendre equation reducing to Legendre's equation, as it must be when m is set equal to zero. Expressed in spherical polar coordinates, the associated Legendre equation is,

$$\frac{1}{\sin\theta}\frac{\theta}{d\theta}\left(\sin\theta\frac{dv}{d\theta}\right) + \left[n(n + 1) - \frac{m^2}{\sin^2\theta}\right]v = 0. \tag{12.83}$$

Associated Legendre polynomials.   The regular solutions, relabeled $P_n^m(x)$ are

$$v \equiv P_n^m(x) = (1 - x^2)^{m/2} \frac{d^m}{dx^m} P_n(x). \tag{12.84}$$

There are the associated Legendre polynomials From the form of Eq. 12.84 we might expect m to be non-negative, differentiating a negative number of times not having been defined. However, if $P_n(x)$ is expressed by Rodrigues' formula, this

---

[1] Leibnitz' formula for the nth derivative of a product is

$$\frac{d^n}{dx^n}[A(x)\,B(x)] = \sum_{s=0}^{n}\binom{n}{s}\frac{d^{n-s}}{dx^{n-s}}A(x)\frac{d^s}{dx^s}B(x).$$

limitation on m is relaxed and we may have $-n \leqslant m \leqslant n$, negative as well as positive values of m being permitted. Equation 12.83 owes its importance primarily to its occurrence in the separation of variables of Laplace's or Helmholtz' equation in spherical polar coordinates for cases with nonvanishing azimuthal dependence.

From our definition of the associated Legendre polynomials, $P_n^m(x)$,

$$P_n^0(x) = P_n(x). \tag{12.85}$$

In addition, we may develop Table 12.2.

TABLE 12.2

Associated Legendre Polynomials

$P_1^1(x) = (1 - x^2)^{1/2} = \sin \theta$

$P_2^1(x) = 3(1 - x^2)^{1/2} = 3 \cos \theta \sin \theta$

$P_2^2(x) = 3(1 - x^2) = 3 \sin^2 \theta$

$P_3^1(x) = \frac{3}{2}(5x^2 - 1)(1 - x^2)^{1/2} = \frac{3}{2}(5 \cos^2 \theta - 1) \sin \theta$

$P_3^2(x) = 15(1 - x^2) = 15 \cos \theta \sin^2 \theta$

$P_3^3(x) = 15(1 - x^2)^{3/2} = 15 \sin^3 \theta$

$P_4^1(x) = \frac{5}{2}(7x^3 - 3x)(1 - x^2)^{1/2} = \frac{5}{2}(7 \cos^3 \theta - 3 \cos \theta) \sin \theta$

$P_4^2(x) = \frac{1.5}{2}(7x^2 - 1)(1 - x^2) = \frac{1.5}{2}(7 \cos^2 \theta - 1) \sin^2 \theta$

$P_4^3(x) = 105x(1 - x^2)^{3/2} = 105 \cos \theta \sin^3 \theta$

$P_4^4(x) = 105(1 - x^2)^2 = 105 \sin^4 \theta$

As with the Legendre polynomials, a generating function for the associated Legendre polynomials does exist.

$$\frac{(2m)!(1 - x^2)^{m/2}}{2^m m!(1 - 2tx + t^2)^{m + 1/2}} = \sum_{s=0}^{\infty} P_{s+m}^m(x)t^s. \tag{12.86}$$

However, because of its more cumbersome form and lack of any direct physical application, it is seldom used.

Recurrence relations.   As expected, the associated Legendre polynomials satisfy recurrence relations. Because of the existence of two indices instead of just one, we have a wide variety of recurrence relations.

$$P_n^{m+1} - \frac{2mx}{(1 - x^2)^{1/2}} P_n^m + [n(n + 1) - m(m - 1)]P_n^{m-1} = 0, \tag{12.87}$$

$$(2n + 1)xP_n^m = (n + m)P_{n-1}^m + (n - m + 1)P_{n+1}^m, \tag{12.88}$$

$$(2n + 1)(1 - x^2)^{1/2}P_n^m$$
$$= P_{n+1}^{m+1} - P_{n-1}^{m+1}$$
$$= (n + m)(n + m - 1)P_{n-1}^{m-1} - (n - m + 1)(n - m + 2)P_{n+1}^{m-1}, \tag{12.89}$$

$$(1 - x^2)^{1/2} P_n^{m\prime} = \tfrac{1}{2} P_n^{m+1} - \tfrac{1}{2}(n + m)(n - m + 1)P_n^{m-1}. \qquad (12.90)$$

These relations, and many other similar ones, may be verified by use of the generating function (Eq. 12.4), by substitution of the series solution of the associated Legendre equation (12.82), or by reduction to the Legendre polynomial recurrence relations, using Eq. 12.84. As an example of the last method, consider the third equation in the preceding set. It is similar to Eq. 12.23.

$$(2n + 1) P_n(x) = P_{n+1}'(x) - P_{n-1}'(x). \qquad (12.91)$$

Let us differentiate this Legendre polynomial recurrence relation m times to obtain

$$(2n + 1) \frac{d^m}{dx^m} P_n(x) = \frac{d^m}{dx^m} P_{n+1}'(x) - \frac{d^m}{dx^m} P_{n-1}'(x)$$

$$= \frac{d^{m+1}}{dx^{m+1}} P_{n+1}(x) - \frac{d^{m+1}}{dx^{m+1}} P_{n-1}(x). \qquad (12.92)$$

Now multiplying by $(1 - x^2)^{(m+1)/2}$ and using the definition of $P_n^m(x)$, we obtain Eq. 12.89.

Parity.   The parity relation satisfied by the associated Legendre polynomials may be determined by examination of the defining equation (12.84). As $x \to -x$, we already know that $P_n(x)$ contributes a $(-1)^n$. The m-fold differentiation yields a factor of $(-1)^m$. Hence we have

$$P_n^m(-x) = (-1)^{n+m} P_n^m(x). \qquad (12.93)$$

A glance at Table 12.2 verifies this for $m \leqslant 4$.
Also, from the definition in Eq. 12.84

$$P_n^m(\pm 1) = 0, \quad \text{for} \quad m > 0. \qquad (12.94)$$

Orthogonality.   The orthogonality of the $P_n^m(x)$ follows from the differential equation just as in $P_n(x)$ (Section 12.3); the term $-m^2/(1 - x^2)$ cancels out, assuming m is the same in both cases. However, it is instructive to demonstrate the orthogonality by another method, a method that will also provide the normalization constant.
Using the definition in Eq. 12.84 and Rodrigues' formula (Eq. 12.65) for $P_n(x)$, we find

$$\int_{-1}^{1} P_p^m(x) P_q^m(x) \, dx = \frac{(-1)^m}{2^{p+q}p!q!} \int_{-1}^{1} X^m \frac{d^{p+m}}{dx^{p+m}} X^p \frac{d^{q+m}}{dx^{q+m}} X^q \, dx. \qquad (12.95)$$

The function X is given by $X \equiv (x^2 - 1)$. If $p \neq q$, let us assume that $p < q$. Notice that the subscript m is the same for both polynomials. This is an essential condition. The technique is to integrate repeatedly by parts; all the integrated parts will vanish as long as there is a factor $X = x^2 - 1$. Let us integrate $q + m$ times to obtain

$$\int_{-1}^{1} P_p^m(x)\, P_q^m(x)\, dx = \frac{(-1)^m (-1)^{q+m}}{2^{p+q} p!\, q!} \int_{-1}^{1} \frac{d^{q+m}}{dx^{q+m}} \left(X^m \frac{d^{p+m}}{dx^{p+m}} X^p \right) X^q\, dx.$$

(12.96)

The integrand on the right-hand side is now expanded by Leibnitz' formula to give

$$X^q \frac{d^{q+m}}{dx^{q+m}} \left(X^m \frac{d^{p+m}}{dx^{p+m}} X^p \right) = X^q \sum_{i=0}^{i=q+m} \frac{(q+m)!}{i!\,(q+m-i)!} \frac{d^{q+m-i}}{dx^{q+m-i}} X^m \frac{d^{p+m+i}}{dx^{p+m+i}} X^p.$$

(12.97)

Since the term X^m contains no power to x greater than x^{2m}, we must have

$$q + m - i \leqslant 2m$$

(12.98)

or the derivative will vanish. Similarly,

$$p + m + i \leqslant 2p.$$

(12.99)

In the solution of these equations for the index i, the conditions for a nonzero result are

$$i \geqslant q - m,$$
$$i \leqslant p - m,$$

(12.100)

If $p < q$, as assumed, there is no solution and the integral vanishes. The same result obviously must follow if $p > q$.

For the remaining case, $p = q$, we may still have the single term corresponding to $i = q - m$. Putting Eq. 12.97 into Eq. 12.96, we have

$$\int_{-1}^{1} [P_q^m(x)]^2\, dx = \frac{(-1)^{q+2m}(q+m)!}{2^{2q} q!\, q!\,(2m)!\,(q-m)!} \int_{-1}^{1} X^q \left(\frac{d^{2m}}{dx^{2m}} X^m \right)\left(\frac{d^{2q}}{dx^{2q}} X^q \right) dx. \quad (12.101)$$

Since

$$X^m = (x^2 - 1)^m = x^{2m} - m x^{2m-2} + \cdots,$$

(12.102)

$$\frac{d^{2m}}{dx^{2m}} X^m = (2m)!,$$

(12.103)

Eq. 12.101 reduces to

$$\int_{-1}^{1} [P_q^m(x)]^2\, dx = \frac{(-1)^{q+2m}(2q)!\,(q+m)!}{2^{2q} q!\, q!\,(q-m)!} \int_{-1}^{1} X^q\, dx.$$

(12.104)

The integral on the right is just

$$(-1)^q \int_{0}^{\pi} \sin^{2q+1}\theta\, d\theta = \frac{(-1)^q 2^{2q+1} q!\, q!}{(2q+1)!}$$

(12.105)

(cf. Exercise 10.4.1). Combining Eqs. 12.104 and 12.105, we have the orthogonality integral

$$\int_{-1}^{1} P_p^m(x)\, P_q^m(x)\, dx = \frac{2}{2q+1} \cdot \frac{(q+m)!}{(q-m)!}\, \delta_{p,q}$$

(12.106)

or, in spherical polar coordinates,

$$\int_0^\pi P_p^m(\cos\theta)\,P_q^m(\cos\theta)\,\sin\theta\,d\theta = \frac{2}{2q+1}\cdot\frac{(q+m)!}{(q-m)!}\,\delta_{p,q}. \qquad (12.107)$$

The orthogonality of the Legendre polynomials is actually a special case of this result, obtained by setting m equal to zero; that is, for $m=0$, Eq. 12.106 reduces to Eqs. 12.43 and 12.48.

It is possible to develop an orthogonality relation for associated Legendre polynomials of the same lower index but different upper index. We find

$$\int_{-1}^1 P_n^m(x)P_n^k(x)(1-x^2)^{-1}\,dx = \frac{(n+m)!}{m(n-m)!}\,\delta_{m,k}. \qquad (12.108)$$

Note that a new weighting factor, $(1-x^2)^{-1}$, has been introduced. The proof of Eq. 12.108 is left as an exercise.

EXAMPLE 12.5.1. MAGNETIC FIELD OF A CURRENT LOOP.

Like the other differential equations of mathematical physics, the associated Legendre equation is likely to pop up quite unexpectedly. As an illustration, consider the magnetic field **B** and magnetic vector potential **A** created by a single circular current loop in the equatorial plane (Fig. 12.10).

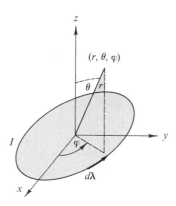

FIG. 12.10   Circular current loop

We know from electromagnetic theory that the contribution of current element $I\,d\lambda$ to the magnetic vector potential is

$$d\mathbf{A} = \frac{\mu_0}{4\pi}\frac{I\,d\lambda}{r}. \qquad (12.109)$$

This, plus the symmetry of our system, shows that **A** has only a φ_0-component and that the component is independent of φ[1]

[1] Pair off corresponding current elements $I\,d\lambda(\varphi_1)$ and $I\,d\lambda(\varphi_2)$, where $\varphi - \varphi_1 = \varphi_2 - \varphi$.

$$\mathbf{A} = \boldsymbol{\varphi}_0 \, A_\varphi(r, \theta). \tag{12.110}$$

By Maxwell's equations

$$\nabla \times \mathbf{H} = \mathbf{J}, \qquad (\mathbf{D} = 0, \text{ mks units}). \tag{12.111}$$

Since

$$\mu_0 \mathbf{H} = \mathbf{B} = \nabla \times \mathbf{A}, \tag{12.112}$$

we have

$$\nabla \times \nabla \times \mathbf{A} = \mu_0 \mathbf{J}, \tag{12.113}$$

where $\mathbf{J}$ is the current density. In our problem $\mathbf{J}$ is zero everywhere except in the current loop. Therefore, away from the loop,

$$\nabla \times \nabla \times \boldsymbol{\varphi}_0 \, A_\varphi(r, \theta) = 0, \tag{12.114}$$

which introduces Eq. 12.110.

Using the expression for the curl in spherical polar coordinates (Section 2.4), we obtain

$$\nabla \times \nabla \times \boldsymbol{\varphi}_0 \, A_\varphi(r, \theta) = \boldsymbol{\varphi}_0 \left[-\frac{\partial^2 A_\varphi}{\partial r^2} - \frac{2}{r}\frac{\partial A_\varphi}{\partial r} - \frac{1}{r^2}\frac{\partial^2 A_\varphi}{\partial \theta^2} - \frac{1}{r^2}\frac{\partial}{\partial \theta}\left(\cot \theta A_\varphi\right) \right]$$

$$= 0. \tag{12.115}$$

Letting $A_\varphi(r, \theta) = R(r)\Theta(\theta)$ and separating variables, we have

$$r^2 \frac{d^2R}{dr^2} + 2r\frac{dR}{dr} - n(n+1)R = 0, \tag{2.1116}$$

$$\frac{d^2\Theta}{d\theta^2} + \cot \theta \frac{d\Theta}{d\theta} + n(n+1)\Theta - \frac{\Theta}{\sin^2 \theta} = 0. \tag{12.117}$$

The second equation is the associated Legendre equation (12.83) with $m = 1$, and we may immediately write

$$\Theta(\theta) = P_n^1(\cos \theta). \tag{12.118}$$

The separation constant $n(n+1)$ was chosen to keep this solution well behaved.

By trial, letting $R(r) = r^\alpha$, we find that $\alpha = n, -n-1$. The first possibility is discarded, for our solution must vanish as $r \to \infty$. Hence

$$A_{\varphi n} = \frac{b_n}{r^{n+1}} \, P_n^1(\cos \theta) = c_n \left(\frac{a}{r}\right)^{n+1} P_n^1(\cos \theta) \tag{12.119}$$

and

$$A_\varphi(r, \theta) = \sum_{n=1}^{\infty} c_n \left(\frac{a}{r}\right)^{n+1} P_n^1(\cos \theta), \qquad (r > a). \tag{12.120}$$

Since A_φ must be invariant to reflection in the equatorial plane by the symmetry of our problem,

$$A_\varphi(r, \cos \theta) = A_\varphi(r, -\cos \theta), \tag{12.121}$$

the parity property of $P_n^m(\cos \theta)$ (Eq. 12.93) shows that $c_n = 0$ for n even.

To complete the evaluation of the constants, we may use Eq. 12.109 to calculate B_z along the z-axis $[B_z = B_r(r, \theta = 0)]$ and compare with the expression obtained from the Biot and Savart law. We have

$$B_r = \mathbf{V} \times \mathbf{A} \mid_r$$

$$= \frac{1}{r \sin \theta} \left[\frac{\partial}{\partial \theta} (\sin \theta \, A_\varphi) \right] \tag{12.122}$$

$$= \frac{\cot \theta}{r} A_\varphi + \frac{1}{r} \frac{\partial A_\varphi}{\partial \theta}.$$

Using

$$\frac{\partial P_n^1(\cos \theta)}{\partial \theta} = -\sin \theta \, \frac{dP_n^1(\cos \theta)}{d(\cos \theta)}$$

$$= -\frac{1}{2} P_n^2 + \frac{n(n + 1)}{2} P_n^0 \tag{12.123}$$

and Eq. 12.87 with $m = 1$,

$$P_n^2(\cos \theta) - \frac{2 \cos \theta}{\sin \theta} P_n^1(\cos \theta) + n(n + 1) P_n(\cos \theta) = 0, \tag{12.124}$$

we obtain

$$B_r(r, \theta) = \sum_{n=1}^{\infty} c_n n(n + 1) \frac{a^{n+1}}{r^{n+2}} P_n(\cos \theta), \qquad r > a \tag{12.125}$$

(for all θ). In particular, for $\theta = 0$,

$$B_r(r, 0) = \sum_{n=1}^{\infty} c_n n(n + 1) \frac{a^{n+1}}{r^{n+2}}. \tag{12.126}$$

We may also obtain

$$B_\theta(r, \theta) = -\frac{1}{r} \frac{\partial(r A_\varphi)}{\partial r}$$

$$= \sum_{n=1}^{\infty} c_n n \frac{a^{n+1}}{r^{n+2}} P_n^1(\cos \theta), \qquad r > a. \tag{12.127}$$

The Biot and Savart law states that

$$d\mathbf{B} = \frac{\mu_0}{4\pi} I \frac{d\boldsymbol{\lambda} \times \mathbf{r}_0}{r^2} \qquad \text{(mks units)}. \tag{12.128}$$

We now integrate over the perimeter of our loop (radius a); the magnetic field along the z-axis is $\mathbf{k} B_z$, where

$$B_z = \frac{\mu_0 I}{2} a^2 (a^2 + z^2)^{-3/2}$$

$$= \frac{\mu_0 I}{2} \frac{a^2}{z^3} \left(1 + \frac{a^2}{z^2} \right)^{-3/2}. \tag{12.129}$$

Expanding by the binomial theorem

$$B_z = \frac{\mu_0 I}{2} \frac{a^2}{z^3} \left[1 - \frac{3}{2}\left(\frac{a}{z}\right)^2 + \frac{15}{8}\left(\frac{a}{z}\right)^4 - \cdots \right]$$

$$= \frac{\mu_0 I}{2} \frac{a^2}{z^3} \sum_{n=1\,\text{odd}}^{\infty} (-1)^{(n-1)/2} \frac{(n/2)!}{[(n-1)/2]!(1/2)!}\left(\frac{a}{z}\right)^{n-1}, \qquad z > a. \qquad (12.130)$$

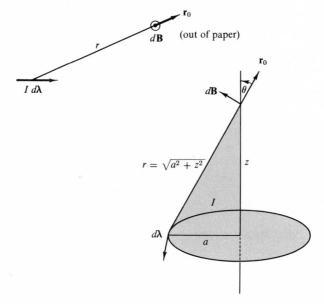

FIG. 12.11   Law of Biot and Savart applied to a circular loop

Equating Eqs. 12.126 and 12.130 term by term (with $r = z$),[1] we find

$$c_1 = \frac{\mu_0 I}{4}, \qquad c_3 = -\frac{\mu_0 I}{16},$$

$$c_n = (-1)^{(n-1)/2} \frac{\mu_0 I}{2n(n+1)} \times \frac{(n/2)!}{[(n-1)/2]!(\frac{1}{2})!}, \qquad n \text{ odd.} \qquad (12.131)$$

Equivalently, we may write

$$c_{2n+1} = (-1)^n \frac{\mu_0 I}{2^{2n+2}} \cdot \frac{(2n)!}{n!(n+1)!} \qquad (12.132)$$

and

$$A_\varphi(r, \theta) = \left(\frac{a}{r}\right)^2 \sum_{n=0}^{\infty} c_{2n+1}\left(\frac{a}{r}\right)^{2n} P_{2n+1}^1(\cos\theta), \qquad (12.133)$$

$$B_r(r, \theta) = \frac{a^2}{r^3} \sum_{n=0}^{\infty} c_{2n+1}(2n+1)(2n+2)\left(\frac{a}{r}\right)^{2n} P_{2n+1}(\cos\theta), \qquad (12.134)$$

[1] The descending power series is also unique.

$$B_\theta(r, \theta) = \frac{a^2}{r^3} \sum_{n=0}^{\infty} c_{2n+1}(2n+1)\left(\frac{a}{r}\right)^{2n} P_{2n+1}^1(\cos\theta). \tag{12.135}$$

These fields may be described in closed form by the use of elliptic integrals. A third possibility is direct integration of Eq. 12.109 by expanding the factor $1/r$ as a Legendre polynomial generating function. These methods have the advantage of yielding the constants c_n directly.

A comparison of magnetic current loop dipole fields and finite electric dipole fields may be of interest. For the magnetic current loop dipole the preceding analysis gives

$$B_r(r, \theta) = \frac{\mu_0 I}{2} \frac{a^2}{r^3}\left[P_1 - \frac{3}{2}\left(\frac{a}{r}\right)^2 P_3 + \cdots\right], \tag{12.136}$$

$$B_\theta(r, \theta) = \frac{\mu_0 I}{4} \frac{a^2}{r^3}\left[P_1^1 - \frac{3}{4}\left(\frac{a}{r}\right)^2 P_3^1 + \cdots\right]. \tag{12.137}$$

From the finite electric dipole potential of Section 12.1 we have

$$E_r(r, \theta) = \frac{qa}{\pi\varepsilon_0 r^3}\left[P_1 + 2P_3\left(\frac{a}{r}\right)^2 + \cdots\right], \tag{12.138}$$

$$E_\theta(r, \theta) = \frac{qa}{2\pi\varepsilon_0 r^3}\left[P_1^1 + \left(\frac{a}{r}\right)^2 P_3^1 + \cdots\right]. \tag{12.139}$$

The two fields agree in form as far as the leading term is concerned, and this is the basis for calling them both dipole fields.

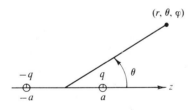

(r, θ, φ)

$-q$

q

θ

$-a$

a

z

FIG. 12.12

EXERCISES

12.5.1 (a) Prove

$$(L - M + 1)^2(P_L^{M-1})^2 + (P_L^M)^2 = (L + M - 1)^2(P_{L-1}^{M-1})^2 + (P_{L-1}^M)^2.$$

(b) Prove

$$(L - M + 1)(L + M)(P_L^{M-1})^2 - (P_L^M)^2$$
$$= (L + M - 1)(L - M + 2)P_{L-1}^{M-1}P_{L+1}^{M-1} - P_{L-1}^M P_{L+1}^M.$$

These two associated Legendre function identities appeared in an investigation of angular distributions of internal conversion electrons.

12.5.2 The associated Legendre polynomial $P_n^m(x)$ satisfies the self-adjoint differential equation

$$(1 - x^2)P_n^{m''}(x) - 2x\,P_n^{m'}(x) + \left[n(n+1) - \frac{m^2}{1-x^2}\right]P_n^m(x) = 0.$$

From the differential equations for $P_n^m(x)$ and $P_n^k(x)$ show that

$$\int_{-1}^{1} P_n^m(x)\,P_n^k(x)\,\frac{dx}{1-x^2} = 0$$

for $k \neq m$.

12.5.3 Prove that

$$\int_{-1}^{1} (1-x^2)^{-1}P_n^m(x)\,P_n^k(x)\,dx = \frac{(n+m)!}{m(n-m)!}\,\delta_{mk}.$$

12.5.4 Express $P_L^{|M|}(\cos\theta)e^{iM\varphi}$ in terms of cartesian coordinates for

$$L = 0, 1, 2, \qquad -L \leqslant M \leqslant L.$$

$$P_0(\cos\theta)e^{0i\varphi} = 1,$$

$$P_1^{\pm 1}(\cos\theta)e^{\pm i\varphi} = \sin\theta\,(\cos\varphi \pm i\sin\varphi) = \frac{1}{r}(x \pm iy),$$

$$P_1(\cos\theta)e^{0i\varphi} = \cos\theta = \frac{z}{r},$$

$$P_2(\cos\theta)e^{0i\varphi} = \frac{3}{2}\cos^2\theta - \frac{1}{2} = \frac{1}{2r^2}(2z^2 - x^2 - y^2),$$

$$P_2^{\pm 1}(\cos\theta)e^{\pm i\varphi} = 3\cos\theta\sin\theta\,(\cos\varphi \pm i\sin\varphi) = \frac{3}{r^2}z(x \pm iy),$$

$$P_2^{\pm 2}(\cos\theta)e^{\pm 2i\varphi} = 3\sin^2\theta\,(\cos\varphi \pm i\sin\varphi)^2 = \frac{3(x \pm iy)^2}{r^2}.$$

12.5.5 Prove that

$$P_n^{-m}(x) = (-1)^m\frac{(n-m)!}{(n+m)!}\,P_n^m(x),$$

where $P_n^m(x)$ is defined by

$$P_n^m(x) = \frac{1}{2^n\,n!}(1-x^2)^{m/2}\frac{d^{n+m}}{dx^{n+m}}(x^2-1)^n.$$

Hint. One approach is to apply Leibnitz' formula to $(x+1)^n(x-1)^n$.

12.5.6 Show that

(a) $\displaystyle \int_0^\pi \left(\frac{dP_n^m}{d\theta}\frac{dP_{n'}^m}{d\theta} + \frac{m^2 P_n^m P_{n'}^m}{\sin^2\theta}\right)\sin\theta\,d\theta = \frac{2n(n+1)}{2n+1}\frac{(n+m)!}{(n-m)!}\,\delta_{nn'},$

(b) $\displaystyle \int_0^\pi \left(\frac{P_n^1}{\sin\theta}\frac{dP_{n'}^1}{d\theta} + \frac{P_{n'}^1}{\sin\theta}\frac{dP_n^1}{d\theta}\right)\sin\theta\,d\theta = 0.$

These integrals occur in the theory of scattering of electromagnetic waves by spheres.

12.5.7 Show that

$$P_n^1(0) = \begin{cases} 0, & n\text{ even} \\[2mm] \dfrac{(-1)^{(n-1)/2}n!}{\{[(n-1)/2]!\,2^{(n-1)/2}\}^2}, & n\text{ odd} \end{cases}$$

by (a) use of recurrence relations, (b) expansion of the generating function.

12.5.8 Determine the vector potential of a magnetic quadrupole by differentiating the magnetic dipole potential.

$$\mathbf{A}_{MQ} = \frac{\mu_0}{2}(Ia^2)(dz)\,\boldsymbol{\varphi}_0\,\frac{P_2^1(\cos\theta)}{r^3} + \text{higher-order terms.}$$

$$\mathbf{B}_{MQ} = \mu_0(Ia^2)(dz)\left[\mathbf{r}_0\frac{3P_2(\cos\theta)}{r^4} + \boldsymbol{\theta}_0\frac{P_2^1(\cos\theta)}{r^4}\right].$$

This corresponds to placing a current loop of radius a at $z = dz$, an oppositely directed current loop at $z = -dz$, and letting $a \to 0$ subject to $(dz)x$ (dipole strength) equal constant.

Another approach to this problem would be to integrate dA (Eq. 12.109), to expand the denominator in a series of Legendre polynomials, and to use the Legendre polynomial addition theorem (Section 12.7).

12.5.9 A single loop of wire of radius a carries a current I.
(a) Find the magnetic inductance $\mathbf{B}$ for $r < a$.
(b) Calculate the integral of the magnetic flux ($\mathbf{B} \cdot d\boldsymbol{\sigma}$) over the area of the current loop, that is,

$$\int_0^a \int_0^{2\pi} B_\theta\left(r, \theta = \frac{\pi}{2}\right) d\varphi\, r\, dr.$$

Ans. ∞.

The earth is within such a ring current in which I approximates millions of amperes arising from the drift of charged particles in the Van Allen belt.

12.5.10 A uniformly charged spherical shell is rotating with constant angular velocity.
(a) Calculate the magnetic inductance $\mathbf{B}$ along the axis of rotation outside the sphere.
(b) Using the vector potential series of Section 12.5, find $\mathbf{A}$ and then $\mathbf{B}$ for all space outside the sphere.

12.5.11 Derive Eq. 12.86, the generating function for associated Legendre polynomials, by differentiating the Legendre polynomial generating function.

12.5.12 In the liquid drop model of the nucleus, the spherical nucleus is subjected to small deformations. Consider a sphere of radius r_0 that is deformed so that its new surface is given by

$$r = r_0[1 + \alpha_2 P_2(\cos\theta)].$$

Find the area of the deformed sphere through terms of order α_2^2.
Hint.

$$dA = \left[r^2 + \left(\frac{dr}{d\varphi}\right)^2\right]^{1/2} r \sin\theta\, d\theta\, d\varphi.$$

Ans. $A = 4\pi r_0^2[1 + \tfrac{4}{5}\alpha_2^2 + \theta(\alpha_2^3)]$.

12.5.13 Repeat Exercise 12.5.12 with the surface described by

$$r = r_0(1 + \alpha_2 P_2 + \alpha_4 P_4).$$

12.5.14 Calculate the volume of the deformed sphere for

$$r = r_0[\alpha_0 + \alpha_2 P_2(\cos\theta)].$$

If the material in the sphere is incompressible, what relation is imposed on α_0 and α_2?

2.5.15 A nuclear particle is in a potential $V(r, \theta, \varphi) = V_0$, a constant for $0 \leqslant r \leqslant a$. It is described by a wave function $\psi(r, \theta, \varphi)$ which satisfies the wave equation

$$-\frac{\hbar}{2M}\nabla^2\psi + V_0\psi = E\psi$$

and the boundary condition

$$\psi(r = a) = 0.$$

Show that for the energy E to be a minimum there must be no angular dependence in the wave function, that is, $\psi = \psi(r)$.

12.5.16 Derive the associated Legendre recurrence relation

$$P_n^{m+1}(x) - \frac{2mx}{(1-x^2)^{1/2}}\, P_n^m(x) + [n(n+1) - m(m-1)]P_n^{m-1}(x) = 0.$$

12.5.17 Show that

$$\sin\theta\, P_n'(\cos\theta) = P_n^1(\cos\theta).$$

12.6 Spherical Harmonics

In the separation of variables of (a) Laplace's equation, (b) Helmholtz's or the space-dependence of the classical wave equation, and (c) the Schrodinger wave equation for central force fields,

$$\nabla^2\psi + k^2 f(r)\psi = 0, \tag{12.140}$$

the angular dependence, coming entirely from the Laplacian operator, is

$$\frac{\Phi(\varphi)}{\sin\theta}\frac{d}{d\theta}\left(\sin\theta\frac{d\Theta}{d\theta}\right) + \frac{\Theta(\theta)}{\sin^2\theta}\frac{d^2\Phi(\varphi)}{d\varphi^2} + n(n+1)\,\Theta(\theta)\,\Phi(\varphi) = 0. \tag{12.141}$$

Orthogonality.   Splitting off the azimuthal dependence, the polar angle dependence (θ) leads to the associated Legendre equation (12.83), which is satisfied by the associated Legendre polynomials, that is, $\Theta(\theta) = P_n^m(\cos\theta)$. The separated azimuthal equation is

$$\frac{1}{\Phi(\varphi)}\frac{d^2\Phi(\varphi)}{d\varphi^2} = -m^2, \tag{12.142}$$

with solutions

$$\Phi(\varphi) = e^{im\varphi}, \tag{12.143}$$

which readily satisfy the orthogonal condition

$$\int_0^{2\pi} e^{-im_1\varphi}e^{im_2\varphi}\, d\varphi = 2\pi\delta_{m_1,m_2}. \tag{12.144}$$

Notice that it is the product $\Phi_{m_1}^*(\varphi)\,\Phi_{m_2}(\varphi)$ that is taken and that $*$ is used to indicate the complex conjugate function. This choice is not required, but it is convenient for quantum mechanical calculations. We could have used

$$\Phi = \sin m\varphi, \qquad \cos m\varphi \tag{12.145}$$

and the conditions of orthogonality that form the basis for Fourier series (Chapter 14).

In electrostatics and most other physical problems we require m to be an integer in order that $\Phi(\varphi)$ may be a single-valued function of the azimuth angle. In quantum mechanics the question is much more involved because the observable quantity that must be single-valued is the square of the magnitude of the wave function, $\Phi^*\Phi$. However, it can be shown that we must still have m integral or nonsensical currents will result.

By means of Eq. 12.144,

$$\frac{1}{\sqrt{2\pi}} e^{im\varphi} \tag{12.146}$$

is orthonormal (orthogonal and normalized) with respect to integration over the azimuth angle φ.

Now there is a little problem. Equations 12.142 and 12.83 are invariant to $m \rightarrow -m$ but we have not yet explicitly defined the associated Legendre polynomials $P_n^m(\cos\theta)$ for negative index m. One possibility is simply to assert that

$$P_n^m(\cos\theta) = P_n^{|m|}(\cos\theta), \qquad m = 0, \pm 1, \pm 2, \ldots, \tag{12.147}$$

taking the absolute value of m whenever it appears. An alternative, which has the advantage that the same recurrence relations derived for $m \geqslant 0$ still hold for $m < 0$, is to return to the definition of $P_n^m(\cos\theta)$ in Eq. 12.84 and replace the $P_n(\cos\theta)$ by Rodrigues' formula (Eq. 12.65).

This leads to

$$P_n^m(\cos\theta) = \frac{1}{2^n n!} (1 - x^2)^{m/2} \frac{d^{m+n}}{dx^{m+n}} (x^2 - 1)^n, \qquad -n \leqslant m \leqslant n. \tag{12.148}$$

Now we may permit m to go negative, as far as $-n$. Further, we see immediately that $P_n^m(\cos\theta)$ vanishes for $m > n$. Hence the index m must lie in the range $-n \leqslant m \leqslant n$ as already indicated.

Normalizing the associated Legendre polynomial by Eq. 12.106, we obtain the orthonormal function

$$\mathscr{P}_n^m(\cos\theta) = \sqrt{\frac{2n+1}{2} \frac{(n-m)!}{(n+m)!}} \, P_n^m(\cos\theta), \qquad -n \leqslant m \leqslant n. \tag{12.149}$$

Since we can show that (Exercise 12.5.5)

$$P_n^{-m}(\cos\theta) = (-1)^m \frac{(n-m)!}{(n+m)!} P_n^m(\cos\theta). \tag{12.150}$$

Eq. 12.149 holds for both positive and negative values of m, within a possible $(-1)^m$.

The function $\Phi_m(\varphi)$ (Eq. 12.143) is orthonormal with respect to the azimuthal angle φ, whereas the function $\mathscr{P}_n^m(\cos\theta)$ (Eq. 12.149) is orthonormal with respect to the polar angle θ. We take the product of the two and define

$$Y_n^m(\theta, \varphi) \equiv \sqrt{\frac{2n+1}{4\pi} \frac{(n-m)!}{(n+m)!}} \, P_n^m(\cos\theta) e^{im\varphi} \tag{12.151}$$

to obtain functions of two angles (and two indices) which are orthonormal over the spherical surface. These $Y_n^m(\theta, \varphi)$ are spherical harmonics. The complete orthogonality integral becomes

$$\int_{\varphi=0}^{2\pi} \int_{\theta=0}^{\pi} Y_{n_1}^{m_1,*}(\theta, \varphi) \, Y_{n_2}^{m_2}(\theta, \varphi) \sin\theta \, d\theta \, d\varphi = \delta_{n_1,n_2} \delta_{m_1,m_2}. \tag{12.152}$$

For convenient reference, the first few spherical harmonics defined by Eq. 12.151 are listed in Table 12.3. Note that in accordance with Eq. 12.150 Y_n^{-m} and Y_n^m differ in phase by $(-1)^m$. For convenience in certain quantum mechanical calculations, particularly in the quantum theory of angular momentum, it is customary to associate the $(-1)^m$ with the *positive* m spherical harmonic. This choice is called the Condon-Shortley phase. (In many other applications of spherical harmonics it is customary to ignore the relative phase, using Eq. 12.151 for $m \geqslant 0$ and $Y_n^{-m} = Y_n^{m*}$ for negative superscript.)

Table 12.3

Spherical Harmonics (Condon-Shortley Phase)

$$Y_0^0(\theta, \varphi) = \frac{1}{\sqrt{4\pi}}$$

$$Y_1^1(\theta, \varphi) = -\sqrt{\frac{3}{8\pi}} \sin \theta e^{i\varphi}$$

$$Y_1^0(\theta, \varphi) = \sqrt{\frac{3}{4\pi}} \cos \theta$$

$$Y_1^{-1}(\theta, \varphi) = +\sqrt{\frac{3}{8\pi}} \sin \theta e^{-i\varphi}$$

$$Y_2^2(\theta, \varphi) = \sqrt{\frac{5}{96\pi}} 3 \sin^2 \theta e^{2i\varphi}$$

$$Y_2^1(\theta, \varphi) = -\sqrt{\frac{5}{24\pi}} 3 \sin \theta \cos \theta e^{i\varphi}$$

$$Y_2^0(\theta, \varphi) = \sqrt{\frac{5}{4\pi}} \left(\frac{3}{2} \cos^2 \theta - \frac{1}{2}\right)$$

$$Y_2^{-1}(\theta, \varphi) = +\sqrt{\frac{5}{24\pi}} 3 \sin \theta \cos \theta e^{-i\varphi}$$

$$Y_2^{-2}(\theta, \varphi) = \sqrt{\frac{5}{96\pi}} 3 \sin^2 \theta \, e^{-2i\varphi}$$

Laplace series, fundamental expansion theorem.   Part of the importance of spherical harmonics lies in the completeness property, a consequence of the Sturm-Liouville form of Laplace's equation. This property, in this case, means that any function $f(\theta, \varphi)$ (with sufficient continuity properties) evaluated over the surface of the sphere can be expanded in a uniformly convergent double series of spherical harmonics[1] (Laplace's series),

$$f(\theta, \varphi) = \sum_{m,n} a_{mn} Y_n^m(\theta, \varphi). \tag{12.153}$$

If $f(\theta, \varphi)$ is known, the coefficients can be immediately found by the use of the orthogonality integral.

---

[1] For a proof of this fundamental theorem see E. W. Hobson, *The Theory of Spherical and Ellipsoidal Harmonics.* New York: Chelsea (1955), Chapter VII.

EXERCISES

12.6.1 Prove that

$$Y_L^M(0, \varphi) = \left(\frac{2L+1}{4\pi}\right)^{1/2} \delta_{M0}.$$

12.6.2 In the theory of Coulomb excitation of nuclei we encounter $Y_L^M(\pi/2, 0)$. Show that

$$Y_L^M\left(\frac{\pi}{2}, 0\right) = \left(\frac{2L+1}{4\pi}\right)^{1/2} \frac{[(L-M)!(L+M)!]^{1/2}}{(L-M)!!(L+M)!!} (-1)^{(L+M)/2} \quad \text{for} \quad L+M \text{ even}$$

$$= 0 \quad \text{for} \quad L+M \text{ odd}.$$

Here $(2n)!! = 2n(2n-2) \cdots 6.4.2,$

$(2n+1)!! = (2n+1)(2n-1) \cdots 5.3.1.$

12.6.3 Express the elements of the quadrupole moment tensor $x_i x_j$ as a linear combination of the spherical harmonics Y_2^M (and Y_0).

12.6.4 Maxwell's electromagnetic equations in spherical polar coordinates are satisfied by

$$E_r = \frac{\psi}{r},$$

$$E_\theta = \frac{1}{l(l+1)} \frac{1}{r} \frac{\partial}{\partial\theta} \frac{\partial}{\partial r}(r\psi),$$

$$E_\varphi = \frac{1}{l(l+1)} \frac{1}{r\sin\theta} \frac{\partial}{\partial\varphi} \frac{\partial}{\partial r}(r\psi),$$

$$B_r = 0,$$

$$B_\theta = \frac{i\omega}{l(l+1)c^2} \frac{1}{r\sin\theta} \frac{\partial}{\partial\varphi}(r\psi),$$

$$B_\varphi = \frac{-i\omega}{l(l+1)c^2} \frac{1}{r} \frac{\partial}{\partial\theta}(r\psi),$$

where

$$\psi(r, \theta, \varphi, t) = R(r)\,\Theta(\theta)\,\Phi(\varphi)e^{i\omega t}$$

and the functions R, Θ, and Φ satisfy

$$\frac{1}{r^2}\frac{d}{dr}\left(r^2 \frac{dR}{dr}\right) + \left(\frac{\omega^2}{c^2} - \frac{l(l+1)}{r^2}\right)R = 0,$$

$$\frac{1}{\sin\theta}\frac{d}{d\theta}\left(\sin\theta \frac{d\Theta}{d\theta}\right) + \left[l(l+1) - \frac{m^2}{\sin^2\theta}\right]\Theta = 0,$$

$$\frac{d^2\Phi}{d\varphi^2} + m^2\Phi = 0.$$

(a) For the particular case $l = 1$ and $m = 0$ show that

$$E_r = ke^{i(\omega t-kr)}\cos\theta\left[-\frac{1}{(kr)^2} + \frac{i}{(kr)^3}\right],$$

$$E_\theta = \frac{k}{2} e^{i(\omega t - kr)} \sin\theta \left[-\frac{i}{kr} - \frac{1}{(kr)^2} + \frac{i}{(kr)^3} \right],$$

$$B_\varphi = \frac{k}{2c} e^{i(\omega t - kr)} \sin\theta \left[-\frac{i}{kr} - \frac{1}{(kr)^2} \right],$$

provided $R(r)$ is chosen to represent an *outgoing* spherical wave.

(b) For $kr \gg 1$ show that the solution of (a) represents a *transverse* wave.

(c) For $kr \ll 1$ show that the solution reduces to the time-dependent field of an oscillating *electric* dipole.

12.6.5 In some circumstances it is desirable to replace the imaginary exponential of our spherical harmonic by sine or cosine. Morse and Feshbach define

$$Y^e_{mn} = P^m_n(\cos\theta) \cos m\varphi,$$
$$Y^0_{mn} = P^m_n(\cos\theta) \sin m\varphi,$$

where

$$\int_0^{2\pi} \int_0^\pi Y^{e\,\text{or}\,0}_{mn}(\theta, \varphi)]^2 \sin\theta \, d\theta \, d\varphi$$

$$= \frac{4\pi}{2(2n+1)} \frac{(n+m)!}{(n-m)!} \quad \text{for} \quad n = 1, 2, 3, \ldots$$

$$= 4\pi \quad \text{for} \quad n = 0 \;(Y^0_{00} \text{ does not exist}).$$

These spherical harmonics are often named according to the patterns of their positive and negative regions on the surface of a sphere—zonal harmonics for $m = 0$, sectoral harmonics for $m = n$, and tesseral harmonics for $0 < m < n$. For Y^e_{mn}, $n = 4$, $m = 0, 2, 4$, indicate on a diagram of a hemisphere (one diagram for each spherical harmonic) the regions in which the spherical harmonic is positive.

12.7   The Addition Theorem for Spherical Harmonics

Trigonometric identity.   In the following discussion (θ_1, φ_1) and (θ_2, φ_2) denote two different directions in our spherical coordinate system, separated by an angle γ. These angles satisfy the trigonometric identity

$$\cos\gamma = \cos\theta_1 \cos\theta_2 + \sin\theta_1 \sin\theta_2 \cos(\varphi_1 - \varphi_2), \qquad (12.154)$$

which is perhaps most easily proved by vector methods (cf. Chapter 1).

The addition theorem, then, asserts that

$$P_n(\cos\gamma) = \frac{4\pi}{2n+1} \sum_{m=-n}^{n} (-1)^m Y^m_n(\theta_1, \varphi_1) Y^{-m}_n(\theta_2, \varphi_2) \qquad (12.155)$$

or equivalently

$$P_n(\cos\gamma) = \frac{4\pi}{2n+1} \sum_{m=-n}^{n} Y^m_n(\theta_1, \varphi_1) Y^{m*}_n(\theta_2, \varphi_2), \qquad (12.156)$$

In terms of the associated Legendre polynomials the addition theorem is

$$P_n(\cos\gamma) = P_n(\cos\theta_1) P_n(\cos\theta_2)$$

$$+ 2 \sum_{m=1}^{n} \frac{(n-m)!}{(n+m)!} P^m_n(\cos\theta_1) P^m_n(\cos\theta_2) \cos m(\varphi_1 - \varphi_2). \qquad (12.157)$$

Derivation of addition theorem.   We now derive Eq. 12.156. Let $g(\theta, \varphi)$ be a function that may be expanded in a Laplace series

$$g(\theta_1, \varphi_1) = Y_n^m(\theta_1, \varphi_1) \qquad \text{relative to } x_1, y_1, z_1$$

$$= \sum_{m=-n}^{n} a_{nm} Y_n^m(\gamma, \psi) \qquad \text{relative to } x_2, y_2, z_2. \qquad (12.158)$$

Actually, the choice of the 0 of the azimuth angle ψ is irrelevant. At $\gamma = 0$ we have

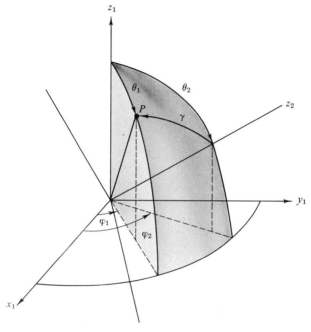

FIG. 12.13

$$g(\theta_1, \varphi_1) \mid_{\gamma=0} = a_{n0} \left(\frac{(2n+1)}{4\pi} \right)^{1/2} \qquad (12.159)$$

since $P_n(1) = 1$, whereas $P_n^m(1) = 0 \ (m \neq 0)$. Multiplying Eq. (12.158) by $Y_n^{0*}(\gamma, \psi)$ and integrating over the sphere, we obtain

$$\int g(\theta_1, \varphi_1) \, Y_n^{0*}(\gamma, \psi) \, d\Omega_{\gamma, \psi} = a_{n0}. \qquad (12.160)$$

Now, using Eq. 12.158, we may rewrite Eq. 12.160

$$\int Y_n^m(\theta_1, \varphi_1) \, Y_n^{0*}(\gamma, \psi) \, d\Omega = a_{n0}. \qquad (12.161)$$

As for Eq. 12.158, we assume that $P_n(\cos \gamma)$ has an expansion of the form

$$P_n(\cos \gamma) = \sum_{m=-n}^{n} b_{nm} Y_n^m(\theta_1, \varphi_1), \qquad (12.162)$$

where the b_{nm} will, of course, depend on θ_2, φ_2, that is, on the orientation of the z_2-axis. Multiplying by $Y_n^{m*}(\theta_1, \varphi_1)$ and integrating with respect to θ_1 and φ_1 over the sphere, we have

$$\int P_n(\cos \gamma) \, Y_n^{m*}(\theta_1, \varphi_1) \, d\Omega_{\theta_1, \, \varphi_1} = b_{nm}. \tag{12.163}$$

In terms of spherical harmonics, Eq. 12.163 becomes

$$\left(\frac{4\pi}{2n + 1}\right)^{1/2} \int Y_n^0(\gamma, \psi) \, Y_n^{m*}(\theta_1, \varphi_1) \, d\Omega = b_{nm}. \tag{12.164}$$

Note that the subscripts have been dropped from the solid angle element $d\Omega$. Since the range of integration is over all solid angles, the choice of polar axis is irrelevant. Then in a comparison of Eqs. 12.161 and 12.164,

$$b_{nm}^* = a_{n0} \left(\frac{4\pi}{2n + 1}\right)^{1/2}$$

$$= \frac{4\pi}{2n + 1} \, g(\theta_1, \varphi_1)|_{\gamma = 0} \quad \text{by Eq. 12.159}$$

$$= \frac{4\pi}{2n + 1} \, Y_n^m(\theta_2, \varphi_2) \quad \text{by Eq. 12.158.} \tag{12.165}$$

The change in subscripts occurs because

$$\begin{aligned} \theta_1 &\to \theta_2 \\ \varphi_1 &\to \varphi_2 \end{aligned} \quad \text{for} \quad \gamma \to 0.$$

Substituting back into Eq. 12.162, we obtain Eq. 12.156, thus proving our addition theorem.

The reader familiar with group theory will find a much more elegant proof of Eq. 12.156 by using the rotation group.[1]

One application of the addition theorem is in the construction of Green's function for the three-dimensional Laplace equation in spherical polar coordinates. If the source is on the polar axis at the point ($r = a$, $\theta = 0$, $\varphi = 0$), then by Eq. 12.4

$$\frac{1}{R} = \frac{1}{|\mathbf{r} - \mathbf{k}a|} = \sum_{n=0}^{\infty} P_n(\cos \gamma) \, \frac{a^n}{r^{n+1}}, \qquad r > a$$

$$= \sum_{n=0}^{\infty} P_n(\cos \gamma) \, \frac{r^n}{a^{n+1}}, \qquad r < a \tag{12.166}$$

Rotating our coordinate system to put the source at (a, θ_2, φ_2) and the point of

[1] Cf. M. E. Rose, *Elementary Theory of Angular Momentum*. New York: Wiley (1957)

observation at (r, θ_1, φ_1), we obtain

$$G(r, \theta_1, \varphi_1, a, \theta_2, \varphi_2) = \frac{1}{R}$$

$$= \sum_{n=0}^{\infty} \sum_{m=-n}^{n} \frac{4\pi}{2n+1} Y_n^{m*}(\theta_1, \varphi_1) Y_n^m(\theta_2, \varphi_2) \frac{a^n}{r^{n+1}}, \qquad r > a,$$

$$= \sum_{n=0}^{\infty} \sum_{m=-n}^{n} \frac{4\pi}{2n+1} Y_n^{m*}(\theta_1, \varphi_1) Y_n^m(\theta_2, \varphi_2) \frac{r^n}{a^{n+1}}, \qquad r < a.$$

$$(12.167)$$

In Section 16.5 (Exercises 16.5.9 and 10) this argument is reversed to provide another derivation of the Legendre polynomial addition theorem.

EXERCISES

12.7.1 In proving the addition theorem it was assumed that $Y_n^k(\theta_1, \varphi_1)$ could be expanded in a series of $Y_n^m(\theta_2, \varphi_2)$ in which m varied from $-n$ to $+n$ but n was held fixed. What arguments can you develop to justify summing only over the upper index m and *not* over the lower index n? *Hints.* One possibility is to examine the homogeneity of the Y_n^m, that is, Y_n^m may be expressed entirely in terms of the form $\cos^{n-p} \theta \sin^p \theta$ or $x^{n-p-s} y^p z^s / r^n$. Another possibility is to examine the behavior of the Legendre equation $[\nabla^2 + n(n+1)/r^2] P_n (\cos \theta) = 0$ under rotation of the coordinate system.

12.7.2 An atomic electron with angular momentum L and magnetic quantum number M has a wave function

$$\psi(r, \theta, \varphi) = f(r) Y_L^M(\theta, \varphi).$$

Show that the sum of the electron densities in a given complete shell is spherically symmetric, that is, that $\sum_{M=-L}^{L} \psi^*(r, \theta, \varphi) \psi(r, \theta, \varphi)$ is independent of θ and φ.

12.7.3 The potential of an electron at point $\mathbf{r}_e$ in the field of Z protons at $\mathbf{r}_p$ is

$$\varphi = -\frac{e^2}{4\pi\varepsilon_0} \sum_{p=1}^{Z} \frac{1}{|\mathbf{r}_e - \mathbf{r}_p|}.$$

Show that this may be written

$$\varphi = -\frac{e^2}{4\pi\varepsilon_0 r_e} \sum_{p=1}^{Z} \sum_{L,M} \left(\frac{r_p}{r_e}\right)^L \frac{4\pi}{2L+1} Y_L^M{}^*(\theta_p, \varphi_p) Y_L^{M*}(\theta_e, \varphi_e),$$

where $r_e > r_p$. How should φ be written for $r_e < r_p$?

12.7.4 Two protons are *uniformly* distributed within the same spherical volume. If the coordinates of one element of charge are $(r_1, \theta_1, \varphi_1)$ and the coordinates of the other are $(r_2, \theta_2, \varphi_2)$ and r_{12} is the distance between them, the element of energy of repulsion will be given by

$$d\psi = \rho^2 \frac{dv_1\, dv_2}{r_{12}} = \rho^2 \frac{r_1^2\, dr_1 \sin \theta_1\, d\theta_1\, d\varphi_1\, r_2^2\, dr_2 \sin \theta_2\, d\theta_2\, d\varphi_2}{r_{12}}.$$

Here $\rho = \dfrac{\text{charge}}{\text{volume}} = \dfrac{3e}{4\pi R^3}$,   charge density,

$$r_{12}^2 = r_1^2 + r_2^2 - 2r_1 r_2 \cos \gamma.$$

Calculate the total electrostatic energy (of repulsion) of the two protons. This calculation is used in accounting for the mass difference in "mirror" nuclei, such as O^{15} and N^{15}.

$$\textit{Ans. For } \begin{array}{ll} r_2 > r_1 & \dfrac{3}{5}\dfrac{e^2}{R} \\[2mm] r_2 < r_1 & \dfrac{3}{5}\dfrac{e^2}{R} \end{array} \left.\begin{array}{l} \\ \end{array}\right\} \dfrac{6}{5}\dfrac{e^2}{R} \text{ (total)}.$$

This is *double* that required to create a uniformly charged sphere because we have two separate cloud charges interacting, *not* one charge interacting with itself (with permutation of pairs *not* considered).

12.7.5   Each of the two $1s$ electrons in helium may be described by a hydrogenic wave function

$$\psi(\mathbf{r}) = \left(\frac{Z^3}{\pi a_0^3}\right)^{1/2} e^{-Zr/a0}$$

in the absence of the other electron. Here Z, the atomic number, is 2. The symbol a_0 is the Bohr radius, $\hbar^2/me^2$. Find the mutual potential energy of the two electrons given by

$$\int \psi^*(\mathbf{r}_1)\, \psi^*(\mathbf{r}_2)\, \frac{e^2}{r_{12}}\, \psi(\mathbf{r}_1) \psi(\mathbf{r}_2)\, d\mathbf{r}_1\, d\mathbf{r}_2. \qquad\qquad \textit{Ans. } \frac{5e^2 Z}{8a_0}.$$

Note. $d\mathbf{r}_1 = r_1^2\, dr_1 \sin\theta_1\, d\theta_1\, d\varphi_1$,
$\qquad r_{12} = |\mathbf{r}_1 - \mathbf{r}_2|$.

12.7.6   A hydrogen electron in a $2p$ orbit has a charge distribution

$$\rho = \frac{1}{64\pi a_0^5}\, r^2 e^{-r/a_0} \sin^2\theta,$$

where a_0 is the Bohr radius, $\hbar^2/me^2$. Find the electrostatic potential corresponding to this charge distribution.

12.7.7   The electric current density produced by a $2p$ electron in a hydrogen atom is

$$\mathbf{J} = \boldsymbol{\varphi}_0\, \frac{\hbar}{32ma_0^5}\, e^{-r/a_0}\, r \sin\theta.$$

Using

$$\mathbf{A}(\mathbf{r}_1) = \int \frac{\mathbf{J}(\mathbf{r}_2)}{|\mathbf{r}_1 - \mathbf{r}_2|}\, d\mathbf{r}_2,$$

find the magnetic vector potential produced by this hydrogen electron. *Hint.* Use the addition theorem to eliminate γ, the angle included between $\mathbf{r}_1$ and $\mathbf{r}_2$. Integrate $d\mathbf{r}_2$ over the sphere to get the total coulomb energy.

12.8 Integrals of the Product of Three Spherical Harmonics

Frequently in quantum mechanics we encounter integrals of the general form

$$\int Y_{L_1}^{M_1*} Y_{L_2}^{M_2} Y_{L_3}^{M_3}\, d\Omega \quad \text{or} \quad \int Y_{L_1}^{M_1*} P_{L_2} Y_{L_3}^{M_3}\, d\Omega,$$

in which the integration is over all solid angles. The first factor in the integrand may come from the wave function of a final state and the third factor from an initial state, whereas the middle factor may represent an operator that is being evaluated or whose "matrix element" is being determined.

By using group theoretical methods, as in the quantum theory of angular momentum, it is possible to give a general expression for the forms listed. The analysis involves the vector-addition or Clebsch-Gordan coefficients, which have been tabulated. Three general restrictions appear.[1] (1) The integral vanishes unless the *vector* sum of the L's (angular momentum) is zero, $|L_1 - L_3| \leqslant L_2 \leqslant L_1 + L_3$. (2) The integral vanishes unless $M_2 + M_3 = M_1$. Here we have the theoretical foundation of the vector model of atomic spectroscopy. (3) Finally, the integral vanishes unless the product $Y_{L_1}^{M_1*} \, Y_{L_2}^{M_2} \, Y_{L_3}^{M_3}$ is even, that is, unless $M_1 + M_2 + M_3 + L_1 + L_2 + L_3$ is an even integer. This is a parity conservation law.

Details of this general and powerful approach will be found in the references. The reader will note that the vector-addition coefficients are developed in terms of the Condon-Shortley phase convention in which the $(-1)^m$ of Eq. 12.150 is associated with the positive m.

It is possible to evaluate many of the commonly encountered integrals of this form with the techniques already developed. The integration over azimuth may be carried out by inspection,

$$\int_0^{2\pi} e^{-iM_1\varphi} e^{iM_2\varphi} e^{iM_3\varphi} \, d\varphi = 2\pi \delta_{M_2 + M_3 - M_1, 0} \, . \tag{12.168}$$

Physically this corresponds to the conservation of the z-component of angular momentum.

Application of recurrence relations.   A glance at Table 12.3 will show that the θ-dependence of $Y_{L_2}^{M_2}$, that is, $P_{L_2}^{M_2}(\theta)$, can be expressed in terms of $\cos \theta$ and $\sin \theta$. However, a factor of $\cos \theta$ or $\sin \theta$ may be combined with the $Y_{L_3}^{M_3}$ factor by using the associated Legendre polynomial recurrence relations. For instance, from Eqs. 12.88 and 12.89 we get

$$\cos \theta Y_L^M = + \left[\frac{(L - M + 1)(L + M + 1)}{(2L + 1)(2L + 3)} \right]^{1/2} Y_{L+1}^M + \left[\frac{(L - M)(L + M)}{(2L - 1)(2L + 1)} \right]^{1/2} Y_{L-1}^M \tag{12.169}$$

$$\sin \theta Y_L^M = + \left[\frac{(L + M + 1)(L + M + 2)}{(2L + 1)(2L + 3)} \right]^{1/2} Y_{L+1}^{M+1} e^{-i\varphi}$$

$$- \left[\frac{(L - M)(L - M - 1)}{(2L - 1)(2L + 1)} \right]^{1/2} Y_{L-1}^{M+1} e^{-i\varphi} \tag{12.170}$$

$$\sin \theta Y_L^M = - \left[\frac{(L - M + 1)(L - M + 2)}{(2L + 1)(2L + 3)} \right]^{1/2} Y_{L+1}^{M-1} e^{i\varphi}$$

$$+ \left[\frac{(L + M)(L + M - 1)}{(2L - 1)(2L + 1)} \right]^{1/2} Y_{L-1}^{M-1} e^{i\varphi}. \tag{12.171}$$

[1] E. U. Condon and G. H. Shortley, *The Theory of Atomic Spectra*. Cambridge: Cambridge University Press (1951). M. E. Rose, *Elementary Theory of Angular Momentum*. New York: Wiley (1957). A. Edmonds, *Angular Momentum in Quantum Mechanics*. Princeton, New Jersey: Princeton University Press (1957). E. P. Wigner, *Group Theory and Its Applications to Quantum Mechanics* (translated by J. J. Griffin). New York: Academic Press (1959).

These equations do *not* include the possible $(-1)^M$ factor.

Using these equations, we obtain

$$\int Y_{L_1}^{M_1*} \cos\theta\, Y_L^M \, d\Omega = \left[\frac{(L-M+1)(L+M+1)}{(2L+1)(2L+3)}\right]^{1/2} \delta_{M_1,M}\,\delta_{L_1,L+1}$$

$$+ \left[\frac{(L-M)(L+M)}{(2L-1)(2L+1)}\right]^{1/2} \delta_{M_1,M}\delta_{L_1,L-1}. \qquad (12.172)$$

The occurence of the Kronecker delta $(L_1, L \pm 1)$ is an aspect of the conservation of angular momentum. Physically, this integral arises in a consideration of ordinary atomic electromagnetic radiation (electric dipole). It leads to the familiar selection rule that transitions to an atomic level with orbital angular momentum quantum number L_1 can originate only from atomic levels with quantum numbers $L_1 - 1$ or $L_1 + 1$. The application to expressions such as

$$\text{quadrupole moment} \sim \int Y_L^{M*} P_2(\cos\theta) Y_L^M \, d\Omega$$

is more involved but perfectly straightforward (cf. Exercise 12.8.4).

Slater coefficients.　　　Integrals of the product of three spherical harmonics are also encountered in the evaluation of the interaction energy between two atomic electrons. We have integrals of the form

$$\int \psi_\alpha^*(1)\, \psi_\alpha(1)\, \frac{1}{r_{12}}\, \psi_\beta^*(2)\, \psi_\beta(2)\, d\tau_1\, d\tau_2.$$

If we expand $r_{12} = |\mathbf{r}_1 - \mathbf{r}_2|$ by the generating function expansion, expand the resulting $P_k(\cos\gamma)$ by the addition theorem, and assume the angular dependence of wave functions $\psi(1)$ and $\psi(2)$ to be $Y_{l_1}^{m_1}(\theta_1, \varphi_1)$ and $Y_{l_2}^{m_2}(\theta_2, \varphi_2)$, respectively, the foregoing integral will separate, giving us a radial integral and *two* integrals of the form

$$a_k'(l_1, m_1) \equiv \sqrt{\frac{4\pi}{2k+1}} \int Y_{l_1}^{m_1*} Y_k^0 Y_{l_1}^{m_1} \, d\Omega. \qquad (12.173)$$

From exchange terms in our total wave function $[\psi_\alpha(1)\to\psi_\alpha(2),\ \psi_\beta(2)\to\psi_\beta(1)]$ we get more integrals of the form

$$b_k'(l_1, m_1, l_2, m_2) \equiv \sqrt{\frac{4\pi}{2k+1}} \int Y_{l_2}^{m_2*} Y_k^{m_2-m_1} Y_{l_1}^{m_1} \, d\Omega. \qquad (12.174)$$

The combinations needed for the computation of atomic wave functions are

$$a_k(l_1, m_1, l_2, m_2) = a_k'(l_1, m_1) \cdot a_k'(l_2, m_2) \qquad (12.175)$$

$$b_k(l_1, m_1, l_2, m_2) = [b_k'(l_1, m_1, l_2, m_2)]^2. \qquad (12.176)$$

These a_k and b_k, often called Slater coefficients, are tabulated in texts that deal with atomic structure.[1]

EXERCISES

12.8.1 Evaluate

$$\int P_{L+1}^{M+1}(\cos \theta) \sin \theta \, P_L^M (\cos \theta) \, d\Omega.$$

12.8.2 Verify

(a) $a_0'(l, m) = 1$,

(b) $a_1'(1, m) = 0$,

(c) $a_2'(0, 0) = 0$,

(d) $a_2'(1, 0) = \frac{2}{5}$,

(e) $a_2'(1, \pm 1) = -\frac{1}{5}$.

12.8.3 Verify

(a) $\int Y_L^M Y_0^0 Y_L^{M*} \, d\Omega = \dfrac{1}{\sqrt{4\pi}}$,

(b) $\int Y_L^M Y_1^0 Y_{L+1}^{M*} \, d\Omega = \sqrt{\dfrac{3}{4\pi}} \sqrt{\dfrac{(L+M+1)(L-M+1)}{(2L+1)(2L+3)}}$,

(c) $\int Y_L^M Y_1^1 Y_{L+1}^{M+1*} \, d\Omega = \sqrt{\dfrac{3}{8\pi}} \sqrt{\dfrac{(L+M+1)(L+M+2)}{(2L+1)(2L+3)}}$,

(d) $\int Y_L^M Y_1^1 Y_{L-1}^{M+1*} \, d\Omega = \sqrt{\dfrac{3}{8\pi}} \sqrt{\dfrac{(L-M)(L-M-1)}{(2L-1)(2L+1)}}$.

These integrals were used in an investigation of the angular correlation of internal conversion electrons.

12.8.4 The theory of nuclear quadrupole moments contains the expression

$$\int Y_L^{M*} (\theta, \varphi) \cos^2 \theta \, Y_L^M(\theta, \varphi) \, d\Omega = \frac{1}{2L+3}\left[\frac{2(L-M)(L+M)}{2L-1} + 1\right].$$

Verify this relation.

12.8.5 The quantum mechanical angular momentum operators $L_x \pm iL_y$ are given by

$$L_x + iL_y = e^{i\varphi}\left(\frac{\partial}{\partial\theta} + i \cot \theta \frac{\partial}{\partial\varphi}\right),$$

$$L_x - iL_y = -e^{-i\varphi}\left(\frac{\partial}{\partial\theta} - i \cot \theta \frac{\partial}{\partial\varphi}\right).$$

Show that

(a) $(L_x + iL_y)Y_{LM}(\theta, \varphi) = -\sqrt{(L - M)(L + M + 1)} \; Y_{L,M+1}(\theta, \varphi)$

(b) $(L_x - iL_y)Y_{LM}(\theta, \varphi) = -\sqrt{(L + M)(L - M + 1)} \; Y_{L,M-1}(\theta, \varphi)$.

Use of the Condon-Shortley phase would eliminate the minus sign before the square roots.

[1] D. R. Hartree, *The Calculation of Atomic Structures*. New York: Wiley (1953), Chapter 3. Condon-Shortley, *The Theory of Atomic Spectra*, §9[6], Tables 1[6], 2[6].

12.9   Legendre Functions of the Second Kind, $Q_n(z)$

In all the analysis so far in this chapter we have been dealing with one solution of Legendre's equation, the solution $P_n(\cos \theta)$, which is regular (finite) at the two singular points of the differential equation, $\cos \theta = \pm 1$. From the general theory of differential equations it is known that a second solution exists. We shall develop this second solution, Q_n, by a series solution of Legendre's equation. Later a closed form will be obtained.

Series solutions of Legendre's equation.   To solve

$$\frac{d}{dx}\left[(1 - x^2)\frac{dy}{dx}\right] + n(n + 1)y = 0 \tag{12.177}$$

we proceed as in Chapter 8, letting

$$y = \sum_{\lambda=0}^{\infty} a_\lambda x^{k+\lambda}{}^1, \tag{12.178}$$

with

$$y' = \sum_{\lambda-0}^{\infty} (k + \lambda)a_\lambda x^{k+\lambda-1}, \tag{12.179}$$

$$y'' = \sum_{\lambda=0}^{\infty} (k + \lambda)(k + \lambda - 1)a_\lambda x^{k+\lambda-2}. \tag{12.180}$$

Substitution into the original differential equation gives

$$\sum_{\lambda=0}^{\infty} (k + \lambda)(k + \lambda - 1)a_\lambda x^{k+\lambda-2}$$
$$+ \sum_{\lambda=0}^{\infty} [n(n + 1) - 2(k + \lambda) - (k + \lambda)(k + \lambda - 1)]a_\lambda x^{k+\lambda} = 0. \tag{12.181}$$

The *indicial equation is*

$$k(k - 1) = 0, \tag{12.182}$$

with solutions $k = 0, 1$. We try first $k = 0$ with $a_0 = 1$, $a_1 = 0$. Then our series is described by the recurrence relation

$$(\lambda + 2)(\lambda + 1)a_{\lambda+2} + [n(n + 1) - 2\lambda - \lambda(\lambda - 1)]a_\lambda = 0, \tag{12.183}$$

which becomes

$$a_{\lambda+2} = -\frac{(n + \lambda + 1)(n - \lambda)}{(\lambda + 1)(\lambda + 2)} a_\lambda. \tag{12.184}$$

Labeling this series p_n, we have

$$p_n(x) = 1 - \frac{n(n + 1)}{2!} x^2 + \frac{(n - 2)n(n + 1)(n + 3)}{4!} x^4 + \cdots. \tag{12.185}$$

---

[1] Note that x may be replaced by the complex variable z.

The second solution of the indicial equation, $k = 1$, with $a_0 = 1$, $a_1 = 0$, leads to the recurrence relation

$$a_{\lambda+2} = -\frac{(n + \lambda + 2)(n - \lambda - 1)}{(\lambda + 2)(\lambda + 3)} a_\lambda. \qquad (12.186)$$

Labeling this series q_n, we obtain

$$q_n(x) = x - \frac{(n - 1)(n + 2)}{3!} x^3 + \frac{(n - 3)(n - 1)(n + 2)(n + 4)}{5!} x^5 - \cdots. \qquad (12.187)$$

Our general solution of Eq. 12.177, then, is

$$y_n(x) = A_n p_n(x) + B_n q_n(x), \qquad (12.188)$$

provided we have convergence.

For n, a positive even integer (or zero), series p_n terminates, and with a proper choice of normalizing factor

$$P_n(x) = (-1)^{n/2} \frac{n!}{2^n[(n/2)!]^2} p_n(x)$$

$$= (-1)^s \frac{(2s)!}{2^{2s}(s!)^2} p_{2s}(x) = (-1)^s \frac{(2s - 1)!!}{(2s)!!} p_{2s}(x), \qquad \text{for} \quad n = 2s. \qquad (12.189)$$

If n is a positive odd integer, series q_n terminates after a finite number of terms, and we may write

$$P_n(x) = (-1)^{(n-1)/2} \frac{n!}{2^{n-1}\{[(n - 1)/2]!\}^2} q_n(x)$$

$$= (-1)^s \frac{(2s + 1)!}{2^{2s}(s!)^2} q_{2s+1}(x) = (-1)^s \frac{(2s + 1)!!}{(2s)!!} q_{2s+1}(x), \qquad \text{for } n = 2s + 1.$$
$$(12.190)$$

Note that these expressions hold for all real values of x, $-\infty < x < \infty$, and for complex values in the finite complex plane. The constants that multiply p_n and q_n are chosen to make P_n agree with Legendre polynomials given by the generating function.

It is sometimes convenient to reverse the order of the terms in the series. This may be done by putting

$$s = \frac{n}{2} - \lambda \qquad \text{in the first form of } P_n(x), \qquad n \text{ even,}$$

$$s = \frac{n - 1}{2} - \lambda \qquad \text{in the second form of } P_n(x), \qquad n \text{ odd,}$$

so that Eqs. 12.189 and 12.190 become

$$P_n(x) = \sum_{s=0}^{[n/2]} (-1)^s \frac{(2n - 2s)!}{2^n s!(n - s)!(n - 2s)!} x^{n-2s}, \qquad (12.191)$$

where the upper limit $m = n/2$ (for n even) or $(n - 1)/2$ (for n odd). This reproduces Eq. 12.8 of Section 12.1, which is obtained directly from the generating function. This agreement with Eq. 12.8 is the reason for the particular choice of normalization in Eqs. 12.189 and 12.190.

We see immediately that for very large x

$$P_n(x) \to \frac{(2n)!}{2^n(n!)^2} \, x^n. \tag{12.192}$$

For use in Section 12.10 we need P_n of pure imaginary argument. If x in Eq. 12.191 is replaced by $i\zeta$, we have

$$P_n(i\zeta) = (-1)^{n/2} \sum_{s=0}^{[n/2]} \frac{(2n - 2s)!}{2^n s!(n - s)!(n - 2s)!} \, \zeta^{n-2s}. \tag{12.193}$$

$Q_n(x)$, functions of the second kind.   It will be noticed that we have used only p_n for n even and q_n for n odd (because they terminated for this choice of n). We may now define a second solution of Legendre's equation by

$$Q_n(x) = (-1)^{n/2} \frac{[(n/2)!]^2 2^n}{n!} \, q_n(x) = (-1)^s \frac{(2s)!!}{(2s - 1)!!} \, q_{2s}(x), \qquad \text{for } n \text{ even, } n = 2s,$$
$$\tag{12.194}$$

$$Q_n(x) = (-1)^{(n+1)/2} \frac{\{[(n - 1)/2]!\}^2 2^{n-1}}{n!} \, p_n(x)$$

$$= (-1)^{s+1} \frac{(2s)!!}{(2s + 1)!!} \, p_{2s+1}(x), \qquad \text{for } n \text{ odd, } n = 2s + 1. \tag{12.195}$$

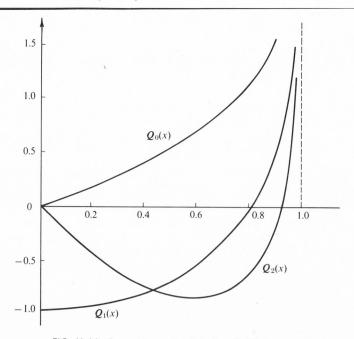

FIG. 12.14   Second Legendre function, $Q_n(x)$, $0 \leqslant x < 1$

This choice of normalizing factors forces Q_n to satisfy the same recurrence relations as P_n. This may be verified by substituting Eqs. 12.194 and 12.195 into Eq. 12.17 and 12.26. Inspection of the (series) recurrence relations (Eqs. 12.184 and 12.186), that is by the Cauchy ratio test shows that $Q_n(x)$ will converge for $-1 < x < 1$. If $|x| \geqslant 1$, our second solution *diverges*.

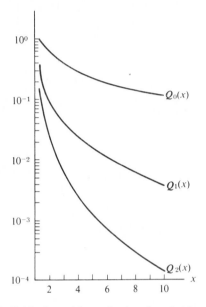

FIG. 12.15   Second Legendre function, $Q_n(x)$, $x > 1$

To develop a second solution in the range $x^2 > 1$, we seek a solution of Eq. 12.177 in the form of a *descending* power series. Let

$$y = \sum_{\lambda=0}^{\infty} b_{-\lambda} x^{k-\lambda} \tag{12.196}$$

with

$$y' = \sum_{\lambda=0}^{\infty} (k - \lambda) b_{-\lambda} x^{k-\lambda-1} \tag{12.197}$$

$$y'' = \sum_{\lambda=0}^{\infty} (k - \lambda)(k - \lambda - 1) b_{-\lambda} x^{k-\lambda-2}. \tag{12.198}$$

Substitution of these equations into Eq. 12.177 gives

$$\sum_{\lambda=0}^{\infty} (k - \lambda)(k - \lambda - 1) b_{-\lambda} x^{k-\lambda-2}$$
$$+ \sum_{\lambda=0}^{\infty} [n(n + 1) - 2(k - \lambda) - (k - \lambda)(k - \lambda - 1)] b_{-\lambda} x^{k-\lambda} = 0. \tag{12.199}$$

Requiring the coefficient of x^k to vanish leads to the indicial equation

$$k(k + 1) - n(n + 1) = 0, \tag{12.200}$$

with solutions

$$k = n, \qquad -n - 1. \tag{12.201}$$

For integral n, the solution $k = n$ $(n \geqslant 0)$ leads to the familiar Legendre polynomials $P_n(x)$. The second solution, $k = -n - 1$, leads to a series with a recurrence relation

$$b_{-\lambda}(n + \lambda + 1)(n + \lambda + 2) + [n(n + 1) - (n + \lambda + 3)(n + \lambda + 2)]b_{-\lambda - 2} = 0 \tag{12.202}$$

or

$$b_{-\lambda - 2} = \frac{(n + \lambda + 1)(n + \lambda + 2)}{(\lambda + 2)(2n + \lambda + 3)} b_{-\lambda}. \tag{12.203}$$

This gives

$$y(x) = b_0 x^{-n-1}\left[1 + \frac{(n + 1)(n + 2)}{2(2n + 3)} x^{-2} + \frac{(n + 1)(n + 2)(n + 3)(n + 4)}{2 \cdot 4 \cdot (2n + 3)(2n + 5)} x^{-4} + \cdots \right] \tag{12.204}$$

with

$$b_{-2s} = \frac{(n + 1)(n + 2) \cdots (n + 2s)}{2 \cdot 4 \cdots (2s)(2n + 3)(2n + s) \cdots (2n + 2s + 1)} b_0. \tag{12.205}$$

This may also be written

$$y(x) = b_0 x^{-n-1} \sum_{s=0}^{\infty} \frac{(n + s)!(n + 2s)!(2n + 1)!}{s!(n!)^2(2n + 2s + 1)!} x^{-2s}. \tag{12.206}$$

One of the standard forms of the second solution is obtained by choosing

$$b_0 = \frac{2^n(n!)^2}{(2n + 1)!}, \tag{12.207}$$

which leads to

$$Q_n(x) = 2^n x^{-n-1} \sum_{s=0}^{\infty} \frac{(n + s)!(n + 2s)!}{s!(2n + 2s + 1)!} x^{-2s}, \qquad x^2 > 1. \tag{12.208}$$

By substituting in this series we see that $Q_n(x)$, $x^2 > 1$, still satisfies the same recurrence relations as $P_n(x)$.

Closed form solutions.   Frequently, a closed form of the second solution, $Q_n(z)$, is desirable. This may be obtained by the method discussed in Section 8.5. We may write

$$Q_n(z) = P_n(z)\left\{ A_n + B_n \int^z \frac{dx}{(1 - x^2)[P_n(x)]^2} \right\}, \tag{12.209}$$

in which the constant A_n replaces the evaluation of the integral at the arbitrary lower limit. Both constants, A_n and B_n, may be determined for special cases.

For $n = 0$, Eq. 12.209 yields

$$Q_0(z) = P_0(z)\left\{A_0 + B_0 \int^z \frac{dx}{(1 - x^2)[P_0(x)]^2}\right\}$$

$$= A_0 + B_0 \frac{1}{2} \ln \frac{1 + z}{1 - z}$$

$$= A_0 + B_0\left(z + \frac{z^3}{3} + \frac{z^5}{5} + \cdots + \frac{z^{2s+1}}{2s + 1} + \cdots\right), \qquad (12.210)$$

the last expression following from a Maclaurin expansion of the logarithm. Comparing this with the series solution (Eq. 12.187), we obtain

$$Q_0(z) = q_0(z) = z + \frac{z^3}{3} + \frac{z^5}{5} + \cdots + \frac{z^{2s+1}}{2s + 1} + \cdots, \qquad (12.211)$$

we have $A_0 = 0$, $B_0 = 1$. Similar results follow for $n = 1$. We obtain

$$Q_1(z) = z\left[A_1 + B_1 \int^z \frac{dx}{(1 - x^2)x^2}\right]$$

$$= A_1 z + B_1 z\left(\frac{1}{2} \ln \frac{1 + z}{1 - z} - \frac{1}{z}\right). \qquad (12.212)$$

Expanding in a power series and comparing with $Q_1(z) = -p_1(z)$, we have $A_1 = 0$, $B_1 = 1$. Therefore we may write

$$Q_0(z) = \frac{1}{2} \ln \frac{1 + z}{1 - z}$$

$$Q_1(z) = \frac{1}{2} z \ln \frac{1 + z}{1 - z} - 1, \qquad |z| < 1. \qquad (12.213)$$

Perhaps the best way of determining the higher-order $Q_n(z)$ is to use the recurrence relation (Eq. 12.17), which may be verified for both $x^2 < 1$ and for $x^2 > 1$ by substituting in the series forms. This recurrence relation technique yields

$$Q_2(z) = \frac{1}{2} P_2(z) \ln \frac{1 + z}{1 - z} - \frac{3}{2} P_1(z). \qquad (12.214)$$

Repeated application of the recurrence formula leads to

$$Q_n(z) = \frac{1}{2} P_n(z) \ln \frac{1 + z}{1 - z} - \frac{2n - 1}{1 \cdot n} P_{n-1}(z) - \frac{2n - 5}{3(n - 1)} P_{n-3}(z) - \cdots. \qquad (12.215)$$

From the form $\ln[(1 + z)/(1 - z)]$ it will be seen that if z is real these expressions hold in the range $-1 < x < 1$. If we wish to have closed forms valid outside this range we need only replace B_n by $B_n \ln(-1)$. We obtain

$$Q_0(z) = \frac{1}{2} \ln \frac{z + 1}{z - 1} \qquad (12.216)$$

$$Q_1(z) = \frac{1}{2} z \ln \frac{z+1}{z-1} - 1, \qquad |z| > 1. \qquad (12.217)$$

and so on. Actually, these expressions hold over the entire complex plane if we treat the line segment $-1 \leqslant x \leqslant 1$ on the real axis as a cut line. Care must be used in the complex plane, for the logarithm is a multivalued function. For instance,

$$\ln(-1) = \ln e^{i\pi + 2n\pi i} \qquad (12.218)$$

$$= i\pi + 2n\pi i,$$

with n any integer. The reader may verify that Eqs. 12.216 and 12.217 agree with Eq. 12.208. This was the basis for our choice of b_0.

In the next section we shall want $Q_n(y)$ on the imaginary axis. From the series form of $Q_n(y)$, $|z| > 1$, we may write

$$Q_n(iy) = (-i)^{n+1} 2^n y^{-n-1} \sum_{s=0}^{\infty} \frac{(n+s)!(n+2s)!(-i)^{2s}}{s!(2n+2s+1)!} y^{-2s}, \qquad (12.219)$$

replacing y by iy. In the closed form it is convenient to take

$$\ln \frac{iy+1}{iy-1} = 2i\left(-\frac{1}{y} + \frac{1}{3y^3} - \frac{1}{5y^5} + \cdots\right)$$

$$= -2i \cot^{-1} y. \qquad (12.220)$$

With this substitution, Eq. 12.215 becomes

$$Q_n(iy) = \frac{1}{2} P_n(iy)(-2i)\cot^{-1} y - \frac{2n-1}{n} P_{n-1}(iy) - \frac{2n-5}{3(n-1)} P_{n-3}(iy) - \cdots, \qquad (12.221)$$

with special cases,

$$Q_0(iy) = -i \cot^{-1} y, \qquad (12.222)$$

$$Q_1(iy) = y \cot^{-1} y - 1. \qquad (12.223)$$

There is a discontinuity at $y = 0$ arising from the arc cotangent. Apart from this, Eq. 12.221 defines $Q_n(iy)$ for all real y, $0 < y < \infty$.

For convenient reference some special values of $Q_n(z)$ are given.

1. $Q_n(1) = \infty$, from the logarithmic term (Eq. 12.215).

2. $Q_n(\infty) = 0$, from the series expansion, (Eq. 12.208).

3. $Q_n(-z) = (-1)^{n+1} Q_n(z)$. This follows from the series form. It may also be derived by using $Q_0(z)$, $Q_1(z)$ and the recurrence relation (Eq. 12.17).

4. $Q_n(0) = 0$, for n even, by (3) above.

5. $Q_n(0) = (-1)^{(n+1)/2} \frac{\{[(n-1)/2]!\}^2}{n!} 2^{n-1} = (-1)^{s+1} \frac{(2s)!!}{(2s+1)!!}$,

$$\text{for} \quad n \text{ odd}, n = 2s+1.$$

This last result comes from the series form (Eq. 12.195) with $p_n(0) = 1$.

As with the Bessel functions, a Wronskian relation can be developed.[1] We find

$$(1 - z^2)[P_n(z) Q_n'(z) - P_n'(z) Q_n(z)] = 1, \tag{12.224}$$

the constant being independent of n, $n = 0, 1, 2, 3, \ldots$. If we use Eq. 12.26 to eliminate the derivatives P_n' and Q_n', Eq. 12.224 becomes

$$P_n(z)Q_{n-1}(z) - P_{n-1}(z) Q_n(z) = \frac{1}{n}. \tag{12.225}$$

Associated Legendre functions of the second kind, $Q_n^m(x)$, may be developed in analogy to the associated Legendre polynomials of Section 12.5. Analogous to Eq. 12.84, we may define

$$Q_n^m(x) = (-1)^m (1 - x^2)^{m/2} \frac{d^m}{dx^m} Q_n(x) \tag{12.226}$$

and

$$Q_n^{-m}(x) = (-1)^m \frac{(n - m)!}{(n + m)!} Q_n^m(x), \qquad -1 < x < 1, m \geqslant 0. \tag{12.227}$$

Some authors omit either or both of the $(-1)^m$ factors. Using these definitions, we readily obtain

$$Q_1^1(x) = -(1 - x^2)^{1/2}\left(\frac{x}{1 - x^2} + \frac{1}{2} \ln \frac{1 + x}{1 - x}\right),$$

$$Q_1^{-1}(x) = -\tfrac{1}{2} Q_1^1(x). \tag{12.228}$$

The $\ln[(1 + x)/(1 - x)]$ is characteristic of these $Q_n^m(x)$ for $m \neq 0$ as well as $m = 0$. For large x ($x^2 > 1$) or for the entire complex plane with $-1 < x < 1$ as a cut line AMS-55 gives

$$Q_n^m(z) = (z^2 - 1)^{m/2} \frac{d^m}{dz^m} Q_n(z), \qquad m \geqslant 0 \tag{12.229}$$

and Eq. 12.227 for negative superscript.

Integral representations. From the Schaefli integral analysis (Section 12.4) a second, independent solution of Legendre's equation is

$$\int_C \frac{(t^2 - 1)^\nu}{(t - z)^{\nu+1}} dt,$$

in which the figure-eight contour (a) keeps the integrated function single-valued and (b) develops a solution distinct from $P_\nu(z)$. With the normalizing factor $(4i \sin \pi \nu)^{-1}$, we have

$$Q_\nu(z) = \frac{1}{4i \sin \pi \nu} \int_C \frac{(t^2 - 1)^\nu}{(t - z)^{\nu+1}} dt.$$

---

[1] This Wronskian relation was used to get $Q_n(z)$ in closed form (Eq. 12.209).

By deforming the contour, as shown in Fig. 12.17, we obtain

$$Q_v(z) = \frac{1}{2^{v+1}} \int_{-1}^{1} \frac{(1-t^2)^v}{(z-t)^{v+1}} \, dt, \qquad v > -1. \tag{12.230}$$

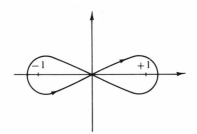

FIG. 12.16   Schlaefi integral contour for $Q_v(x)$

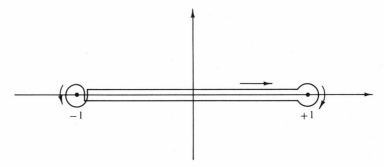

FIG. 12.17   Deformed Schaefi contour

The identification of this integral as $Q_v(z)$ is left as Exercise 12.9.7.

The substitution

$$\gamma = \frac{e^\varphi \sqrt{z+1} - \sqrt{z-1}}{e^\varphi \sqrt{z+1} + \sqrt{z-1}}$$

leads (after considerable manipulation) to

$$Q_v(z) = \int_0^\infty \frac{d\varphi}{[z + \sqrt{z^2 - 1} \cosh \varphi]^{v+1}}, \qquad v > -1, \tag{12.231}$$

analogous to Eq. 12.73 for $P_n(z)$. To hold $Q_v(z)$ analytic and single-valued a cut line is run from $+1$ to $-\infty$.

EXERCISES

12.9.1   Derive the parity relation for $Q_n(x)$.

12.9.2 Verify that the Legendre functions of the second kind, $Q_n(x)$, satisfy the same recurrence relations as $P_n(x)$, both for $|x| < 1$ and for $|x| > 1$.

$$(2n + 1)x \, Q_n(x) = (n + 1) \, Q_{n+1}(x) + n \, Q_{n-1}(x),$$

$$(2n + 1) \, Q_n(x) = Q'_{n+1}(x) - Q'_{n-1}(x).$$

12.9.3 (a) Using the recurrence relations, prove (independently of the Wronskian relation) that

$$n[P_n(x) \, Q_{n-1}(x) - P_{n-1}(x) \, Q_n(x)] = P_1(x) \, Q_0(x) - P_0(x) \, Q_1(x).$$

(b) By direct substitution show that the right-hand side of this equation equals 1.

12.9.4 Prove that

$$P_{n+1}(x) \, Q_{n-1}(x) - P_{n-1}(x) \, Q_{n+1}(x) = \frac{2n + 1}{n(n + 1)} x.$$

12.9.5 Prove that

$$Q_n(\cos \theta) = (-1)^n \frac{r^{n+1}}{n!} \frac{\partial^n}{\partial z^n} \left[\frac{1}{2r} \ln \left(\frac{r - z}{r + z} \right) \right].$$

12.9.6 Assuming that

$$\int_{-1}^{1} \frac{(1 - t^2)^\nu}{(z - t)^{\nu+1}} \, dt$$

satisfies Legendre's equation ($\nu > -1$), show from the parity that it cannot involve any $P_\nu(z)$.

12.9.7 Assuming that

$$\int_{-1}^{1} \frac{(1 - t)^\nu}{(z - t)^{\nu+1}} \, dt$$

satisfies Legendre's equation ($\nu > -1$), show that the integral is $2^{\nu+1} Q_\nu(z)$. *Hint.* We can expand the denominator in powers of t/z (for $|z| > t$) and integrate by using the beta function (Section 10.4).

12.10 Application to Spheroidal Coordinate Systems

Let us consider the physical problems of dielectric and conducting spheroids placed in a uniform electric field. For simplicity the axis of symmetry of the spheroid will be taken parallel to the direction of the original electric field. This gives us complete axial symmetry and eliminates all azimuthal dependence.

Oblate spheroidal coordinates.   If our spheroid is oblate, it will be convenient to choose oblate spheroidal coordinates so that one coordinate surface describes the spheroid. We can use the system defined by the transformation equations[1]

$$x = a \cosh u \sin v \cos \varphi,$$

$$y = a \cosh u \sin v \sin \varphi, \tag{12.232}$$

$$z = a \sinh u \cos v,$$

[1] This is the coordinate same system as the oblate spheroidal system defined in Section 2.11, except that $v_{12.10} = \pi/2 - v_{2.11}$.

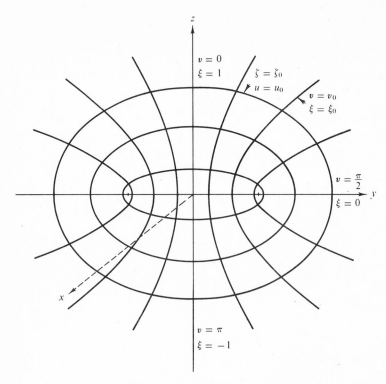

FIG. 12.18　Oblate spheroidal coordinates

the surface $u = u_0$ being an oblate spheroid, the surface $v = v_0$, a hyperboloid of one sheet, and the surface $\varphi = \varphi_0$, a half plane through the z-axis.

Here it is somewhat more convenient to replace this set (u, v, φ) by the coordinates (ξ, ζ, φ), defined by

$$\xi = \cos v, \qquad -1 \leqslant \xi \leqslant 1,$$
$$\zeta = \sinh u, \qquad 0 \leqslant \zeta < \infty. \tag{12.233}$$

In this new system the surface $\zeta = 0$ is a circular disk, whereas $\zeta = \zeta_0 > 0$ is an ellipsoid of revolution (oblate spheroid). The surface $\xi = 0$ is a plane with a circular hole, whereas $\xi = 1$ is a line, perpendicular to the hole, $\xi = 0$, and the disk $\zeta = 0$ and passing through their common center. Eqs. 12.232 become

$$x = \rho \cos \varphi$$
$$y = \rho \sin \varphi \tag{12.234}$$
$$z = a\xi\zeta,$$

in which

$$\rho = a[(1 - \xi^2)(1 + \zeta^2)]^{1/2}. \tag{12.235}$$

The triad (ξ, ζ, φ) form a right-handed set, $\boldsymbol{\xi}_0 \times \boldsymbol{\zeta}_0 = \boldsymbol{\varphi}_0$.

We seek solutions of Laplace's equation, which has become

$$\frac{\partial}{\partial \xi}\left[(1 - \xi^2)\frac{\partial V}{\partial \xi}\right] + \frac{\partial}{\partial \zeta}\left[(1 + \zeta^2)\frac{\partial V}{\partial \zeta}\right] + \frac{\xi^2 + \zeta^2}{(1 - \xi^2)(1 + \zeta^2)}\frac{\partial^2 V}{\partial \varphi^2} = 0. \quad (12.236)$$

Here we have used the scale factors

$$h_\xi = a\left(\frac{\xi^2 + \zeta^2}{1 - \xi^2}\right)^{1/2},$$

$$h_\zeta = a\left(\frac{\xi^2 + \zeta^2}{1 + \zeta^2}\right)^{1/2}, \quad (12.237)$$

$$h_\varphi = a[(1 - \xi^2)(1 + \zeta^2)]^{1/2} = \rho.$$

We assume a solution of the form $X(\xi)\,Z(\zeta)\,\Phi(\varphi)$. Then, separating variables (cf. Section 2.5), we find that $X(\xi)$ must satisfy the associated Legendre equation, $Z(\zeta)$ the associated Legendre equation of pure imaginary argument, and $\Phi(\varphi)$ the usual simple harmonic oscillator equation. The potential V may be written

$$V(\xi, \zeta, \varphi) = \sum_{m,n} X_{mn}(\xi)\, Z_{mn}(\zeta)\, \Phi_m(\varphi), \quad (12.238)$$

where

$$X_{mn}(\xi) = A\, P_n^m(\xi) + B\, Q_n^m(\xi)$$

$$Z_{mn}(\zeta) = A'\, P_n^m(i\zeta) + B'\, Q_n^m(i\zeta) \quad (12.239)$$

$$\Phi(\varphi) = C \cos m\varphi + D \sin m\varphi.$$

By applying our condition of axial symmetry, we set $m = 0$, eliminating all the associated Legendre functions. However, we still need P_n and Q_n for both real and imaginary arguments.

Our boundary conditions, for the simpler case of a *conducting* oblate spheroid, are

$$V = 0 \quad \text{for} \quad \zeta = \zeta_0 \quad \text{(surface of spheroid)},$$

$$V \to -E_0 a\xi\zeta \quad \text{for} \quad \zeta \to \infty,$$

where E_0 is the original, unperturbed electric field. To construct the proper ξ dependence we must have $n = 1$ and $B = 0$. (If $B \neq 0$, there will be trouble at $\xi = 1$, $Q_n(1) = \infty$.) This yields

$$V(\xi, \zeta) = P_1(\xi)[A'P_1(i\zeta) + B'Q_1(i\zeta)]$$
$$= \xi[A'i\zeta + B'(\zeta \cot^{-1}\zeta - 1)]. \quad (12.240)$$

As $\zeta \to \infty$, $Q_1(i\zeta) \to 0$. Applying the second boundary condition,

$$A' = iE_0 a, \quad (12.241)$$

we obtain

$$V(\xi, \zeta) = \xi[-E_0 a\zeta + B'(\zeta \cot^{-1}\zeta - 1)]. \quad (12.242)$$

By the first boundary condition the potential V vanishes on the spheroidal surface, $\zeta = \zeta_0$, or

$$0 = \xi[-E_0 a\zeta_0 + B'(\zeta_0 \cot^{-1}\zeta_0 - 1)], \quad (12.243)$$

and

$$B' = \frac{E_0 a \zeta_0}{\zeta_0 \cot^{-1} \zeta_0 - 1}. \tag{12.244}$$

The final result for $V(\xi, \zeta)$ is

$$V(\xi, \zeta) = -E_0 a \xi \zeta_0 \left(\frac{\zeta}{\zeta_0} - \frac{\zeta \cot^{-1} \zeta - 1}{\zeta_0 \cot^{-1} \zeta_0 - 1} \right), \zeta \geqslant \zeta_0. \tag{12.245}$$

To recapitulate, we have taken a summation of solutions of Laplace's equation to describe the potential. The arbitrary constants have been determined by demanding that the solution fit the boundary conditions. This gives Eq. 12.245. Finally, from Section 1.15, we know that our solution is unique.

The corresponding spherical problem (Section 12.3) is a limiting case. The limit, $\zeta_0 \to \infty$, $a \to 0$, with $a\zeta_0 = r_0$, a constant, will carry the oblate spheroidal system into the spherical system.

If our oblate spheroid is a *dielectric* spheroid, permittivity ε, the first boundary condition is replaced by

(a') V is continuous at $\zeta = \zeta_0,$[1]

(a'') $D_n = -\dfrac{\varepsilon}{h_\zeta} \dfrac{\partial V}{\partial \zeta}$ is continuous at $\zeta = \zeta_0$.

Let us *assume* that the electric field inside the dielectric is constant and parallel to the z(symmetry)-axis.[2] The justification of this assumption is that it works! Then, applying the boundary condition at infinity, we have

$$V_{\text{outside}} = \xi[-E_0 a \zeta + B'(\zeta \cot^{-1} \zeta - 1)] \tag{12.246}$$

$$V_{\text{inside}} = -E_{\text{in}} a \xi \zeta. \tag{12.247}$$

At $\zeta = \zeta_0$ conditions (a') and (a'') give

$$-E_{\text{in}} a \zeta_0 = -E_0 a \zeta_0 + B'(\zeta_0 \cot^{-1} \zeta_0 - 1) \tag{12.248}$$

$$\varepsilon E_{\text{in}} a = \varepsilon_0 E_0 a - \varepsilon_0 B' \left(\cot^{-1} \zeta_0 - \frac{\zeta_0}{1 + \zeta_0^2} \right), \tag{12.249}$$

the factor h_ζ cancelling out. Eliminating B', we find that the ratio of the original field E_0 to the field in the interior of the dielectric E_{in} is

$$\frac{E_0}{E_{\text{in}}} = 1 + \left(\frac{\varepsilon}{\varepsilon_0} - 1 \right)(1 + \zeta_0^2)(1 - \zeta_0 \cot^{-1} \zeta_0). \tag{12.250}$$

It is convenient to separate the geometric effect from the physical effect ($\varepsilon \neq \varepsilon_0$). We may *define* a depolarizing factor, L, by

$$E_{\text{in}} = E_0 - LP. \tag{12.251}$$

---

[1] This is equivalent to requiring the tangential component of **E** to be continuous.

[2] The alternative is to set up the interior potential as a summation of solutions of Laplace's equation analogous to Eq. 12.238.

where P, the polarization, is $E_{in}(\varepsilon - \varepsilon_0)$. Solving for L, we find

$$L = \frac{1}{\varepsilon_0}(1 + \zeta_0^2)(1 - \zeta_0 \cot^{-1} \zeta_0), \qquad (12.252)$$

a function of the geometry of our oblate spheroid.

In the limit as $\zeta_0 \to \infty$

$$\lim_{\zeta_0 \to \infty} L = \frac{1}{3\varepsilon_0}, \qquad (12.253)$$

which is just the value for a dielectric sphere. At the other extreme

$$\lim_{\zeta_0 \to 0} L = \frac{1}{\varepsilon_0}, \qquad (12.254)$$

and this is just the value for a thin dielectric slab perpendicular to the uniform electric field.

Prolate spheroidal coordinates.   The analysis of a dielectric *prolate* spheroid in a uniform electric field proceeds along the same lines, except that prolate spheroidal coordinates are used. We shall use[1]

$$x = \rho \cos \varphi,$$

$$y = \rho \sin \varphi, \qquad (12.255)$$

$$z = a\xi\eta,$$

$$\eta = \cosh u, \qquad 1 \leqslant \eta < \infty,$$

$$\xi = \cos v, \qquad -1 \leqslant \xi \leqslant 1, \qquad (12.256)$$

and

$$\rho = a[(1 - \xi^2)(\eta^2 - 1)]^{1/2}.$$

If we express the Laplacian in terms of (ξ, η, φ) (cf. Eq. 2.105, Section 2.10) the variables will separate. Both the ξ- and η-dependence lead to the associated Legendre equation. The φ-dependence once again yields the simple harmonic oscillator equation. Hence $V(\xi, \eta, \varphi)$ is the same as $V(\xi, \zeta, \varphi)$ (Eqs. 12.238 and 12.239) but with the arguments $i\zeta$ replaced by real η. If $m = 0$ is set by azimuthal symmetry and boundary conditions are applied, the external potential becomes

$$V_{\text{outside}} = \xi\left[A'\eta + B'\left(\frac{1}{2}\eta \ln \frac{\eta + 1}{\eta - 1} - 1\right)\right]. \qquad (12.257)$$

Leaving the intervening steps for the reader to supply by analogy with the oblate spheroid, we finally obtain a depolarizing factor L,

$$L = \frac{1}{\varepsilon_0}(\eta_0^2 - 1)\left(\frac{1}{2}\eta_0 \ln \frac{\eta_0 + 1}{\eta_0 - 1} - 1\right), \qquad (12.258)$$

in which $\eta = \eta_0$ describes the prolate spheroidal surface. In the limit as $\eta_0 \to 1$

---

[1] This follows Section 2.10 exactly.

the prolate spheroid becomes an infinitely long thin needle. As expected,

$$\lim_{\eta_0 \to 1} L = 0. \tag{12.259}$$

On the other hand,

$$\lim_{\eta_0 \to \infty} L = \frac{1}{3\varepsilon_0}, \tag{12.260}$$

again corresponding to the spherical case.

It might perhaps be mentioned that although these electrostatic cases have only a little application the corresponding magnetic problems are rather important. The analysis for paramagnetic and diamagnetic spheroids in a uniform magnetic field is just like that of the electrostatic cases. Both electrostatic and magnetostatic problems involve solutions of Laplace's equation.

EXERCISES

12.10.1 Show that the depolarizing factor for a prolate spheroid ($\eta = \eta_0$) aligned in a uniform electric field is

$$L = \frac{1}{\varepsilon_0}(\eta_0^2 - 1)\left(\frac{1}{2}\eta_0 \ln \frac{\eta_0 + 1}{\eta_0 - 1} - 1\right).$$

12.10.2 A charged conducting isolated prolate spheroidal shell ($\eta = \eta_0$) is at a potential V_0.
(a) Show that the electrostatic potential outside the shell is

$$V = V_0 \frac{Q_0(\eta)}{Q_0(\eta_0)} = V_0 \frac{\ln[(\eta + 1)/(\eta - 1)]}{\ln[(\eta_0 + 1)/(\eta_0 - 1)]}.$$

(b) What is the capacitance of the spheroid?
Hint. Investigate the behavior of this potential at large distances from the shell.

12.10.3 (a) A charged isolated oblate spheroidal shell ($\zeta = \zeta_0$) is at a potential $V = V_0$. Show that the electrostatic potential outside the shell is

$$V = V_0 \frac{Q_0(i\zeta)}{Q_0(i\zeta_0)} = V_0 \frac{\cot^{-1}\zeta}{\cot^{-1}\zeta_0}.$$

(b) By letting $\zeta_0 \to 0$ we obtain a disk of radius a. Find the potential of this disk at large distances and from it calculate the total charge on the disk. Use this result to show that the capacitance of the disk is $C = 8\varepsilon_0 a$ (mks units).

12.10.4 A quantum mechanical particle is confined to the interior of a prolate spheroid. Find the minimum permitted energy of the particle as a function of spheroid volume and eccentricity. Assume small eccentricity.

12.11 Vector Spherical Harmonics

Most of our attention in this chapter has been directed toward solving the equations of scalar fields such as the electrostatic field. This was done primarily because the scalar fields are easier to handle than vector fields! However, with scalar field problems under firm control, more and more attention is being paid to vector field problems.

Magnetic field of a current loop.   To illustrate the difficulties let us consider the equation[1]

$$\nabla \times \nabla \times \mathbf{A} = \mu_0 \mathbf{J} \tag{12.261}$$

for the magnetic vector potential. Let us further suppose that the boundary conditions are best expressed in spherical polar coordinates. In the example of a current loop (Section 12.5) it was possible to handle this equation because the form of $\mathbf{A}$ was highly restricted. In general, this equation will yield three scalar equations, each involving all three components of A, A_r, A_θ, and A_φ. Such coupled differential equations can be solved, but the complexities are formidable.

Setting $\nabla \cdot \mathbf{A} = 0$, we can convert our equation into the vector Laplacian $\nabla^2 \mathbf{A}$. This will separate into one equation for each component in *cartesian* coordinates. Unfortunately, our boundary conditions (for the current loop) are in spherical coordinates. To satisfy them we would still have to mix the cartesian components A_x, A_y, and A_z in a form that would probably be both awkward and difficult to handle.

To facilitate the solution of Eq. 12.261 and other equations, such as the vector Helmholtz and the vector wave equation, various combinations of the (scalar) spherical harmonics have been used to construct vectors in spherical polar coordinates. One set, useful in quantum mechanics, has been described by Hill.[2] His three vector spherical harmonics are

$$\mathbf{V}_{LM} = \mathbf{r}_0 \left[-\left(\frac{L+1}{2L+1} \right)^{1/2} Y_L^M \right] + \mathbf{\theta}_0 \left\{ \frac{1}{[(L+1)(2L+1)]^{1/2}} \frac{\partial Y_L^M}{\partial \theta} \right\}$$
$$+ \mathbf{\varphi}_0 \left\{ \frac{iM}{[(L+1)(2L+1)]^{1/2} \sin \theta} Y_L^M \right\}, \tag{12.262}$$

$$\mathbf{W}_{LM} = \mathbf{r}_0 \left[\left(\frac{L}{2L+1} \right)^{1/2} Y_L^M \right] + \mathbf{\theta}_0 \left\{ \frac{1}{[L(2L+1)]^{1/2}} \frac{\partial Y_L^M}{\partial \theta} \right\}$$
$$+ \mathbf{\varphi}_0 \left\{ \frac{iM}{[L(2L+1)]^{1/2} \sin \theta} Y_L^M \right\}, \tag{12.263}$$

$$\mathbf{X}_{LM} = \mathbf{\theta}_0 \left\{ \frac{-M}{[L(L+1)]^{1/2} \sin \theta} Y_L^M \right\} + \mathbf{\varphi}_0 \left\{ \frac{-i}{[L(L+1)]^{1/2}} \frac{\partial Y_L^M}{\partial \theta} \right\}. \tag{12.264}$$

These functions satisfy a general orthogonality relation

$$\int \mathbf{A}_{LM} \cdot \mathbf{B}_{L'M'}^* \, d\Omega = \delta_{AB} \delta_{LL'} \delta_{MM'}, \tag{12.265}$$

---

[1] Cf. Section 12.5 for a derivation from Maxwell's equations.

[2] E. H. Hill, Theory of Vector Spherical Harmonics, *Am. J. Phys.* **22**, 211 (1954); also J. M. Blatt and V. Weisskopf, *Theoretical Nuclear Physics*. New York: Wiley (1952). Note that Hill assigns phases in accordance with the Condon-Shortley phase convention (Section 12.6).

where $\mathbf{A}$ and $\mathbf{B}$ may be $\mathbf{V}$, $\mathbf{X}$, or $\mathbf{W}$. This may be verified by using the definitions of $\mathbf{V}$, $\mathbf{X}$, and $\mathbf{W}$ and reducing the integral to one of ordinary orthonormal spherical harmonics, $Y_L^M(\theta, \varphi)$.

Under the parity operations (coordinate inversion) the vector spherical harmonics transform as

$$\mathbf{V}_{LM}(\theta', \varphi') = (-1)^{L+1}\mathbf{V}_{LM}(\theta, \varphi),$$

$$\mathbf{W}_{LM}(\theta', \varphi') = (-1)^{L+1}\mathbf{W}_{LM}(\theta, \varphi), \qquad (12.266)$$

$$\mathbf{X}_{LM}(\theta', \varphi') = (-1)^{L}\mathbf{X}_{LM}(\theta, \varphi),$$

where

$$\theta' = \pi - \theta$$
$$\phi' = \pi + \varphi. \qquad (12.267)$$

In verifying these relations the reader should remember that the spherical polar coordinate unit vectors $\mathbf{r}_0$ and $\boldsymbol{\varphi}_0$ are odd and $\boldsymbol{\theta}_0$ is even. These properties may be verified by expressing the unit vectors $\mathbf{r}_0$, $\boldsymbol{\theta}_0$, and $\boldsymbol{\varphi}_0$ in terms of the cartesian unit vectors $\mathbf{i}$, $\mathbf{j}$, and $\mathbf{k}$ and spherical polar coordinates.

To demonstrate the use of the vector spherical harmonics consider Eq. 12.261 again. From Hill's table of differential relations

$$\nabla \cdot [F(r) \, \mathbf{V}_{LM}(\theta, \varphi)] = -\left(\frac{L+1}{2L+1}\right)^{1/2}\left[\frac{dF}{dr} + \frac{L+2}{r} F\right] Y_L^M(\theta, \varphi), \quad (12.268)$$

$$\nabla \cdot [F(r) \, \mathbf{W}_{LM}(\theta, \varphi)] = \left(\frac{L}{2L+1}\right)^{1/2}\left[\frac{dF}{dr} - \frac{L-1}{r} F\right] Y_L^M(\theta, \varphi), \qquad (12.269)$$

$$\nabla \cdot [F(r) \, \mathbf{X}_{LM}(\theta, \varphi)] = 0. \qquad (12.270)$$

The condition

$$\nabla \cdot \mathbf{A} = 0 \qquad (12.271)$$

eliminates $\mathbf{V}_{LM}$ and $\mathbf{W}_{LM}$, leaving only $\mathbf{X}_{LM}$. In the absence of current ($\mathbf{J} = 0$), that is, away from the current loop, Eq. 12.261, subject to Eq. 12.271, becomes

$$\nabla^2 \mathbf{A} = 0. \qquad (12.272)$$

Using another of Hill's differential relations with $\mathbf{A}_{LM} = R(r) \, \mathbf{X}_{LM}(\theta, \varphi)$, we obtain

$$\nabla^2[R(r) \, \mathbf{X}_{LM}(\theta, \varphi)] = \left[\frac{d^2R}{dr^2} + \frac{2}{r}\frac{dR}{dr} - \frac{L(L+1)}{r^2} R\right]\mathbf{X}_{LM} = 0, \quad (12.273)$$

in agreement with our Eq. 12.116. We have

$$\mathbf{A}_{LM} = a_{LM} r^{-L-1} \, \mathbf{X}_{LM}(\theta, \varphi). \qquad (12.274)$$

We note that there can be no azimuthal dependence because of the symmetry of our loop, $M = 0$, and our solution reduces to

$$\mathbf{A}_L = a_L r^{-L-1}\left\{\frac{-i}{[L(L+1)]^{1/2}} \frac{\partial Y_L^0}{\partial \theta}\right\}\boldsymbol{\varphi}_0. \qquad (12.275)$$

This is equivalent to Eq. 12.119. The constants a_L are determined by fitting boundary conditions, as done in Section 12.5 for c_n. The magnetic field may be found from

$$\mathbf{V} \times [F(r)\mathbf{X}_{LM}] = i\left(\frac{L}{2L+1}\right)^{1/2}\left[\frac{dF}{dr} - \frac{L}{r}F\right]\mathbf{V}_{LM}$$

$$+ i\left(\frac{L+1}{2L+1}\right)^{1/2}\left[\frac{dF}{dr} + \frac{(L+1)}{r}F\right]\mathbf{W}_{LM},$$

(12.276)

which corresponds to Eq. 12.122. [Here $F(r) = a_L r^{-L-1}$.]

The definitions of the vector spherical harmonics given here are dictated by convenience, primarily in quantum mechanical calculations, in which the angular momentum is a significant parameter. Morse and Feshbach describe another set of vector spherical harmonics, **B**, **C**, and **P**, in which the radial dependence is entirely in **P** and the angular dependence entirely in **B** and **C**. This set offers advantages in treating the wave equation when we want to separate the longitudinal and transverse parts of the wave.

Further examples of the usefulness and power of the vector spherical harmonics will be found in Blatt and Weisskopf, in Morse and Feshbach, and in Jackson's *Classical Electrodynamics*, which uses vector spherical harmonics in a description of multipole radiation and related electromagnetic problems.

EXERCISES

12.11.1 In *Classical Electrodynamics* Jackson defines $\mathbf{X}_{LM}$ by the equation

$$\mathbf{X}_{LM}(\theta, \varphi) = \frac{1}{\sqrt{L(L+1)}} \mathbf{L} Y_L^M(\theta, \varphi),$$

in which the angular momentum operator **L** is given by

$$\mathbf{L} = -i(\mathbf{r} \times \mathbf{V}).$$

Show that this definition agrees with Eq. 12.264.

12.11.2 Verify that the parity of $\mathbf{V}_{LM}$ is $(-1)^{L+1}$, the parity of $\mathbf{X}_{LM}$ is $(-1)^L$, and that of $\mathbf{W}_{LM}$ is $(-1)^{L+1}$. What happened to the M-dependence of the parity? *Hint.* r_0 and φ_0 have odd parity; θ_0 has even parity (cf. Exercise 2.4.14).

12.11.3 Verify the orthonomality of the vector spherical harmonics $\mathbf{V}_{LM}$, $\mathbf{X}_{LM}$, and $\mathbf{W}_{LM}$.

12.11.4 (a) Show that

$$\mathbf{E} = \sqrt{4\pi\varepsilon_0} \sum_{L,M} a_{LM} g_L(kr) \mathbf{X}_{LM}(\theta, \varphi),$$

$$\mathbf{B} = \sqrt{\frac{4\pi}{\mu_0}} \sum_{L,M} -\frac{i}{k} a_{LM} \mathbf{V} \times g_L(kr) \mathbf{X}_{LM}(\theta, \varphi),$$

are solutions of Maxwell's electromagnetic equations (mks units). The radial functions $g_L(kr)$ are spherical Hankel functions and $k = \omega/c$.

(b) Show that this is magnetic multipole radiation; or is it electric multipole radiation?

REFERENCES

HOBSON, E. W., *The Theory of Spherical and Ellipsoidal Harmonics.* New York: Chelsea (1955). A most complete reference. This is the classic text on Legendre polynomials and all related functions.
See also the references listed at the end of Chapter 13.

CHAPTER 13

SPECIAL FUNCTIONS

In this chapter we shall study four sets of orthogonal polynomials, Hermite, Laguerre, and Chebyshev[1] of first and second kinds. Although these four sets are of less importance in mathematical physics than the Bessel and Legendre functions of Chapters 11 and 12, they do occur. They are of occasional use and therefore deserve at least a little attention. Because the general mathematical techniques duplicate those of the preceding two chapters, the development of these functions is only outlined. Detailed proofs, along the lines of Chapters 11 and 12, are left to the reader. To conclude the chapter, these polynomials and other functions are expressed in terms of hypergeometric and confluent hypergeometric functions.

13.1 Hermite Functions

Generating functions—Hermite polynomials.   The Hermite polynomials, $H_n(x)$, may be defined by the generating function

$$g(x, t) = e^{-t^2 + 2tx} = \sum_{n=0}^{\infty} H_n(x) \frac{t^n}{n!}. \tag{13.1}$$

Recurrence relations.   Note the absence of a superscript, which distinguishes it from the unrelated Hankel functions. From the generating function we find that the Hermite polynomials satisfy the recurrence relations

$$H_{n+1}(x) = 2x\, H_n(x) - 2n\, H_{n-1}(x) \tag{13.2}$$

and

$$H_n'(x) = 2n\, H_{n-1}(x). \tag{13.3}$$

---

[1] This is the spelling choice of AMS-55. However a variety of forms, such as Tschebyscheff is encountered

477

Equation 13.2 may be obtained by differentiating the generating function with respect to t; differentiation with respect to x leads to Eq. 13.3.

Direct expansion of the generating function easily gives $H_0(x) = 1$ and $H_1(x) = 2x$. Then Eq. 13.2 permits the construction of any $H_n(x)$ desired (integral n). For convenient reference the first several Hermite polynomials are listed in Table 13.1.

TABLE 13.1

Hermite Polynomials

$H_0(x) = 1$

$H_1(x) = 2x$

$H_2(x) = 4x^2 - 2$

$H_3(x) = 8x^3 - 12x$

$H_4(x) = 16x^4 - 48x^2 + 12$

$H_5(x) = 32x^5 - 160x^3 + 120x$

$H_6(x) = 64x^6 - 480x^4 + 720x^2 - 120$

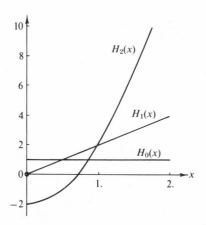

FIG. 13.1 Hermite polynomials

Special values of the Hermite polynomials follow from the generating function, that is,

$$H_{2n}(0) = (-1)^n \frac{(2n)!}{n!} \qquad (13.4)$$

$$H_{2n+1}(0) = 0. \qquad (13.5)$$

We also obtain from the generating function the important parity relation

$$H_n(x) = (-1)^n H_n(-x). \qquad (13.6)$$

Alternate representations.   Differentiation of the generating function[1] n times with respect to t and then setting t equal to zero yields

$$H_n(x) = (-1)^n e^{x^2} \frac{d^n}{dx^n} (e^{-x^2}).\tag{13.7}$$

This gives us a Rodrigues representation of $H_n(x)$. A second representation may be obtained by using the calculus of residues (Chapter 7). If we multiply Eq. 13.7 by t^{-m-1} and integrate around the origin, only the term with $H_m(x)$ will survive.

$$H_m(x) = \frac{m!}{2\pi i} \oint t^{-m-1} e^{-t^2 + 2tx} \, dt.\tag{13.8}$$

Also from Eq. 13.1, we may write our Hermite polynomial $H_n(x)$ in series form.

$$\begin{aligned}
H_n(x) &= (2x)^n - \frac{2\,n!}{(n-2)!2!} (2x)^{n-2} + \frac{4\,n!}{(n-4)!4!} (2x)^{n-4} 1 \cdot 3 \cdots \\
&= \sum_{s=0}^{[n/2]} (-2)^s (2x)^{n-2s} \binom{n}{2s} 1 \cdot 3 \cdot 5 \cdots (2s-1) \\
&= \sum_{s=0}^{[n/2]} (-1)^s (2x)^{n-2s} \frac{n!}{(n-2s)!s!}.
\end{aligned}\tag{13.9}$$

This terminates for integral n and yields our Hermite polynomial.

Orthogonality.   The recurrence relations (Eqs. 13.2 and 13.3) lead to the second-order linear differential equation

$$H_n''(x) - 2x\, H_n'(x) + 2n\, H_n(x) = 0.\tag{13.10}$$

which is clearly *not* self-adjoint. To develop the orthogonal properties of the Hermite polynomials it is convenient to introduce a set of (unnormalized) functions φ_n by

$$\varphi_n(x) = e^{-x^2/2} H_n(x).\tag{13.11}$$

Substitution into Eq. 13.10 yields the differential equation for $\varphi_n(x)$,

$$\varphi_n''(x) + (2n + 1 - x^2)\, \varphi_n(x) = 0.\tag{13.12}$$

This is the differential equation for a quantum mechanical, simple harmonic oscillator which is perhaps the most important single application of the Hermite polynomials. Equation 13.12 is self-adjoint and the solutions $\varphi_n(x)$ are orthogonal for the interval $(-\infty < x < \infty)$.

The problem of normalizing these functions remains. Proceeding as in Section 12.3, we multiply Eq. 13.1 by itself and then by e^{-x^2}. This yields

$$e^{-x^2} e^{-s^2 + 2sx} e^{-t^2 + 2tx} = \sum_{m,n=0}^{\infty} e^{-x^2} H_m(x) H_n(x) \frac{s^m t^n}{m!n!}.\tag{13.13}$$

---

[1] Rewrite the generating functions as $g(x, t) = e^{x^2} e^{-(t-x)^2}$. Note that

$$\frac{d}{dt} e^{-(t-x)^2} = -\frac{d}{dx} e^{-(t-x)^2}.$$

When integrating over x from $-\infty$ to $+\infty$, the cross terms of the double sum drop out because of the orthogonality property[1]

$$\sum_{n=0}^{\infty} \frac{(st)^n}{n!n!} \int_{-\infty}^{\infty} e^{-x^2} [H_n(x)]^2 \, dx = \int_{-\infty}^{\infty} e^{-x^2 - s^2 + 2sx - t^2 + 2tx} \, dx$$

$$= \int_{-\infty}^{\infty} e^{-(x-s-t)^2} e^{2st} \, dx$$

$$= \pi^{1/2} e^{2st} = \pi^{1/2} \sum_{n=0}^{\infty} \frac{2^n (st)^n}{n!}. \qquad (13.14)$$

By equating coefficients of like powers of st we obtain

$$\int_{-\infty}^{\infty} e^{-x^2} [H_n(x)]^2 \, dx = 2^n \pi^{1/2} n!. \qquad (13.15)$$

As already indicated, the Hermite polynomials are used in analyzing the quantum mechanical simple harmonic oscillator. For a potential energy $V = \frac{1}{2} Kz^2$ (force $F = -\mathbf{\nabla} V = -Kz$), the Schrödinger wave equation is

$$-\frac{\hbar^2}{2m} \mathbf{\nabla}^2 \, \Psi(z) + \frac{1}{2} Kz^2 \, \Psi(z) = E \, \Psi(z). \qquad (13.16)$$

Our oscillating particle has mass m and total energy E. By use of the abbreviations

$$x = \alpha z \quad \text{with} \quad \alpha^4 = \frac{mK}{\hbar^2},$$

$$\lambda = \frac{2E}{\hbar} \left(\frac{m}{K}\right)^{1/2} = \frac{2E}{\hbar\omega}, \qquad (13.17)$$

in which ω is the angular frequency of the corresponding classical oscillator, Eq. 13.16 becomes [with $\Psi(z) = \Psi(x/\alpha) = \psi(x)$]

$$\frac{d^2\psi(x)}{dx^2} + (\lambda - x^2) \, \psi(x) = 0. \qquad (13.18)$$

This is Eq. 13.12 with $\lambda = 2n + 1$. Hence

$$\psi_n(x) = 2^{-n/2} \pi^{-1/4} (n!)^{-1/2} e^{-x^2/2} \, H_n(x) \qquad \text{(normalized)}. \qquad (13.19)$$

The requirement that n be an integer is dictated by the boundary conditions of the quantum mechanical system,

$$\lim_{\lim \to \pm\infty} \Psi(z) = 0.$$

Specifically, if $n \to \nu$, not an integer, a power-series solution of Eq. 13.10 shows that $H_\nu(x)$ will behave as $x^\nu e^{x^2}$ for large x. The functions $\psi_\nu(x)$ and $\Psi_\nu(z)$ will therefore blow up at infinity, and it will be impossible to normalize the wave function $\Psi(z)$. With this requirement, energy E becomes

---

[1] The cross terms ($m \neq n$) may be left in, if desired. Then, when the coefficients of $s^\alpha t^\beta$ are equated, the orthogonality will be apparent.

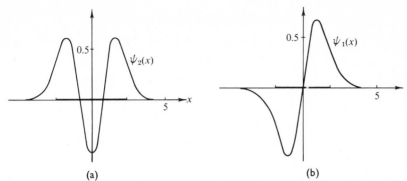

FIG. 13.2 Quantum mechanical oscillator wave functions

$$E = (n + \tfrac{1}{2})\hbar\omega. \tag{13.20}$$

As n ranges over integral values ($n \geq 0$), we see that the energy is quantized and that there is a minimum or zero point energy

$$E_{min} = \tfrac{1}{2}\hbar\omega. \tag{13.21}$$

This zero point energy is an aspect of the uncertainty principle, a purely quantum phenomenon.

In quantum mechanical problems, particularly in molecular spectroscopy, a number of integrals of the form

$$\int_{-\infty}^{\infty} x^r e^{-x^2} H_n(x) H_m(x)\, dx$$

are needed. Examples for $r = 1$ and $r = 2$ (with $n = m$) are included in the exercises at the end of this chapter. A large number of other examples are contained in Wilson, Decius, and Cross.[1]

The oscillator potential has also been employed extensively in calculations of nuclear structure (nuclear shell model).

There is a second independent solution of Eq. 13.10. This Hermite function of the second kind is an infinite series (Sections 8.4, 8.5) and of no physical interest, at least not yet.

EXERCISES

13.1.1 From the generating function show that

$$H_n(x) = \sum_{s=0}^{} (-1)\, \frac{n!}{(n-2s)!\,s!}\,(2x)^{n-2s}.$$

[1] Wilson, E., B. Jr., J. C. Decius, and P. C. Cross, *Molecular Vibrations*. New York: McGraw-Hill (1955).

13.1.2 (a) Using the Cauchy integral theorem, develop an integral representation of $H_n(x)$ based on Eq. 13.1 with the contour enclosing the point $z = -x$.

$$Ans.\ H_n(x) = \frac{n!}{2\pi i} e^{x^2} \oint \frac{e^{-z^2}}{(z+x)^{n+1}}\, dz.$$

(b) Show by direct substitution that this result satisfies the Hermite equation.

13.1.3 The transition probability between two oscillator states, m and n, depends on

$$\int_{-\infty}^{\infty} xe^{-x^2}\, H_n(x)\, H_m(x)\, dx.$$

Show that this integral equals $\pi^{1/2} 2^{n-1} n!\ \delta_{m,n-1} + \pi^{1/2} 2^n (n+1)!\ \delta_{m,n+1}$.
This result shows that such transitions can occur only between states of adjacent energy

levels, $m = n \pm 1$. *Hint.* Multiply the generating function (Eq. 13.1) by itself using two different sets of variables (x, s) and (x, t).

13.1.4 Show that

$$\int_{-\infty}^{\infty} x^2 e^{-x^2}\, H_n(x)\, H_n(x)\, dx = \pi^{1/2} 2^n n!\left(n + \frac{1}{2}\right).$$

This integral occurs in the calculation of the mean-square displacement of our quantum oscillator. *Hint.* Use the recurrence relation Eq. 13.2 and the orthogonality integral.

13.1.5 Show that

$$\int_{-\infty}^{\infty} x^m e^{-x^2}\, H_n(x)\, dx = 0 \quad \text{for} \quad m \text{ an integer}, \qquad 0 \leqslant m \leqslant n - 1.$$

13.1.6 There are numerous odd relations between the special functions. One relating Hermite and Legendre polynomials is

$$P_n(x) = \frac{2}{\pi^{1/2} n!} \int_0^{\infty} t^n e^{-t^2}\, H_n(xt)\, dt.$$

Verify this relation. *Hint.* Use the series representation of H_n and then term-by-term integration.

13.1.7 Prove that

$$\left(2x - \frac{d}{dx}\right)^n 1 = H_n(x).$$

Hint. Check out the first couple of examples and then use mathematical induction.

13.1.8 Starting with the generating function and using the method of steepest descent, develop an asymptotic expansion of $H_n(x)$.

13.1.9 From the generating function derive the recurrence relations

$$H_{n+1}(x) = 2x\, H_n(x) - 2n\, H_{n-1}(x),$$
$$H_n'(x) = 2n\, H_{n-1}(x).$$

13.2 Laguerre Functions

Differential equation—Laguerre polynomials.   If we start with the appropriate generating function, it is possible to develop the Laguerre polynomials in exact analogy with the Hermite polynomials. Alternatively, a series solution may be developed by the methods of Section 8.4. Instead, to illustrate a different technique, let us start with Laguerre's differential equation and obtain a solution in the form of a contour integral, as we did with the modified Bessel function $K_v(x)$ (Section 10.5). From this integral representation a generating function will be derived.

Laguerre's differential equation is

$$xy''(x) + (1 - x) y'(x) + n\, y(x) = 0. \tag{13.22}$$

We shall attempt to represent y, or rather y_n, since y will depend on n, by the contour integral

$$y_n(x) = \frac{1}{2\pi i} \oint \frac{e^{-xz/(1-z)}}{(1-z)z^{n+1}}\, dz. \tag{13.23}$$

The contour includes the origin but does not enclose the point $z = 1$. From Section 6.3

$$y_n'(x) = -\frac{1}{2\pi i} \oint \frac{e^{-xz/(1-z)}}{(1-z)^2 z^n}\, dz, \tag{13.24}$$

$$y_n''(x) = \frac{1}{2\pi i} \oint \frac{e^{-xz/(1-z)}}{(1-z)^3 z^{n-1}}\, dz. \tag{13.25}$$

Substituting into the left-hand side of Eq. 13.22 we obtain

$$\frac{1}{2\pi i} \oint \left[\frac{x}{(1-z)^3 z^{n-1}} - \frac{1-x}{(1-z)^2 z^n} + \frac{n}{(1-z)z^{n+1}} \right] e^{-xz/(1-z)}\, dz,$$

which is equal to

$$\frac{1}{2\pi i} \oint \frac{d}{dz}\left[\frac{e^{-xz/(1-z)}}{(1-z)z^n} \right]\, dz. \tag{13.26}$$

If we integrate our perfect differential around a contour chosen so that the final value equals the initial value (Fig. 13.3), the integral will vanish, thus verifying that $y_n(x)$ (Eq. 13.23) is a solution of Laguerre's equation.

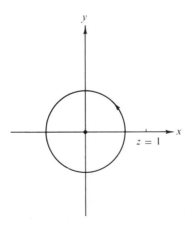

FIG. 13.3 Laguerre function contour

It has become customary to define $L_n(x)$, the Laguerre polynomial, by

$$L_n(x) = \frac{1}{2\pi i} \oint \frac{e^{-xz/(1-z)}}{(1-z)z^{n+1}}\, dz. \tag{13.27}$$

This is exactly what we would obtain from the series

$$g(x, z) = \frac{e^{-xz/(1-z)}}{1-z} = \sum_{n=0}^{\infty} L_n(x)z^n, \qquad |z| < 1 \tag{13.28}$$

if we multiplied by z^{-n-1} and integrated around the origin. As in the development of the calculus of residues (Section 7.3), only the z^{-1} term in the series survives. On this basis, we identify $g(x, z)$ as the generating function for the Laguerre polynomials.

With the transformation

$$\frac{xz}{1-z} = s - x \qquad z = \frac{s-x}{s}, \tag{13.29}$$

$$L_n(x) = \frac{e^x}{2\pi i} \oint \frac{s^n e^{-s}}{(s-x)^{n+1}}\, ds, \tag{13.30}$$

the new contour enclosing the point $s = x$ in the s-plane. By Cauchy's integral theorem (for derivatives)

$$L_n(x) = \frac{e^x}{n!} \frac{d^n}{dx^n} (x^n e^{-x}), \qquad \text{(integral } n), \tag{13.31}$$

giving us Rodrigues' formula for Laguerre polynomials. From these representations of $L_n(x)$ we find the series form (for integral n):

$$L_n(x) = \frac{(-1)^n}{n!}\left[x^n - \frac{n^2}{1!}x^{n-1} + \frac{n^2(n-1)^2}{2!}x^{n-2} - \cdots + (-1)^n n! \right],$$

$$= \sum_{m=0}^{n} (-1)^m \frac{n!}{(n-m)!m!m!}x^m = \sum_{s=0}^{n}(-1)^{n-s}\frac{n!x^{n-s}}{(n-s)!(n-s)!s!} \tag{13.32}$$

and the specific polynomials listed in Table 13.2.

TABLE 13.2

Laguerre Polynomials

$L_0(x) = 1$

$L_1(x) = -x + 1$

$2!\, L_2(x) = x^2 - 4x + 2$

$3!\, L_3(x) = -x^3 + 9x^2 - 18x + 6$

$4!\, L_4(x) = x^4 - 16x^3 + 72x^2 - 96x + 24$

$5!\, L_5(x) = -x^5 + 25x^4 - 200x^3 + 600x^2 - 600x + 120$

$6!\, L_6(x) = x^6 - 36x^5 + 450x^4 - 2400x^3 + 5400x^2 - 4320x + 720$

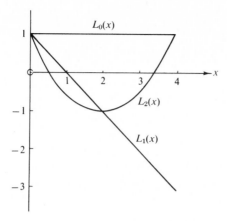

FIG. 13.4 Laguerre polynomials

By differentiating the generating function in Eq. 13.28, with respect to x and z, we obtain the recurrence relations

$$(n + 1)L_{n+1}(x) = (2n + 1 - x)L_n(x) - n L_{n-1}(x), \qquad (13.33)$$

$$x L'_n(x) = n L_n(x) - n L_{n-1}(x). \qquad (13.34)$$

Also from Eq. 13.28 we find the special value

$$L_n(0) = 1. \qquad (13.35)$$

As may be seen from the form of the generating function, the form of Laguerre's differential equation, or from Table 13.2, the Laguerre polynomials have neither odd nor even symmetry (parity).

The Laguerre differential equation is not self-adjoint and the Laguerre polynomials, $L_n(x)$, do not by themselves form a orthogonal set. However, the related set of functions[1]

$$\varphi_n(x) = e^{-x/2} L_n(x) \qquad (13.36)$$

is orthonormal for the interval ($0 \leqslant x < \infty$), that is,

$$\int_0^\infty e^{-x}L_m(x) L_n(x) \, dx = \delta_{m,n}. \qquad (13.37)$$

Our new orthonormal function $\varphi_n(x)$ satisfies the differential equation

$$x \varphi''_n(x) + \varphi'_n(x) + \left(n + \frac{1}{2} - \frac{x}{4}\right) \varphi_n(x) = 0, \qquad (13.38)$$

which is seen to have the Sturm-Liouville form (self-adjoint). Note that it is the boundary conditions in the Sturm-Liouville theory that fix our interval as

---

[1] The factor $e^{-x/2}$ may be *derived* by the method of Section 9.1.

$(0 \leqslant x < \infty)$. Equation 13.37 may be verified by using the generating function (Eq. 13.28).

Associated Laguerre polynomials.   In many applications, particularly in quantum theory, we need the associated Laguerre polynomials defined by[1]

$$L_n^k(x) = (-1)^k \frac{d^k}{dx^k} [L_{n+k}(x)].$$ (13.39)

From the series form of $L_n(x)$

$$L_0^k(x) = 1$$

$$L_1^k(x) = -x + k + 1$$ (13.40)

$$L_2^k(x) = \frac{x^2}{2} - (k + 2)x + \frac{(k + 2)(k + 1)}{2}.$$

In general

$$L_n^k(x) = \sum_{m=0}^{n} (-1)^m \frac{(n + k)!}{(n - m)!(k + m)!m!} x^m \qquad (k > -1).$$ (13.41)

A generating function may be developed by differentiating the Laguerre generating function k times. Adjusting the index to L_{n+k}, we obtain

$$\frac{e^{-xz/(1-z)}}{(1 - z)^{k+1}} = \sum_{n=0}^{\infty} L_n^k(x)z^n, \qquad |z| < 1.$$ (13.42)

From this

$$L_n^k(0) = \frac{(n + k)!}{n!k!}.$$ (13.43)

Recurrence relations can easily be derived from the generating function or by differentiating the Laguerre polynomial recurrence relations. Among the numerous possibilities are

$$(n + 1)L_{n+1}^k(x) = (2n + k + 1 - x) L_n^k(x) - (n + k) L_{n-1}^k(x)$$ (13.44)

$$xL_n^{k'}(x) = n L_n^k(x) - (n + k) L_{n-1}^k(x).$$ (13.45)

From these or from differentiating Laguerre's differential equation k times we have the associated Laguerre equation

$$L_n^{k''}(x) + (k + 1 - x) L_n^{k'}(x) + n L_n^k(x) = 0.$$ (13.46)

A Rodrigues representation of the associated Laguerre polynomial is

$$L_n^k(x) = \frac{e^x x^{-k}}{n!} \frac{d^n}{dx^n} (e^{-x}x^{n+k}).$$ (13.47)

The reader will note that all of these formulas for $L_n^k(x)$ reduce to the corresponding expressions for $L_n(x)$ when $k = 0$.

The associated Laguerre equation (13.46) is not self-adjoint but it can be put in

[1] Some authors use $\mathscr{L}_{n+k}^k(x) = (d^k/dx^k)[L_{n+k}(x)]$. Hence our $L_n^k(x) = (-1)^k \mathscr{L}_{n+k}^k(x)$.

self-adjoint form by multiplying by $e^{-x}x^k$, which becomes the weighting function (Section 9.1). We obtain

$$\int_0^\infty e^{-x}x^k \, L_n^k(x) \, L_m^k(x) \, dx = \frac{(n+k)!}{n!} \delta_{m,n}.$$ (13.48)

By letting $\psi_n^k(x) = e^{-x/2}x^{k/2} \, L_n^k(x)$, $\psi_n^k(x)$ satisfies the self-adjoint equation

$$x \, \psi_n^{k\prime\prime}(x) + \psi_n^{k\prime}(x) + \left(-\frac{x}{4} + \frac{2n+k+1}{2} - \frac{k^2}{4x} \right) \psi_n^k(x) = 0.$$ (13.49)

A further useful form is given by defining[1]

$$\Phi_n^k(x) = e^{-x/2}x^{(k+1)/2} \, L_n^k(x).$$ (13.50)

Substitution into the associated Laguerre equation yields

$$\Phi_n^{k\prime\prime}(x) + \left(-\frac{1}{4} + \frac{2n+k+1}{2x} - \frac{k^2-1}{4x^2} \right) \Phi_n^k(x) = 0.$$ (13.51)

The corresponding normalization integral is

$$\int_0^\infty e^{-x}x^{k+1} \, L_n^k(x) \, L_n^k(x) \, dx = \frac{(n+k)!}{n!}(2n+k+1).$$ (13.52)

The reader may show that the $\Phi_n^k(x)$ do *not* form an orthogonal set (except with x^{-1} as a weighting function) because of the x^{-1} in the term $(2n+k+1)/2x$.

Perhaps the most important single application of the Laguerre polynomials is in the solution of the Schrödinger wave equation for the hydrogen atom. This equation is

$$-\frac{\hbar^2}{2m}\nabla^2\psi - \frac{Ze^2}{r}\psi = E\psi,$$ (13.53)

in which $Z = 1$ for hydrogen, 2 for singly ionized helium, and so on. Separating variables, we find that the angular dependence of ψ is $Y_L^M(\theta, \varphi)$. The radial part, $R(r)$, satisfies the equation

$$-\frac{\hbar^2}{2m}\frac{1}{r^2}\frac{d}{dr}\left(r^2 \frac{dR}{dr} \right) - \frac{Ze^2}{r}R + \frac{\hbar^2}{2m}\frac{L(L+1)}{r^2}R = ER.$$ (13.54)

By use of the abbreviations

$$\rho = \alpha r \quad \text{with } \alpha^2 = -\frac{8mE}{\hbar^2}, \qquad (E < 0),$$

$$\lambda = \frac{2mZe^2}{\alpha\hbar^2},$$ (13.55)

Eq. 13.54 becomes

$$\frac{1}{\rho^2}\left(\frac{d}{d\rho}\rho^2\frac{d\Phi(\rho)}{d\rho} \right) + \left(\frac{\lambda}{\rho} - \frac{1}{4} - \frac{L(L+1)}{\rho^2} \right) \Phi(\rho) = 0,$$ (13.56)

[1] This corresponds to modifying the function ψ in Eq. 13.49 to eliminate the first derivative (Cf. Exercise 8.5.4).

where $\Phi(\rho) = R(\rho/\alpha)$. A comparison with Eq. 13.51 for $\Phi_n^k(x)$ shows that Eq. 13.56 is satisfied by

$$\rho \, \Phi(\rho) = e^{-\rho/2} \rho^{L+1} L_{\lambda-L-1}^{2L+1}(\rho), \qquad (13.57)$$

in which k is replaced by $2L + 1$ and n by $n + L$.

We must restrict the parameter λ by requiring it to be an integer n, $n = 1, 2 \ 3, \ldots$[1]

This is necessary because the Laguerre function of nonintegral n would diverge as $\rho^n e^\rho$, which is unacceptable for our physical problem in which

$$\lim_{r \to \infty} R(r) = 0.$$

This restriction on λ, imposed by our boundary condition, has the effect of quantizing the energy

$$E_n = -\frac{Z^2 m e^4}{2n^2 \hbar^2}. \qquad (13.58)$$

The negative sign enters because we are dealing here with bound states, $E = 0$ corresponding to an electron that is just able to escape to infinity. Using this result for E_n, we may rewrite ρ as

$$\rho = \frac{2Z}{n a_0} r \qquad (13.59)$$

with

$$a_0 = \frac{\hbar^2}{m e^2} \qquad \text{the Bohr radius.}$$

The final normalized hydrogen wave function may be written

$$\psi_{nLM}(r, \theta, \varphi) = \left[\left(\frac{2Z}{n a_0} \right)^3 \frac{(n - L - 1)!}{2n(n + L)!} \right]^{1/2} \times e^{-\alpha r/2} (\alpha r)^L \, L_{n-L-1}^{2L+1}(\alpha r) \, Y_L^M(\theta, \varphi).$$

$$(13.60)$$

EXERCISES

13.2.1 Show with the aid of the Leibnitz formula, that the series expansion of $L_n(x)$ (Eq. 13.32) follows from the Rodrigues representation (Eq. 13.31).

13.2.2 From Eq. 13.60 the normalized radial part of the hydrogenic wave function is

$$R_{nL}(r) = \left[\alpha^3 \frac{(n - L - 1)!}{2n(n + L)!} \right]^{1/2} e^{-\alpha r/2} (\alpha r)^L \, L_{n-L-1}^{2L+1}(\alpha r),$$

in which $\alpha = 2Z/n a_0 = 2Zme^2/n\hbar^2$. Evaluate

[1] This is the conventional notation for λ. It is *not* the same n as the index n in $\Phi_n^k(x)$.

(a) $\bar{r} = \int_0^\infty r \, R_{nL}(\alpha r) \, R_{nL}(\alpha r) r^2 \, dr,$ (b) $\overline{r^{-1}} = \int_0^\infty r^{-1} R_{nL}(\alpha r) \, R_{nL}(\alpha r) r^2 \, dr.$

The quantity $\bar{r}$ is the average displacement of the electron from the nucleus, whereas $\overline{r^{-1}}$ is the average of the reciprocal displacement.

$$Ans. \; \bar{r} = \frac{a_0}{2} \, [3n^2 - L(L+1)]$$

$$\overline{r^{-1}} = \frac{1}{n^2 a_0}.$$

13.2.3 From the generating function derive the Rodrigues representation

$$L_n^k(x) = \frac{e^x x^{-k}}{n!} \frac{d^n}{dx^n} (e^{-x} x^{n+k}).$$

13.2.4 Derive the generalized integral

$$\int_0^\infty e^{-x} x^{k+a} \, L_n^k(x) \, L_n^k(x) \, dx = \frac{(n+k)!}{n!} (2n+k+1)^a$$

and show that we must require $a > -k - 1$. *Hint.* For integral a note that

$$x L_n^k = (2n+k+1) L_n^k - (n+k) L_{n-1}^k - (n-1) L_{n+1}^k.$$

13.2.5 (a) Rewrite the Schrödinger wave equation for hydrogen in parabolic coordinates.
(b) Separate the variables and show that the (unnormalized) solutions are
   (1) $e^{iM\varphi},$
   (2) $e^{-\alpha \xi/2} \xi^{M/2} L_{n_1}^M(\alpha \xi),$
   (3) $e^{-\alpha \eta/2} \eta^{M/2} L_{n_2}^M(\alpha \eta),$ $(M \geqslant 0),$
   in which n_1 and n_2 are non-negative integers and

$$\alpha = \frac{Z}{(n_1 + n_2 + M + 1)a_0}.$$

(c) Show that the normalized wave function is

$$\psi_{n_1 n_2 M}(\xi, \eta, \varphi) = \left[\frac{\alpha^3 n_1! n_2!}{\pi (n_1 + M)!(n_2 + M)!(n_1 + n_2 + M + 1)} \right]^{1/2}$$
$$\times \alpha^M (\xi \eta)^{M/2} e^{-\alpha(\xi+\eta)/2} L_{n_1}^M(\alpha \xi) L_{n_2}^M(\alpha \eta) e^{iM\varphi}.$$

(d) Since the choice of coordinates cannot alter the behavior of our physical system, there must be a correspondence between $\psi(r, \theta, \varphi)$, spherical polar coordinates, $\psi(\xi, \eta, \varphi)$, parabolic coordinates. Show that

$$\psi_{nLM}(r, \theta, \varphi) = \psi_{100}(r, \theta, \varphi) = \psi_{000}(\xi, \eta, \varphi) = \psi_{n_1 n_2 M}(\xi, \eta, \varphi),$$

$$\psi_{200}(r, \theta, \varphi) = \frac{1}{\sqrt{2}}[\psi_{010}(\xi, \eta, \varphi) + \psi_{100}(\xi, \eta, \varphi)],$$

$$\psi_{210}(r, \theta, \varphi) = \frac{1}{\sqrt{2}}[\psi_{010}(\xi, \eta, \varphi) - \psi_{100}(\xi, \eta, \varphi)].$$

The general relation among quantum numbers is

Spherical		Parabolic
n	$=$	$n_1 + n_2 + M + 1$
M	$=$	$M.$

It may be seen that the first of these numbers is required to match the radial exponential dependence, whereas the second is needed to match the azimuthal portions.

13.2.6 The wave equation for the three-dimensional harmonic oscillator is

$$-\frac{\hbar^2}{2m} \nabla^2 \psi + \frac{1}{2} kr^2 \psi = E\psi.$$

Show that the radial part of ψ may be written in terms of Laguerre functions of argument $(\sqrt{m/k}\ r^2)$.

13.2.7 (a) Using the explicit series form (Eq. 13.32) show that
$$L_n'(0) = -n$$
$$L_n''(0) = \tfrac{1}{2}n(n-1).$$
(b) Repeat without using the explicit series form of $L_n(x)$.

13.2.8 The radial solution of the Schrödinger equation for the bound hydrogen atom may be developed from the Laguerre polynomial defined by
$$L_\lambda = \frac{e^\rho}{\lambda!}\frac{d^\lambda}{d\rho^\lambda}(e^{-\rho}\rho^\lambda).$$

Here λ is a positive integer ($\lambda = n + l$) and
$$\rho = 2\sqrt{-2E}\ r = \frac{2Zr}{n}$$

with $E < 0$ for bound states. For free states $E > 0$ and $\rho \to i\rho$. The change in sign of the energy also means that
$$n \to -i\frac{Z}{\sqrt{2E}} = -in',$$

in which n' is real and n pure imaginary. Show that the differential representation of L_λ can be continued for all λ (real or complex) by using the Cauchy integral formula to obtain
$$L_\lambda(\rho) = \frac{2}{2\pi i}e^\rho \int \frac{c^{-s}s^\lambda}{(s-\rho)^{\lambda+1}}\,ds$$
$$= \frac{1}{2\pi i}\int e^{-t}(t+\rho)^\lambda t^{-\lambda-1}\,dt.$$

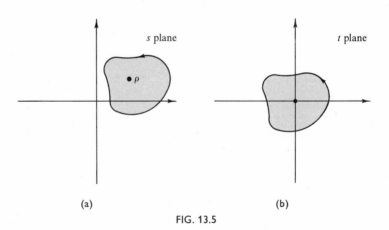

FIG. 13.5

13.2.9 The radial eigenfunction of the hydrogen atom problem is given in terms of the associate Laguerre polynomial,
$$R = c_1 e^{-\rho/2}\rho^l L_{\lambda-\mu}^\mu(\rho) = c_1 e^{-\rho/2}\rho^l \frac{d^\mu}{d\rho^\mu}L_\lambda(\rho)$$
in which $\lambda = n + l$, $\mu = 2l + 1$. Here c_1 is a constant involving the energy and angular momentum of the electron.

(a) From the result of Exercise 13.2.8 show that

$$R = c_2(-ip)^l e^{-\rho/2} \frac{1}{2\pi i} \int e^{-t}(t+\rho)^{n-l-1} t^{n-l-1}\, dt$$

$$= c_2 \frac{(ip)^{-l-1}}{2\pi} \int e^{-\rho\xi}\left(\xi + \frac{1}{2}\right)^{-in'-l-1}\left(\xi - \frac{1}{2}\right)^{in'-l-1}\, d\xi.$$

(b) Show that R is real if ρ and n are purely imaginary.

13.2.10 There are three possible contours of physical interest for the complex integral representation of the radial wave function of Exercise 13.2.9 (see Fig. 13.6).
Show that
(a) contour $(a) \longrightarrow$ stationary state,
(b) contour $(b) \longrightarrow$ asymptotic incoming wave,
(c) contour $(c) \longrightarrow$ asymptotic outgoing wave.

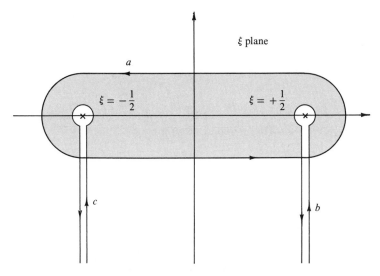

FIG. 13.6   Laguerre function contours

13.3   Chebyshev (Tschebyscheff) Polynomials

Generating function.   In Chapter 12 the generating function for the ultraspherical or Gegenbauer polynomials[1]

$$\frac{2^\beta}{(1 - 2xt + t^2)^{\beta + 1/2}} = \frac{\pi^{1/2}}{(\beta - \frac{1}{2})!} \sum_{n=0}^{\infty} T_n^\beta(x) t^n, \qquad |t| < 1. \tag{13.61}$$

was mentioned, with $\beta = 0$ giving rise to the Legendre polynomials. In this chapter,
by letting $\beta = \pm\frac{1}{2}$, we may generate two sets of polynomials known as the
Chebyshev polynomials.

[1] AMS-55 denotes the ultraspherical polynomials by $C_n^{(\alpha)}(x)$:

$$C_n^{(\alpha)}(x) = \frac{\pi^{1/2}}{2^{\alpha-1/2}(\alpha - 1)!}\, T_n^{\alpha-1/2}(x), \qquad C_n^{(1)}(x) = U_n(x).$$

Type II.   With $\beta = +\frac{1}{2}$, Eq. 13.61 becomes

$$\frac{2^{1/2}}{(1 - 2xt + t^2)} = \pi^{1/2} \sum_{n=0}^{\infty} T_n^{1/2}(x)t^n. \tag{13.62}$$

It will be convenient to change the notation slightly and to use

$$\sqrt{\frac{\pi}{2}} \, T_n^{1/2}(x) \equiv U_n(x). \tag{13.63}$$

This gives us

$$\frac{1}{1 - 2xt + t^2} = \sum_{n=0}^{\infty} U_n(x)t^n. \tag{13.64}$$

The functions $U_n(x)$ generated by $(1 - 2xt + t^2)^{-1}$ are labeled Chebyshev polynomials type II.

Type I.   With $\beta = -\frac{1}{2}$ there is trouble. The t- and x-dependence on the left disappears and the $(\beta - \frac{1}{2})!$ blows up. We may avoid this difficulty by first differentiating Eq. 13.61 with respect to t and then setting $\beta = -\frac{1}{2}$. This yields

$$\frac{x - t}{1 - 2xt + t^2} = \sqrt{\frac{\pi}{2}} \sum_{n=0}^{\infty} n \, T_n^{-1/2}(x)t^{n-1}. \tag{13.65}$$

By multiplying Eq. 13.65 by $2t$ and adding one we obtain

$$\frac{1 - t^2}{1 - 2tx + t^2} = 1 + \sqrt{\frac{\pi}{2}} \sum_{n=0}^{\infty} 2n \, T_n^{-1/2}(x)t^n. \tag{13.66}$$

For $n > 0$ we define $T_n(x)$ by

$$T_n(x) = \sqrt{\frac{\pi}{2}} \, n \, T_n^{-1/2}(x). \tag{13.67}$$

Then

$$\frac{1 - t^2}{1 - 2tx + t^2} = 1 + 2 \sum_{n=1}^{\infty} T_n(x)t^n. \tag{13.68}$$

For $n = 0$ we define

$$T_0(x) = 1 \tag{13.69}$$

to preserve the recurrence relation (Eq. 13.70). We label $T_n(x)$ the Chebyshev polynomials type I. The reader should be warned that the notation for these functions differs from reference to reference. There is almost no general agreement. Here we follow the usage of AMS-55.

These Chebyshev polynomials (type I) combine useful features of (a) Fourier series and (b) orthogonal polynomials. They are of great interest in numerical computation. For example, a least squares approximation minimizes the average squared error. An approximation using Chebyshev polynomials allows a larger average squared error but may keep extreme errors down.

From the generating functions (Eqs. 13.64 and 13.68) we obtain recurrence relations

$$T_{n+1}(x) - 2x \, T_n(x) + T_{n-1}(x) = 0, \tag{13.70}$$

$$U_{n+1}(x) - 2x \, U_n(x) + U_{n-1}(x) = 0. \tag{13.71}$$

Then, using the generating functions for the first few values of n and these recurrence relations for the higher-order polynomials, we get Tables 13.3 and 13.4.

TABLE 13.3

Chebyshev Polynomials, Type I

$T_0 = 1$
$T_1 = x$
$T_2 = 2x^2 - 1$
$T_3 = 4x^3 - 3x$
$T_4 = 8x^4 - 8x^2 + 1$
$T_5 = 16x^5 - 20x^3 + 5x$
$T_6 = 32x^6 - 48x^4 + 18x^2 - 1$

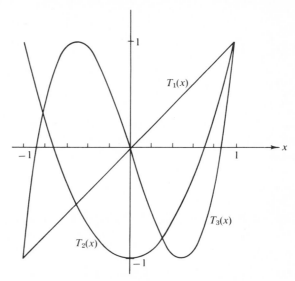

FIG. 13.7   Chebyshev polynomials, $T_n(x)$

Table 13.4

Chebyshev Polynomials, Type II

$U_0 = 1$
$U_1 = 2x$
$U_2 = 4x^2 - 1$
$U_3 = 8x^3 - 4x$
$U_4 = 16x^4 - 12x^2 + 1$
$U_5 = 32x^5 - 32x^3 + 6x$
$U_6 = 64x^6 - 80x^4 + 24x^2 - 1$

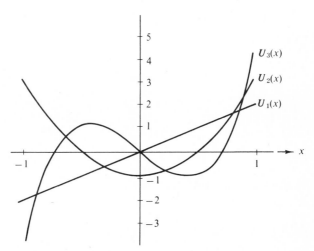

FIG. 13.8   Chebyshev polynomials, $U_n(x)$

Again, from the generating functions, we have the special values

$$T_n(1) = 1$$
$$T_n(-1) = (-1)^n$$
$$T_{2n}(0) = (-1)^n$$
$$T_{2n+1}(0) = 0$$

(13.72)

$$U_n(1) = n + 1$$
$$U_n(-1) = (-1)^n(n + 1)$$
$$U_{2n}(0) = (-1)^n \tag{13.73}$$
$$U_{2n+1}(0) = 0.$$

The parity relations for T_n and U_n are

$$T_n(x) = (-1)^n T_n(-x)$$
$$U_n(x) = (-1)^n U_n(-x). \tag{13.74}$$

Rodrigues' representations of $T_n(x)$ and $U_n(x)$ are

$$T_n(x) = \frac{(-1)^n \pi^{1/2} (1 - x^2)^{1/2}}{2^n (n - \frac{1}{2})!} \frac{d^n}{dx^n} [(1 - x^2)^{n - 1/2}], \tag{13.75}$$

and

$$U_n(x) = \frac{(-1)^n (n + 1) \pi^{1/2}}{2^{n+1} (n + \frac{1}{2})! (1 - x^2)^{1/2}} \frac{d^n}{dx^n} [(1 - x^2)^{n + 1/2}]. \tag{13.76}$$

Recurrence relations.   From the generating functions for $T_n(x)$ and $U_n(x)$ we can obtain a variety of recurrence relations involving derivatives. Among the more useful equations are

$$(1 - x^2) T_n'(x) = -nx T_n(x) + n T_{n-1}(x), \tag{13.77}$$

and

$$(1 - x^2) U_n'(x) = -nx U_n(x) + (n + 1) U_{n-1}(x). \tag{13.78}$$

From Eqs. 13.70 and 13.77 $T_n(x)$, the Chebyshev polynomial type I, satisfies

$$(1 - x^2) T_n''(x) - x T_n'(x) + n^2 T_n(x) = 0, \tag{13.79}$$

whereas $U_n(x)$ the Chebyshev polynomial of type II satisfies

$$(1 - x^2) U_n''(x) - 3x U_n'(x) + n(n + 2) U_n(x) = 0. \tag{13.80}$$

Gegenbauer's equation,

$$(1 - x^2)y'' - 2(1 + \beta)xy' + n(n + 2\beta + 1)y = 0, \tag{13.81}$$

is a generalization of these equations reducing to Eq. 13.79 for $\beta = -\frac{1}{2}$, to Eq. 13.80 for $\beta = +\frac{1}{2}$, and to Legendre's equation for $\beta = 0$.

It is sometimes convenient to define a new function, $V_n(x)$, in terms of the type II polynomials by

$$V_{n+1}(x) = \sqrt{1 - x^2} \, U_n(x). \tag{13.82}$$

Note that the index has been increased from n to $n + 1$. It may be shown that $V_n(x)$ satisfies Eq. 13.79.

From the generating functions, or from the differential equations, power series representations are

$$T_n(x) = \frac{n}{2} \sum_{m=0}^{[n/2]} (-1)^m \frac{(n-m-1)!}{m!(n-2m)!} (2x)^{n-2m}$$

$$= x^n - \binom{n}{2} x^{n-2}(1-x^2) + \binom{n}{4} x^{n-4}(1-x^2)^2 - \cdots, \tag{13.83}$$

$$U_n(x) = \sum_{m=0}^{[n/2]} (-1)^m \frac{(n-m)!}{m!(n-2m)!} (2x)^{n-2m}. \tag{13.84}$$

Using Eq. 13.82, we obtain

$$V_n(x) = \sqrt{1-x^2} \left[\binom{n}{1} x^{n-1} - \binom{n}{3} x^{n-3}(1-x^2) \right.$$

$$\left. + \binom{n}{5} x^{n-5}(1-x^2)^2 - \cdots \right], \tag{13.85}$$

A combination of Eqs. 13.83 and 13.85 produces

$$T_n(x) + i \, V_n(x) = [x + i(1-x^2)^{1/2}]^n \qquad |x| \leqslant 1. \tag{13.86}$$

Orthogonality.   If Eq. 13.79 is put into self-adjoint form (Section 9.1), we obtain $w(x) = (1-x^2)^{-1/2}$ as a weighting factor. For Eq. 13.80 the corresponding weighting factor is $(1-x^2)^{+1/2}$. The resulting orthogonality integrals are

$$\int_{-1}^{1} T_m(x) \, T_n(x)(1-x^2)^{-1/2} \, dx = \begin{cases} 0 & m \neq n, \\ \dfrac{\pi}{2}, & m = n \neq 0, \\ \pi, & m = n = 0, \end{cases} \tag{13.87}$$

$$\int_{-1}^{1} V_m(x) \, V_n(x)(1-x^2)^{-1/2} \, dx = \begin{cases} 0, & m \neq n, \\ \dfrac{\pi}{2}, & m = n \neq 0, \\ 0, & m = n = 0, \end{cases} \tag{13.88}$$

and

$$\int_{-1}^{1} U_m(x) \, U_n(x)(1-x^2)^{1/2} \, dx = \frac{\pi}{2} \, \delta_{m,n}. \tag{13.89}$$

The $\pi/2$ factors may be obtained from the generating functions by using a technique similar to that in Section 12.3. Notice the change in pattern when $m = n = 0$. The orthogonal relations for sine and cosine needed for the development of Fourier series (Chapter 14) show this same behavior.

EXERCISES

13.3.1 From

$$T_n(x) + i \, V_n(x) = [x + i(1 - x^2)^{1/2}]^n$$

let $x = \cos \theta$ and show that

(a) $T_n(x) = \cos n\theta = \cos (n \cos^{-1} x)$,   (b) $V_n(x) = \sin n\theta = \sin (n \cos^{-1} x)$,

(c) $U_n(x) = \dfrac{\sin [(n + 1)\theta]}{\sin \theta} = \dfrac{\sin [(n + 1) \cos^{-1} x]}{\sin (\cos^{-1} x)}$.

The result in part (a) shows that the expansion of an even function in a series of $T_n(x)$ is equivalent to a Fourier cosine approximation (cf. Section 14.1).

13.3.2 Derive

(a) $T_{n+1}(x) + T_{n-1}(x) = 2x \, T_n(x)$,   (b) $T_{m+n}(x) + T_{m-n}(x) = 2T_m(x) \, T_n(x)$,

from the "corresponding" cosine identities.

13.3.3 Starting with $x = \cos \theta$ and $T_n(\cos \theta) = \cos n\theta$, expand

$$x^k = \left(\frac{e^{i\theta} + e^{-i\theta}}{2} \right)^k$$

and show that

$$x^k = \frac{1}{2^{k-1}} \left[T_k(x) + \binom{k}{1} T_{k-2}(x) + \binom{k}{2} T_{k-4}(x) + \cdots \right],$$

the series in brackets terminating with $\binom{k}{m} T_1(x)$ for $k = 2m + 1$ or $\frac{1}{2}\binom{k}{m} T_0$ for $k = 2m$.

13.3.4 Given

$$(1 - x^2) \, U_n''(x) - 3x \, U_n'(x) + n(n + 2) \, U_n(x) = 0,$$

show that $V_n(x)$ satisfies

$$(1 - x^2) \, V_n''(x) - x \, V_n'(x) + n^2 \, V_n(x) = 0,$$

which is Chebyshev's equation.

13.3.5 Show that the Wronskian of $T_n(x)$ and $V_n(x)$ is given by

$$T_n(x) \, V_n'(x) - T_n'(x) \, V_n(x) = - \frac{n}{(1 - x^2)^{1/2}} \, .$$

This verifies that T_n and $V_n (n \neq 0)$ are independent solutions of Eq. 13.79.

13.3.6 Another Chebyshev generating function is

$$\frac{1 - xt}{1 - 2xt + t^2} = \sum_{n=0}^{\infty} W_n(x)t^n, \qquad |t| < 1.$$

How is $W_n(x)$ related to our $T_n(x)$ and $U_n(x)$?

13.3.7 Show that $V_n(x)$ satisfies the same three-term recurrence relation as $T_n(x)$ (Eq. 13.70).

13.3.8 Verify the series solutions for $T_n(x)$ and $U_n(x)$ (Eqs. 13.83 and 13.84).

13.3.9 A number of equations relate the two types of Chebyshev polynomials. As examples show that

$$T_n(x) = U_n(x) - x\, U_{n-1}(x)$$

and

$$(1 - x^2)\, U_n(x) = 2T_{n+1}(x) - T_{n+2}(x).$$

13.3.10 Show that

(a) $\cos xy = J_0(x) + 2 \sum_{n=1}^{\infty} (-1)^n J_{2n}(x)\, T_{2n}(y)$,

(b) $\sin xy = 2 \sum_{n=0}^{\infty} (-1)^n J_{2n+1}(x)\, T_{2n+1}(y)$,

(c) $e^{xy} = I_0(x) + 2 \sum_{n=1}^{\infty} I_n(x)\, T_n(y)$.

Here $J_n(x)$ is the regular Bessel function and $I_n(x)$ is the modified Bessel function (Section 11.4).

13.3.11 Verify the following integral representations

(a) $T_n(z) = \dfrac{1}{4\pi i} \oint \dfrac{(1 - t^2)\, dt}{(1 - 2zt + t^2)t^{n+1}}$,   (b) $U_n(z) = \dfrac{1}{2\pi i} \oint \dfrac{dt}{(1 - 2zt + t^2)t^{n+1}}$.

In each case the path of integration encircles the origin in the positive sense and does *not* include the zeros of $(1 - 2zt + t^2)$.

13.3.12 The curves plotted in Fig. 13.7 suggest that $|T_n(x)| \leqslant 1$ for $-1 \leqslant x \leqslant 1$ (real x). Prove this.

13.3.13 Show that

$$\frac{dV_n(x)}{dx} = -n \frac{T_n(x)}{\sqrt{1 - x^2}},$$

(a) using the trigonometric forms of V_n and T_n,
(b) using the Rodrigues representation.

13.3.14 Derive the Rodrigues representation of $T_n(x)$.

$$T_n(x) = \frac{(-1)^n \pi^{1/2}(1 - x^2)^{1/2}}{2^n(n - \frac{1}{2})!} \frac{d^n}{dx^n} [(1 - x^2)^{n-1/2}].$$

Hints. One possibility is to use the hypergeometric function relation

$$_2F_1(a, b, c; z) = (1 - z)^{-a}\, _2F_1\left(a,\, c - b,\, c;\, \frac{-z}{1 - z}\right),$$

with $z = (1 - x)/2$. An alternate approach is to develop a first-order differential equation for $y = (1 - x^2)^{n-1/2}$. Repeated differentiation of this equation leads to the Chebyshev equation.

13.4 Hypergeometric Functions

In Chapter 8 the hypergeometric equation[1]

$$x(1 - x)\, y''(x) + [c - (a + b + 1)x]\, y'(x) - ab\, y(x) = 0 \qquad (13.90)$$

---

[1] This is sometimes called Gauss's differential equation. The solutions then become Gauss functions.

was introduced as a canonical form of a linear second-order differential equation with regular singularities at $x = 0$, 1, and ∞. One solution is

$$y(x) = {}_2F_1(a, b, c; x)$$

$$= 1 + \frac{a \cdot b}{c} \frac{x}{1!} + \frac{a(a + 1)b(b + 1)}{c(c + 1)} \frac{x^2}{2!} + \cdots, \qquad c \neq 0, -1, -2, -3, \cdots,$$

(13.91)

which is known as the hypergeometric function or hypergeometric series. In terms of the often-used Pochhammer symbol

$$(a)_n = a(a + 1)(a + 2) \cdots (a + n - 1),$$
$$(a)_0 = 1,$$

(13.92)

the hypergeometric function becomes

$$_2F_1(a, b, c; x) = \sum_{n=0}^{\infty} \frac{(a)_n (b)_n}{(c)_n} \frac{x^n}{n!}.$$

(13.93)

In this form the subscripts 2 and 1 become clear. The leading subscript 2 indicates that two Pochhammer symbols appear in the numerator and the final subscript 1 indicates one Pochhammer symbol in the denominator. The confluent hypergeometric function $_1F_1$ appears in Section 13.5.

From the form of Eq. 13.91 we see that the parameter c may not be zero or a negative integer. On the other hand, if a or b equals 0 or a negative integer, the series terminates and the hypergeometric function becomes a simple polynomial.

Many more or less elementary functions can be represented by the hypergeometric function.[1] We find

$$\ln(1 + x) = x \,_2F_1(1, 1, 2; -x).$$

(13.94)

For the complete elliptic intervals K and E

$$K = \int_0^{\pi/2} (1 - k^2 \sin^2 \theta)^{-1/2} \, d\theta$$

$$= \frac{\pi}{2} \,_2F_1\left(\frac{1}{2}, \frac{1}{2}, 1; k^2\right),$$

(13.95)

$$E = \int_0^{\pi/2} (1 - k^2 \sin^2 \theta)^{1/2} \, d\theta$$

$$= \frac{\pi}{2} \,_2F_1\left(\frac{1}{2}, -\frac{1}{2}, 1; k^2\right).$$

(13.96)

The hypergeometric equation as a second-order linear differential equation has a second independent solution. The usual form is

$$y(x) = x^{1-c} \,_2F_1(a + 1 - c, b + 1 - c, 2 - c; x), \qquad c \neq 2, 3, 4, \cdots.$$ (13.97)

The reader may show (Exercise 13.4.1) that if c is an integer either the two solutions

---

[1] With three parameters, a, b, and c, we can represent almost anything.

coincide or (barring a rescue by integral a or integral b) one of the solutions will blow up. In such a case the second solution is expected to include a logarithmic term.

Alternate forms of the hypergeometric equation include

$$(1 - z^2)\, y''\left(\frac{1 - z}{2}\right) - [(a + b + 1)z - (a + b + 1 - 2c)]y'\left(\frac{1 - z}{2}\right)$$

$$- ab\, y\left(\frac{1 - z}{2}\right) = 0, \quad (13.98)$$

$$(1 - z^2)\, y''\,(z^2) - \left[(2a + 2b + 1)z + \frac{1 - 2c}{z}\right] y'(z^2) - 4ab\, y(z^2) = 0. \quad (13.99)$$

The parameters a, b, and c enter in the same way as the parameter n of Bessel, Legendre, and other special functions. As we found with these functions, we expect recurrence relations involving unit changes in the parameters a, b and c. The usual nomenclature for the hypergeometric functions in which *one* parameter changes by $+$ or -1 is "contiguous function." Generalizing this term to include simultaneous unit changes in more than one parameter, we find 26 functions contiguous to $_2F_1(a, b, c; x)$. Taking them two at a time, we can develop the formidable total of 325 equations among the contiguous functions. One typical example is

$$(a - b)\{c(a + b - 1) + 1 - a^2 - b^2 + [(a - b)^2 - 1](1 - x)\}\, _2F_1(a, b, c; x)$$

$$= (c - a)(a - b + 1)b\, _2F_1(a - 1, b + 1, c; x) \quad (13.100)$$

$$+ (c - b)(a - b - 1)a\, _2F_1(a + 1, b - 1, c; x).$$

Since the Gegenbauer equation (13.61) in Section 13.3 is a special case of Eq. 13.90, we see that Gegenbauer functions (and Legendre and Chebyshev functions) may be expressed as hypergeometric functions. For the Gegenbauer function we obtain

$$T_n^\beta(x) = \frac{(n + 2\beta)!}{2^\beta n!\, \beta!}\, _2F_1\left(-n, n + 2\,\beta + 1, 1 + \beta; \frac{1 - x}{2}\right). \quad (13.101)$$

For Legendre and associated Legendre functions

$$P_n(x) = {_2F_1}\left(-n, n + 1, 1; \frac{1 - x}{2}\right), \quad (13.102)$$

$$P_n^m(x) = \frac{(n + m)!}{(n - m)!} \frac{(1 - x^2)^{m/2}}{2^m m!}\, _2F_1\left(m - n, m + n + 1, m + 1; \frac{1 - x}{2}\right). \quad (13.103)$$

Alternate forms are

$$P_{2n}(x) = (-1)^n \frac{(2n)!}{2^{2n} n!\, n!}\, _2F_1(-n, n + \frac{1}{2}, \frac{1}{2}; x^2), \quad (13.104)$$

$$P_{2n+1}(x) = (-1)^n \frac{(2n + 1)!}{2^{2n} n!\, n!}\, x\, _2F_1(-n, n + \frac{3}{2}, \frac{3}{2}; x^2). \quad (13.105)$$

In terms of hypergeometric functions, the Chebyshev functions become

$$T_n(x) = {}_2F_1\left(-n,\, n,\, \frac{1}{2};\, \frac{1-x}{2}\right),$$ (13.106)

$$U_n(x) = (n+1)\, {}_2F_1\left(-n,\, n+2,\, \frac{3}{2};\, \frac{1-x}{2}\right),$$ (13.107)

$$V_n(x) = \sqrt{1-x^2}\; n\, {}_2F_1\left(-n+1,\, n+1,\, \frac{3}{2};\, \frac{1-x}{2}\right).$$ (13.108)

The leading factors are determined by direct comparison of complete power series, comparison of coefficients of particular powers of the variable, or evaluation at $x = 0$ or 1, etc.

EXERCISES

13.4.1 (a) For c, an integer, and a and b, nonintegral, show that

$$\quad {}_2F_1(a, b, c; x) \text{ and } x^{1-c}\, {}_2F_1(a+1-c, b+1-c, 2-c; x)$$

yield only one solution to the hypergeometric equation.

(b) What happens if a is an integer, say $a = -1$, and $c = -2$?

13.4.2 Find the Legendre, Chebyshev I, and Chebyshev II recurrence relations corresponding to the contiguous hypergeometric function equation (13.100).

13.4.3 Prove that

$$\quad {}_2F_1(a, b, c; x) = (1-x)^{-a}\, {}_2F_1\left(a,\, c-b, c,\, \frac{-x}{1-x}\right).$$

13.4.4 Verify

$$\quad {}_2F_1(-n, b, c; 1) = \frac{(c-b)_n}{(c)_n}.$$

Hint. Here is a chance to use the contiguous function relation

$$[2a - c + (b-a)x]\, F(a, b, c; x) = a(1-x)\, F(a+1, b, c; x) - (c-a)\, F(a-1, b, c; x)$$

and mathematical induction.

13.5 Confluent Hypergeometric Functions

The confluent hypergeometric equation[1]

$$x\, y''(x) + (c-x)\, y'(x) - a\, y(x) = 0$$ (13.109)

may be obtained from the hypergeometric equation of Section 13.4 by merging

---

[1] This is often called Kummer's equation. The solutions, then, are Kummer functions.

two of its singularities. The resulting equation has a regular singularity at $x = 0$ and an irregular one at $x = \infty$. One solution of the confluent hypergeometric equation is

$$y(x) = {}_1F_1(a, c; x) = M(a, c; x)$$

$$= 1 + \frac{a}{c}\frac{x}{1!} + \frac{a(a + 1)}{c(c + 1)}\frac{x^2}{2!} + \cdots, \qquad c \neq 0, -1, -2, \cdots. \qquad (13.110)$$

In terms of the Pochhammer symbols we have

$$M(a, c; x) = \sum_{n=0}^{\infty} \frac{(a)_n}{(c)_n}\frac{x^n}{n!}. \qquad (13.111)$$

Clearly $M(a, c; x)$ becomes a polynomial if the parameter a is 0 or a negative integer. Numerous more or less elementary functions may be represented by the confluent hypergeometric function. Examples are the error function and the incomplete gamma function.

$$\mathrm{erf}(x) = \frac{2}{\pi^{1/2}} \int_0^x e^{-t^2}\, dt$$

$$= \frac{2}{\pi^{1/2}} x\, M\left(\frac{1}{2}, \frac{3}{2}; -x^2\right), \qquad (13.112)$$

$$\gamma(a, x) = \int_0^x e^{-t} t^{a-1}\, dt$$

$$= a^{-1} x^a\, M(a, a + 1; -x), \qquad \mathrm{R.P.}(a) > 0. \qquad (13.113)$$

A second solution of Eq. 13.109 is given by

$$y(x) = x^{1-c}\, M(a + 1 - c, 2 - c; x), \qquad c \neq 2, 3, 4, \ldots. \qquad (13.114)$$

The standard form of the second solution of Eq. 13.109 is a linear combination of Eq. 13.110 and 13.114.

$$U(a, c, x) = \frac{\pi}{\sin \pi c}\left[\frac{M(a, c; x)}{(a - c)!(c - 1)!} - \frac{x^{1-c}\, M(a + 1 - c, 2 - c; x)}{(a - 1)!(1 - c)!}\right]. \qquad (13.115)$$

An alternate form of the confluent hypergeometric equation that will be useful later is obtained by changing the independent variable from x to x^2.

$$y''(x^2) + \left[\frac{2c - 1}{x} - 2x\right] y'(x^2) - 4a\, y(x^2) = 0. \qquad (13.116)$$

As with the hypergeometric functions, contiguous functions exist in which the parameters a and c are changed by ± 1. Including the cases of simultaneous changes in the two parameters,[1] we have eight possibilities. Taking the original function and pairs of the contiguous functions, we can develop a total of 28 equations.[2]

---

[1] Slater refers to these as associated functions.

[2] The recurrence relations for Bessel, Hermite, and Laguerre functions are special cases of these equations.

Bessel and modified Bessel functions.   Kummer's first formula,

$$M(a, c; x) = e^x M(c - a, c; -x), \tag{13.117}$$

is useful in representing the Bessel and modified Bessel functions. The formula may be verified by series expansion (cf. Exercise 13.5.2).

As expected from the form of the confluent hypergeometric equation and the character of its singularities, the confluent hypergeometric functions are useful in representing a number of the special functions of mathematical physics. For the Bessel functions

$$J_v(x) = \frac{e^{-ix}}{v!}\left(\frac{x}{2}\right)^v M\left(v + \frac{1}{2}, 2v + 1; 2ix\right), \tag{13.118}$$

whereas for the modified Bessel functions of the first kind,

$$I_v(x) = \frac{e^{-x}}{v!}\left(\frac{x}{2}\right)^v M\left(v + \frac{1}{2}, 2v + 1; 2x\right). \tag{13.119}$$

Hermite functions.   The Hermite functions are given by

$$H_{2n}(x) = (-1)^n \frac{(2n)!}{n!} M\left(-n, \frac{1}{2}; x^2\right), \tag{13.120}$$

$$H_{2n+1}(x) = (-1)^n \frac{2(2n + 1)!}{n!} x\, M\left(-n, \frac{3}{2}; x^2\right), \tag{13.121}$$

using Eq. 13.116.

Comparing the Laguerre differential equation with the confluent hypergeometric equation, we have

$$L_n(x) = M(-n, 1; x). \tag{13.122}$$

The constant is fixed as unity by noting Eq. 13.35 for $x = 0$. For the associated Laguerre functions

$$L_n^m(x) = (-1)^m \frac{d^m}{dx^m} L_{n+m}(x)$$

$$= \frac{(n + m)!}{n!\,m!} M(-n, m + 1; x). \tag{13.123}$$

Alternate verification is obtained by comparing Eq. 13.123 with the power series solution (Eq. 13.41 of Section 13.2). Note that in the hypergeometric form, as distinct from a Rodrigues representation, the indices n and m need not be integers and, if they are not integers, $L_n^m(x)$ will not be a polynomial.

Miscellaneous cases.   There are certain advantages in expressing our special functions in terms of hypergeometric and confluent hypergeometric functions. If the general behavior of the latter functions is known, the behavior of the special functions we have investigated follows as a series of special cases. This may be useful in determining asymptotic behavior or evaluating normalization integrals.

The further advantage is that the relations between the special functions are clarified. For instance, an examination of Eqs. 13.120, 13.121, and 13.123 suggests that the Laguerre and Hermite functions are related. Verification is given as Exercise 13.5.4.

The confluent hypergeometric equation (13.109) is clearly not self-adjoint. For this and other reasons it is convenient to define

$$M_{k\mu}(x) = e^{-x/2} x^{\mu + 1/2} M(\mu - k + \tfrac{1}{2}, 2\mu + 1; x). \tag{13.124}$$

This new function $M_{k\mu}(x)$ is a Whittaker function which satisfies the self-adjoint equation

$$M''_{k\mu}(x) + \left(-\frac{1}{4} + \frac{k}{x} + \frac{\tfrac{1}{4} - \mu^2}{x^2} \right) M_{k\mu}(x) = 0. \tag{13.125}$$

The corresponding second solution is

$$W_{k\mu}(x) = e^{-x/2} x^{\mu + 1/2} U(\mu - k + \tfrac{1}{2}, 2\mu + 1; x). \tag{13.126}$$

EXERCISES

13.5.1 Show that the Wronskian of the two confluent hypergeometric functions, $M(a, c; x)$ and $U(a, c; x)$ is given by

$$MU' - M'U = -\frac{(c-1)! \, e^x}{(a-1)! \, x^c}.$$

What happens if a is 0 or a negative integer?

13.5.2 Verify the Kummer transformations:
(a) $M(a, c; x) = e^x M(c - a, c; -x)$, (b) $U(a, c; x) = x^{1-c} U(a - c + 1, 2 - c; x)$.

13.5.3 Verify the following integral representations:

(a) $M(a, c; x) = \dfrac{\Gamma(c)}{\Gamma(a)\Gamma(c - a)} \displaystyle\int_0^1 e^{xt} t^{a-1} (1 - t)^{c-a-1} \, dt$,

(b) $U(a, c; x) = \dfrac{1}{\Gamma(a)} \displaystyle\int_0^\infty e^{-xt} t^{a-1} (1 + t)^{c-a-1} \, dt$.

13.5.4 The confluent function facilitates the establishment of some odd relations among the special functions of mathematical physics. For example, show that
(a) $H_{2n}(x) = (-1)^n 2^{2n} n! \, L_n^{-1/2}(x^2)$, (b) $H_{2n+1}(x) = (-1)^n 2^{2n+1} n! x \, L_n^{1/2}(x^2)$.

13.5.5 Show that the modified Bessel function of the second kind $K_\nu(x)$ is given by
$$K_\nu(x) = \pi^{1/2} e^{-x} (2x)^\nu U(\nu + \tfrac{1}{2}, 2\nu + 1; 2x).$$

13.5.6 Show that the contiguous confluent hypergeometric function equation,
$$(c - a) M(a - 1, c; x) + (2a - c + x) M(a, c; x) - a M(a + 1, c; x) = 0,$$
leads to the associated Laguerre function recurrence relation (Eq. 13.44).

13.5.7   By direct differentiation and substitution verify that

$$y = ax^{-a} \int_0^x e^{-t} t^{a-1} \, dt$$

actually does satisfy

$$xy'' + (a + 1 + x)y' + ay = 0.$$

13.5.8   Verify the confluent hypergeometric form of the Hermite polynomial $H_{2n+1}(x)$ (Eq. 13.121) by showing that

(a) $H_{2n+1}(x)/x$ satisfies the confluent hypergeometric equation with $a = -n$, $c = \frac{3}{2}$ and argument x^2,

(b) $\displaystyle\lim_{x \to 0} \frac{H_{2n+1}(x)}{x} = (-1)^n \frac{2(2n + 1)!}{n!}$.

REFERENCES

ABRAMOWITZ, M., and I. A. STEGUN, editors, *Handbook of Mathematical Functions*. Washington, D.C.: National Bureau of Standards, Applied Mathematics Series-55 (1964). Chapter 22 is a detailed summary of the properties and representations of orthogonal polynomials. Other chapters summarize properties of Bessel, Legendre, hypergeometric, and confluent hypergeometric functions and much more.

MAGNUS, W., and F. OBERHETTINGER, *Formulas and Theorems for the Special Functions of Mathematical Physics*. Translated by J. Wermer. New York: Chelsea (1949). An excellent summary of just what the title says, including the topics of Chapters 10–13.

RAINVILLE, E. D., *Special Functions*. New York: Macmillan (1960). A coherent, comprehensive account of almost all the special functions of mathematical physics that the reader is likely to encounter.

SANSONE, G. *Orthogonal Functions*. Translated by A. H. Diamond. New York: Interscience Publishers (1959).

SLATER, L. J., *Confluent Hypergeometric Functions*. Cambridge: Cambridge University Press (1960). A clear and detailed development of the properties of the confluent hypergeometric functions and of relations of the confluent hypergeometric equation to other differential equations of mathematical physics.

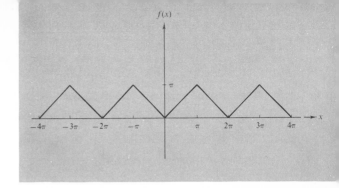

CHAPTER 14

FOURIER SERIES

14.1 General Properties

Fourier series.   A Fourier series may be defined as an expansion of a function or representation of a function in a series of sines and cosines such as

$$f(x) = \frac{a_0}{2} + \sum_{n=1}^{\infty} a_n \cos nx + \sum_{n=1}^{\infty} b_n \sin nx. \tag{14.1}$$

The conditions imposed on $f(x)$ to make this equation valid are that $f(x)$ has only a finite number of finite discontinuities and only a finite number of extreme values, maxima, and minima.[1] Functions satisfying these conditions may be called piecewise regular. The conditions themselves are known as the Dirichlet conditions. Although there are some functions that do not obey these Dirichlet conditions, they may well be labeled pathological for purposes of Fourier expansions. In the vast majority of physical problems involving a Fourier series these conditions will be satisfied.

Expressing $\cos nx$ and $\sin nx$ in exponential form, we may rewrite Eq. 14.1 as

$$f(x) = \sum_{n=-\infty}^{\infty} c_n e^{inx} \tag{14.2}$$

in which

$$c_n = \tfrac{1}{2}(a_n - ib_n),$$
$$c_{-n} = \tfrac{1}{2}(a_n + ib_n), \qquad n > 0, \tag{14.3}$$

and

$$c_0 = \tfrac{1}{2}a_0.$$

[1] These conditions are *sufficient* but not *necessary*.

14 FOURIER SERIES

If we expand $f(z)$ in a Laurent series[1] (assuming $f(z)$ is analytic),

$$f(z) = \sum_{n=-\infty}^{\infty} d_n z^n. \tag{14.4}$$

On the unit circle $z = e^{i\theta}$ and

$$f(z) = f(e^{i\theta}) = \sum_{n=-\infty}^{\infty} d_n e^{in\theta}. \tag{14.5}$$

Completeness—Laurent series.   The Laurent expansion on the unit circle (Eq. 14.5) has the same form as the complex Fourier series (Eq. 14.2), which shows the equivalence between the two expansions. Since the Laurent series as a power series has the property of completeness, we see that the Fourier functions, e^{inx}, form a complete set; that is the series (Eqs. 14.1 and 14.2) is able to represent any piecewise regular function in the range $(0, 2\pi)$. This range and the related question of periodicity are considered in the next section.

The Fourier expansion and the completeness property may be expected, for the functions $\sin nx$, $\cosine nx$, e^{inx} are all eigenfunctions of a self-adjoint linear differential equation,

$$y'' + n^2 y = 0. \tag{14.6}$$

We obtain orthogonal eigenfunctions for different values of the eigenvalue n by choosing the interval $[0, p\pi]$, p an integer, to satisfy the boundary conditions in the Sturm-Liouville theory (Chapter 9). If we further choose $p = 2$, the different eigenfunctions for the same eigenvalue n may be orthogonal. We have

$$\int_0^{2\pi} \sin mx \sin nx \, dx = \begin{cases} \pi\delta_{m,n}, & m \neq 0, \\ 0, & m = 0, \end{cases} \tag{14.7}$$

$$\int_0^{2\pi} \cos mx \cos nx \, dx = \begin{cases} \pi\delta_{m,n}, & m \neq 0, \\ 2\pi, & m = n = 0, \end{cases} \tag{14.8}$$

$$\int_0^{2\pi} \sin mx \cos nx \, dx = 0 \quad \text{for all integral } m \text{ and } n. \tag{14.9}$$

Note carefully that any interval $x_0 \leqslant x \leqslant x_0 + 2\pi$ will be equally satisfactory. Frequently we shall use $x_0 = -\pi$ to obtain the interval $-\pi \leqslant x \leqslant \pi$. For the complex eigenfunctions $e^{\pm inx}$ orthogonality is usually *defined* in terms of the complex conjugate of one of the two factors,

$$\int_0^{2\pi} (e^{imx})^* e^{inx} \, dx = 2\pi\delta_{m,n}. \tag{14.10}$$

This agrees with the treatment of the spherical harmonics (Section 12.6).

Sturm-Liouville theory.   The Sturm-Liouville theory guarantees the validity of Eq. 14.1 (for functions satisfying the Dirichlet conditions) and, by use of the

[1] Section 6.4.

orthogonality relations, allows us to compute the expansion coefficients

$$a_n = \frac{1}{\pi} \int_0^{2\pi} f(t) \cos nt\, dt, \tag{14.11}$$

$$b_n = \frac{1}{\pi} \int_0^{2\pi} f(t) \sin nt\, dt, \qquad n = 0, 1, 2, \dots . \tag{14.12}$$

This, of course, is subject to the requirement that the integrals exist. They do if $f(t)$ is piecewise continuous. Substituting Eqs. 14.11 and 14.12 into Eq. 14.1, we write our Fourier expansion

$$f(x) = \frac{1}{2\pi} \int_0^{2\pi} f(t)\, dt + \frac{1}{\pi} \sum_{n=1}^{\infty} \left(\cos nx \int_0^{2\pi} f(t) \cos nt\, dt + \sin nx \int_0^{2\pi} f(t) \sin nt\, dt \right)$$

$$= \frac{1}{2\pi} \int_0^{2\pi} f(t)\, dt + \frac{1}{\pi} \sum_{n=1}^{\infty} \int_0^{2\pi} f(t) \cos n(t - x)\, dt, \tag{14.13}$$

the first (constant) term being the average value of $f(x)$ over the interval $[0, 2\pi]$.

Sawtooth wave. An idea of the convergence of a Fourier series and the error in using only a finite number of terms in the series may be obtained by considering the expansion of

$$f(x) = \begin{cases} x, & 0 \leqslant x < \pi, \\ x - 2\pi, & \pi < x \leqslant 2\pi. \end{cases} \tag{14.14}$$

This is a sawtooth wave, and for convenience we shall shift our interval from $[0, 2\pi]$ to $[-\pi, \pi]$. In this interval we have simply $f(x) = x$. Using Eqs. 14.11 and 14.12 we may show the expansion to be

$$f(x) = x = 2 \left[\sin x - \frac{\sin 2x}{2} + \frac{\sin 3x}{3} - \cdots - (-1)^{n+1} \frac{\sin nx}{n} + \cdots \right], \tag{14.15}$$

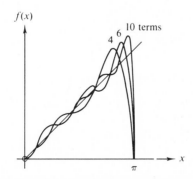

FIG. 14.1 Fourier representation of sawtooth wave

Figure 14.1 shows $f(x)$ for $0 \leqslant x < \pi$ for the sum of two, four, six, and ten terms of the series. Three features deserve comment.

1. There is a steady increase in the accuracy of the representation as the number of terms included is increased.

2. All the curves pass through the midpoint $y = 0$ at $x = \pi$.

3. In the vicinity of $x = \pi$ there is an overshoot that persists and shows no sign of diminishing.

Behavior of discontinuities.   The behavior at $x = \pi$ is an example of a general rule that at a finite discontinuity the series converges to the arithmetic mean. For a discontinuity at $x = x_0$ the series yields

$$f(x_0) = \tfrac{1}{2}[f(x_0+) + f(x_0-)], \tag{14.16}$$

the arithmetic mean of the right and left approaches to $x = x_0$. A general proof is given by Jeffreys and by Carslaw.

The overshoot just before $x = \pi$ is an example of the Gibbs phenomenon, discussed in Section 14.5.

EXERCISES

14.1.1 A function $f(x)$ (quadratically integrable) is to be represented by a *finite* Fourier series. A convenient measure of the accuracy of the series is given by the integrated square of the deviation

$$\Delta_p = \int_0^{2\pi} \left[f(x) - \frac{a_0}{2} - \sum_{n=1}^{p} (a_n \cos nx + b_n \sin nx) \right]^2 dx.$$

Show that the requirement that Δ_p be minimized, that is,

$$\frac{\partial \Delta_p}{\partial a_n} = 0, \qquad \frac{\partial \Delta_p}{\partial b_n} = 0,$$

for all n, leads to choosing a_n and b_n, as given in Eqs. 14.11 and 14.12.

14.2 Advantages, Uses of Fourier Series

Discontinuous function.   One of the advantages of a Fourier representation over some other representation, such as a Taylor series, is that it may represent a discontinuous function. An example is the sawtooth wave in the preceding section. Other examples are considered in Section 14.3 and in the exercises.

Periodic functions.   Related to this advantage is the usefulness of a Fourier series in representing a periodic function. If $f(x)$ has a period of 2π, perhaps it is only natural that we expand it in a series of functions with period 2π, $2\pi/2$, $2\pi/3$, ... This guarantees that if our periodic $f(x)$ is represented over one interval $[0, 2\pi]$ or $[-\pi, \pi]$ the representation holds for all finite x.

At this point we may conveniently consider the properties of symmetry. Using the interval $[-\pi, \pi]$, $\sin x$ is odd and $\cos x$ is an even function of x. Hence by Eqs. 14.11 and 14.12,[1] if $f(x)$ is odd, all $a_n = 0$ and if $f(x)$ is even all $b_n = 0$. In other words,

$$f(x) = \frac{a_0}{2} + \sum_{n=1}^{\infty} a_n \cos nx, \qquad f(x) \text{ even}, \tag{14.17}$$

$$f(x) = \sum_{n=1}^{\infty} b_n \sin nx, \qquad f(x) \text{ odd}. \tag{14.18}$$

Frequently these properties are helpful in expanding a given function.

We have noted that the Fourier series is periodic. This is important in considering whether Eq. 14.1 holds outside the initial interval. Suppose we are given only that

$$f(x) = x, \qquad 0 \leqslant x < \pi \tag{14.19}$$

and are asked to represent $f(x)$ by a series expansion. Let us take three of the infinite number of possible expansions.

1. If we assume a Taylor expansion, we have

$$f(x) = x, \tag{14.20}$$

a one-term series. This (one term) series is defined for all finite x.

2. Using the Fourier cosine series (Eq. 14.17), we predict that

$$f(x) = -x, \qquad -\pi < x \leqslant 0,$$
$$f(x) = 2\pi - x, \qquad \pi < x < 2\pi. \tag{14.21}$$

3. Finally, from the Fourier sine series (Eq. 14.18), we have

$$f(x) = x, \qquad -\pi < x \leqslant 0,$$
$$f(x) = x - 2\pi, \qquad \pi < x < 2\pi. \tag{14.22}$$

These three possibilities, Taylor series, Fourier cosine series, and Fourier sine series, are each perfectly valid in the original interval $[0, \pi]$. Outside, however, their behavior is strikingly different (cf. Fig. 14.2). Which of the three, then, is correct? This question has no answer, unless we are given more information about $f(x)$. It may be any of the three or none of them. Our Fourier expansions are valid over the basic interval. Unless the function $f(x)$ is known to be periodic with a period equal to our basic interval, or $(1/n)$th of our basic interval, there is no assurance whatever that the representation (Eq. 14.1) will have any meaning outside the basic interval.

In addition to the advantages of representing discontinuous and periodic functions, there is a third very real advantage in using a Fourier series. Suppose that we are solving the equation of motion of an oscillating particle subject to a periodic driving force. The Fourier expansion of the driving force then gives us the fundamental term and a series of harmonics. The (linear) differential equation may

[1] With the range of integration $-\pi \leqslant x \leqslant \pi$.

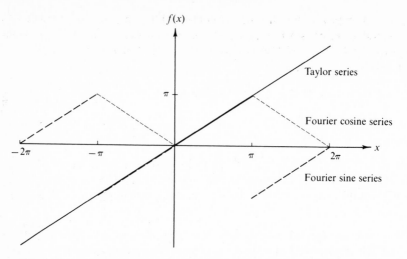

FIG. 14.2 Comparison of Fourier cosine series, Fourier sine series, and Taylor series

be solved for each of these harmonics individually, a process that may be much easier than dealing with the original driving force. Then, as long as the differential equation is linear, all the solutions may be added together to obtain the final solution.[1] This is more than just a clever mathematical trick. It corresponds to finding the response of the system to the fundamental frequency and to each of the harmonic frequencies.

One question that is sometimes raised is, " Were the harmonics there all along or were they created by our Fourier analysis?" One answer compares the functional resolution into harmonics with the resolution of a vector into rectangular components. The components may have been present in the sense that they may be isolated and observed, but the resolution is certainly not unique. Hence many authorities prefer to say that the harmonics were created by our choice of expansion. Other expansions in other sets of orthogonal functions would give different results. For further discussion the reader should consult a series of notes and letters in the *American Journal of Physics*.[2]

Change of interval.   So far attention has been restricted to an interval of length 2π. This restriction may easily be relaxed. If $f(x)$ is periodic with a period $2L$, we may write

$$f(x) = \frac{a_0}{2} + \sum_{n=1}^{\infty}\left[a_n \cos\frac{n\pi x}{L} + b_n \sin\frac{n\pi x}{L}\right] \qquad (14.23)$$

[1] One of the nastier features of nonlinear differential equations is that this principle of superposition is not valid.

[2] B. L. Robinson, *Am. J. Phys.* **21**, 391 (1953).

F. W. Van Name, Jr., *Am. J. Phys.* **22**, 94 (1954).

with

$$a_n = \frac{1}{L} \int_{-L}^{L} f(t) \cos \frac{n\pi t}{L} dt, \qquad n = 0, 1, 2, 3, \ldots, \tag{14.24}$$

$$b_n = \frac{1}{L} \int_{-L}^{L} f(t) \sin \frac{n\pi t}{L} dt, \qquad n = 1, 2, 3, \ldots, \tag{14.25}$$

replacing x in Eq. 14.1 with $\pi x/L$ and t in Eqs. 14.11 and 14.12 with $\pi t/L$. (For convenience the interval in Eqs. 14.11 and 14.12 is shifted to $-\pi \leqslant x \leqslant \pi$.)

14.3 Applications of Fourier Series

EXAMPLE 14.1.1. SQUARE WAVE—HIGH FREQUENCIES

One simple application of Fourier series, the analysis of a "square" wave in terms of its Fourier components, may occur in electronic circuits designed to handle sharply rising pulses. Suppose that our wave is defined by

$$\begin{aligned} f(x) &= 0, & -\pi < x < 0, \\ f(x) &= h, & 0 < x < \pi. \end{aligned} \tag{14.26}$$

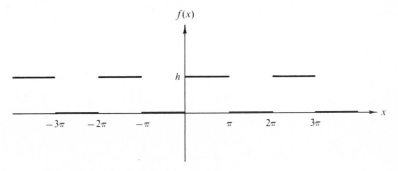

FIG. 14.3   Square wave

From Eqs. 14.11 and 14.12 we find

$$a_0 = \frac{1}{\pi} \int_0^{\pi} h \, dx = h, \tag{14.27}$$

$$a_n = \frac{1}{\pi} \int_0^{\pi} h \cos nx \, dx = 0, \qquad n = 1, 2, 3, \ldots, \tag{14.28}$$

$$b_n = \frac{1}{\pi} \int_0^{\pi} h \sin nx \, dx = \frac{h}{n\pi} (1 - \cos n\pi); \tag{14.29}$$

$$\therefore \quad b_n = \frac{2h}{n\pi}, \qquad n \text{ odd}, \tag{14.30}$$

$$b_n = 0, \qquad n \text{ even}. \tag{14.31}$$

The resulting series is

$$f(x) = \frac{h}{2} + \frac{2h}{\pi}\left(\frac{\sin x}{1} + \frac{\sin 3x}{3} + \frac{\sin 5x}{5} + \cdots\right). \qquad (14.32)$$

Except for the first term which represents an average of $f(x)$ over the interval $[-\pi, \pi]$ all the cosine terms have vanished. Since $f(x) - h/2$ is odd, we have a Fourier sine series. Although only the odd terms in the sine series occur, they fall only as n^{-1}. This is similar to the convergence (or lack of convergence) of the harmonic series. Physically this means that our square wave contains a lot of high-frequency components. If the electronic apparatus will not pass these components, our square wave input will emerge more or less rounded off, perhaps as an amorphous blob.

Example 14.3.2.   Full Wave Rectifier

As a second example, let us ask how well the output of a full wave rectifier approaches pure direct current. Our rectifier may be thought of as having passed the positive peaks of an incoming sine wave and inverting the negative peaks. This yields

$$f(t) = \sin \omega t, \qquad 0 < \omega t < \pi,$$
$$f(t) = -\sin \omega t, \qquad -\pi < \omega t < 0. \qquad (14.33)$$

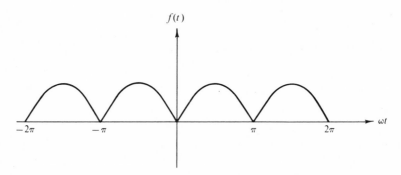

FIG. 14.4   Full wave rectifier

Since $f(t)$ defined here is even, no terms of the form $\sin n\omega t$ will appear. Again, from Eqs. 14.11 and 14.12, we have

$$a_0 = \frac{1}{\pi} \int_{-\pi}^{0} -\sin \omega t \, d(\omega t) + \frac{1}{\pi} \int_{0}^{\pi} \sin \omega t \, d(\omega t)$$
$$= \frac{2}{\pi} \int_{0}^{\pi} \sin \omega t \, d(\omega t) = \frac{4}{\pi}, \qquad (14.34)$$

$$a_n = \frac{2}{\pi} \int_0^\pi \sin \omega t \cos n\omega t \, d(\omega t)$$

$$= -\frac{2}{\pi} \frac{2}{n^2 - 1}, \qquad n \text{ even}$$

$$= 0, \qquad n \text{ odd}. \tag{14.35}$$

Note carefully that $[0, \pi]$ is not an orthogonality interval and we do not get zero for even n. The resulting series is

$$f(t) = \frac{2}{\pi} - \frac{4}{\pi} \sum_{n=2,4,6,\ldots} \frac{\cos n\omega t}{n^2 - 1}. \tag{14.36}$$

The original frequency ω has been eliminated. The lowest frequency oscillation is 2ω. The high-frequency components fall off as n^{-2}, showing that the full wave rectifier does a fairly good job of approximating direct current. Whether this good approximation is adequate depends on the particular application. If the remaining ac components are objectionable, they may be further suppressed by appropriate filter circuits.

These two examples bring out two features characteristic of Fourier expansions. [1]
1. If $f(x)$ has discontinuities (as in the square wave in Example 14.3.1), we can expect the nth coefficient to be decreasing as $1/n$. Convergence is relatively slow.
2. If $f(x)$ is continuous (though possibly with discontinuous derivatives as in the full wave rectifier of Example 14.3.2), we can expect the nth coefficient to be decreasing as $1/n^2$.

EXAMPLE 14.3.3. INFINITE SERIES, RIEMANN ZETA FUNCTION

As a final example, we consider the purely mathematical problem of expanding x^2. Let

$$f(x) = x^2, \qquad -\pi < x < \pi. \tag{14.37}$$

By symmetry all $b_n = 0$. For the a_n's we have

$$a_0 = \frac{1}{\pi} \int_{-\pi}^\pi x^2 \, dx = \frac{2\pi^2}{3}, \tag{14.38}$$

$$a_n = \frac{2}{\pi} \int_0^\pi x^2 \cos nx \, dx$$

$$= \frac{2}{\pi} \cdot (-1)^n \frac{2\pi}{n^2}$$

$$= (-1)^n \frac{4}{n^2}. \tag{14.39}$$

[1] G. Raisbeck, "Order of Magnitude of Fourier Coefficients," *Am. Math. Monthly* **62**, 149–155 (1955).

From this we obtain

$$x^2 = \frac{\pi^2}{3} + 4 \sum_{n=1}^{\infty} (-1)^n \frac{\cos nx}{n^2}. \tag{14.40}$$

As it stands, Eq. 14.40 is of no particular importance, but if we set $x = \pi$ [1]

$$\cos n\pi = (-1)^n \tag{14.41}$$

and Eq. 14.40 becomes

$$\pi^2 = \frac{\pi^2}{3} + 4 \sum_{n=1}^{\infty} \frac{1}{n^2} \tag{14.42}$$

or

$$\frac{\pi^2}{6} = \sum_{n=1}^{\infty} \frac{1}{n^2} \equiv \zeta(2), \tag{14.43}$$

thus yielding the Riemann zeta function, $\zeta(2)$, in closed form. From our expansion of x^2 and expansions of other powers of x numerous other infinite series can be evaluated. A few are included in the list of exercises at the end of the chapter.

EXERCISES

14.3.1   Develop the Fourier series representation of

$$f(t) = \begin{cases} 0, & -\pi \leqslant \omega t \leqslant 0, \\ \sin \omega t, & 0 \leqslant \omega t \leqslant \pi. \end{cases}$$

This is the output of a simple half-wave rectifier. It is also an approximation of the solar thermal effect that produces "tides" in the atmosphere.

$$\text{Ans. } f(t) = \frac{1}{\pi} + \frac{1}{2} \sin \omega t - \frac{2}{\pi} \sum_{\substack{n=2,4,6,\dots \\ \text{even}}}^{\infty} \frac{\cos n\omega t}{n^2 - 1}.$$

14.3.2   A metal cylindrical tube of radius a is split lengthwise into two nontouching halves. The

FIG. 14.5

[1] Note that the point $x = \pi$ is *not* a point of discontinuity.

top half is maintained at a potential $+V$, the bottom half at a potential $-V$. Separate the variables in Laplace's equation and solve for the electrostatic potential for $r \leqslant a$. Observe the resemblance between your solution for $r = a$ and the Fourier series for a square wave. *Note.* A closed form solution is obtained in Section 6.6 by complex variable analysis.

14.3.3 A metal cylinder is placed in a (previously) uniform electric field, E_0, the axis of the cylinder perpendicular to that of the original field.
(a) Find the perturbed electrostatic potential.
(b) Find the induced surface charge on the cylinder as a function of angular position.

14.3.4 A quantum mechanical particle in a rectangular box (sides a, b, and c) satisfies the Schrödinger wave equation

$$-\frac{\hbar^2}{2m} \nabla^2 \psi(x, y, z) = E \psi(x, y, z),$$

where E is the energy of the particle. It also satisfies the boundary condition that the wave function ψ vanish on the surface of the box. Determine the wave function $\psi(x, y, z)$. Note that the choice of geometry and boundary conditions leads to a solution in the form of a triple product of Fourier series.

14.3.5 A sawtooth wave is given by

$$f(x) = x, \qquad -\pi < x < \pi.$$

Show that

$$f(x) = 2 \sum_{n=1}^{\infty} \frac{(-1)^{n+1}}{n} \sin nx.$$

14.3.6 A triangular wave is represented by

$$f(x) = \begin{cases} x, & 0 < x < \pi \\ -x, & -\pi < x < 0. \end{cases}$$

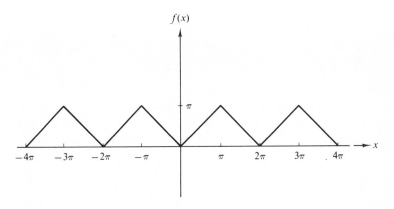

FIG. 14.6   Triangular wave

Represent $f(x)$ by a Fourier series.

$$Ans. \, f(x) = \frac{\pi}{2} - \frac{4}{\pi} \sum_{\substack{n=1,3,5,\ldots \\ \text{odd}}} \frac{\cos nx}{n^2}.$$

14.3.7 Derive the Fourier series expansion of the Dirac delta function in the interval $-\pi < x < \pi$.
(a) What significance can be attached to the constant term?
(b) In what region is this representation valid?

14.3.8 (a) Using

$$f(x) = x^2, \qquad -\pi < x < \pi,$$

show that

$$\sum_{n=1}^{\infty} \frac{(-1)^{n+1}}{n^2} = \frac{\pi^2}{12}.$$

(b) Using the Fourier series for a triangular wave developed in Exercise 14.3.6 show that

$$\sum_{n=1}^{\infty} \frac{1}{(2n-1)^2} = \frac{\pi^2}{8}.$$

(c) Using

$$f(x) = x^4, \qquad -\pi < x < \pi,$$

show that

$$\sum_{n=1}^{\infty} \frac{1}{n^4} = \frac{\pi^4}{90} = \zeta(4),$$

$$\sum_{n=1}^{\infty} \frac{(-1)^{n+1}}{n^4} = \frac{7\pi^4}{720}.$$

(d) Using

$$f(x) = \begin{cases} x(\pi - x), & 0 < x < \pi, \\ -x(\pi + x), & -\pi < x < 0, \end{cases}$$

derive

$$f(x) = \frac{8}{\pi} \sum_{\substack{n=1,3,5,\cdots \\ \text{odd}}}^{\infty} \frac{\sin nx}{n^3}$$

and show that

$$\sum_{\substack{n=1,3,5,\cdots \\ \text{odd}}}^{\infty} (-1)^{(n-1)/2} n^{-3} = 1 - \frac{1}{3^3} + \frac{1}{5^3} - \frac{1}{7^3} + \cdots = \frac{\pi^3}{32}.$$

(e) Using the Fourier series for a square wave, show that

$$\sum_{\substack{n=1,3,5,\cdots \\ \text{odd}}}^{\infty} (-1)^{(n-1)/2} n^{-1} = 1 - \frac{1}{3} + \frac{1}{5} - \frac{1}{7} + \cdots = \frac{\pi}{4}.$$

14.4 Properties of Fourier Series

Convergence.   It might be noted, first, that our Fourier series should not be expected to be uniformly convergent if it represents a discontinuous function. A uniformly convergent series of continuous functions ($\sin nx$, $\cos nx$) always yields a continuous function (cf. Section 5.5). If, however, (a) $f(x)$ is continuous, $-\pi \leqslant x \leqslant \pi$, (b) $f(-\pi) = f(+\pi)$, and (c) $f'(x)$ is sectionally continuous, the Fourier series for $f(x)$ will converge uniformly. These restrictions do not demand that $f(x)$ be periodic, but they will be satisfied by continuous, differentiable, periodic functions (period of 2π). For a proof of uniform convergence the reader is referred to the literature.[1]

Integration.   Term-by-term integration of the series

$$f(x) = \frac{a_0}{2} + \sum_{n=1}^{\infty} a_n \cos nx + \sum_{n=1}^{\infty} b_n \sin nx \qquad (14.44)$$

[1] See, for instance, R. V. Churchill, *Fourier Series and Boundary Value Problems*. New York: McGraw-Hill (1941), Section 38.

yields

$$\int_{x_0}^{x} f(x)\, dx = \frac{a_0 x}{2}\Big|_{x_0}^{x} + \sum_{n=1}^{\infty} \frac{a_n}{n} \sin nx \Big|_{x_0}^{x} - \sum_{n=1}^{\infty} \frac{b_n}{n} \cos nx \Big|_{x_0}^{x}. \tag{14.45}$$

Clearly, the effect of integration is to place an additional power of n in the denominator of each coefficient. This results in more rapid convergence than before. Consequently, a convergent Fourier series may always be integrated term by term, the resulting series converging uniformly to the integral of the original function. Indeed, term-by-term integration may be valid even if the original series (Eq. 14.44) is not itself convergent! A discussion will be found in Jeffreys and Jeffreys, Section 14.06.

Strictly speaking, Eq. 14.45 may not be a Fourier series; that is, if $a_0 \neq 0$, there will be a term $\frac{1}{2}a_0 x$. However,

$$\int_{x_0}^{x} f(x)\, dx - \frac{1}{2}a_0 x \tag{14.46}$$

will still be a Fourier series.

Differentiation.   The situation regarding differentiation is quite different from that of integration. Here, the word is *caution*. Consider the series for

$$f(x) = x, \qquad -\pi < x < \pi. \tag{14.47}$$

We readily find that the Fourier series is

$$x = 2 \sum_{n=1}^{\infty} (-1)^{n+1} \frac{\sin nx}{n}, \qquad -\pi < x < \pi. \tag{14.48}$$

Differentiating term by term, we obtain

$$1 = 2 \sum_{n=1}^{\infty} (-1)^n \cos nx, \tag{14.49}$$

which is not convergent!

For a triangular wave (Exercise 14.3.6), in which the convergence is more rapid (and uniform),

$$f(x) = \frac{\pi}{2} - \frac{4}{\pi} \sum_{n=1,\text{odd}}^{\infty} \frac{\cos nx}{n^2}. \tag{14.50}$$

Differentiating term by term

$$f'(x) = \frac{4}{\pi} \sum_{n=1,\text{odd}}^{\infty} \frac{\sin nx}{n}, \tag{14.51}$$

which is the Fourier expansion of a square wave

$$f'(x) = \begin{cases} 1, & 0 < x < \pi, \\ -1, & -\pi < x < 0. \end{cases} \tag{14.52}$$

Inspection of Fig. 14.6 verifies that this is indeed the derivative of our triangular wave.

As the inverse of integration, the operation of differentiation has placed an additional factor n in the numerator of each term. This reduces the rate of convergence and may, as in the first case mentioned, render the differentiated series divergent.

In general, term-by-term differentiation is permissible under the same conditions listed for uniform convergence.

Lanczos convergence factors.   The operation of differentiation is also troublesome in another way. Lanczos has pointed out the danger and a possible remedy. First we note that the use of an *infinite* number of terms in the Fourier expansion is an often unobtainable ideal. Instead, let

$$f(x) = f_m(x) + \eta_m(x), \tag{14.53}$$

with

$$f_m(x) = \sum_{n=-(m-1)}^{m-1} c_n e^{inx}, \tag{14.54}$$

reverting to the exponential form for convenience, and η_m is a remainder or error term given by

$$\eta_m(x) = \sum_{n=m}^{\infty} (c_n e^{inx} + c_{-n} e^{-inx})$$

$$= e^{imx} \sum_{n=0}^{\infty} c_{m+n} e^{inx} + e^{-imx} \sum_{n=0}^{\infty} c_{-m-n} e^{-inx}$$

$$= e^{imx} \rho_m(x) + e^{-imx} \rho_{-m}(x). \tag{14.55}$$

In electronic terms $\eta_m(x)$ is a modulated carrier wave with a high-frequency carrier, e^{imx}, and a modulation, $\rho_m(x)$. Differentiation of this remainder term, $\eta_m(x)$, leads to

$$\frac{d\eta_m(x)}{dx} = ime^{imx} \rho_m(x) + e^{imx} \frac{d\rho_m(x)}{dx} + \cdots. \tag{14.56}$$

The trouble arises in the first term on the right which blows up as $m \to \infty$. Now this corresponds to differentiating the carrier frequency e^{imx}. Actually we want only to differentiate the modulation $\rho_m(x)$, and this part is well behaved.

Lanczos suggested that we could do what we wanted to do and avoid the extraneous infinity by defining a new difference operator, $\mathscr{D}_m$, by the equation

$$\mathscr{D}_m f(x) = \frac{f(x + \pi/m) - f(x - \pi/m)}{2\pi/m}. \tag{14.57}$$

This represents a sort of average derivative. Clearly

$$\lim_{m \to \infty} \mathscr{D}_m = \frac{d}{dx}. \tag{14.58}$$

By applying $\mathscr{D}_m$ to the remainder, $\eta_m(x)$, we obtain

$$\mathscr{D}_m \, \eta_m(x) = \frac{e^{im(x + \pi/m)} \rho_m(x + \pi/m) - e^{im(x - \pi/m)} \rho_m(x - \pi/m)}{2\pi/m}$$

$$+ \frac{e^{-im(x + \pi/m)} \rho_{-m}(x + \pi/m) - e^{-im(x - \pi/m)} \rho_{-m}(x - \pi/m)}{2\pi/m}, \quad (14.59)$$

$$\mathscr{D}_m \, \eta_m(x) = -e^{imx} \mathscr{D}_m \, \rho_m(x) - e^{-imx} \mathscr{D}_m \, \rho_{-m}(x),$$

showing that $\mathscr{D}_m$ effectively operates on the modulation ρ_m and *not* on the carrier e^{imx}. The diverging terms of the forms $ime^{imx} \rho_m(x)$ have been eliminated. (The minus signs appearing in this case are the result of picking points $x \pm \pi/m$ which are shifted one half cycle of e^{imx}.)

Applied to a complex Fourier series,

$$\mathscr{D}_m e^{inx} = \frac{e^{in(x + \pi/m)} - e^{+in(x - \pi/m)}}{2\pi/m}$$

$$= ine^{inx} \frac{\sin(n\pi/m)}{n\pi/m}. \quad (14.60)$$

Hence

$$\mathscr{D}_m e^{inx} = \left[\frac{\sin(n\pi/m)}{n\pi/m} \right] \frac{d}{dx} e^{inx}. \quad (14.61)$$

The additional factor $\sin(n\pi/m)/(n\pi/m)$ is called a Lanczos smoothing factor, or Lanczos convergence factor, σ_n; that is

$$\sigma_n = \frac{\sin(n\pi/m)}{n\pi/m}. \quad (14.62)$$

The inclusion of these σ_n's in a differentiated series is sometimes helpful to convergence. The *finite* Fourier series

$$f(x) = \frac{a_0}{2} + \sum_{n=1}^{m-1} (a_n \cos nx + b_n \sin nx) \quad (14.63)$$

is replaced with

$$f(x) = \frac{a_0}{2} + \sum_{n=1}^{m-1} \frac{\sin(n\pi/m)}{n\pi/m} (a_n \cos nx + b_n \sin nx). \quad (14.64)$$

As will be seen in Section 14.5, the Lanczos σ_n's can almost eliminate the Gibbs phenomenon.

EXERCISES

14.4.1 Show that integration of the Fourier expansion of $f(x) = x$, $-\pi < x < \pi$, leads to

$$\frac{\pi^2}{12} = \sum_{n=1}^{\infty} (-1)^{n+1} n^{-2}$$

$$= 1 - \tfrac{1}{4} + \tfrac{1}{9} - \tfrac{1}{16} + \cdots .$$

14.4.2. Parseval's identity.

(a) Assuming that the Fourier expansion of $f(x)$ is uniformly convergent, show that

$$\frac{1}{\pi} \int_{-\pi}^{\pi} [f(x)]^2 \, dx = \frac{a_0^2}{2} + \sum_{n=1}^{\infty} (a_n^2 + b_n^2).$$

This is Parseval's identity.

(b) Given

$$x^2 = \frac{\pi^2}{3} + 4 \sum_{n=1}^{\infty} \frac{(-1)^n \cos nx,}{n^2}$$

apply Parseval's identity to obtain $\zeta(4)$ in closed form.

14.5 Gibbs Phenomenon

This is a peculiarity of the Fourier series at a simple discontinuity. An example is seen in Fig. 14.1. For convenience of numerical calculation we consider the behavior of the Fourier series which represents the periodic square wave

$$f(x) = \begin{cases} \dfrac{h}{2}, & 0 < x < \pi, \\[2mm] -\dfrac{h}{2}, & -\pi < x < 0. \end{cases} \tag{14.65}$$

This is essentially the square wave used in Section 14.3, and we see immediately that the solution is

$$f(x) = \frac{2h}{\pi} \left(\frac{\sin x}{1} + \frac{\sin 3x}{3} + \frac{\sin 5x}{5} + \cdots \right) \tag{14.66}$$

Summation of series.[1]   In Section 14.1 the sum of the first several terms of the Fourier series for a sawtooth wave was plotted (Fig. 14.1). Now we develop an analytic method of summing the first r terms of our Fourier series (Eq. 14.66).

From Eq. 14.13

$$a_n \cos nx + b_n \sin nx = \frac{1}{\pi} \int_{-\pi}^{\pi} f(t) \cos n(t - x) \, dt. \tag{14.67}$$

Then the rth partial sum becomes

$$s_r(x) = \sum_{n=0}^{r} (a_n \cos nx + b_n \sin nx)$$

$$= \text{R.P.} \frac{1}{\pi} \int_{-\pi}^{\pi} f(t) \left[\frac{1}{2} + \sum_{n=1}^{r} e^{-i(t-x)n} \right] dt. \tag{14.68}$$

[1] It is of some interest to note that this series also occurs in the analysis of the diffraction grating (r slits).

Summing the finite series of exponentials (geometric progression), we obtain

$$s_r(x) = \frac{1}{2\pi} \int_{-\pi}^{\pi} f(t) \frac{\sin(r + \frac{1}{2})(t - x)}{\sin \frac{1}{2}(t - x)} \, dt. \tag{14.69}$$

This is convergent at all points, including $t = x$.

Square wave.   Applying this result to our square wave (Eq. 14.66), we have the sum of the first r terms (plus $\frac{1}{2}a_0$, which is zero here).

$$s_r(x) = \frac{h}{4\pi} \int_0^{\pi} \frac{\sin(r + \frac{1}{2})(t - x)}{\sin \frac{1}{2}(t - x)} \, dt - \frac{h}{4\pi} \int_{-\pi}^0 \frac{\sin(r + \frac{1}{2})(t - x)}{\sin \frac{1}{2}(t - x)} \, dt$$

$$= \frac{h}{4\pi} \int_0^{\pi} \frac{\sin(r + \frac{1}{2})(t - x)}{\sin \frac{1}{2}(t - x)} \, dt - \frac{h}{4\pi} \int_0^{\pi} \frac{\sin(r + \frac{1}{2})(t + x)}{\sin \frac{1}{2}(t + x)} \, dt. \tag{14.70}$$

This last result follows from the transformation

$$t = -t \quad \text{in the second integral.} \tag{14.71}$$

Replacing $t - x$ in the first term with s and $t + x$ in the second term with s we obtain

$$s_r(x) = \frac{h}{4\pi} \int_{-x}^{\pi - x} \frac{\sin(r + \frac{1}{2})s}{\sin \frac{1}{2}s} \, ds - \frac{h}{4\pi} \int_x^{\pi + x} \frac{\sin(r + \frac{1}{2})s}{\sin \frac{1}{2}s} \, ds$$

$$= \frac{h}{4\pi} \int_{-x}^{x} \frac{\sin(r + \frac{1}{2})s}{\sin \frac{1}{2}s} \, ds - \frac{h}{4\pi} \int_{\pi - x}^{\pi + x} \frac{\sin(r + \frac{1}{2})s}{\sin \frac{1}{2}s} \, ds. \tag{14.72}$$

As $x \to 0$, the second integral becomes negligible, and we associate the first

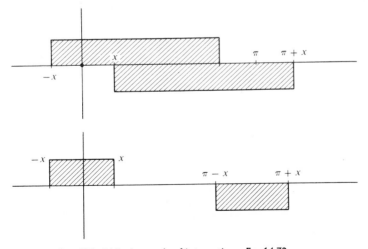

FIG. 14.7   Intervals of integration—Eq. 14.72

integral with the discontinuity at $x = 0$. Using $(r + \frac{1}{2}) = p$ and $ps = \xi$, we obtain

$$s_r(x) = \frac{h}{2\pi} \int_0^{px} \frac{\sin \xi}{\sin(\xi/2p)} \cdot \frac{d\xi}{p}. \tag{14.73}$$

Our partial sum, $s_r(x)$, starts at zero when $x = 0$ (in agreement with Eq. 14.16) and increases until $px = \pi$, at which point the numerator, $\sin \xi$, goes negative. For large r, and therefore large p, our denominator remains positive.

The maximum value of the partial sum is then

$$s_r(x)_{max} = \frac{h}{2} \cdot \frac{1}{\pi} \int_0^\pi \frac{\sin \xi \, d\xi}{\sin(\xi/2p)p}$$

$$\approx \frac{h}{2} \cdot \frac{2}{\pi} \int_0^\pi \frac{\sin \xi}{\xi} \, d\xi. \tag{14.74}$$

The integral is clearly greater than $\pi/2$, since it can be written

$$\left(\int_0^\infty - \int_\pi^{3\pi} - \int_{3\pi}^{5\pi} - \cdots \right) \frac{\sin \xi}{\xi} \, d\xi = \int_0^\pi \frac{\sin \xi}{\xi} \, d\xi. \tag{14.75}$$

Calculation of overshoot.   We saw in Section 7.2 that the integral from 0 to ∞ is $\pi/2$. From this integral we are subtracting a series of *negative* terms. A power series expansion and term-by-term integration yields

$$\frac{2}{\pi} \int_0^\pi \frac{\sin \xi}{\xi} \, d\xi = 1.1789798 \ldots, \tag{14.76}$$

which means that the Fourier series tends to overshoot the positive corner by some 18 per cent and to undershoot the negative corner by the same amount, as suggested in Fig. 14.8. The inclusion of more terms (increasing r) does nothing to remove this overshoot but merely moves it closer to the point of discontinuity. The overshoot

FIG. 14.8   Square wave—Gibbs phenomenon

is the Gibbs phenomenon, and because of it the Fourier series representation may be highly unreliable for precise numerical work, especially in the vicinity of a discontinuity.

As suggested in Section 14.4, the Gibbs phenomenon may be suppressed drastically by the use of Lanczos convergence factors. Considering our square wave to be the derivative of a triangular wave, we replace Eq. 14.66 with $h = 2$ with

$$f(x) = \frac{4}{\pi} \sum_{n=1}^{m} \frac{\sin\{[(2n-1)\pi]/2m\}}{[(2n-1)\pi]/2m} \cdot \frac{\sin(2n-1)x}{(2n-1)}. \tag{14.77}$$

The results, with $m = 100$, are plotted in Fig. 14.9. The 18 per cent overshoot is sharply reduced, but the reader will note that a price has been paid for this smoothing: the rate of rise has been cut roughly in half.

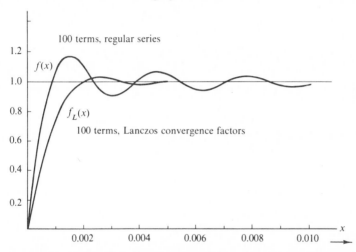

FIG. 14.9   Square wave—smoothing effect of Lanczos convergence factors

REFERENCES

CARSLAW, H. S., *Introduction to the Theory of Fourier's Series and Integrals*. 2nd Ed. London: Macmillan (1921). A detailed and classic work. Includes a considerable discussion of Gibbs phenomenon in Chapter IX.

JEFFREYS, H. and B. S. JEFFREYS, *Methods of Mathematical Physics*, 2nd Ed. Cambridge: Cambridge University Press (1950).

LANCZOS, C., *Applied Analysis*. Englewood Cliffs, New Jersey: Prentice-Hall (1956). A well-written presentation of the Lanczos convergence technique for Fourier series. This and several other topics are presented from the point of view of a mathematician who wants useful numerical results and not just abstract existence theorems.

ZYGMUND, A., *Trigonometric Series*, Vols. I and II. Cambridge: Cambridge University Press (1959). An extremely complete exposition, including relatively recent results in the realm of pure mathematics.

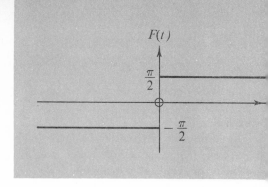

CHAPTER 15

INTEGRAL TRANSFORMS

15.1 Integral Transforms

Frequently in mathematical physics we encounter pairs of functions related by an expression of the following form:

$$g(\alpha) = \int_a^b f(t)\, K(\alpha, t)\, dt. \qquad (15.1)$$

The function $g(\alpha)$ is called the (integral) transform of $f(t)$ by the kernel $K(\alpha, t)$.

Fourier transform.   One of the most useful of the infinite number of possible transforms is the Fourier given by

$$g(\alpha) = \frac{1}{\sqrt{2\pi}} \int_{-\infty}^{\infty} f(t) e^{i\alpha t}\, dt. \qquad (15.2)$$

Two modifications of this form, developed in Section 15.3, are the Fourier cosine and Fourier sine transforms:

$$g_c(\alpha) = \sqrt{\frac{2}{\pi}} \int_0^{\infty} f(t) \cos \alpha t\, dt, \qquad (15.3)$$

$$g_s(\alpha) = \sqrt{\frac{2}{\pi}} \int_0^{\infty} f(t) \sin \alpha t\, dt. \qquad (15.4)$$

524

The Fourier transform is based on the kernel $e^{i\alpha t}$ and its real and imaginary parts taken separately, $\cos \alpha t$ and $\sin \alpha t$.

Three other useful kernels are

$$e^{-\alpha t}, \qquad t\, J_n(\alpha t), \qquad t^{\alpha-1}.$$

Laplace, Mellin, and Hankel transforms. These give rise to the following transforms

$$g(\alpha) = \int_0^\infty f(t)\, e^{-\alpha t}\, dt, \qquad \text{Laplace transform} \qquad (15.5)$$

$$g(\alpha) = \int_0^\infty f(t) t\, J_n(\alpha t)\, dt, \qquad \text{Hankel transform (Fourier-Bessel)} \qquad (15.6)$$

$$g(\alpha) = \int_0^\infty f(t) t^{\alpha-1}\, dt, \qquad \text{Mellin transform.} \qquad (15.7)$$

Clearly the possible types are unlimited. These transforms have been useful in mathematical analysis and in physical applications. We have actually used the Mellin transform without calling it by name; that is, $g(\alpha) = (\alpha - 1)!$ is the Mellin transform of $f(t) = e^{-t}$. Of course, we could just as well say $g(\alpha) = n!/\alpha^{n+1}$ is the Laplace transform of $f(t) = t^n$. Of the three, the Laplace transform is by far the most used. It is discussed at length in Sections 15.7–15.11. The Hankel transform, a Fourier transform for a Bessel function expansion, represents a limiting case of a Fourier-Bessel series.

Linearity. All of these integral transforms are linear; that is

$$\int_a^b [c_1 f_1(t) + c_2 f_2(t)]\, K(\alpha, t)\, dt$$

$$= \int_a^b c_1 f_1(t)\, K(\alpha, t)\, dt + \int_a^b c_2 f_2(t)\, K(\alpha, t)\, dt, \qquad (15.8)$$

$$\int_a^b c f(t)\, K(\alpha, t)\, dt = c \int_a^b f(t)\, K(\alpha, t)\, dt, \qquad (15.9)$$

where c_1 and c_2 are constants and $f_1(t)$ and $f_2(t)$ are functions for which the transform operation is defined.

Representing our linear integral transform by the operator $\mathscr{L}$, we obtain

$$g(\alpha) = \mathscr{L} f(t). \qquad (15.10)$$

We expect an inverse operator $\mathscr{L}^{-1}$ exists such that

$$f(t) = \mathscr{L}^{-1} g(\alpha). \qquad (15.11)$$

For our three Fourier transforms $\mathscr{L}^{-1}$ is given in Section 15.3. In general, the determination of the inverse transform is the main problem in using integral transforms. The inverse Laplace transform is discussed in Section 15.11. For details of the inverse Hankel and inverse Mellin transforms the reader is referred to the references at the end of the chapter.

EXERCISES

15.1.1   The Fourier transforms for a function of two variables are

$$F(u, v) = \frac{1}{2\pi} \int\!\!\int_{-\infty}^{\infty} f(x, y) e^{i(ux+vy)} \, dx \, dy,$$

$$f(x, y) = \frac{1}{2\pi} \int\!\!\int_{-\infty}^{\infty} F(u, v) e^{-i(ux+vy)} \, du \, dv.$$

Using $f(x, y) = f([x^2 + y^2]^{1/2})$, show that the *zero*-order Hankel transforms

$$F(\rho) = \int_0^{\infty} r f(r) J_0(\rho r) \, dr,$$

$$f(r) = \int_0^{\infty} \rho F(\rho) J_0(\rho r) \, d\rho,$$

are a special case of the Fourier transform.

15.1.2   Verify the following Mellin transforms:

(a) $\displaystyle\int_0^{\infty} x^{\alpha-1} \sin (kx) \, dx = k^{-\alpha}(\alpha - 1)! \sin \frac{\pi\alpha}{2}, \qquad -1 < \alpha < \frac{1}{2}.$

(b) $\displaystyle\int_0^{\infty} x^{\alpha-1} \cos (kx) \, dx = k^{-\alpha}(\alpha - 1)! \cos \frac{\pi\alpha}{2}, \qquad 0 < \alpha < \frac{1}{2}.$

15.2 Development of the Fourier Integral

In Chapter 14 it was shown that Fourier series are useful in representing certain functions (a) over a limited range $[0, 2\pi]$, $[-L, L]$, etc., or (b) for the infinite interval $(-\infty, \infty)$, *if the function is periodic.* We now turn our attention to the problem of representing a nonperiodic function over the infinite range. Physically this means resolving a single pulse or wave packet into sinusoidal waves.

We have seen (Section 14.2) that for the interval $[-L, L]$ the coefficients a_n and b_n could be written

$$a_n = \frac{1}{L} \int_{-L}^{L} f(t) \cos \frac{n\pi t}{L} \, dt \tag{15.12}$$

$$b_n = \frac{1}{L} \int_{-L}^{L} f(t) \sin \frac{n\pi t}{L} \, dt. \tag{15.13}$$

The resulting Fourier series is

$$f(x) = \frac{1}{2L} \int_{-L}^{L} f(t) \, dt + \frac{1}{L} \sum_{n=1}^{\infty} \cos \frac{n\pi x}{L} \int_{-L}^{L} f(t) \cos \frac{n\pi t}{L} \, dt$$

$$+ \frac{1}{L} \sum_{n=1}^{\infty} \sin \frac{n\pi x}{L} \int_{-L}^{L} f(t) \sin \frac{n\pi t}{L} \, dt \tag{15.14}$$

or

$$f(x) = \frac{1}{2L} \int_{-L}^{L} f(t)\, dt + \frac{1}{L} \sum_{n=1}^{\infty} \int_{-L}^{L} f(t) \cos \frac{n\pi}{L}(t-x)\, dt. \qquad (15.15)$$

We now let the parameter L approach infinity, transforming the finite interval $[-L, L]$ into the infinite interval $(-\infty, \infty)$. We set

$$\frac{n\pi}{L} = \omega, \qquad \frac{\pi}{L} = \Delta\omega, \qquad \text{with } L \to \infty.$$

Then we have

$$f(x) \to \frac{1}{\pi} \sum_{n=1}^{\infty} \Delta\omega \int_{-\infty}^{\infty} f(t) \cos \omega(t-x)\, dt \qquad (15.16)$$

$$f(x) = \frac{1}{\pi} \int_{0}^{\infty} d\omega \int_{-\infty}^{\infty} f(t) \cos \omega(t-x)\, dt, \qquad (15.17)$$

replacing the infinite sum by the integral over ω. The first term (corresponding to a_0) has vanished, assuming that $\int_{-\infty}^{\infty} f(t)\, dt$ exists.

It must be emphasized that this result (Eq. 15.17) is purely formal. It is not intended as a rigorous derivation, but it can be made rigorous (cf. I. N. Sneddon, *Fourier Transforms*, Section 3.2). However, for those interested in contour integration, a completely different derivation, based on the Cauchy integral formula, is given in our Section 6.3. We shall take Eq. 15.17 as the Fourier integral. It is subject to the restrictions that $f(x)$ satisfy the Dirichlet conditions (Chapter 14) and that $\int_{-\infty}^{\infty} |f(t)|\, dt$ be convergent.

Our Fourier integral (Eq. 15.17), may be put into exponential form by noting that

$$f(x) = \frac{1}{2\pi} \int_{-\infty}^{\infty} d\omega \int_{-\infty}^{\infty} f(t) \cos \omega(t-x)\, dt, \qquad (15.18)$$

whereas

$$\frac{1}{2\pi} \int_{-\infty}^{\infty} d\omega \int_{-\infty}^{\infty} f(t) \sin \omega(t-x)\, dt = 0; \qquad (15.19)$$

$\cos \omega(t-x)$ is an even function of ω and $\sin \omega(t-x)$ is an odd function of ω. Adding Eqs. 15.18 and 15.19 (with a factor i), we obtain

$$f(x) = \frac{1}{2\pi} \int_{-\infty}^{\infty} e^{-i\omega x}\, d\omega \int_{-\infty}^{\infty} f(t) e^{i\omega t}\, dt. \qquad (15.20)$$

The variable ω introduced here is an arbitrary mathematical variable. In many physical problems, however, it corresponds to the angular frequency ω. We may then interpret Eq. 15.18 or 15.20 as a representation of $f(x)$ in terms of a distribution of infinitely long sinusoidal wave trains of angular frequency ω in which this frequency is a *continuous* variable.

15.3 Fourier Transforms—Inversion Theorem

Let us *define* $g(\omega)$, the Fourier transform of the function $f(t)$, by

$$g(\omega) \equiv \frac{1}{\sqrt{2\pi}} \int_{-\infty}^{\infty} f(t)e^{i\omega t}\, dt. \tag{15.21}$$

Exponential transform.   Then from Eq. 15.20 (or Section 6.3) we have the inverse relation

$$f(x) = \frac{1}{\sqrt{2\pi}} \int_{-\infty}^{\infty} g(\omega)e^{-i\omega x}\, d\omega. \tag{15.22}$$

It will be noted that Eqs. 15.21 and 15.22 are almost but not quite symmetrical, differing in the sign of i.

Cosine transform.   If $f(x)$ is odd or even, these transforms may be expressed in a somewhat different form. Consider, first, $f(x) = f(-x)$, even. Writing the exponential of Eq. 15.21 in trigonometric form, we have

$$g(\omega) = \frac{1}{\sqrt{2\pi}} \int_{-\infty}^{\infty} f(t)(\cos \omega t + i \sin \omega t)\, dt$$

$$= \sqrt{\frac{2}{\pi}} \int_{0}^{\infty} f(t) \cos \omega t\, dt, \tag{15.23}$$

the $\sin \omega t$ dependence vanishing on integration over the symmetric interval $(-\infty, \infty)$. Similarly, Eq. 15.22 transforms to

$$f(x) = \sqrt{\frac{2}{\pi}} \int_{0}^{\infty} g(\omega) \cos \omega x\, d\omega. \tag{15.24}$$

Equations 15.23 and 15.24 are known as Fourier cosine transforms.

Sine transform.   The corresponding pair of Fourier sine transforms is obtained by assuming that $f(x) = -f(-x)$, odd, and applying the same symmetry arguments. The equations are

$$g(\omega) = \sqrt{\frac{2}{\pi}} \int_{0}^{\infty} f(t) \sin \omega t\, dt \,^{1} \tag{15.25}$$

$$f(x) = \sqrt{\frac{2}{\pi}} \int_{0}^{\infty} g(\omega) \sin \omega x\, d\omega. \tag{15.26}$$

From the last equation we may develop the physical interpretation that $f(x)$ is being described by a continuum of sine waves. The amplitude of $\sin \omega t$ is given by $\sqrt{2/\pi}\, g(\omega)$, in which $g(\omega)$ is the Fourier sine transform of $f(x)$. It will be seen that Eq. 15.26 is the integral analog of the summation (Eq. 14.18). Similar interpretations hold for the cosine and exponential cases.

If we take Eqs. 15.21, 15.23, and 15.25 as the direct integral transforms, described by $\mathscr{L}$ in Eq. 15.10 (Section 15.1), the corresponding inverse transforms, $\mathscr{L}^{-1}$ of Eq. 15.11, are given by Eqs. 15.22, 15.24, and 15.26.

---

[1] Note that a factor $-i$ has been absorbed into this $g(\omega)$.

EXAMPLE 15.3.1. FINITE WAVE TRAIN

An important application of the Fourier transform is the resolution of a finite pulse into sinusoidal waves. Imagine that an infinite wave train $\sin \omega_0 t$ is clipped by Kerr cell shutters so that we have

$$f(t) = \begin{cases} \sin \omega_0 t, & |t| < \dfrac{N\pi}{\omega_0}, \\ 0, & |t| > \dfrac{N\pi}{\omega_0}. \end{cases} \tag{15.27}$$

This corresponds to N cycles of our original wave train. Since $f(t)$ is odd, we may use the Fourier sine transform (Eq. 15.25) to obtain

$$g(\omega) = \sqrt{\frac{2}{\pi}} \int_0^{N\pi/\omega_0} \sin \omega_0 t \sin \omega t \, dt. \tag{15.28}$$

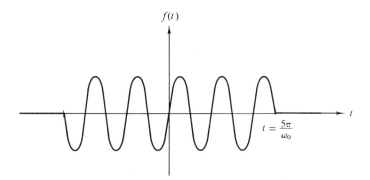

FIG. 15.1 Finite wave train

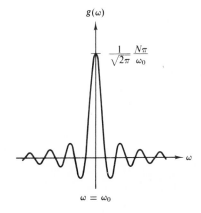

FIG. 15.2 Fourier transform of finite wave train

Integrating, we find our amplitude function

$$g(\omega) = \sqrt{\frac{2}{\pi}} \left[\frac{\sin[(\omega_0 - \omega)(N\pi/\omega_0)]}{2(\omega_0 - \omega)} - \frac{\sin[(\omega_0 + \omega)(N\pi/\omega_0)]}{2(\omega_0 + \omega)} \right]. \qquad (15.29)$$

It is of some considerable interest to see how $g(\omega)$ depends on frequency. For large ω_0 and $\omega \approx \omega_0$ only the first term will be of any importance. It is plotted in Fig. 15.2. This is the amplitude curve for the single slit diffraction pattern. There are zeroes at

$$\frac{\omega_0 - \omega}{\omega_0} = \frac{\Delta\omega}{\omega_0} = \pm\frac{1}{N}, \qquad \pm\frac{2}{N}, \text{ etc.} \qquad (15.30)$$

Since the contributions outside the central maximum are small, we may take

$$\Delta\omega = \frac{\omega_0}{N} \qquad (15.31)$$

as a good measure of the spread in frequency of our wave pulse. Clearly, if N is large (a long pulse), the frequency spread will be small. On the other hand, if our pulse is clipped short, N small, the frequency distribution will be wider.

Uncertainty principle.   Here is a classical analog of the famous uncertainty principle of quantum mechanics. If we are dealing with electromagnetic waves,

$$\frac{h\omega}{2\pi} = E, \qquad \text{energy (of our wave pulse or photon)}$$

$$\frac{h\,\Delta\omega}{2\pi} = \Delta E, \qquad (15.32)$$

h being Planck's constant, which represents an uncertainty in the energy of our pulse. There is also an uncertainty in the time, for our wave of N cycles requires $2N\pi/\omega_0$ seconds to pass. Taking

$$\Delta t = \frac{2N\pi}{\omega_0}, \qquad (15.33)$$

we have the product of these two uncertainties:

$$\Delta E \cdot \Delta t = \frac{h\,\Delta\omega}{2\pi} \cdot \frac{2\pi N}{\omega_0}$$

$$= h\,\frac{\omega_0}{2\pi N} \cdot \frac{2\pi N}{\omega_0} = h. \qquad (15.34)$$

The Heisenberg uncertainty principle actually states

$$\Delta E \cdot \Delta t \geqslant \frac{h}{2\pi} \qquad (15.35)$$

and this is clearly satisfied in our example.

EXERCISE

15.3.1 Verify that the following are Fourier integral transforms of one another:

(a) $\sqrt{\dfrac{2}{\pi}} \cdot \dfrac{1}{\sqrt{a^2 - x^2}}$, $\quad |x| < a$, and $J_0(ay)$,

$\qquad 0, \qquad\qquad\qquad |x| > a$,

(b) 0, $\qquad\qquad\qquad\qquad |x| < a$, and $N_0(a|y|)$,

$\qquad -\sqrt{\dfrac{\pi}{2}} \cdot \dfrac{1}{\sqrt{x^2 - a^2}}$, $\quad |x| > a$,

(c) $\sqrt{\dfrac{\pi}{2}} \cdot \dfrac{1}{\sqrt{x^2 + a^2}}$ and $K_0(a|y|)$.

(d) Can you suggest why $I_0(ay)$ is not included in this list?

Hint. J_0, N_0, and K_0 may be transformed most easily by using an exponential representation, reversing the order of integration, and employing the Dirac delta function exponential representation (Section 15.6).

15.4 Fourier Transform of Derivatives

Using the exponential form, the Fourier transform of $f(x)$ is

$$g(\omega) = \frac{1}{\sqrt{2\pi}} \int_{-\infty}^{\infty} f(x) e^{i\omega x} \, dx \qquad (15.36)$$

and for $df(x)/dx$

$$g_1(\omega) = \frac{1}{\sqrt{2\pi}} \int_{-\infty}^{\infty} \frac{d f(x)}{dx} e^{i\omega x} \, dx. \qquad (15.37)$$

Integrating Eq. 15.37 by parts, we obtain

$$g_1(\omega) = \frac{e^{i\omega x}}{\sqrt{2\pi}} f(x) \Big|_{-\infty}^{\infty} - \frac{i\omega}{\sqrt{2\pi}} \int_{-\infty}^{\infty} f(x) e^{i\omega x} \, dx. \qquad (15.38)$$

If $f(x)$ vanishes as $x \to \pm\infty$, we obtain

$$g_1(\omega) = -i\omega \, g(\omega); \qquad (15.39)$$

that is, the transform of the derivative is $(-i\omega)$ times the transform of the original function. This may readily be generalized to the nth derivative to yield

$$g_n(\omega) = (-i\omega)^n \, g(\omega), \qquad (15.40)$$

provided all the integrated parts vanish as $x \to \pm\infty$.

EXAMPLE 15.4.1.   WAVE EQUATION

This technique may be used to advantage in handling partial differential equations. To illustrate the technique let us derive a familiar expression of elementary physics. An infinitely long string is vibrating freely. The amplitude y of the (small) vibrations satisfies the wave equation

$$\frac{\partial^2 y}{\partial x^2} = \frac{1}{v^2} \frac{\partial^2 y}{\partial t^2}. \tag{15.41}$$

We shall assume that

$$y = f(x) \tag{15.42}$$

at $t = 0$.

Applying our Fourier transform, which means multiplying by $e^{i\alpha x}$ and integrating over x, we obtain

$$\int_{-\infty}^{\infty} \frac{\partial^2 y(x, t)}{\partial x^2} e^{i\alpha x}\, dx = \frac{1}{v^2} \int_{-\infty}^{\infty} \frac{\partial^2 y(x, t)}{\partial t^2} e^{i\alpha x}\, dx \tag{15.43}$$

or

$$(-i\alpha)^2 Y(\alpha, t) = \frac{1}{v^2} \frac{\partial^2 Y(\alpha, t)}{\partial t^2}. \tag{15.44}$$

Here we have used

$$Y(\alpha, t) = \frac{1}{\sqrt{2\pi}} \int_{-\infty}^{\infty} y(x, t) e^{i\alpha x}\, dx \tag{15.45}$$

and Eq. 15.40 for the second derivative. Note that the integrated part of Eq. 15.38 vanishes. The wave has not yet got out to ∞. Since no derivatives with respect to α appear, Eq. 15.44 is actually an ordinary differential equation—in fact the linear oscillator equation. This transformation, from a partial to an ordinary differential equation, is a significant achievement. We solve Eq. 15.44 subject to the appropriate initial conditions. At $t = 0$, applying Eq. 15.42, Eq. 15.45 reduces to

$$Y(\alpha, 0) = \frac{1}{\sqrt{2\pi}} \int_{-\infty}^{\infty} f(x) e^{i\alpha x}\, dx \tag{15.46}$$

$$= F(\alpha).$$

The general solution of Eq. 15.44 in exponential form is

$$Y(\alpha, t) = F(\alpha) e^{\pm iv\alpha t}. \tag{15.47}$$

Using the inversion formula (Eq. 15.22), we have

$$y(x, t) = \frac{1}{\sqrt{2\pi}} \int_{-\infty}^{\infty} Y(\alpha, t) e^{-i\alpha x}\, d\alpha \tag{15.48}$$

and, by Eq. 15.47,

$$y(x, t) = \frac{1}{\sqrt{2\pi}} \int_{-\infty}^{\infty} F(\alpha) e^{-i\alpha(x \mp vt)}\, d\alpha. \tag{15.49}$$

Since $f(x)$ is the Fourier inverse transform of $F(\alpha)$,

$$y(x, t) = f(x \mp vt), \tag{15.50}$$

corresponding to waves advancing in the $+x$- and $-x$-directions, respectively.

The particular linear combinations of waves is given by the boundary condition of Eq. 15.42 and some other boundary condition such as a restriction on $\partial y/\partial t$.

EXERCISES

15.4.1 The one-dimensional Fermi age equation for the diffusion of neutrons slowing down in some medium (such as graphite) is

$$\frac{\partial^2 q(x, \tau)}{\partial x^2} = \frac{\partial q(x, \tau)}{\partial \tau}.$$

Here q is the number of neutrons that "slow down," falling below some given energy per second per unit volume. The Fermi age, τ, is a measure of the energy loss.

If $q(x, 0) = S\, \delta(x)$, corresponding to a plane source of neutrons at $x = 0$, emitting S neutrons per unit area per second, derive the solution

$$q = S \frac{e^{-x^2/4\pi\tau}}{\sqrt{4\pi\tau}}.$$

Hint: Replace $q(x, \tau)$ with

$$p(k, \tau) = \frac{1}{\sqrt{2\pi}} \int_{-\infty}^{\infty} q(x, \tau) e^{ikx}\, dx.$$

This is analogous to the diffusion of heat in an infinite medium.

15.4.2 The orthogonalized Hermite function $\varphi_n(x) = e^{-x^2/2}\, H_n(x)$ satisfies the differential equation

$$\varphi_n''(x) + (2n + 1 - x^2)\, \varphi_n(x) = 0$$

(Section 13.1). From this differential equation develop the Fourier transform of $\varphi_n(x)$.

15.5 Convolution Theorem

We consider two functions $f(x)$ and $g(x)$ with Fourier transforms $F(t)$ and $G(t)$, respectively. We define the operation

$$f * g \equiv \frac{1}{\sqrt{2\pi}} \int_{-\infty}^{\infty} g(y) f(x - y)\, dy \tag{15.51}$$

as the *convolution* of the two functions f and g over the interval $(-\infty, \infty)$. In other works this is sometimes referred to as the *Faltung*, to use the German term for "folding."[1] We now transform the integral in Eq. 15.51 by introducing the Fourier transforms.

---

[1] For $f(y) = e^{-y}$, $f(y)$ and $f(x - y)$ are plotted in Fig. 15.3. Clearly, $f(y)$ and $f(x - y)$ are mirror images of each other in relation to the vertical line $y = x/2$, that is, we could generate $f(x - y)$ by "folding" over $f(y)$ on the line $y = x/2$.

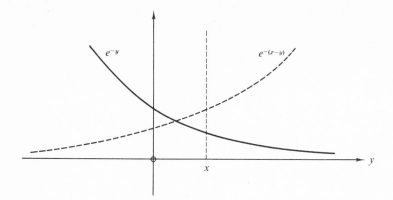

FIG. 15.3

$$\int_{-\infty}^{\infty} g(y) f(x-y)\, dy = \frac{1}{\sqrt{2\pi}} \int_{-\infty}^{\infty} g(y) \int_{-\infty}^{\infty} F(t) e^{-it(x-y)} dt\, dy$$

$$= \frac{1}{\sqrt{2\pi}} \int_{-\infty}^{\infty} F(t) e^{-itx} dt \int_{-\infty}^{\infty} g(y) e^{ity}\, dy$$

$$= \int_{-\infty}^{\infty} F(t)\, G(t) e^{-itx}\, dt, \qquad (15.52)$$

interchanging the order of integration and transforming $g(y)$. This result may be interpreted as follows: the Fourier inverse transform of a *product* of Fourier transforms is the convolution of the original functions, $f * g$.

For the special case $x = 0$ we have

$$\int_{-\infty}^{\infty} F(t)\, G(t)\, dt = \int_{-\infty}^{\infty} f(-y)\, g(y)\, dy. \qquad (15.53)$$

Parseval's relation.   Analagous results may be derived for the Fourier sine and cosine transforms (Exercises 15.5.1, 2). Equation 15.53 and the corresponding sine and cosine convolutions are often labeled "Parseval's relations" by analogy with Parseval's theorem for Fourier series (Chapter 14, Exercise 14.4.2).

Parseval's relations may be developed independently of the inverse Fourier transform and then used rigorously to derive the inverse transform. Details are given by Morse and Feshbach,[1] Section 4.8 (see also Exercise 15.5.3).

EXERCISES

15.5.1 Work out the convolution equation corresponding to Eq. 15.52 for

[1] Morse, P. M. and H. Feshbach, *Methods of Theoretical Physics*. New York: McGraw-Hill (1953).

(a) Fourier sine transforms.

$$\int_0^\infty g(y)f(x-y)\,dy = -\int_0^\infty F_s(s)\,G_s(s)\cos sx\,ds.$$

(b) Fourier cosine transforms.

$$\int_0^\infty g(y)f(x-y)\,dy = \int_0^\infty F_c(s)\,G_c(s)\cos sx\,ds.$$

15.5.2 Show that for both Fourier sine and Fourier cosine transforms Parseval's relation has the form

$$\int_0^\infty F(t)\,G(t)\,dt = \int_0^\infty f(x)\,g(x)\,dx.$$

15.5.3 Starting from Parseval's relation (Eq. 15.53), let $g(y) = 1$, $0 \leqslant y \leqslant \alpha$, and zero elsewhere. From this derive the Fourier inverse transform, (Eq. 15.22). *Hint.* Differentiate with respect to α.

15.6 Momentum Representation

In advanced dynamics and in quantum mechanics linear momentum and spacial position occur on an equal footing. In this section we shall start with the usual space distribution and derive the corresponding momentum distribution. For the one-dimensional case our wave function $\psi(x)$, a solution of the Schrödinger wave equation, has the following properties:

1. $\psi^*(x)\,\psi(x)\,dx$ is the probability of finding the quantum particle between x and $x + dx$ and

2.
$$\int_{-\infty}^\infty \psi^*(x)\,\psi(x)\,dx = 1, \qquad (15.54)$$

corresponding to *one* particle (along the x-axis).
  In addition, we have

3.
$$\bar{x} = \int_{-\infty}^\infty \psi^*(x)x\,\psi(x)\,dx \qquad (15.55)$$

for the *average* position of the particle[1] along the x-axis.
  We want a function $g(p)$ that will give the same information about the momentum.

1. $g^*(p)\,g(p)\,dp$ is the probability that our quantum particle has a momentum between p and $p + dp$.

2.
$$\int_{-\infty}^\infty g^*(p)\,g(p)\,dp = 1. \qquad (15.56)$$

3.
$$\bar{p} = \int_{-\infty}^\infty g^*(p)p\,g(p)\,dp \qquad (15.57)$$

As shown below, such a function is given by the Fourier transform of our space function $\psi(x)$. Specifically,

[1] This is often called an expectation value and denoted by $\langle x \rangle$.

$$g(p) = \frac{1}{\sqrt{2\pi\hbar}} \int_{-\infty}^{\infty} \psi(x) e^{-ipx/\hbar} \, dx \tag{15.58}$$

$$g^*(p) = \frac{1}{\sqrt{2\pi\hbar}} \int_{-\infty}^{\infty} \psi^*(x) e^{ipx/\hbar} \, dx. \tag{15.59}$$

To verify this, let us check on properties 2 and 3. Our normalization integral becomes

$$\int_{-\infty}^{\infty} g^*(p)\, g(p) \, dp = \int_{-\infty}^{\infty} \int_{-\infty}^{\infty} \left(\frac{1}{2\pi\hbar} \int_{-\infty}^{\infty} e^{-ip(x-x')/\hbar} \, dp \right) \psi^*(x')\, \psi(x) \, dx' \, dx. \tag{15.60}$$

The expression in the parentheses is a Fourier representation of the Dirac delta function[1] and

$$\int_{-\infty}^{\infty} g^*(p)\, g(p) \, dp = \int_{-\infty}^{\infty} \int_{-\infty}^{\infty} \delta(x - x')\, \psi^*(x')\, \psi(x) \, dx' \, dx. \tag{15.61}$$

Integrating over x', property 2 is verified. This is almost equivalent to applying the relations of the preceding section. Equation 15.61 corresponds to the Parseval relations

$$\int_{-\infty}^{\infty} F(t)\, G^*(t) \, dt = \int_{-\infty}^{\infty} f(y)\, g^*(y) \, dy, \tag{15.62}$$

$$\int_{-\infty}^{\infty} |F(t)|^2 \, dt = \int_{-\infty}^{\infty} |f(y)|^2 dy. \tag{15.63}$$

To check on property 3 we must show that

$$\bar{p} = \int_{-\infty}^{\infty} g^*(p) p\, g(p) \, dp = \int_{-\infty}^{\infty} \psi^*(x) \frac{\hbar}{i} \frac{d}{dx} \psi(x) \, dx, \tag{15.64}$$

where $(\hbar/i)(d/dx)$ is the momentum operator in the space representation. We replace the momentum functions and the first integral becomes

$$\frac{1}{2\pi\hbar} \iiint_{-\infty}^{\infty} p e^{-ip(x-x')/\hbar} \, \psi^*(x')\, \psi(x) \, dp \, dx' \, dx. \tag{15.65}$$

Now

$$p e^{-ip(x-x')/\hbar} = \frac{d}{dx} \left[-\frac{\hbar}{i} e^{-ip(x-x')/\hbar} \right]. \tag{15.66}$$

Substituting into Eq. 15.65 and integrating by parts, holding x' and p constant, we obtain

$$\bar{p} = \iint_{-\infty}^{\infty} \left[\frac{1}{2\pi\hbar} \int_{-\infty}^{\infty} e^{-ip(x-x')/\hbar} \, dp \right] \cdot \psi^*(x') \frac{\hbar}{i} \frac{d}{dx} \psi(x) \, dx' \, dx. \tag{15.67}$$

Here we assume $\psi(x)$ vanishes as $x \to \pm\infty$, eliminating the integrated part. Again

[1] Cf. Exercises 15.6.1 and 15.6.2.

using the Dirac delta function, Exercise 15.6.1, Eq. 15.67 reduces to Eq. 15.64 to verify our momentum representation. The reader will note that technically we have employed the inverse Fourier transform in Eq. 15.58. This was chosen to yield the proper sign in Eq. 15.67.

EXAMPLE 15.6.1. HYDROGEN ATOM

The hydrogen atom ground state may be described by the spacial wave function

$$\psi(\mathbf{r}) = \left(\frac{1}{\pi a_0^3}\right)^{1/2} e^{-r/a_0}, \tag{15.68}$$

a_0 being the Bohr radius, $\hbar^2/me^2$. We now have a three-dimensional wave function. The transform corresponding to Eq. 15.58 is

$$g(\mathbf{p}) = \frac{1}{(2\pi\hbar)^{3/2}} \int \psi(\mathbf{r}) e^{-i\mathbf{p}\cdot\mathbf{r}/\hbar} \, d\mathbf{r}. \tag{15.69}$$

Substituting Eq. 15.68 into Eq. 15.69 and using

$$\int e^{-ar + i\mathbf{b}\cdot\mathbf{r}} \, d\mathbf{r} = \frac{8\pi a}{(a^2 + b^2)^2}, \tag{15.70}$$

we obtain the hydrogenic momentum wave function

$$g(\mathbf{p}) = \pi^{-5/2} \frac{a_0^{3/2}\hbar^{5/2}}{(a_0^2 p^2 + \hbar^2)^2}. \tag{15.71}$$

Such momentum functions have been found useful in problems like Compton scattering from atomic electrons, the wavelength distribution of the scattered radiation depending on the momentum distribution of the target electrons.

The relation between the ordinary space representation and the momentum representation may be clarified by considering the basic commutation relations of quantum mechanics. We can go from a classical Hamiltonian to the Schrödinger wave equation by requiring that momentum p and position x *not* commute. Instead, we require that

$$[p, x] \equiv (px - xp) = -i\hbar. \tag{15.72}$$

For the multidimensional case Eq. 15.72 is replaced by

$$[p_i, x_j] = -i\hbar\delta_{ij}. \tag{15.73}$$

The Schrödinger (space) representation is obtained by using

$$x_j \rightarrow x_j,$$
$$p_i \rightarrow -i\hbar \frac{\partial}{\partial x_i}, \tag{x}$$

replacing the momentum by a partial space derivative. The reader will easily see that

$$[p, x]\psi(x) = -i\hbar \, \psi(x). \tag{15.74}$$

However, Eq. 15.72 can equally well be satisfied by using

$$x_j \to i\hbar \frac{\partial}{\partial p_j},$$ (p)

$$p_i \to p_i.$$

This is the momentum representation. Then

$$[p, x]\, g(p) = -i\hbar\, g(p).$$ (15.75)

Hence the representation (x) is not unique; (p) is an alternate possibility.

In general the Schrödinger representation (x) leading to the Schrödinger wave equation is more convenient because the potential energy V is generally given as a function of position $V(x, y, z)$. The momentum representation (p) usually leads to an integral equation (cf. Chapter 16 for the pros and cons of the integral equations). For an exception, consider the harmonic oscillator.

EXAMPLE 15.6.2. HARMONIC OSCILLATOR

The classical Hamiltonian (kinetic energy + potential energy = total energy) is

$$H(p, x) = \frac{p^2}{2m} + \frac{1}{2} kx^2 = E.$$ (15.76)

In the Schrödinger representation we obtain

$$-\frac{\hbar^2}{2m} \frac{d^2\psi(x)}{dx^2} + \frac{1}{2} kx^2\, \psi(x) = E\, \psi(x).$$ (15.77)

For total energy E equal to $\sqrt{(k/m)}\hbar/2$ there is a solution

$$\psi(x) = e^{-(\sqrt{mk}/2\hbar)x^2}.$$ (15.78)

The momentum representation leads to

$$\frac{p^2}{2m} g(p) - \frac{\hbar^2 k}{2} \frac{d^2 g(p)}{dp^2} = E\, g(p).$$ (15.79)

Again for

$$E = \sqrt{\frac{k}{m}} \frac{\hbar}{2}$$ (15.80)

the momentum wave equation (15.79) is satisfied by

$$g(p) = e^{-p^2/(2\hbar\sqrt{mk})}.$$ (15.81)

Either representation, space or momentum (and an infinite number of other possibilities), may be used, depending on which is more convenient for the particular problem under attack.

The demonstration that $g(p)$ is the momentum wave function corresponding to Eq. 15.78, that it is the Fourier inverse transform of Eq. 15.78, is left as Exercise 15.6.5.

EXERCISES

15.6.1 Find the Fourier transform of the Dirac delta function and then by inverting the transform obtain an integral expression for the Dirac delta function:

$$\delta(x) = \frac{1}{2\pi} \int_{-\infty}^{\infty} e^{-ikx} \, dk.$$

This constitutes an orthogonality relation for our continuum of exponentials, the Dirac delta replacing the Kronecker delta of the discrete system.

15.6.2 Using
(a) $$\delta(x) = \lim_{a \to \infty} \delta(x, a)$$
    and

(b) $$\delta(x, a) = \frac{a}{\sqrt{\pi}} e^{-a^2 x^2}$$

as a model of the Dirac delta function, show that

$$\delta(x) = \frac{1}{2\pi} \int_{-\infty}^{\infty} e^{-ikx} \, dk.$$

15.6.3 An infinite plane wave in quantum mechanics may be represented by the function

$$\psi(x) = e^{ip'x/\hbar}.$$

Find the corresponding momentum distribution function. Note that it has an infinity and that $\psi(x)$ is not normalized.

15.6.4 A quantum mechanical particle in a one-dimensional " box," $0 \leqslant x \leqslant a$, has a space wave function

$$\psi(x) = \sin \frac{n\pi x}{a}$$

in which n is an integer. Find the corresponding momentum wave functions and comment on their physical interpretation. *Hint.* To avoid problems of reflections at the walls let the wave function extend over *all* space and let the box be the interval between 0 and a.

15.6.5 A linear quantum oscillator in its ground state has a wave function

$$\psi(x) = a^{-1/2}\pi^{-1/4}e^{-x^2/2a^2}.$$

Show that the corresponding momentum function is

$$g(p) = a^{1/2}\pi^{-1/4}\hbar^{-1/2}e^{-a^2 p^2/2\hbar^2}.$$

15.6.6 We define

$$\delta(x, \varepsilon) = \begin{cases} \varepsilon^{-1}, & 0 < x < \varepsilon, \\ 0, & x < 0, \quad x > \varepsilon. \end{cases}$$

Express $\delta(x, \varepsilon)$ as a Fourier integral (via the Fourier integral theorem, inverse transforms, etc.). Finally show that

$$\lim_{\varepsilon \to 0} \delta(x, \varepsilon) = \frac{1}{2\pi} \int_{-\infty}^{\infty} e^{-ikx} \, dk.$$

15.6.7 From 15.6.1, 2, or 6 develop the representation

$$\delta(x) = \lim_{\alpha \to \infty} \frac{\sin \alpha x}{\pi x}.$$

This has been used as a starting point in a rigorous development of Fourier series.

15.6.8 A free particle in quantum mechanics is described by a plane wave

$$\psi_k(x, t) = e^{i[kx - (\hbar k^2/2m)t]}.$$

Combining waves of adjacent momentum with an amplitude weighting factor $\varphi(k)$ we form a wave packet

$$\Psi(x, t) = \int_{-\infty}^{\infty} \varphi(k)e^{i[kx - (\hbar k^2/2m)t]} \, dk.$$

(a) Solve for $\varphi(k)$ given that

$$\Psi(x, 0) = e^{-x^2/2a^2}.$$

(b) Using the known value of $\varphi(k)$ integrate to get the explicit form of $\Psi(x, t)$. Note that this wave packet diffuses or spreads out with time.

$$\textit{Ans.} \quad \Psi(x, t) = \frac{e^{-\{x^2/2[(a^2 + (i\hbar/m)t]\}}}{[1 + (i\hbar t/ma^2)]^{1/2}}.$$

15.7 Elementary Laplace Transforms

The Laplace transform $f(s)$ or $\mathcal{L}$ of a function $F(t)$ is defined by[1]

$$f(s) = \mathcal{L}\{F(t)\} = \lim_{a \to \infty} \int_0^a e^{-st} F(t) \, dt$$

$$= \int_0^{\infty} e^{-st} F(t) \, dt. \tag{15.82}$$

A few comments on the existence of the integral might be in order. The infinite integral of $F(t)$,

$$\int_0^{\infty} F(t) \, dt,$$

need not exist. For instance, $F(t)$ may diverge exponentially for large t. However, if there is some *constant* s_0 such that

$$|e^{-s_0 t} F(t)| \leqslant M, \tag{15.83}$$

a positive constant for sufficiently large t, $t > t_0$, the Laplace transform (Eq. 15.82), will exist for $s > s_0$; $F(t)$ is said to be of exponential order. As a counterexample, $F(t) = e^{t^2}$ does not satisfy the condition given by Eq. 15.83 and is *not* of exponential order. $\mathcal{L}\{e^{t^2}\}$ does *not* exist.

The Laplace transform may also fail to exist because of a sufficiently strong singularity in the function $F(t)$ as $t \to 0$; that is,

$$\int_0^{\infty} e^{-st} t^n \, dt$$

diverges at the origin for $n \leqslant -1$. The Laplace transform $\mathcal{L}\{t^n\}$ does not exist for $n \leqslant -1$.

---

[1] This is sometimes called a one-sided Laplace transform; the integral from $-\infty$ to $+\infty$ is referred to as a two-sided Laplace transform. Some authors introduce an additional factor of s. This extra s appears to have little advantage and continually gets in the way (cf. Jeffreys and Jeffreys, Section 14.13 for additional comments). Generally we take s to be real and positive. It is possible to have s complex provided R.P.(s) > 0.

Since, for two functions $F(t)$ and $G(t)$, for which the integrals exist

$$\mathscr{L}\{a\,F(t) + b\,G(t)\} = a\mathscr{L}\{F(t)\} + b\mathscr{L}\{G(t)\}, \tag{15.84}$$

the operation denoted by $\mathscr{L}$ is *linear*.

To introduce the Laplace transform, let us apply the operation to some of the elementary functions. In all cases we assume that $F(t) = 0$ for $t < 0$.

$$F(t) = 1 \qquad (t > 0).$$

Then

$$\mathscr{L}\{1\} = \int_0^\infty e^{-st}\,dt = \frac{1}{s}, \qquad \text{for } s > 0. \tag{15.85}$$

Again, let

$$F(t) = e^{kt} \qquad (t > 0).$$

The Laplace transform becomes

$$\mathscr{L}\{e^{kt}\} = \int_0^\infty e^{-st}e^{kt}\,dt = \frac{1}{s - k} \qquad \text{for } s > k. \tag{15.86}$$

Using this relation we may easily obtain the Laplace transform of certain other functions. Since

$$\cosh kt = \tfrac{1}{2}(e^{kt} + e^{-kt}),$$
$$\sinh kt = \tfrac{1}{2}(e^{kt} - e^{-kt}), \tag{15.87}$$

we have

$$\mathscr{L}\{\cosh kt\} = \frac{1}{2}\left(\frac{1}{s - k} + \frac{1}{s + k}\right) = \frac{s}{s^2 - k^2},$$
$$\mathscr{L}\{\sinh kt\} = \frac{1}{2}\left(\frac{1}{s - k} - \frac{1}{s + k}\right) = \frac{k}{s^2 - k^2}, \tag{15.88}$$

both valid for $s > k$. By the relations

$$\cos kt = \cosh ikt,$$
$$\sin kt = -i \sinh ikt, \tag{15.89}$$

the Laplace transforms are

$$\mathscr{L}\{\cos kt\} = \frac{s}{s^2 + k^2},$$
$$\mathscr{L}\{\sin kt\} = \frac{k}{s^2 + k^2}, \tag{15.09}$$

both valid for $s > 0$. Another derivation of this last transform is given in the next section.

Finally, for $F(t) = t^n$, we have

$$\mathscr{L}\{t^n\} = \int_0^\infty e^{-st}t^n\,dt,$$

which is just the factorial function. Hence

$$\mathscr{L}\{t^n\} = \frac{n!}{s^{n+1}}, \qquad s > 0. \tag{15.91}$$

There is little point to these operations unless we can carry out the inverse transform, as in Fourier transforms, that is, with

$$\mathscr{L}\{F(t)\} = f(s),$$

then

$$\mathscr{L}^{-1}\{f(s)\} = F(t). \tag{15.92}$$

Taken literally, this inverse transform is *not* unique; that is, two functions $F_1(t)$ and $F_2(t)$ may have the same transform, $f(s)$. However, in this case

$$F_1(t) - F_2(t) = N(t)$$

where $N(t)$ is a null function meaning that

$$\int_0^{t_0} N(t)\, dt = 0.$$

for all positive t_0. This result is known as Lerch's theorem. Therefore to the physicist and engineer $N(t)$ may almost always be taken as zero and the inverse operation becomes unique.

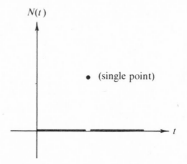

FIG. 15.4   A possible null function

The determination of the inverse transform can be done in two ways. (1) a general technique for $\mathscr{L}^{-1}$ will be developed in Section 15.11 by using the calculus of residues. (2) A table of transforms can be built up and used to carry out the inverse transforms exactly as we can use a table of logarithms to look up antilogarithms. These transforms constitute the embryonic beginnings of such a table. For a more complete set, see Table 15.2 page 573.

Utilization of such a table of transforms (or inverse transforms) is facilitated by expanding $f(s)$ in *partial fractions*.

Frequently $f(s)$, our transform, occurs in the form $g(s)/h(s)$, where $g(s)$ and $h(s)$ are polynomials with no common factors, $g(s)$ being of lower degree than $h(s)$. If the factors of $h(s)$ are all linear and distinct, then by the theory of partial fractions we may write

$$f(s) = \frac{c_1}{s - a_1} + \frac{c_2}{s - a_2} + \cdots + \frac{c_n}{s - a_n}, \tag{15.93}$$

where the c_i's are independent of s. If any of the roots, say a_1, is multiple (occurring

m times), then $f(s)$ has the form

$$f(s) = \frac{c_{1,m}}{(s - a_1)^m} + \frac{c_{1,m-1}}{(s - a_1)^{m-1}} + \cdots + \frac{c_{1,1}}{s - a_1} + \sum_{i=2}^{n} \frac{c_i}{s - a_i}. \tag{15.94}$$

Finally, if one of the factors is quadratic, $(s^2 + ps + q)$, the numerator, instead of being a simple constant, will have the form

$$\frac{as + b}{s^2 + ps + q}.$$

There are various ways of determining the constants introduced. For instance, in Eq. 15.93 we may multiply through by $(s - a_i)$ and obtain

$$c_i = \lim_{s \to a_i} (s - a_i) f(s). \tag{15.95}$$

In elementary cases a direct solution is often the easiest.

EXAMPLE 15.7.1

Let

$$f(s) = \frac{k^2}{s(s^2 + k^2)} = \frac{c}{s} + \frac{as + b}{s^2 + k^2} \tag{15.96}$$

Putting the right side of the equation over a common denominator and equating like powers of s in the numerator,

$$\frac{k^2}{s(s^2 + k^2)} = \frac{c(s^2 + k^2) + s(as + b)}{s(s^2 + k^2)}, \tag{15.97}$$

$$c + a = 0, \qquad s^2,$$

$$b = 0, \qquad s^1,$$

and

$$ck^2 = k^2, \qquad s^0.$$

Solving these $(s \neq 0)$,

$$c = 1,$$

$$b = 0,$$

$$a = -1,$$

giving

$$f(s) = \frac{1}{s} - \frac{s}{s^2 + k^2}. \tag{15.98}$$

and

$$\mathscr{L}^{-1}\{f(s)\} = 1 - \cos kt \tag{15.99}$$

by Eqs. 15.85 and 15.90.

EXAMPLE 15.7.2

As one application of Laplace transforms, consider the evaluation of

$$F(t) = \int_0^\infty \frac{\sin tx}{x} \, dx. \tag{15.100}$$

Suppose we take the Laplace transform of this definite (and improper) integral:

$$\mathscr{L}\left\{\int_0^\infty \frac{\sin tx}{x}\,dx\right\} = \int_0^\infty e^{-st} \int_0^\infty \frac{\sin tx}{x}\,dx\,dt. \qquad (15.101)$$

Now, interchanging the order of integration (which must be justified!),[1] we get

$$\int_0^\infty \frac{1}{x}\left[\int_0^\infty e^{-st}\sin tx\,dt\right]dx = \int_0^\infty \frac{dx}{s^2 + x^2}, \qquad (15.102)$$

since the factor in square brackets is just the Laplace transform of $\sin xt$. From the integral tables

$$\int_0^\infty \frac{dx}{s^2 + x^2} = \frac{1}{s}\tan^{-1}\left(\frac{x}{s}\right)\Big|_0^\infty = \frac{\pi}{2s} = f(s). \qquad (15.103)$$

By Eq. 15.85 we carry out the inverse transformation to obtain

$$F(t) = \frac{\pi}{2}, \qquad t > 0, \qquad (15.104)$$

in agreement with an evaluation by the calculus of residues (Section 7.2). It has been assumed that $t > 0$ in $F(t)$. For $F(-t)$ we need note only that $\sin(-tx) = -\sin tx$, giving $F(-t) = -F(t)$. Finally, if $t = 0$, $F(0)$ is clearly zero. Therefore

$$\int_0^\infty \frac{\sin tx}{x}\,dx = \begin{cases} \dfrac{\pi}{2}, & t > 0 \\[2mm] 0, & t = 0 \\[2mm] -\dfrac{\pi}{2}, & t < 0. \end{cases} \qquad (15.105)$$

Note that $\int_0^\infty (\sin tx/x)\,dx$, taken as a function of t, describes a step function, a step of height π at $t = 0$.

FIG. 15.5 $f(t)$ $\displaystyle\int_0^\infty \frac{\sin tx}{x}\,dx$, a step function

EXERCISES

15.7.1 Prove that

$$\lim_{s\to\infty} sf(s) = \lim_{t\to +0} F(t).$$

Hint. Assume that $F(t)$ can be expressed as $F(t) = \displaystyle\sum_{n=0}^\infty a_n t^n$.

[1] See Jeffreys and Jeffreys, Chapter 1.

15.7.2 Show that

$$\frac{1}{\pi} \lim_{s \to 0} \mathscr{L}\{\cos xt\} = \delta(x).$$

15.8 Laplace Transform of Derivatives

Perhaps the main application of Laplace transforms is in converting differential equations into simpler forms that may be solved more easily. It will be seen, for instance, that coupled differential equations with constant coefficients transform to simultaneous linear algebraic equations.

Let us transform the first derivative of $F(t)$.

$$\mathscr{L}\{F'(t)\} = \int_0^\infty e^{-st} \frac{d\,F(t)}{dt}\, dt$$

$$= e^{-st}\, F(t)\Big|_0^\infty + s \int_0^\infty e^{-st}\, F(t)\, dt$$

$$= s\mathscr{L}\{F(t)\} - F(0). \tag{15.106}$$

Strictly speaking $F(0) = F(+0)$[1] and dF/dt is required to be at least piecewise continuous for $0 \leqslant t < \infty$. Naturally both $F(t)$ and its derivative must be such that the integrals do not diverge. Incidentally Eq. 15.106 provides another proof of Exercise 15.7.1.

An extension gives

$$\mathscr{L}\{F^{(2)}(t)\} = s^2 \mathscr{L}\{F(t)\} - sF(+0) - F'(+0), \tag{15.107}$$

$$\mathscr{L}\{F^{(n)}(t)\} = s^n \mathscr{L}\{F(t)\} - s^{n-1} F(+0) - s^{n-2} F'(+0) - \cdots - F^{(n-1)}(+0). \tag{15.108}$$

Note carefully how the initial conditions, $F(+0)$, $F'(+0)$, and so on, are incorporated into the transform. Equation 15.107 may be used to derive $\mathscr{L}\{\sin kt\}$. We use the identity

$$-k^2 \sin kt = \frac{d^2}{dt^2} \sin kt. \tag{15.109}$$

Then, applying the Laplace transform operation,

$$-k^2 \mathscr{L}\{\sin kt\} = \mathscr{L}\left\{\frac{d^2}{dt^2} \sin kt\right\}$$

$$= s^2 \mathscr{L}\{\sin kt\} - s \sin(0) - \frac{d}{dt} \sin kt\,|_{t=0}. \tag{15.110}$$

Since $\sin(0) = 0$ and $d/dt \sin kt|_{t=0} = k$,

$$\mathscr{L}\{\sin kt\} = \frac{k}{s^2 + k^2}, \tag{15.111}$$

verifying Eq. 15.90.

---

[1] Zero is approached from the *positive* side.

EXAMPLE 15.8.1. SIMPLE HARMONIC OSCILLATOR

As a simple but reasonably physical example, consider a mass m oscillating under the influence of an ideal spring, spring constant k. As usual, friction is neglected. Then Newton's second law becomes

$$m\,\frac{d^2\,X(t)}{dt^2} + k\,X(t) = 0; \tag{15.112}$$

also

$$X(0) = X_0,$$
$$X'(0) = 0.$$

Applying the Laplace transform, we obtain

$$m\mathscr{L}\left\{\frac{d^2X}{dt^2}\right\} + k\mathscr{L}\{X(t)\} = 0, \tag{15.113}$$

and by use of Eq. 15.107 this becomes

$$ms^2\,x(s) - msX_0 + k\,x(s) = 0, \tag{15.114}$$

$$x(s) = X_0\,\frac{s}{s^2 + \omega_0^2}, \qquad \text{with } \omega_0^2 \equiv \frac{k}{m}. \tag{15.115}$$

From Eq. 15.90 this is seen to be the transform of $\cos \omega_0 t$, which gives

$$X(t) = X_0 \cos \omega_0 t \tag{15.116}$$

as expected.

EXAMPLE 15.8.2. EARTH'S NUTATION

A somewhat more involved example is provided by the nutation of the earth's poles (force-free procession). Treating the earth as a rigid (oblate) spheroid, the Euler equations of motion reduce to

$$\frac{dX}{dt} = -a\,Y$$

$$\frac{dY}{dt} = +a\,X \tag{15.117}$$

where $a \equiv [(I_z - I_x)/I_z]\omega_z$,

   $X = \omega_x$,

   $Y = \omega_y$ with angular velocity vector $\boldsymbol{\omega} = (\omega_x, \omega_y, \omega_z)$,

   I_z = moment of interia about the z-axis and $I_y = I_x$ moment of interia about x (or y)-axis.

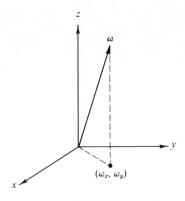

FIG. 15.6

The z-axis coincides with the axis of symmetry of the earth. It differs from the axis for the earth's daily rotation, $\boldsymbol{\omega}$, by some 15 meters, measured at the poles. Transformation of these coupled differential equations yields

$$s\, x(s) - X(0) = -a\, y(s),$$
$$s\, y(s) - Y(0) = a\, x(s). \tag{15.118}$$

Combining to eliminate $y(s)$, we have

$$s^2\, x(s) - s\, X(0) + a\, Y(0) = -a^2\, x(s)$$

or

$$x(s) = X(0)\, \frac{s}{s^2 + a^2} - Y(0)\, \frac{a}{s^2 + a^2}. \tag{15.119}$$

Hence

$$X(t) = X(0)\cos at - Y(0)\sin at. \tag{15.120}$$

Similarly,

$$Y(t) = X(0)\sin at + Y(0)\cos at. \tag{15.121}$$

This is seen to be a rotation of the vector $(X,\ Y)$ counterclockwise (for $a > 0$) about the z-axis with angle $\theta = at$ and angular velocity a.

A direct interpretation may be found by choosing the time axis so that $Y(0) = 0$. Then

$$X(t) = X(0)\cos at,$$
$$Y(t) = X(0)\sin at, \tag{15.122}$$

which are the parametric equations for rotation of $(X,\ Y)$ in a circular orbit of radius $X(0)$ with angular velocity a in the counterclockwise sense.

In the case of the earth's angular velocity vector $X(0)$ is about 15 meters, whereas a, as defined here, corresponds to a period $(2\pi/a)$ of some 300 days. Actually, because of departures from the idealized rigid body assumed in setting up Euler's equations, the period is about 427 days.[1]

[1] Menzel, D., ed., *Fundamental Formulas of Physics*, p. 695. New York: Prentice Hall (1955).

If in Eq. 15.117 we set

$$X(t) = L_x,$$

$$Y(t) = L_y,$$

where L_x and L_y = the x- and y-components of the angular momentum **L**,

$$a = -g_L B_z,$$

g_L = gyromagnetic ratio,

B_z = magnetic field (along the z-axis),

Eq. 15.117 describes the Larmor precession of charged bodies in a uniform magnetic field, B_z.

Dirac delta function.   For use with differential equations one further transform is helpful—that of the Dirac delta function:

$$\mathcal{L}\{\delta(t - t_0)\} = \int_0^\infty e^{-st}\delta(t - t_0)\, dt = e^{-st_0}, \qquad \text{for } t_0 \geqslant 0, \qquad (15.123)$$

and for $t_0 = 0$

$$\mathcal{L}\{\delta(t)\} = 1, \qquad (15.124)$$

where it is assumed that we are using a representation of the delta function such that

$$\int_0^\infty \delta(t)\, dt = 1, \qquad \delta(t) = 0 \quad \text{for} \quad t > 0. \qquad (15.125)$$

As an alternate method, $\delta(t)$ may be considered the limit as $\varepsilon \to 0$ of $F(t)$, where

$$F(t) = \begin{cases} 0, & t < 0, \\ \varepsilon^{-1}, & 0 < t < \varepsilon, \\ 0, & t > \varepsilon. \end{cases} \qquad (15.126)$$

By direct calculation

$$\mathcal{L}\{F(t)\} = \frac{1 - e^{-\varepsilon s}}{\varepsilon s}. \qquad (15.127)$$

Taking the limit of the integral (instead of the integral of the limit),

$$\lim_{\varepsilon \to 0} \mathcal{L}\{F(t)\} = 1$$

or Eq. 15.124

$$\mathcal{L}\{\delta(t)\} = 1.$$

This delta function is frequently called the impulse function because it is so useful in describing impulsive forces, that is, forces lasting only a short time.

EXAMPLE 15.8.3. IMPULSIVE FORCE

Newton's second law for impulsive force acting on a particle of mass m becomes

$$m\,\frac{d^2 X}{dt^2} = P\,\delta(t) \qquad (15.128)$$

where P is a constant.

Transforming, we obtain

$$ms^2 \, x(s) - ms \, X(0) - m \, X'(0) = P. \qquad (15.129)$$

For a particle starting from rest, $X'(0) = 0.$[1] We shall also take $X(0) = 0$. Then

$$x(s) = \frac{P}{ms^2}, \qquad (15.130)$$

and

$$X(t) = \frac{P}{m} \, t, \qquad (15.131)$$

$$\frac{dX(t)}{dt} = \frac{P}{m}, \qquad \text{a constant.} \qquad (15.132)$$

The effect of the impulse $P \, \delta(t)$ is to transfer (instantaneously) P units of linear momentum to the particle.

A similar analysis applies to the ballistic galvanometer. The torque on the galvanometer is given initially by ki, in which i is a pulse of current and k is a proportionality constant. Since i is of short duration, we set

$$ki = kq \, \delta(t) \qquad (15.133)$$

where q is the total charge carried by the current i. Then, with I the moment of inertia,

$$I \frac{d^2\theta}{dt^2} = kq \, \delta(t), \qquad (15.134)$$

and transforming as above, we find that the effect of the current pulse is a transfer of kq units of *angular* momentum to the galvanometer.

EXERCISES

15.8.1 Use the expression for the transform of a second derivative to obtain the transform of $\cos kt$.

15.8.2 If $F(t)$ can be expanded in a power series (Taylor or Laurent), that is,

$$F(t) = \sum_n a_n t^n,$$

and

$$\int_0^\infty e^{-st} \sum_m a_n t^n \, dt$$

or

$$\sum_n a_n \int_0^\infty e^{-st} \, t^n \, dt$$

---

[1] This really should be $X'(+0)$. To include the effect of the impulse consider that the impulse will occur at $t = \varepsilon$ and let $\varepsilon \to 0$.

exists, show that $f(s)$, the Laplace transform of $F(t)$, contains no powers of s greater than s^{-1}. Check your result by calculating $\mathcal{L}\{\delta(t)\}$ and comment intelligently on this fiasco.

15.8.3   Radioactive nuclei decay according to the law

$$\frac{dN}{dt} = -\lambda N,$$

N being the concentration of a given nuclide and λ, the particular decay constant. This equation may be interpreted as stating that the rate of decay is proportional to the number of these radioactive nuclei present. They all decay independently.

In a radioactive series of n different nuclides, starting with N_1,

$$\frac{dN_1}{dt} = -\lambda_1 N_1,$$

$$\frac{dN_2}{dt} = \lambda_1 N_1 - \lambda_2 N_2, \text{ etc.},$$

$$\frac{dN_n}{dt} = \lambda_{n-1} N_{n-1}, \quad \text{stable.}$$

Find $N_1(t)$, $N_2(t)$, and $N_3(t)$, $n = 3$, with $N_1(0) = N_0$, $N_2(0) = N_3(0) = 0$.

$$\textit{Ans.} \quad N_1(t) = N_0 e^{-\lambda_1 t},$$

$$N_2(t) = N_0 \frac{\lambda_1}{\lambda_2 - \lambda_1} (e^{-\lambda_1 t} - e^{-\lambda_2 t}),$$

$$N_3(t) = N_0 \left(1 - \frac{\lambda_2}{\lambda_2 - \lambda_1} e^{-\lambda_1 t} + \frac{\lambda_1}{\lambda_2 - \lambda_1} e^{-\lambda_2 t} \right).$$

Find an approximate expression for N_2 and N_3, valid for small t when $\lambda_1 \approx \lambda_2$.

$$\textit{Ans.} \quad N_2 \approx N_0 \lambda_1 t$$

$$N_3 \approx \frac{N_0}{2} \lambda_1 \lambda_2 t^2.$$

Find approximate expressions for N_2 and N_3, valid for large t, when
(a) $\lambda_1 \gg \lambda_2$,   (b) $\lambda_1 \ll \lambda_2$.

$\textit{Ans.}$ (a) $N_2 \approx N_0 e^{-\lambda_2 t}$ (b) $N_2 \approx N_0 \dfrac{\lambda_1}{\lambda_2} e^{-\lambda_1 t}$,

         $N_3 \approx N_0(1 - e^{-\lambda_2 t})$, $\lambda_1 t \gg 1$. $N_3 \approx N_0(1 - e^{-\lambda_1 t})$, $\lambda_2 t \gg 1$.

15.8.4   The formation of an isotope in a nuclear reactor is given by

$$\frac{dN_2}{dt} = nv\sigma_1 N_{10} - \lambda_2 N_2(t) - nv\sigma_2 N_2(t).$$

Here the product nv is the neutron flux, neutrons per cubic centimeter, times centimeters per second mean velocity; σ_1 and σ_2 (cm^2) are measures of the probability of neutron absorption by the original isotope, concentration N_{10}, which is assumed constant and the newly formed isotope, concentration N_2, respectively. The radioactive decay constant for the isotope is λ_2.

(a) Find the concentration N_2 of the new isotope as a function of time.

(b) If the original element is Eu^{153}, $\sigma, = 400$ barns $= 400 \times 10^{-24}$ cm^2, $\sigma_2 = 1000$ barns $= 1000 \times 10^{-24}$ cm^2, and $\lambda_2 = 1.4 \times 10^{-9}$ sec^{-1}. If $N_{10} = 10^{20}$ and $(nv) = 10^9$ cm^{-2} sec^{-1}, find N_2, the concentration of Eu^{154} after one year of continuous irradiation. Is the assumption that N_1 is constant justified?

15.8.5 In a nuclear reactor Xe^{135} is formed both as a direct fission product and as a decay product of I^{135}, half-life, 6.7 hours. The half-life of Xe^{135} is 9.2 hours. As Xe^{135} strongly absorbs thermal neutrons thereby "poisoning" the nuclear reactor, its concentration is a matter of great interest. The relevant equations are

$$\frac{dN_I}{dt} = \gamma_I \varphi \sigma_f N_U - \lambda_I N_I,$$

$$\frac{dN_X}{dt} = \lambda_I N_I + \gamma_X \varphi \sigma_f N_U - \lambda_X N_X - \varphi \sigma_X N_X.$$

Here N_I = concentration of I^{135} (Xe^{135}, U^{235}), Assume N_U = constant.

γ_I = yield of I^{135} per fission = 0.060,

γ_X = yield of Xe^{135} direct from fission = 0.003,

$\lambda_I = I^{135}$ (Xe^{135}) decay constant $= \dfrac{\ln 2}{t^{1/2}} = \dfrac{0.693}{t^{1/2}}$

σ_f = thermal neutron fission cross section for U^{235},

σ_X = thermal neutron absorption cross section for Xe^{135} = 3.5×10^6 barns,

$\qquad\qquad\qquad\qquad\qquad\qquad\qquad\qquad\qquad\quad = 3.5 \times 10^{-18} \text{ cm}^2$.

(σ_I, the absorption cross section of I^{135} is negligible.)

φ = neutron flux = neutrons/cm³ × mean velocity (cm/sec)

1. Find $N_X(t)$ in terms of neutron flux φ and the product $\sigma_f N_U$.
2. Find $N_X(t \rightarrow \infty)$.
3. After N_X has reached equilibrium, the reactor is shut down, $\varphi = 0$. Find $N_X(t)$ following shut down. Notice the increase in N_X which may for a few hours interfere with starting the reactor up again.

15.8.6 Derive the Laplace transform of the Gauss error function

$$\Phi(t) = \frac{2}{\sqrt{\pi}} \int_0^t e^{-x^2}\, dx.$$

Ans. $\mathcal{L}\{\Phi(t)\} = \dfrac{1}{s} e^{s^2/4}\left[1 - \Phi\left(\dfrac{s}{2}\right)\right].$

15.9 Other Properties

Substitution.   If we replace the parameter s by $s - a$ in the definition of the Laplace transform (Eq. 15.82), we have

$$f(s - a) = \int_0^\infty e^{-(s-a)t}\, F(t)\, dt = \int_0^\infty e^{-st} e^{at}\, F(t)\, dt \tag{15.135}$$

$$= \mathcal{L}\{e^{at}\, F(t)\}.$$

Hence the replacement of s with $s - a$ corresponds to multiplying $F(t)$ by e^{at} and conversely. This result can be used to good advantage in extending our table of transforms. From Eq. 15.90 we find immediately that

$$\mathcal{L}\{e^{at} \sin kt\} = \frac{k}{(s - a)^2 + k^2}\,; \tag{15.136}$$

also

$$\mathcal{L}\{e^{at} \cos kt\} = \frac{s - a}{(s - a)^2 + k^2}, \qquad s > a.$$

EXAMPLE 15.9.1.   DAMPED OSCILLATOR

These expressions are useful when we consider an oscillating mass with damping proportional to the velocity. Equation 15.112, with such damping added, becomes

$$m\,X''(t) + b\,X'(t) + k\,X(t) = 0, \tag{15.137}$$

in which b is a proportionality constant. Let us assume that the particle starts from rest at $X(0) = X_0$, $X'(0) = 0$. The transformed equation is

$$m[s\,x(s) - sX_0] + b[s\,x(s) - X_0] + k\,x(s) = 0 \tag{15.138}$$

and

$$x(s) = X_0 \frac{ms + b}{ms^2 + bs + k}. \tag{15.139}$$

This may be handled by completing the square of the denominator,

$$s^2 + \frac{b}{m}s + \frac{k}{m} = \left(s + \frac{b}{2m}\right)^2 + \left(\frac{k}{m} - \frac{b^2}{4m^2}\right). \tag{15.140}$$

If the damping is small, $b^2 < 4\,km$, the last term is positive and will be denoted by ω_1^2.

$$x(s) = X_0 \frac{s + b/m}{(s + b/2m)^2 + \omega_1^2}$$

$$= X_0 \frac{s + b/2m}{(s + b/2m)^2 + \omega_1^2} + X_0 \frac{(b/2m\omega_1)\omega_1}{(s + b/2m)^2 + \omega_1^2}. \tag{15.141}$$

By Eqs. 15.136

$$X(t) = X_0 e^{-(b/2m)t}\left(\cos \omega_1 t + \frac{b}{2m\omega_1}\sin \omega_1 t\right)$$

$$= X_0 \frac{\omega_0}{\omega_1} e^{-(b/2m)t}\cos(\omega_1 t - \varphi) \tag{15.142}$$

where

$$\tan \varphi = \frac{b}{2m\omega_1},$$

$$\omega_0^2 = \frac{k}{m}.$$

Of course, as $b \to 0$, this solution goes over to the undamped solution, (Section 15.8).

RLC analog.   It is worth noting the similarity between this damped simple harmonic oscillation of a mass on a spring and an RLC circuit (resistance, inductance, and capacitance). At any instant the sum of the potential differences around the loop must be zero (Kirchhoff's law, conservation of energy). This gives

$$L\frac{dI}{dt} + RI + \frac{1}{C}\int^t I\,dt = 0. \tag{15.143}$$

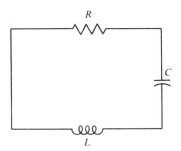

FIG. 15.7 *RLC* circuit

Differentiating the current I with respect to time (to eliminate the integral), we have

$$L \frac{d^2 I}{dt^2} + R \frac{dI}{dt} + \frac{1}{C} I = 0. \tag{15.144}$$

If we replace
  $I(t)$ with $X(t)$,

  L with m,

  R with b,

  C^{-1} with k,

this is identical with the mechanical problem. It is but one example of the unification of diverse branches of physics by mathematics. A more complete discussion will be found in Olson's book.[1]

  Translation.   This time let $f(s)$ be multiplied by e^{-bs}, $b > 0$.

$$e^{-bs} f(s) = e^{-bs} \int_0^\infty e^{-st} F(t) \, dt$$

$$= \int_0^\infty e^{-s(t+b)} F(t) \, dt. \tag{15.145}$$

Now let $t + b = \tau$. Eq. 15.145 becomes

$$e^{-bs} f(s) = \int_b^\infty e^{-s\tau} F(\tau - b) \, d\tau. \tag{15.146}$$

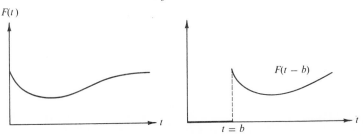

FIG. 15.8 Translation

[1] Olsen, H. F., *Dynamical Analogies*. New York: Van Nostrand (1943).

Since $F(t)$ is assumed to be equal to zero for $t < 0$, $F(\tau - b) = 0$ for $0 \leqslant \tau < b$. Therefore we can extend the lower limit to zero without changing the value of the integral. Then, noting that τ is only a variable of integration,

$$e^{-bs} f(s) = \mathscr{L}\{F(t - b)\}. \tag{15.147}$$

EXAMPLE 15.9.2.   ELECTROMAGNETIC WAVES

The electromagnetic wave equation with $E = E_y$ or E_z, a transverse wave propagating along the x-axis, is

$$\frac{\partial^2 E(x, t)}{\partial x^2} - \frac{1}{v^2} \frac{\partial^2 E(x, t)}{\partial t^2} = 0. \tag{15.148}$$

Transforming this equation with respect to t,

$$\frac{\partial^2}{\partial x^2} \mathscr{L}\{E(x, t)\} - \frac{s^2}{v^2} \mathscr{L}\{E(x, t)\} + \frac{s}{v^2} E(x, 0) + \frac{1}{v^2} \frac{\partial E(x, t)}{\partial t}\bigg|_{t=0} = 0. \tag{15.149}$$

If we have the initial condition $E(x, 0) = 0$ and

$$\frac{\partial E(x, t)}{\partial t}\bigg|_{t=0} = 0,$$

then

$$\frac{\partial^2}{\partial x^2} \mathscr{L}\{E(x, t)\} = \frac{s^2}{v^2} \mathscr{L}\{E(x, t)\}. \tag{15.150}$$

The solution (of this *ordinary* differential equation) is

$$\mathscr{L}\{E(x, t)\} = c_1 e^{-(s/v)x} + c_2 e^{+(s/v)x}; \tag{15.151}$$

c_1 and c_2 are obtained by additional boundary conditions. If our wave remains finite as $x \to \infty$, $\mathscr{L}\{E(x, t)\}$ will also. Hence $c_2 = 0$.
   If $E(0, t)$ is denoted by $F(t)$, then $c_1 = f(s)$ and

$$\mathscr{L}\{E(x, t)\} = e^{-(s/v)x} f(s). \tag{15.152}$$

From the translation property (Eq. 15.147) we find immediately

$$E(x, t) = \begin{cases} F\left(t - \dfrac{x}{v}\right), & t \geqslant \dfrac{x}{v}, \\[2mm] 0, & t < \dfrac{x}{v}. \end{cases} \tag{15.153}$$

Differentiation and substitution into Eq. 15.148 verifies Eq. 15.153. Our solution represents a wave (or pulse) moving in the positive x-direction with velocity v. Note that for $x > vt$ the region remains undisturbed; the pulse has not had time to get there. If we had wanted a signal propagated along the negative x-axis, c_1 would have been set equal to 0 and we would have obtained

$$E(x, t) = \begin{cases} F\left(t + \dfrac{x}{v}\right), & t \geqslant -\dfrac{x}{v}, \\ 0, & t < -\dfrac{x}{v}, \end{cases} \qquad (15.154)$$

a wave along the negative x-axis.

Derivative of a transform.   When $F(t)$, which is at least piecewise continuous, and s is chosen so that $e^{-st} F(t)$ converges exponentially for large s, the integral

$$\int_0^\infty e^{-st} F(t)\, dt$$

is uniformly convergent and may be differentiated (under the integral sign) with respect to s. Then

$$f'(s) = \int_0^\infty (-t) e^{-st} F(t)\, dt = \mathscr{L}\{-t\, F(t)\}. \qquad (15.155)$$

Continuing this process,

$$f^{(n)}(s) = \mathscr{L}\{(-t)^n\, F(t)\}. \qquad (15.156)$$

All the integrals so obtained will be uniformly convergent because of the decreasing exponential behavior of $e^{-st} F(t)$.

This same technique may be applied to generate more transforms. For example

$$\mathscr{L}\{e^{kt}\} = \int_0^\infty e^{-st} e^{kt}\, dt$$

$$= \frac{1}{s - k}, \qquad (s > k). \qquad (15.157)$$

Differentiating with respect to s (or with respect to k), we obtain

$$\mathscr{L}\{te^{kt}\} = \frac{1}{(s - k)^2}, \qquad s > k. \qquad (15.158)$$

EXAMPLE 15.9.3. BESSEL'S EQUATION

An interesting application of a differentiated Laplace transform appears in the solution of Bessel's equation with $n = 0$. From Chapter 11 we have

$$x^2\, y''(x) + x\, y'(x) + x^2\, y(x) = 0. \qquad (15.159)$$

Dividing by x and substituting $t = x$ and $F(t) = y(x)$ to agree with the present notation, the Bessel equation becomes

$$t\, F''(t) + F'(t) + t\, F(t) = 0. \qquad (15.160)$$

We need a regular solution, in particular $F(0) = 1$. Also we assume that our unknown $F(t)$ has a transform. Then, transforming and using Eqs. 15.107 and 15.155, we have

$$-\frac{d}{ds}[s^2 f(s) - s] + s f(s) - 1 - \frac{d}{ds} f(s) = 0. \qquad (15.161)$$

Since $F(0)$ is finite, substitution into Eq. 15.160 indicates that $F'(0) = 0$. Rearranging Eq. 15.161, we obtain

$$(s^2 + 1) f'(s) + s f(s) = 0 \qquad (15.162)$$

or

$$\frac{df}{f} = -\frac{s \, ds}{s^2 + 1}. \qquad (15.163)$$

By integration,

$$\ln f(s) = -\tfrac{1}{2} \ln (s^2 + 1) + \ln C, \qquad (15.164)$$

which may be rewritten

$$f(s) = \frac{C}{\sqrt{s^2 + 1}}. \qquad (15.165)$$

To make use of Eq. 15.91, $f(s)$ is expanded in a series of negative powers of s, convergent for $s > 1$.

$$f(s) = \frac{C}{s}\left(1 + \frac{1}{s^2}\right)^{-1/2}$$

$$= \frac{C}{s}\left[1 - \frac{1}{2s^2} + \frac{1 \cdot 3}{2^2 \cdot 2! s^4} - \cdots + \frac{(-1)^n(2n)!}{(2^n n!)^2 s^{2n}} + \cdots\right]. \qquad (15.166)$$

Inverting, term by term, we obtain

$$F(t) = C \sum_{n=0}^{\infty} \frac{(-1)^n t^{2n}}{(2^n n!)^2}. \qquad (15.167)$$

When C is set equal to 1, as required by the initial condition $F(0) = 1$, $F(t)$ is just $J_0(t)$, our familiar Bessel function of order zero. Hence

$$\mathscr{L}\{J_0(t)\} = \frac{1}{\sqrt{s^2 + 1}}. \qquad (15.168)$$

Note that we assumed $s > 1$. The proof for $s > 0$ is left as a problem.

It is perhaps worth noting that this application was successful and relatively easy because we took $n = 0$ in Bessel's equation. This made it possible to divide out a factor of x (or t). If this had not been done, the terms of the form $t^2 F(t)$ would have introduced a second derivative of $f(s)$. The resulting equation would have been no easier to solve than the original one.

When we go beyond linear differential equations with constant coefficients, the Laplace transform may still be applied, but there is no guarantee that it will be helpful.

The application to Bessel's equation, $n \neq 0$, will be found in the references. Alternatively, we can show that

$$\mathscr{L}\{J_n(at)\} = \frac{a^{-n}(\sqrt{s^2 + a^2} - s)^n}{\sqrt{s^2 + a^2}} \tag{15.169}$$

by expressing $J_n(t)$ as an infinite series and transforming term by term (Exercise 15.9.5).

Integration of transforms. Again with $F(t)$ at least piecewise continuous and x large enough so that $e^{-xt} F(t)$ decreases exponentially (as $x \to \infty$), the integral

$$f(x) = \int_0^\infty e^{-xt} F(t) \, dt \tag{15.170}$$

is uniformly convergent with respect to x. This justifies reversing the order of integration in the following equation:

$$\int_s^b f(x) \, dx = \int_s^b \int_0^\infty e^{-xt} F(t) \, dt \, dx$$

$$= \int_0^\infty \frac{F(t)}{t} (e^{-st} - e^{-bt}) \, dt, \tag{15.171}$$

on integrating with respect to x. The lower limit s is chosen large enough so that $f(s)$ is within the region of uniform convergence. Now, letting $b \to \infty$, we have

$$\int_s^\infty f(x) \, dx = \int_0^\infty \frac{F(t)}{t} e^{-st} \, dt$$

$$= \mathscr{L}\left\{\frac{F(t)}{t}\right\}, \tag{15.172}$$

provided that $F(t)/t$ is finite at $t = 0$ or diverges less strongly than t^{-1} (so that $\mathscr{L}\{F(t)/t\}$ will exist).

EXERCISES

15.9.1 Solve Eq. 15.137, which describes a damped simple harmonic oscillator for $X(0) = X_0$, $X'(0) = 0$, and
(a) $b^2 = 4 \, km$ (critically damped), (b) $b^2 > 4 \, km$ (overdamped).

Ans. (a) $X(t) = X_0 e^{-(b/2m)t} \left(1 + \frac{b}{2m} t\right)$.

15.9.2 Solve Eq. 15.137, which describes a damped simple harmonic oscillator for $X(0) = 0$, $X'(0) = v_0$, and

(a) $b^2 < 4$ km (underdamped),   (b) $b^2 = 4$ km (critically damped),

$$Ans. \quad \text{(a)} \quad X(t) = \frac{v_0}{\omega_1} e^{-(b/2m)t} \sin \omega_1 t,$$

$$\text{(b)} \quad X(t) = v_0 t\, e^{-(b/2m)t}.$$

(c) $b^2 > 4$ km (overdamped).

15.9.3 Ringing circuit. In certain electronic circuits resistance, inductance, and capacitance are placed in the plate circuit in parallel (Fig. 15.9). A constant voltage is maintained across the parallel elements, keeping the capacitor charged. At time $t = 0$ the circuit is disconnected from the voltage source. Find the voltages across the parallel elements R, L, and C as a function of time. Assume R to be *large*. *Hint.* By Kirchoff's laws

$$I_R + I_C + I_L = 0 \quad \text{and} \quad E_R = E_C = E_L$$

where

$$E_R = I_R R,$$

$$E_C = \frac{q_0}{C} + \frac{1}{C}\int_0^t I_C\, dt,$$

$$E_L = L\frac{dI_L}{dt},$$

q_0 = initial charge of capacitor.

FIG. 15.9   Ringing circuit

15.9.4 The motion of a body falling in a resisting medium may be described by

$$m\frac{d^2 X(t)}{dt^2} = mg - b\frac{d X(t)}{dt}$$

when the retarding force is proportional to the velocity. Find $X(t)$ and $dX(t)/dt$ for the initial conditions

$$X(0) = \frac{dX}{dt}\bigg|_{t=0} = 0.$$

15.9.5 Prove

$$\mathcal{L}\{J_\nu(at)\} = a^{-\nu}\frac{(\sqrt{s^2 + a^2} - s)^\nu}{\sqrt{s^2 + a^2}}$$

for $\nu = 1$ and for $\nu = 2$ by using the series expansion of J_ν. What limits are imposed on s and on ν by this method?

$$Ans. \quad s > 1,$$
$$\nu > -1.$$

15.9.6 With $J_0(t)$ expressed as a contour integral, apply the Laplace transform operation, reverse the order of integration, and thus show that

$$\mathcal{L}\{J_0(t)\} = (s^2 + 1)^{-1/2}, \qquad \text{for } s > 0.$$

15.9.7 Develop the Laplace transform of $J_n(t)$ from $\mathcal{L}\{J_0(t)\}$ by using the Bessel function recurrence relations.

15.9.8 Show that

$$\mathcal{L}\{I_0(at)\} = (s^2 - a^2)^{-1/2}, \qquad s > a.$$

15.9.9 Verify the following Laplace transforms:

(a) $\mathcal{L}\{J_{1/2}(at)\} = \dfrac{[(a^2 + s^2)^{1/2} - s]^{1/2}}{a^{1/2}(a^2 + s^2)^{1/2}},$

(b) $\mathcal{L}\{N_{1/2}(at)\} = \dfrac{[(a^2 + s^2)^{1/2} + s]^{1/2}}{a^{1/2}(a^2 + s^2)^{1/2}},$

(c) $\mathcal{L}\{I_{1/2}(at)\} = \dfrac{[s - (s^2 - a^2)^{1/2}]^{1/2}}{a^{1/2}(s^2 - a^2)^{1/2}},$

(d) $\mathcal{L}\{K_{1/2}(at)\} = \dfrac{\pi}{(2a)^{1/2}(s + a)^{1/2}}.$

15.9.10 Verify the following Laplace transforms:

(a) $\mathcal{L}\{j_0(at)\} = \mathcal{L}\left\{\dfrac{\sin at}{at}\right\} = \dfrac{1}{a}\cot^{-1}\left(\dfrac{s}{a}\right),$

(b) $\mathcal{L}\{n_0(at)\}$ does not exist

(c) $\mathcal{L}\{i_0(at)\} = \mathcal{L}\left\{\dfrac{\sinh at}{at}\right\} = \dfrac{1}{2a}\ln\dfrac{s+a}{s-a}$

$$= \dfrac{1}{a}\coth^{-1}\left(\dfrac{s}{a}\right),$$

(d) $\mathcal{L}\{k_0(at)\}$ does not exist.

15.9.11 When functions are used with argument $\sqrt{t}$, some unusual Laplace transforms occur. Show that

(a) $\mathcal{L}\left\{\dfrac{1}{\sqrt{\pi t}}\cos(2\sqrt{kt})\right\} = \dfrac{1}{s^{1/2}}e^{-k/s},$

(b) $\mathcal{L}\{J_0(2\sqrt{kt})\} = \dfrac{1}{s}e^{-k/s},$

(c) $\mathcal{L}\left\{\dfrac{1}{\sqrt{\pi k}}\sinh(2\sqrt{kt})\right\} = \dfrac{1}{s^{3/2}}e^{k/s}.$

15.9.12 Develop a Laplace transform solution of Laguerre's equation

$$t\,F''(t) + (1 - t)\,F'(t) + n\,F(t) = 0.$$

Note that you need a derivative of a transform and a transform of derivatives. Go as far as you can with $n = n$; then (and only then) set $n = 0$.

15.9.13 Show that the Laplace transform of the Laguerre polynomial $L_n(at)$ is given by

$$\mathcal{L}\{L_n(at)\} = \dfrac{(s - a)^n}{s^{n+1}}, \qquad s > 0.$$

15.9.14 Show that

$$\mathcal{L}\{E_1(t)\} = \dfrac{1}{s}\ln(s + 1), \qquad s > 0,$$

where

$$E_1(t) = \int_t^\infty \dfrac{e^{-\tau}d\tau}{\tau} = \int_1^\infty \dfrac{e^{-xt}}{x}\,dx.$$

$E_1(t)$ is the exponential-integral function.

15.9.15 (a) Show that

$$\mathcal{L}\left\{\frac{\sin kt}{t}\right\} = \cot^{-1}\left(\frac{s}{k}\right).$$

(b) Using this result (with $k = 1$), prove that

$$\mathcal{L}\{si(t)\} = -\frac{1}{s}\tan^{-1} s,$$

where

$$si(t) = -\int_t^\infty \frac{\sin x}{x}\,dx, \qquad \text{the sine integral.}$$

15.9.16 If $F(t)$ is periodic with a period a so that $F(t + a) = F(t)$ for all $t \geqslant 0$, show that

$$\mathcal{L}\{F(t)\} = \frac{\int_0^a e^{-st} F(t)\,dt,}{1 - e^{-as},}$$

with the integration now over only the *first period* of $F(t)$.

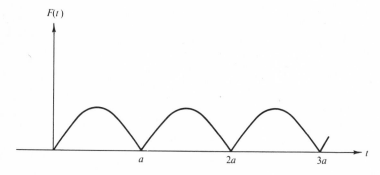

FIG. 15.10   Periodic function

15.10   Convolution or Faltung Theorem

One of the most important properties of the Laplace transform is that given by the convolution or faltung theorem.[1] We take two transforms

$$f_1(s) = \mathcal{L}\{F_1(t)\} \quad \text{and} \quad f_2(s) = \mathcal{L}\{F_2(t)\} \tag{15.173}$$

and multiply them together. To avoid complications when changing variables, the upper limits are held finite.

$$f_1(s) \cdot f_2(s) = \lim_{a \to \infty} \int_0^a e^{-sx} F_1(x)\,dx \int_0^{a-x} e^{-sy} F_2(y)\,dy. \tag{15.174}$$

The upper limits are chosen so that the area of integration, shown in Fig. 15.11a, is the shaded triangle, not the square. This modification is permissible because the two integrands are assumed to decrease exponentially. In the limit $a \to \infty$ the integral over the unshaded triangle will give zero contribution. Substituting

---

[1]An alternate derivation employs the Bromwich integral (Section 15.11). This is Exercise 15.11.7.

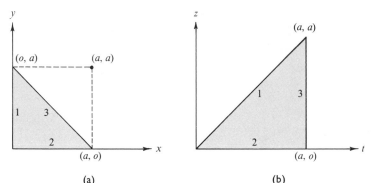

(a)   (b)

FIG. 15.11   Change of variables, (a) xy-plane (b) zt-plane

$x = t - z$, $y = z$ the region of integration is mapped into the triangle shown in Fig. 15.11b. Using Jacobians to transform the element of area, we have

$$dx\,dy = \begin{vmatrix} \dfrac{\partial x}{\partial t} & \dfrac{\partial y}{\partial t} \\[2mm] \dfrac{\partial x}{\partial z} & \dfrac{\partial y}{\partial z} \end{vmatrix} dt\,dz = \begin{vmatrix} 1 & 0 \\[2mm] -1 & 1 \end{vmatrix} dt\,dz \qquad (15.175)$$

or $dx\,dy = dt\,dz$. With this substitution Eq. 15.174 becomes

$$f_1(s) \cdot f_2(s) = \lim_{a \to \infty} \int_0^a e^{-st} \int_0^t F_1(t - z)\,F_2(z)\,dz\,dt$$

$$= \mathscr{L}\left\{ \int_0^t F_1(t - z)\,F_2(z)\,dz \right\}. \qquad (15.176)$$

For convenience this integral is represented by the symbol

$$\int_0^t F_1(t - z)\,F_2(z)\,dz \equiv F_1 * F_2 \qquad (15.177)$$

and referred to as the convolution, closely analogous to the Fourier convolution (Section 15.5). If we substitute $w = t - z$, we find

$$F_1 * F_2 = F_2 * F_1, \qquad (15.178)$$

showing that the relation is symmetric.

Carrying out the inverse transform, we also find

$$\mathscr{L}^{-1}\{f_1(s) \cdot f_2(s)\} = \int_0^t F_1(t - z)\,F_2(z)\,dz. \qquad (15.179)$$

This can be useful in the development of new transforms or as an alternative to a partial fraction expansion. One immediate application is in the solution of integral equations (Chapter 16).

EXAMPLE 15.10.1.   DRIVEN OSCILLATOR WITH DAMPING

As one illustration of the use of the convolution theorem; let us return to the mass m on a spring, with damping and a driving force $F(t)$. The equation of motion (15.112) now becomes

$$m\,X''(t) + b\,X'(t) + k\,X(t) = F(t). \tag{15.180}$$

Initial conditions $X(0) = 0$, $X'(0) = 0$ are used to simplify this illustration, and the transformed equation is

$$ms^2\,x(s) + bs\,x(s) + k\,x(s) = f(s) \tag{15.181}$$

or

$$x(s) = \frac{f(s)}{m} \times \frac{1}{(s + b/2m)^2 + \omega_1^2}, \tag{15.182}$$

where $\omega_1^2 \equiv k/m - b^2/4m^2$, as before.

By the convolution theorem (Eq. 15.176),

$$X(t) = \frac{1}{m\omega_1} \int_0^t F(t - z)e^{-(b/2m)z} \sin \omega_1 z \, dz. \tag{15.183}$$

If the force is impulsive, $F(t) = P\,\delta(t)$,[1]

$$X(t) = \frac{P}{m\omega_1} e^{-(b/2m)t} \sin \omega_1 t. \tag{15.184}$$

P represents the momentum transferred by the impulse and the constant P/m takes the place of an initial velocity $X'(0)$.

If $F(t) = F_0 \sin \omega t$, Eq. 15.183 may be used, but a partial fraction expansion is perhaps more convenient. With

$$f(s) = \frac{F_0\omega}{s^2 + \omega^2}$$

Eq. 15.182 becomes

$$x(s) = \frac{F_0\omega}{m} \times \frac{1}{s^2 + \omega^2} \times \frac{1}{(s + b/2m)^2 + \omega_1^2}$$

$$= \frac{F_0\omega}{m}\left[\frac{a's + b'}{s^2 + \omega^2} + \frac{c's + d'}{(s + b/2m)^2 + \omega_1^2}\right]. \tag{15.185}$$

The coefficients a', b', d', and d' are independent of s. Direct calculation shows

$$a' = \frac{b}{m}\,\omega^2 + \frac{m}{b}\,(\omega_0^2 - \omega^2)^2,$$

$$b' = -\frac{m}{b}\,(\omega_0^2 - \omega^2)\left[\frac{b}{m}\,\omega^2 + \frac{m}{b}\,(\omega_0^2 - \omega^2)^2\right].$$

[1] Note that $\delta(t)$ lies *inside* the interval $[0, t]$.

Since c' and d' will lead to exponentially decreasing terms (transients), they will be discarded here. Carrying out the inverse operation, we find for the steady-state solution

$$X(t) = \frac{F_0}{[b^2\omega^2 + m^2(\omega_0^2 - \omega^2)^2]^{1/2}} \sin(\omega t - \varphi), \qquad (15.186)$$

where

$$\tan \varphi = \frac{b\omega}{m(\omega_0^2 - \omega^2)}.$$

Differentiating the denominator, we find that the amplitude has a maximum when

$$\omega^2 = \omega_0^2 - \frac{b^2}{2m^2} = \omega_1^2 - \frac{b^2}{4m^2}. \qquad (15.187)$$

This is the resonance condition. At resonance the amplitude becomes $F_0/b\omega_1$, showing that the mass m goes into infinite oscillation at resonance if damping is neglected ($b = 0$). It is worth noting that we have had three different characteristic frequencies:

$$\omega_2^2 = \omega_0^2 - \frac{b^2}{2m^2},$$

resonance for forced oscillations, with damping,

$$\omega_1^2 = \omega_2 - \frac{b^2}{4m^2},$$

free oscillation frequency, with damping,

$$\omega_0^2 = \frac{k}{m},$$

free oscillation frequency, no damping. They coincide *only* if the damping is zero.

EXAMPLE 15.10.2. TAUTACHRONE

Another illustration of the convolution theorem is provided by the tautachrone, or equal time, problem, which is related to the famous brachistochrone problem (calculus of variations, Section 17.2). The problem is to determine a curve passing through the origin for which the time required for a particle to slide down the curve to the origin (with no friction) is *independent* of the starting point. The particle starts from rest.

By conservation of energy, kinetic energy gained equals potential energy lost,

$$\frac{1}{2} m \left(\frac{d\lambda}{dt}\right)^2 = mg(y_0 - y), \qquad \left(\frac{d\lambda}{dt} < 0\right), \qquad (15.188)$$

where λ is the distance along the curve from the origin, m is the mass of the particle,

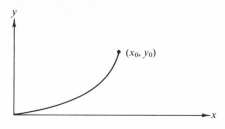

FIG. 15.12   Tautochrone

and g is the acceleration of gravity. Then

$$\frac{-d\lambda}{\sqrt{y_0 - y}} = \sqrt{2g}\, dt. \tag{15.189}$$

Integrating from top to bottom (time $t = 0$ to time $t = T$), we have

$$\sqrt{2g}\, T = -\int_{y=y_0}^{y=0} \frac{d\lambda}{\sqrt{y_0 - y}} = \int_{y=0}^{y=y_0} \frac{d\lambda}{\sqrt{y_0 - y}}. \tag{15.190}$$

The time of descent, T, is to be constant, independent of y_0. Now our path length λ is some function of the height, say $\lambda = F(y)$ and

$$\frac{d\lambda}{dy} = F'(y) = \sqrt{1 + \left(\frac{dx}{dy}\right)^2}. \tag{15.191}$$

Therefore

$$\sqrt{2g}\, T = \int_0^{y_0} (y_0 - y)^{-1/2} \, F'(y) \, dy$$

$$= y^{-1/2} * F'(y), \tag{15.192}$$

by the definition of convolution. Since the transform of the convolution of two functions is the product of the transforms,

$$\sqrt{2g}\, T \frac{1}{s} = \mathscr{L}\{F'(y)\} \cdot \mathscr{L}\{y^{-1/2}\}$$

$$= \mathscr{L}\{F'(y)\} \cdot \sqrt{\frac{\pi}{s}} \tag{15.193}$$

by Eq. 15.91. Note that $(-\frac{1}{2})! = \sqrt{\pi}$. Hence

$$\mathscr{L}\{F'(y)\} = \frac{\sqrt{2g}\, T}{\pi} \sqrt{\frac{\pi}{s}}, \tag{15.194}$$

which may be inverted to give

$$F'(y) = \frac{\sqrt{2g}\, T}{\pi} y^{-1/2}. \tag{15.195}$$

Squaring Eq. 15.191, we obtain

$$1 + \left(\frac{dx}{dy}\right)^2 = \frac{c}{y}, \qquad (15.196)$$

where

$$c = \frac{2gT^2}{\pi^2}.$$

Separation of variables leads to

$$dx = \sqrt{\frac{c - y}{y}}\, dy, \qquad (15.197)$$

which is satisfied by

$$x = \frac{c}{2}(\theta + \sin\theta),$$

$$y = \frac{c}{2}(1 - \cos\theta), \qquad (15.198)$$

the parametric equations for a cycloid passing through the origin.

Figure 15.13 is our tautachrone. This analysis demonstrates that a particle sliding

FIG. 15.13   Tautachrone, cycloidal path

(with no friction) down the curve in the first quadrant, up the reflected curve in the second quadrant, sliding back and forth, would have a period independent of its amplitude. This amplitude independence would also apply to a pendulum whose bob was constrained to follow such a cycloidal path.

EXERCISES

15.10.1 From the convolution theorem show that

$$\frac{1}{s}f(s) = \mathcal{L}\left\{\int_0^t F(x)\, dx\right\}$$

where $f(s) = \mathcal{L}\{F(t)\}$.

15.10.2 If $F(t) = t^a$ and $G(t) = t^b$,

(a) show that the convolution

$$F * G = t^{a+b+1} \int_0^1 y^a (1-y)^b \, dy.$$

(b) By using the convolution theorem show that

$$\int_0^1 y^a (1-y)^b \, dy = \frac{a! \, b!}{(a+b+1)!}.$$

If we replace a by $a - 1$ and b by $b - 1$, this is the Euler formula for the beta function (Chapter 10).

15.10.3 An undamped oscillator is driven by a force $F_0 \sin \omega t$. Find the displacement as a function of time. Notice that it is a linear combination of two simple harmonic motions, one with the frequency of the driving force and one with the frequency ω_0 of the free oscillator. (Assume $X(0) = X'(0) = 0$).

$$Ans. \quad X(t) = \frac{F_0/m}{\omega^2 - \omega_0^2} \left(\frac{\omega}{\omega_0} \sin \omega_0 t - \sin \omega t \right).$$

15.11 Inverse Laplace Transformation

We shall now develop an expression for the inverse Laplace transform, $\mathscr{L}^{-1}$, appearing in the equation

$$F(t) = \mathscr{L}^{-1}\{f(s)\}. \tag{15.199}$$

One approach lies in the Fourier transform for which we know the inverse relation. There is a difficulty, however. Our Fourier transformable function had to satisfy the Dirichlet conditions. In particular, we required that

$$\lim_{\omega \to \infty} G(\omega) = 0. \tag{15.200}$$

Now we wish to treat functions, $F(t)$, that may diverge exponentially. To surmount this difficulty we extract an exponential factor, $e^{\gamma t}$ from our (possibly) divergent Laplace function and write

$$F(t) = e^{\gamma t} G(t). \tag{15.201}$$

If $F(t)$ diverges as $e^{\alpha t}$, we require γ to be greater than α *so that* $G(t)$ *will be convergent*. Now, with $G(t) = 0$ for $t < 0$ and otherwise suitably restricted so that it may be represented by a Fourier integral (Eq. 15.20),

$$G(t) = \frac{1}{2\pi} \int_{-\infty}^{\infty} e^{iut} \, du \int_0^{\infty} G(v) e^{-iuv} \, dv. \tag{15.202}$$

Using Eq. 15.201, we may rewrite (15.202)

$$F(t) = \frac{e^{\gamma t}}{2\pi} \int_{-\infty}^{\infty} e^{iut} \, du \int_0^{\infty} F(v) e^{-\gamma v} e^{-iuv} \, dv. \tag{15.203}$$

Now with the change of variable,

$$s = \gamma + iu, \tag{15.204}$$

the integral over v is thrown into the form of a Laplace transform

$$\int_0^\infty F(v)e^{-sv}\,dv = f(s);$$ (15.205)

s is now a complex variable and R.P. $(s) \geq \gamma$ to guarantee convergence. Notice that the Laplace transform has mapped a function specified on the positive real axis onto the complex plane, R.P.$(s) \geq \gamma$.

With γ as a constant, $ds = i\,du$. Substituting Eq. 15.205 into Eq. 15.203, we obtain

$$F(t) = \frac{1}{2\pi i}\int_{\gamma - i\infty}^{\gamma + i\infty} e^{st}f(s)\,ds.$$ (15.206)

Here is our inverse transform. We have rotated the line of integration through 90° (by using $ds = i\,du$). The path has become an infinite *vertical* line in the complex plane, the constant γ having been chosen so that all the singularities of $f(s)$ are on the left-hand side.

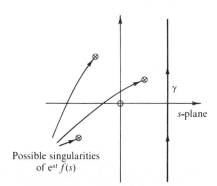

Possible singularities
of $e^{st}f(s)$

FIG. 15.14   Singularities of $e^{st}f(s)$

Bromwich integral.   Equation 15.206, our inverse transformation, is usually known as the Bromwich integral, although sometimes it is referred to as the Fourier-Mellin theorem or Fourier-Mellin integral. This integral may now be evaluated by the regular methods of contour integration (Chapter 7). If $t > 0$, the contour may be closed by an infinite semicircle in the left half plane. Then by the residue theorem (Section 7.2)

$$F(t) = \sum \text{(residues included for R.P.}(s) < \gamma).$$ (15.207)

Possibly this means of evaluation with R.P.(s) ranging through negative values seems paradoxical in view of our previous requirement that R.P.$(s) \geq \gamma$. The paradox disappears when we recall that the requirement R.P.$(s) \geq \gamma$ was imposed to guarantee convergence of the Laplace transform integral that defined $f(s)$. Once $f(s)$ is obtained we may then proceed to exploit its properties as an analytical function in the complex plane wherever we choose. In effect, we are employing analytical continuation to get $\mathscr{L}\{F(t)\}$ in the left half plane exactly as the recurrence relation for the factorial function was used to extend the Euler integral definition (Eq. 10.5) to the left half plane.

Perhaps a pair of examples may clarify the evaluation of Eq. 15.206.

EXAMPLE 15.11.1

If $f(s) = a/(s^2 - a^2)$, then

$$e^{st} f(s) = \frac{ae^{st}}{s^2 - a^2} = \frac{ae^{st}}{(s + a)(s - a)}. \tag{15.208}$$

There is a simple pole at $s = a$, residue $= \frac{1}{2}e^{at}$ and a second pole at $s = -a$, residue $= -\frac{1}{2}e^{-at}$,

$$\sum \text{residues} = \frac{1}{2}(e^{at} - e^{-at}) = \sinh at \tag{15.209}$$

in agreement with Eq. 15.88.

EXAMPLE 15.11.2

If

$$f(s) = \frac{1 - e^{-as}}{s},$$

then we have

$$e^{st}f(s) = \frac{e^{st}}{s} - e^{-as}\left(\frac{e^{st}}{s}\right). \tag{15.210}$$

The first term on the right has a simple pole at $s = 0$, residue $= 1$. Then by Eq. 15.207

$$F_1(t) = \begin{cases} 1, & t > 0, \\ 0, & t < 0. \end{cases} \tag{15.211}$$

Neglecting the minus sign and the e^{-as}, we find that the second term on the right also has a simple pole at $s = 0$, residue $= 1$. Noting the translation property (Eq. 15.147), we have

$$F_2(t) = \begin{cases} 1, & t - a > 0, \\ 0, & t - a < 0. \end{cases} \tag{15.212}$$

Therefore

$$F(t) = F_1(t) - F_2(t) = \begin{cases} 0, & t < 0, \\ 1, & 0 < t < a, \\ 0, & t > a, \end{cases} \tag{15.213}$$

a step function of unit height and length a.

Two general comments may be in order. First, these two examples hardly begin to show the usefulness and power of the Bromwich integral. It is always available for inverting a complicated transform when the tables prove inadequate.

Second, this derivation is not presented as a rigorous one. Rather, it is given more

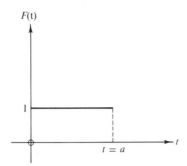

FIG. 15.15   Finite-length step function

as a plausibility argument, though it can be made rigorous. The determination of
the inverse transform is somewhat similar to the solution of a differential equation.
It makes little difference how you get the solution. Guess at it if you want to. The
solution can always be checked by substitiution back into the original differential
equation. Similarly, $F(t)$ can (and, to check on careless errors, should) be checked
by determining whether by Eq. 15.82

$$\mathscr{L}\{F(t)\} = f(s).$$

As a final illustration of the use of the Laplace inverse transform we have some
results from the work of Brillouin and Sommerfeld (1914) in electromagnetic theory.

EXAMPLE 15.11.3.   VELOCITY OF ELECTROMAGNETIC WAVES IN A DISPERSIVE MEDIUM

The group velocity u of traveling waves is related to the phase velocity v by the
equation

$$u = v - \lambda \frac{dv}{d\lambda}. \tag{15.214}$$

Here λ is the wavelength. In the vicinity of an absorption line (resonance) $dv/d\lambda$ may

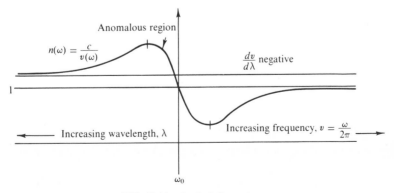

FIG. 15.16   Optical dispersion

be sufficiently negative so that $u > c$. The question immediately arises whether a signal can be transmitted faster than c, the velocity of light in vacuum. This question, which assumes that such a group velocity is meaningful, is of fundamental importance to the theory of special relativity.

We need a solution to the wave equation

$$\frac{\partial^2 \psi}{\partial x^2} = \frac{1}{v^2} \frac{\partial^2 \psi}{\partial t^2} \tag{15.215}$$

corresponding to a harmonic vibration starting at the origin at time zero. Since our medium is dispersive, v is a function of the angular frequency. Imagine, for instance, a plane wave, angular frequency ω, incident on a shutter at the origin. At $t = 0$ the shutter is (instantaneously) opened, and the wave is permitted to advance along the positive x-axis.

Let us then build up a solution starting at $x = 0$. It is convenient to use the **Cauchy** integral

$$\psi(0, t) = \frac{1}{2\pi i} \int_{\gamma - i\infty}^{\gamma + i\infty} \frac{e^{st}}{s + i\omega} \, ds = \begin{cases} 0, & t < 0, \\ e^{-i\omega t}, & t > 0. \end{cases} \tag{15.216}$$

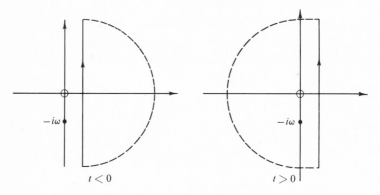

$t < 0$ $t > 0$

FIG. 15.17   Possible closed contours

That this is just the Bromwich integral may be verified by noting that

$$F(t) = \begin{cases} 0, & t < 0, \\ e^{-i\omega t}, & t > 0, \end{cases} \tag{15.217}$$

and applying the Laplace transform. The transformed function $f(s)$ becomes

$$f(s) = \frac{1}{s + i\omega}. \tag{15.218}$$

Our Cauchy-Bromwich integral provides us with the time-dependence of a signal leaving the origin at $t = 0$. To include the space-dependence we note that

$$e^{s(t - x/v)}$$

satisfies the wave equation. With this as a clue, we replace t by $t - x/v$ and write a solution

$$\psi(x, t) = \frac{1}{2\pi i} \int_{\gamma - i\infty}^{\gamma + i\infty} \frac{e^{s(t - x/v)}}{s + i\omega} \, ds. \tag{15.219}$$

It was seen in the derivation of the Bromwich integral that our variable s replaces the ω of the Fourier transformation. Hence the wave velocity v becomes a function of s, that is, $v(s)$. Its particular form need not concern us here. We need only the property

$$\lim_{|s| \to \infty} v(s) = \text{constant}, \, c. \tag{15.220}$$

This is suggested by the asymptotic behavior of the curve on the right side of Fig. 15.16.[1]

Evaluating Eq. 15.219 by the calculus of residues, we may close the path of integration by a semicircle in the *right* half plane, provided

$$t - \frac{x}{c} < 0.$$

Hence

$$\psi(x, t) = 0, \qquad t - \frac{x}{c} < 0, \tag{15.221}$$

which means that the velocity of our signal cannot exceed the velocity of light in vacuum c. This simple but very significant result was extended by Sommerfeld and Brillouin to show just how the wave advanced in the dispersive medium.

EXERCISES

15.11.1 Find

$$\mathscr{L}^{-1}\left\{\frac{s}{s^2 - k^2}\right\}$$

(a) by a partial fraction expansion,
(b) repeat, using the Bromwich integral.

15.11.2 Find

$$\mathscr{L}^{-1}\left\{\frac{k^2}{s(s^2 + k^2)}\right\}$$

(a) by using a partial fraction expansion,
(b) repeat using the convolution theorem,
(c) repeat using the Bromwich integral.

Ans. $F(t) = 1 - \cos kt$.

15.11.3 Use the Bromwich integral to find the function whose transform is $f(s) = s^{-1/2}$. Note that $f(s)$ has a branch point as $s = 0$. The negative x-axis may be taken as a cut line.

Ans. $F(t) = (\pi t)^{-1/2}$.

[1] Equation 15.220 follows rigorously from the theory of anomalous dispersion.

15.11.4 Show that

$$\mathscr{L}^{-1}\{(s^2 + 1)^{-1/2}\} = J_0(t)$$

by evaluation of the Bromwich integral.

FIG. 15.18   A possible contour for the inversion of $J_0(t)$

15.11.5 Evaluate the inverse Laplace transform

(a) $\mathscr{L}^{-1}\{(s^2 - a^2)^{-1/2}\} = I_0(at)$

(b) $\mathscr{L}^{-1}\left\{\dfrac{(s - \sqrt{s^2 - a^2})^\nu \cdot}{\sqrt{s^2 - a^2}}\right\} = a^\nu\, I_\nu(at), \qquad \nu > -1.$

15.11.6 Show that

$$\mathscr{L}^{-1}\left\{\frac{\ln s}{s}\right\} = -\ln t - C,$$

where $C = 0.5772, \cdots$, the Euler-Mascheroni constant.

15.11.7 Derive the Laplace transformation convolution theorem by use of the Bromwich integral.

15.11.8 Derive the Bromwich integral from Cauchy's integral formula. *Hint.* Apply the inverse transform $\mathscr{L}^{-1}$ to

$$f(s) = \frac{1}{2\pi i}\,\lim_{\alpha \to \infty}\int_{\gamma - i\alpha}^{\gamma + i\alpha}\frac{f(z)}{s - z}\,dz,$$

where $f(z)$ is analytic for R.P.$(z) \geqslant \gamma$.

15.11.9 Starting with

$$\frac{1}{2\pi i}\int_{\gamma - i\infty}^{\gamma + i\infty} e^{st} f(s)\, ds,$$

show that by introducing

$$f(s) = \int_0^\infty e^{-sz}\, F(z)\, dz$$

we can convert one integral into the Fourier representation of a Dirac delta function. From this derive the inverse Laplace transform.

TABLE 15.1

Laplace Transform Operations

	Operations		Equation
1.	Laplace transform	$f(s) = \mathscr{L}\{F(t)\} = \int_0^\infty e^{-st} F(t)\, dt$	(15.82)
2.	Transform of derivative	$s f(s) - F(+0) = \mathscr{L}\{F'(t)\}$	(15.106)
		$s^2 f(s) - s F(+0) - F'(+0) = \mathscr{L}\{F''(t)\}$	
3.	Transform of integral	$\dfrac{1}{s} f(s) = \mathscr{L}\left\{\int_0^t F(x)\, dx\right\}$	(Exercise 15.10.1)
4.	Substitution	$f(s-a) = \mathscr{L}\{e^{at} F(t)\}$	(15.135)
5.	Translation	$e^{-bs} f(s) = \mathscr{L}\{F(t-b)\}$	(15.147)
6.	Derivative of transform	$f^{(n)}(s) = \mathscr{L}\{(-t)^n F(t)\}$	(15.156)
7.	Integral of transform	$\int_s^\infty f(x)\, dx = \mathscr{L}\left\{\dfrac{F(t)}{t}\right\}$	(15.172)
8.	Convolution	$f_1(s) \cdot f_2(s) = \mathscr{L}\left\{\int_0^t F_1(t-z) F_2(z)\, dz\right\}$	(15.176)
9.	Inverse transform, Bromwich integral	$\dfrac{1}{2\pi i} \int_{\gamma - i\infty}^{\gamma + i\infty} e^{st} f(s)\, ds = F(t)$	(15.206)

TABLE 15.2

Laplace Transforms

	$f(s)$	$F(t)$	Limitation	Equation
1.	1	$\delta(t)$	Singularity at $+0$	(15.124)
2.	$\dfrac{1}{s}$	1	$s > 0$	(15.85)
3.	$\dfrac{n!}{s^{n+1}}$	t^n	$s > 0$ $n > -1$	(15.91)
4.	$\dfrac{1}{s-k}$	e^{kt}	$s > k$	(15.86)
5.	$\dfrac{1}{(s-k)^2}$	te^{kt}	$s > k$	(15.158)
6.	$\dfrac{s}{s^2-k^2}$	$\cosh kt$	$s > k$	(15.88)
7.	$\dfrac{k}{s^2-k^2}$	$\sinh kt$	$s > k$	(15.88)

	$f(s)$	$F(t)$	Limitation	Equation
8.	$\dfrac{s}{s^2 + k^2}$	$\cos kt$	$s > 0$	(15.90)
9.	$\dfrac{k}{s^2 + k^2}$	$\sin kt$	$s > 0$	(15.90)
10.	$\dfrac{s - a}{(s - a)^2 + k^2}$	$e^{at} \cos kt$	$s > a$	(15.136)
11.	$\dfrac{k}{(s - a)^2 + k^2}$	$e^{at} \sin kt$	$s > a$	(15.136)
12.	$(s^2 + a^2)^{-1/2}$	$J_0(at)$	$s > 0$	(15.168)
13.	$(s^2 - a^2)^{-1/2}$	$I_0(at)$	$s > a$	(Exercise 15.9.8)
14.	$\dfrac{1}{a} \cot^{-1}\left(\dfrac{s}{a}\right)$	$j_0(at)$	$s > 0$	(Exercise 15.9.10)
15.	$\left.\begin{array}{l} \dfrac{1}{2a} \ln \dfrac{s+a}{s-a} \\[2mm] \dfrac{1}{a} \coth^{-1}\left(\dfrac{s}{a}\right) \end{array}\right\}$	$i_0(at)$	$s > a$	(Exercise 15.9.10)
16.	$\dfrac{(s - a)^n}{s^{n+1}}$	$L_n(at)$	$s > 0$	(Exercise 15.9.13)
17.	$\dfrac{1}{s} \ln (s + 1)$	$E_1(x) = -Ei(-x)$	$s > 0$	(Exercise 15.9.14)
18.	$\dfrac{\ln s}{s}$	$-\ln t - C$	$s > 0$	(Exercise 15.11.6)

A more extensive table of Laplace transforms appears in Chapter 29 of AMS–55.

REFERENCES

CARSLAW H. S., and J. C. JAEGER, *Operational Methods in Applied Mathematics*. 2nd Ed. Oxford: Oxford University Press (1947). Here the Laplace transform is developed and applied to a wide variety of fields in physics and engineering.

ERDELYI, A., Ed., *Tables of Integral Transforms*, Volumes I and II. Bateman Manuscript Project. New York: McGraw-Hill. Volume I: *Fourier, Laplace, Mellin Transforms*. Volume II: *Hankel Transforms and Special Functions*. An encyclopedic compilation of transforms, special functions, and their properties. Useful primarily as a reference.

JEFFREYS, H., and B. S. JEFFREYS, *Methods of Mathematical Physics*. 2nd Ed. Cambridge: Cambridge University Press (1950).

LePage, W. R., *Complex Variables and the Laplace Transform for Engineers*. New York: McGraw-Hill (1961). Complex variable analysis is carefully developed and then applied to Fourier and Laplace transforms. Written to be read by students, but intended for the serious student.

Scott, E. J., *Transform Calculus with an Introduction to Complex Variables*. New York: Harper (1955). The primary emphasis is on the Laplace transform. Complex variable contour integration is developed and used extensively.

Sneddon, I. N., *Fourier Transforms*. New York: McGraw-Hill (1951). A detailed comprehensive treatment, loaded with applications to a wide variety of fields of modern and classical physics.

Titchmarsh, E. C., *Introduction to the Theory of Fourier Integrals*. Oxford: Oxford University Press (1948). Comprehensive treatment of Fourier integrals and related integral transforms.

Tranter, C. J., *Integral Transforms in Mathematical Physics*. 2nd Ed. London: Methuen, New York: Wiley (1951) A short, concise, but useful work covering Laplace, Fourier, Hankel, and Mellin transforms and their inverses.

Van der Pol, B., and H. Bremmer, *Operational Calculus Based on the Two-sided Laplace Integral*. 2nd Ed. Cambridge: Cambridge University Press (1955). Here is a development based on the integral range $-\infty$ to $+\infty$, rather than the usual 0 to $+\infty$. Chapter V contains a detailed study of the Dirac delta function (impulse function).

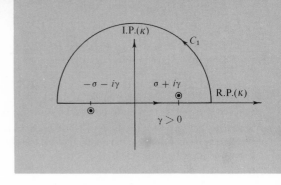

$$\text{I.P.}(\kappa)$$

$$C_1$$

$$-\sigma - i\gamma \qquad \sigma + i\gamma$$

$$\text{R.P.}(\kappa)$$

$$\gamma > 0$$

CHAPTER 16

INTEGRAL EQUATIONS

16.1 Introduction

With the exception of the integral transforms of the last chapter, we have been considering equations with relations between the unknown function $\varphi(x)$ and one or more of its derivatives. We now proceed to investigate equations containing the unknown function within an integral. These equations are classified in two ways:

1. If the limits of integration are fixed, we shall call the equation a Fredholm equation; if one limit is variable, it is a Volterra equation.

2. If the unknown function appears *only* under the integral sign, we shall label it " first kind." If it appears both inside and outside the integral, it will be labeled, " second kind."

Definitions.   Symbolically we have
Fredholm equation of the first kind:

$$f(x) = \int_a^b K(x, t)\, \varphi(t)\, dt. \qquad (16.1)$$

Fredholm equation of the second kind:

$$\varphi(x) = f(x) + \lambda \int_a^b K(x, t)\, \varphi(t)\, dt. \qquad (16.2)$$

Volterra equation of the first kind:

$$f(x) = \int_a^x K(x, t)\, \varphi(t)\, dt. \qquad (16.3)$$

Volterra equation of the second kind:

$$\varphi(x) = f(x) + \int_a^x K(x, t)\, \varphi(t)\, dt. \qquad (16.4)$$

576

In all four cases $\varphi(t)$ is the unknown function. $K(x, t)$, which we call the kernel, and $f(x)$ are assumed to be known. When $f(x) = 0$, the equation is said to be homogeneous.

The reader may wonder, with some justification, why we bother about integral equations. After all, the differential equations have done a rather good job of describing our physical world so far. There are two reasons for introducing integral equations here.

First, we have placed considerable emphasis on the solution of differential equations *subject to particular boundary conditions*. For instance, the boundary condition at $r = 0$ determines whether the Neumann function $N_n(r)$ is present when Bessel's equation is solved. The boundary condition for $r \to \infty$ determines whether the $I_n(r)$ is present in our solution of the modified Bessel equation. The integral equation relates the unknown function not only to its values at neighboring points (derivatives) but also to its values throughout a region, including the boundary. In a very real sense the boundary conditions are built into the integral equation rather than imposed at the final stage of the solution. It will be seen later, when we construct kernels (Section 16.5), that the form of the kernel depends on the values on the boundary. The integral equation, then, is compact and may turn out to be a more convenient or more powerful form than the differential equation. Second, whether we like it or not, there are some problems, such as some diffusion and transport phenomena, that cannot be represented by differential equations. If we wish to solve such problems, we are forced to handle integral equations. A most important example of this sort of physical situation follows.

EXAMPLE 16.1.1. NEUTRON TRANSPORT THEORY—BOLTZMANN EQUATION

The fundamental equation of neutron transport theory is an expression of the equation of continuity for neutrons:

$$\text{production} = \text{losses} + \text{leakage}.$$

Under production we have sources

$$S(v, \mathbf{\Omega}, \mathbf{r})dv \, d\Omega$$

representing the introduction of S neutrons per cubic centimeter per second with *speeds* between v and $v + dv$ and direction of motion $\mathbf{\Omega}$ within a solid angle $d\Omega$.

An additional source is provided by scattering collisions that *scatter* neutrons into the ranges just listed. The rate of scattering is given by

$$\sum_s (v, v', \mathbf{\Omega}, \mathbf{\Omega}') \, \varphi(v', \mathbf{\Omega}', \mathbf{r}),$$

where $\sum_s$ is the (macroscopic) probability that a neutron of speed v', direction $\mathbf{\Omega}'$, will be scattered with resultant speed v, direction $\mathbf{\Omega}$. The quantity $\varphi(v', \mathbf{\Omega}', \mathbf{r})$ is the neutron flux. Expressed as a vector, $\mathbf{\varphi} = \mathbf{\Omega}\varphi$ has the direction of the neutron velocity and a magnitude equal to the number of neutrons per second of speed v crossing a unit area at position $\mathbf{r}$ and in a direction $\mathbf{\Omega}$ (Fig. 16.1).

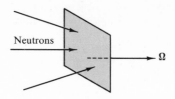

FIG. 16.1   Neutron flux

Integrating over available initial speeds (v') and over all directions $(\mathbf{\Omega}')$, we obtain

$$\iint \sum_s (v, v', \mathbf{\Omega}, \mathbf{\Omega}') \, \varphi(v', \mathbf{\Omega}', \mathbf{r}) \, dv' \, d\mathbf{\Omega}'$$

for the second production term.

Losses come from leakage given by

$$\mathbf{\nabla} \cdot \mathbf{\varphi}(v, \mathbf{\Omega}, \mathbf{r})$$

and from absorption and scattering into another (lower) velocity range. These are

$$\left[\sum_a (v) + \sum_s (v) \right] \varphi(v, \mathbf{\Omega}, \mathbf{r}).$$

If the medium is not homogeneous and isotropic, the $\sum$'s may have position- and direction-dependence in addition to the indicated speed or energy dependence.

Our equation of continuity finally becomes

$$\iint \sum_a (v, v', \mathbf{\Omega}, \mathbf{\Omega}') \, \varphi(v', \mathbf{\Omega}', \mathbf{r}) \, dv' \, d\mathbf{\Omega}' + S(v, \mathbf{\Omega}, \mathbf{r})$$

$$= \mathbf{\nabla} \cdot \mathbf{\varphi}(v, \mathbf{\Omega}, \mathbf{r}) + \left[\sum_a (v) + \sum_s (v) \right] \varphi(v, \mathbf{\Omega}, \mathbf{r}). \qquad (16.5)$$

This is the steady-state Boltzmann equation, an integro-differential equation. In this form the Boltzmann equation is almost impossible to handle. Most of neutron transport theory is a development of methods that are compromises between physical accuracy and mathematical feasibility.[1]

An integral equation may also appear as a matter of deliberate choice based on convenience or the need for the mathematical power of an integral equation formulation.

EXAMPLE 16.1.2.   MOMENTUM REPRESENTATION IN QUANTUM MECHANICS

The Schrödinger equation (in ordinary space representation) is

$$-\frac{\hbar^2}{2m} \mathbf{\nabla}^2 \, \psi(\mathbf{r}) + V(\mathbf{r}) \, \psi(\mathbf{r}) = E \, \psi(\mathbf{r}) \qquad (16.6)$$

[1] Cf. *Reactor Handbook*, 2nd Ed., Vol. III, Part A, *Physics*. H. Soodak, Ed. New York: Interscience Publishers (1962). Cf. Chapter 3.

or

$$(-\nabla^2 + a^2)\,\psi(\mathbf{r}) = v(\mathbf{r})\,\psi(\mathbf{r}) \tag{16.7}$$

where

$$a^2 = -\frac{2m}{\hbar^2}\,E,$$

$$v(\mathbf{r}) = -\frac{2m}{\hbar^2}\,V(\mathbf{r}).$$

We may generalize Eq. 16.7 to

$$(-\nabla^2 + a^2)\,\psi(\mathbf{r}) = \int v(\mathbf{r}, \mathbf{r}')\,\psi(\mathbf{r}')\,d\mathbf{r}'. \tag{16.8}$$

For the special case of

$$v(\mathbf{r}, \mathbf{r}') = v(\mathbf{r}')\,\delta(\mathbf{r} - \mathbf{r}'), \tag{16.9}$$

which represents local interaction Eq. 16.8 reduces to Eq. 16.7. Equation 16.8 is now subjected to the Fourier transform (cf. Section 15.6).

$$\Phi(\mathbf{k}) = \frac{1}{(2\pi)^{3/2}} \int \psi(\mathbf{r})e^{-i\mathbf{k}\cdot\mathbf{r}}\,d\mathbf{r} \tag{16.10}$$

$$\psi(\mathbf{r}) = \frac{1}{(2\pi)^{3/2}} \int \Phi(\mathbf{k})e^{i\mathbf{k}\cdot\mathbf{r}}\,d\mathbf{k}.$$

Here, the abbreviation

$$\frac{p}{\hbar} = k \quad (2\pi \times \text{wave number}) \tag{16.11}$$

has been introduced. Developing Eq. 16.10, we obtain

$$\int (-\nabla^2 + a^2)\,\psi(\mathbf{r})e^{-i\mathbf{k}\cdot\mathbf{r}}\,d\mathbf{r} = \iint v(\mathbf{r}, \mathbf{r}')\,\psi(\mathbf{r}')e^{-i\mathbf{k}\cdot\mathbf{r}}\,d\mathbf{r}'\,d\mathbf{r}. \tag{16.12}$$

Note that the ∇^2 on the left operates only on the $\psi(\mathbf{r})$. Integrating the left-hand side by parts and substituting Eq. 16.10 for $\psi(\mathbf{r}')$ on the right.

$$\int (k^2 + a^2)\,\psi(\mathbf{r})e^{-i\mathbf{k}\cdot\mathbf{r}}\,d\mathbf{r} = (2\pi)^{3/2}(k^2 + a^2)\,\Phi(\mathbf{k})$$

$$= \frac{1}{(2\pi)^{3/2}} \iiint v(\mathbf{r}, \mathbf{r}')\,\Phi(\mathbf{k}')e^{-i(\mathbf{k}\cdot\mathbf{r}-\mathbf{k}'\cdot\mathbf{r}')}\,d\mathbf{r}'\,d\mathbf{r}\,d\mathbf{k}'. \tag{16.13}$$

If we use

$$f(\mathbf{k}, \mathbf{k}') = \frac{1}{(2\pi)^3} \iint v(\mathbf{r}, \mathbf{r}')e^{-i(\mathbf{k}\cdot\mathbf{r}-\mathbf{k}'\cdot\mathbf{r}')}\,d\mathbf{r}'\,d\mathbf{r}, \tag{16.14}$$

Eq. 16.13 becomes

$$(k^2 + a^2)\,\Phi(\mathbf{k}) = \int f(\mathbf{k}, \mathbf{k}')\,\Phi(\mathbf{k}')\,d\mathbf{k}', \tag{16.15}$$

a homogeneous Fredholm equation of the second kind in which the parameter a^2 corresponds to the eigenvalue.

For our special but important case of local interaction, application of Eq. 16.9 leads to

$$f(\mathbf{k}, \mathbf{k}') = f(\mathbf{k} - \mathbf{k}'). \tag{16.16}$$

This is our momentum representation equivalent to an ordinary static interaction potential in ordinary space. Our momentum function $\Phi(\mathbf{k})$ satisfies the integral equation (Eq. 16.15). It must be emphasized that all through here we have assumed that the required Fourier integrals exist. For a linear oscillator potential, $V(\mathbf{r}) = r^2$, the required integrals would not exist. Equation 16.10 would lead to divergent oscillations and we would have no Eq. 16.15.

Often we find that we have a choice. The physical problem may be represented by a differential or an integral equation. Let us assume that we have the differential equation and wish to transform it into an integral equation. Starting with a *linear* second-order differential equation

$$y'' + A(x)y' + B(x)y = g(x) \tag{16.17}$$

with initial conditions

$$y(a) = y_0,$$
$$y'(a) = y'_0,$$

we integrate to obtain

$$y' = -\int_a^x Ay' \, dx - \int_a^x By \, dx + \int_a^x g \, dx + y'_0. \tag{16.18}$$

Integrating the first integral on the right by parts yields

$$y' = -Ay - \int_a^x (B - A')y \, dx + \int_a^x g \, dx + A(a)y_0 + y'_0. \tag{16.19}$$

Notice how the initial conditions are being absorbed into our new version. Integrating a second time, we obtain

$$y = -\int_a^x Ay \, dx - \int_a^x \int_a^x [B(t) - A'(t)]y(t) \, dt \, dx$$

$$+ \int_a^x \int_a^x g(t) \, dt \, dx + [A(a)y_0 + y'_0](x - a) + y_0. \tag{16.20}$$

To transform this equation into a neater form, we use the relation

$$\int_a^x \int_a^x f(t) \, dt \, dx = \int_a^x (x - t) f(t) \, dt. \tag{16.21}$$

This may be verified by differentiating both sides. Since the derivatives are equal, the original expressions can differ only by a constant. Letting $x \to a$, the constant vanishes and Eq. 16.21 is established. Applying it to Eq. 16.20

$$y(x) = -\int_a^x \{A(t) + (x - t)[B(t) - A'(t)]\} \, y(t) \, dt$$

$$+ \int_a^x (x - t) g(t) \, dt + [A(a)y_0 + y'_0](x - a) + y_0. \tag{16.22}$$

If we now introduce the abbreviations

$$K(x, t) = (t - x)[B(t) - A'(t)] - A(t),$$

$$f(x) = \int_a^x (x - t) g(t) \, dt + [A(ay_0 + y_0')](x - a) + y_0,$$

(16.23)

Eq. 16.22 becomes

$$y(x) = f(x) + \int_a^x K(x, t) \, y(t) \, dt,$$

(16.24)

which is a Volterra equation of the second kind.

EXAMPLE 16.1.3

As a simple illustration consider the linear oscillator equation

$$y'' + \omega^2 y = 0$$

(16.25)

with

$$y(0) = 0$$

$$y'(0) = 1.$$

This yields

$$A(x) = 0,$$

$$B(x) = \omega^2,$$

$$g(x) = 0,$$

and our integral equation becomes

$$y(x) = x + \omega^2 \int_0^x (t - x) y(t) \, dt$$

(16.26)

The reader may show that this is indeed satisfied by $y(x) = (1/\omega) \sin \omega x$.

Let us reconsider the linear oscillator equation (16.25) but now with the boundary conditions

$$y(0) = 0,$$

$$y(b) = 0.$$

Since $y'(0)$ is not given, we must modify the procedure. The first integration gives

$$y' = -\omega^2 \int_0^x y \, dx + y'(0).$$

(16.27)

Integrating a second time and again using Eq. 16.21, we have

$$y = -\omega^2 \int_0^x (x - t) y(t) \, dt + y'(0) x.$$

(16.28)

We now impose the condition $y(b) = 0$. This gives

$$\omega^2 \int_0^b (b - t) \, y(t) \, dt = by'(0).$$

(16.29)

Substituting this back into Eq. 16.28, we obtain

$$y(x) = -\omega^2 \int_0^x (x - t)\, y(t)\, dt + \omega^2 \frac{x}{b} \int_0^b (b - t)y(t)\, dt. \tag{16.30}$$

Now let us break the interval $[0, b]$ into two intervals $[0, x]$ and $[x, b]$. Since

$$\frac{x}{b}(b - t) - (x - t) = \frac{t}{b}(b - x), \tag{16.31}$$

we find

$$y(x) = \omega^2 \int_0^x \frac{t}{b}(b - x)\, y(t)\, dt + \omega^2 \int_x^b \frac{x}{b}(b - t)\, y(t)\, dt. \tag{16.32}$$

Finally, if we define a kernel

$$K(x, t) = \begin{cases} \dfrac{t}{b}(b - x), & t < x, \\[2mm] \dfrac{x}{b}(b - t), & x < t, \end{cases} \tag{16.33}$$

we have

$$y(x) = \omega^2 \int_0^b K(x, t)\, y(t)\, dt, \tag{16.34}$$

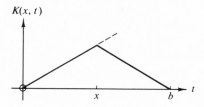

$K(x, t)$

FIG. 16.2

a homogeneous Fredholm equation of the second kind.

Our new kernel, $K(x, t)$, has some interesting properties.

1. It is symmetric, $K(x, t) = K(t, x)$.
2. It is continuous in the sense that

$$\left. \frac{t}{b}(b - x) \right|_{t = x} = \left. \frac{x}{b}(b - t) \right|_{t = x}$$

3. Its derivative with respect to t is *discontinuous*. As t increases through the point $t = x$, there is a discontinuity of -1 in $\partial K(x, t)/\partial t$.

We shall return to these properties in Section 16.5 in which we identify $K(x, t)$ as a **Green's** function.

EXERCISES

16.1.1 Derive the Volterra integral equation corresponding to

(a) $y''(x) - y(x) = 0$; $y(0) = 0$, $y'(0) = 1$.

$$\textit{Ans.}\ y = \int_0^x (x - t)y(t)dt + x.$$

(b) $y''(x) - y(x) = 0$; $y(0) = 1$, $y'(0) = -1$.

$$\textit{Ans.}\ y = \int_0^x (x - t)y(t)dt - x + 1.$$

16.1.2 Derive a Fredholm integral equation corresponding to

$$y''(x) - y(x) = 0; \quad y(1) = 1,$$
$$y(-1) = 1,$$

(a) by integrating twice,   (b) by forming the Green's function.

$$\textit{Ans.}\quad y(x) = 1 - \int_{-1}^1 K(x, t)y(t)dt,$$
$$K(x, t) = \begin{cases} \tfrac{1}{2}(1 - t)(x + 1), & x < t, \\ \tfrac{1}{2}(1 - x)(t + 1), & x > t. \end{cases}$$

16.1.3 The general second-order linear differential equation with constant coefficients is

$$y''(x) + a_1 y'(x) + a_2 y(x) = 0.$$

Given the boundary conditions

$$y(0) = y(1) = 0,$$

integrate twice and develop the integral equation

$$y(x) = \int_0^1 K(x, t) y(t) dt$$

with

$$K(x, t) = \begin{cases} a_2 t(1 - x) + a_1(x - 1), & t < x, \\ a_2 x(1 - t) + a_1 x, & x < t. \end{cases}$$

Note that $K(x, t)$ is symmetric and continuous if $a_1 = 0$. How is this related to self-adjointness of the differential equation?

16.2 Integral Transforms, Generating Functions

Although there is no general method available for inverting integral equations, certain special cases may be treated with our *integral transforms* (Chapter 15.) For convenience, these are listed here. If

$$\psi(x) = \frac{1}{\sqrt{2\pi}} \int_{-\infty}^{\infty} e^{ixt} \varphi(t) \, dt,$$

then

$$\varphi(x) = \frac{1}{\sqrt{2\pi}} \int_{-\infty}^{\infty} e^{-ixt} \psi(t) \, dt \quad \text{(Fourier).} \tag{16.35}$$

If

$$\psi(x) = \int_0^\infty e^{-xt}\, \varphi(t)\, dt,$$

then

$$\varphi(x) = \frac{1}{2\pi i} \int_{\gamma - i\infty}^{\gamma + i\infty} e^{xt}\, \psi(t)\, dt \qquad \text{(Laplace)}. \qquad (16.36)$$

If

$$\psi(x) = \int_0^\infty t^{x-1}\, \varphi(t)\, dt.$$

then

$$\varphi(x) = \frac{1}{2\pi i} \int_{\gamma - i\infty}^{\gamma + i\infty} x^{-t}\, \psi(t)\, dt \qquad \text{(Mellin)}. \qquad (16.37)$$

If

$$\psi(x) = \int_0^\infty t\, \varphi(t)\, J_\nu(xt)\, dt,$$

then

$$\varphi(x) = \int_0^\infty t\, \psi(t)\, J_\nu(xt)\, dt \qquad \text{(Hankel)}. \qquad (16.38)$$

Actually, the usefulness of the integral transform technique extends a bit beyond these four rather specialized forms.

EXAMPLE 16.2.1.   FOURIER TRANSFORM SOLUTION

Let us consider a Fredholm equation of the first kind with a kernel of the general type $k(x - t)$:

$$f(x) = \int_{-\infty}^\infty k(x - t)\, \varphi(t)\, dt, \qquad (16.39)$$

in which $\varphi(t)$ is our unknown function. *Assuming that the needed transforms exist,* we apply the Fourier convolution theorem (Section 15.5) to obtain

$$f(x) = \int_{-\infty}^\infty K(t)\, \Phi(t) e^{-ixt}\, dt. \qquad (16.40)$$

The functions $K(t)$ and $\Phi(t)$ are the Fourier transforms of $k(x)$ and $\varphi(x)$, respectively. Inverting, by Eq. 16.35, we have

$$K(t)\, \Phi(t) = \frac{t}{2\pi} \int_{-\infty}^\infty f(x) e^{ixt}\, dx = \frac{F(t)}{\sqrt{2\pi}}. \qquad (16.41)$$

Then

$$\Phi(t) = \frac{1}{\sqrt{2\pi}} \cdot \frac{F(t)}{K(t)}, \qquad (16.42)$$

and again inverting we have

$$\varphi(x) = \frac{1}{2\pi} \int_{-\infty}^\infty \frac{F(t)}{K(t)} e^{-ixt}\, dt. \qquad (16.43)$$

For a rigorous justification of this result the reader is invited to follow Morse and

Feshbach across complex planes. An extension of this transformation solution appears as Exercise 16.2.1.

EXAMPLE 16.2.2. GENERALIZED ABEL EQUATION, CONVOLUTION THEOREM

In Section 15.10 Laplace transforms were used to solve the integral equation of the tautachrone problem. Generalizing slightly, we write the integral equation as

$$f(x) = \int_0^x \frac{\varphi(t)}{(x-t)^\alpha}\, dt, \qquad 0 < \alpha < 1. \tag{16.44}$$

Taking the Laplace transform of both sides of this equation, we obtain

$$\mathcal{L}\{f(x)\} = \mathcal{L}\left\{\int_0^x \frac{\varphi(t)}{(x-t)^\alpha}\, dt\right\}$$
$$= \mathcal{L}\{x^{-\alpha}\}\mathcal{L}\{\varphi(x)\}, \tag{16.45}$$

the last step following by the Laplace convolution theorem (Section 15.10). Then

$$\mathcal{L}\{\varphi(x)\} = \frac{s^{1-\alpha}\mathcal{L}\{f(x)\}}{(-\alpha)!}. \tag{16.46}$$

Dividing by s, we obtain

$$\frac{1}{s}\mathcal{L}\{\varphi(x)\} = \frac{s^{-\alpha}\mathcal{L}\{f(x)\}}{(-\alpha)!}$$
$$= \frac{\mathcal{L}\{x^{\alpha-1}\}\mathcal{L}\{f(x)\}}{(\alpha-1)!(-\alpha)!}. \tag{16.47}$$

Combining the factorials (Eq. 10.32), and applying the Laplace convolution theorem again, we discover that

$$\frac{1}{s}\mathcal{L}\{\varphi(x)\} = \frac{\sin \pi\alpha}{\pi} \mathcal{L}\left\{\int_0^x \frac{f(t)}{(x-t)^{1-\alpha}}\, dt\right\}. \tag{16.48}$$

Inverting with the aid of equation (15.179), we get

$$\int_0^x \varphi(t)\, dt = \frac{\sin \pi\alpha}{\pi} \int_0^x \frac{f(t)}{(x-t)^{1-\alpha}}\, dt, \tag{16.49}$$

and finally, by differentiating,

$$\varphi(x) = \frac{\sin \pi\alpha}{\pi} \frac{d}{dx} \int_0^x \frac{f(t)}{(x-t)^{1-\alpha}}\, dt. \tag{16.50}$$

Our solution of Abel's equation in Chapter 15 is a special case ($\alpha = \frac{1}{2}$).

Generating functions. Occasionally, the reader may encounter integral equations that involve generating functions. Suppose we have the admittedly special case

$$f(x) = \int_{-1}^1 \frac{\varphi(t)}{(1 - 2xt - x^2)^{1/2}}\, dt, \qquad -1 \leqslant x \leqslant 1. \tag{16.51}$$

We notice two important features:

1. $(1 - 2xt + x^2)^{-1/2}$ generates the Legendre polynomials.
2. $[-1, 1]$ is the orthogonal interval for the Legendre polynomials.

If we now expand the denominator (property 1) and assume that our unknown $\varphi(t)$ may be written as a series of these same Legendre polynomials,

$$f(x) = \int_{-1}^{1} \sum_{n=0}^{\infty} a_n P_n(t) \sum_{r=0}^{\infty} P_r(t) x^r \, dt \tag{16.52}$$

by utilizing the orthogonality of the Legendre polynomials (property 2),

$$f(x) = \sum_{r=0}^{\infty} \frac{2a_r}{2r + 1} x^r. \tag{16.53}$$

We may identify the a_n's by differentiating n times and then setting $x = 0$.

$$f^{(n)}(0) = n! \frac{2}{2n + 1} a_n. \tag{16.54}$$

Hence,

$$\varphi(t) = \sum_{n=0}^{\infty} \frac{2n + 1}{2} \frac{f^{(n)}(0)}{n!} P_n(t). \tag{16.55}$$

Similar results may be obtained with the other generating functions (cf. Exercise 16.2.5).

EXERCISES

16.2.1 The kernel of a Fredholm equation of the second kind,

$$\varphi(x) = f(x) + \lambda \int_{-\infty}^{\infty} K(x, t) \varphi(t) \, dt,$$

is of the form $k(x - t)$.[1] Asssuming that the required transforms exist, show that

$$\varphi(x) = \frac{1}{\sqrt{2\pi}} \int_{-\infty}^{\infty} \frac{F(t) e^{-ixt}}{1 - \sqrt{2\pi} \, \lambda \, K(t)};$$

$F(t)$ and $K(t)$ are the Fourier transforms of $f(x)$ and $k(x)$, respectively.

16.2.2 The kernel of a Volterra equation of the first kind,

$$f(x) = \int_{0}^{x} K(x, t) \varphi(t) \, dt,$$

has the form $k(x - t)$. Assuming that the required transforms exist, show that

$$\varphi(x) = \frac{1}{2\pi i} \int_{\gamma - i\infty}^{\gamma + i\infty} \frac{F(s)}{K(s)} e^{xs} \, ds.$$

[1] This kernel and a range $0 \leqslant x < \infty$ are the characteristics of integral equations of the Wiener-Hopf type. Details will be found in Chapter 8 of Morse and Feshbach.

$F(s)$ and $K(s)$ are the Laplace transforms of $f(x)$ and $k(x)$, respectively.

16.2.3 The kernel of a Volterra equation of the second kind,

$$\varphi(x) = f(x) + \lambda \int_0^x K(x, t) \, \varphi(t), \, dt,$$

has the form $k(x - t)$. Assuming that the required transforms exist, show that

$$\varphi(x) = \frac{1}{2\pi i} \int_{\gamma - i\infty}^{\gamma + i\infty} \frac{F(s)}{1 - \lambda K(s)} e^{xs} \, ds.$$

16.2.4 Using the Laplace transform solution (Exercise 16.2.3), solve

(a) $\varphi(x) = x + \int_0^x (t - x) \, \varphi(t) \, dt, \qquad \varphi(x) = \sin x,$

(b) $\varphi(x) = x - \int_0^x (t - x) \, \varphi(t) \, dt, \qquad \varphi(x) = \sinh x.$

Check your results by substituting back into the original integral equations.

16.2.5 A Fredholm equation of the first kind has a kernel $e^{-(x-t)^2}$.

$$f(x) = \int_{-\infty}^{\infty} e^{-(x-t)^2} \, \varphi(t) \, dt.$$

Show that the solution is

$$\varphi(x) = \frac{1}{\sqrt{\pi}} \sum_{n=0}^{\infty} \frac{f^{(n)}(0)}{2^n n!} H_n(x),$$

in which $H_n(x)$ is an nth-order Hermite polynomial.

16.2.6 Solve Abel's equation,

$$f(x) = \int_0^x \frac{\varphi(t)}{(x - t)^\alpha} \, dt, \qquad 0 < \alpha < 1;$$

by the following method:

(a) Multiply both sides by $(z - x)^{\alpha - 1}$ and integrate with respect to x over the range $0 \leqslant x \leqslant z$.

(b) Reverse the order of integration and evaluate the integral on the right-hand side (with respect to x) by the beta function.

Note:

$$\int_t^z \frac{dx}{(z - x)^{1-\alpha}(x - t)^\alpha} = B\,(1 - \alpha, \, \alpha)$$

$$= (-\alpha)!(\alpha - 1)!$$

$$= \frac{\pi}{\sin \pi\alpha}.$$

16.2.7 A Kirchhoff diffraction theory analysis of a laser leads to the integral equation

$$v(\mathbf{r}_2) = \gamma \iint K(\mathbf{r}_1, \mathbf{r}_2) \, v(\mathbf{r}_1) \, dA.$$

The unknown $v(\mathbf{r}_1)$ gives the geometric distribution of the radiation field over one mirror surface; the range of integration is over the surface of that mirror. For square confocal spherical mirrors the integral equation becomes

$$v(x_2, y_2) = \frac{-i\gamma e^{ikb}}{\lambda b} \int_{-a}^a \int_{-a}^a e^{-(ik/b)(x_1 x_2 + y_1 y_2)} \, v(x_1, y_1) \, dx_1 \, dy_1,$$

in which b is the centerline distance between the laser mirrors. This can be put in a some-what simpler form by the substitutions

$$\frac{kx_i^2}{b} = \xi_i^2, \quad \frac{ky_i^2}{b} = \eta_i^2 \quad \text{and} \quad \frac{ka^2}{b} = \frac{2\pi a^2}{\lambda b} = \alpha^2.$$

(a) Show that the variables separate and we get two integral equations.
(b) Show that the new limits $\pm \alpha$ may be approximated by $\pm \infty$ for a mirror dimension $a \gg \lambda$.
(c) Solve the resulting integral equations.

16.3 Neumann Series, Separable (Degenerate) Kernels

Many and probably most integral equations cannot be solved by the specialized integral transform techniques of the preceding section. Here we develop two rather general techniques for solving integral equations. The first, due largely to Neumann, Liouville, and Volterra, develops the unknown function $\varphi(x)$ as a power series in λ, where λ is a given constant. The method is applicable whenever the series converges.

The second method is somewhat restricted because it requires that the two variables appearing in the kernel $K(x, t)$ be separable. However, there are two major rewards: (1) the relation between an integral equation and a set of simultaneous linear algebraic equations is shown explicitly, and (2) the method leads to eigen-values and eigenfunctions—in close analogy to Section 4.5.

Neumann series.   We solve a linear integral equation of the second kind by successive approximations; our integral equation is the Fredholm equation

$$\varphi(x) = f(x) + \lambda \int_a^b K(x, t)\, \varphi(t)\, dt \tag{16.56}$$

in which $f(x) \neq 0$. If the upper limit of the integral is a variable (Volterra equation), the following development will still hold, but with minor modifications. Let us try (there is no *guarantee* that it will work) to approximate our unknown function by

$$\varphi(x) \approx \varphi_0(x) = f(x). \tag{16.57}$$

This choice is not mandatory. If you can make a better guess, go ahead and guess. The choice here is equivalent to saying that the integral or the constant λ is small. To improve this first crude approximation we feed $\varphi_0(x)$ back into the integral, getting

$$\varphi_1(x) = f(x) + \lambda \int_a^b K(x, t) f(t)\, dt. \tag{16.58}$$

Repeating this process of substituting the new $\varphi_n(x)$ back into Eq. 16.56, we develop the sequence

$$\varphi_2(x) = f(x) + \lambda \int_a^b K(x, t_1) f(t_1)\, dt_1$$

$$+ \lambda^2 \int_a^b \int_a^b K(x, t_1)\, K(t_1, t_2) f(t_2)\, dt_2\, dt_1 \tag{16.59}$$

and

$$\varphi_n(x) = \sum_{i=0}^{n} \lambda^i u_i(x),$$ (16.60)

where

$$u_0(x) = f(x)$$

$$u_1(x) = \int_a^b K(x, t_1) f(t_1)\, dt_1$$

$$u_2(x) = \int_a^b \int_a^b K(x, t_1)\, K(t_1, t_2) f(t_2)\, dt_2\, dt_1.$$ (16.61)

$$u_n(x) = \int\int\int K(x, t_1)\, K(t_1, t_2) \cdots K(t_{n-1}, t_n) \cdot f(t_n)\, dt_n \cdots dt_1.$$

We expect that our solution $\varphi(x)$ will be

$$\varphi(x) = \lim_{n \to \infty} \varphi_n(x) = \lim_{n \to \infty} \sum_{i=0}^{n} \lambda^i u_i(x),$$ (16.62)

provided that our infinite series converges.

We may conveniently check the convergence by the Cauchy ratio test, noting that

$$|\lambda^n u_n(x)| \leqslant |\lambda|^n |f_{max}| |K_{max}|^n |b - a|^n,$$ (16.63)

using f_{max} to represent the *maximum* value of $f(x)$ in the interval $[a, b]$ and K_{max} to represent the maximum value of $K(x, t)$ in its domain in the x, t-plane. We have convergence if

$$|\lambda| |K_{max}| |b - a| < 1.$$ (16.64)

Note that $\lambda u_n(\max)$ is being used as a *comparison* series. If it converges, our actual series must converge. If this condition is not satisfied, we may have convergence or we may not. A more sensitive test is required. Of course, even if the Neumann series diverges, there still may be a solution obtainable by another method.

EXAMPLE 16.3.1

To illustrate the Neumann method we consider the integral equation

$$\varphi(x) = x + \frac{1}{2} \int_{-1}^{1} (t - x)\, \varphi(t)\, dt.$$ (16.65)

The Neumann series yields

$$\varphi_0(x) = x$$

$$\varphi_1(x) = x + \tfrac{1}{3}$$ (16.66)

$$\varphi_2(x) = x + \frac{1}{3} - \frac{x}{3}$$

$$\varphi_3(x) = x + \frac{1}{3} - \frac{x}{3} - \frac{1}{3^2}.$$

and by induction

$$\varphi_n(x) = x + \sum_{s=1}^{n} (-1)^{s-1} 3^{-s} - x \sum_{s=1}^{n} (-1)^{s-1} 3^{-s} \qquad (16.67)$$

Letting $n \to \infty$,

$$\varphi(x) = \tfrac{3}{4} x + \tfrac{1}{4}. \qquad (16.68)$$

It is interesting to note that our series converged easily even though Eq. 16.64 is *not* satisfied in this particular case. Actually Eq. 16.64 is a rather crude upper bound on λ. It can be shown that a necessary and sufficient condition for the convergence of our series solution is that $|\lambda| < |\lambda_e|$, where λ_e is the eigenvalue of smallest magnitude of the corresponding homogeneous equation $[f(x) = 0)]$. For this particular example $\lambda_e = \sqrt{3}/2$ which is clearly greater than $\tfrac{1}{2}$.

The Fredholm method of solving Fredholm equations consists of subdividing the integration interval and essentially replacing the integral by a sum. The single integral equation is replaced by a large number (approaching infinity) of simultaneous linear algebraic equations. For details the reader is again referred to the references listed at the end of this chapter.

Separable kernel.   The technique of replacing our integral equation by simultaneous algebraic equations may also be used whenever our kernel $K(x, t)$ is separable in the sense that

$$K(x, t) = \sum_{j=1}^{n} M_j(x) N_j(t), \qquad (16.69)$$

where n, the upper limit of the sum, is *finite*. Such kernels are sometimes called degenerate. Our class of separable kernels includes all polynomials and many of the elementary transcendental functions, that is,

$$\cos (t - x) = \cos t \cos x + \sin t \sin x. \qquad (16.70)$$

If Eq. 16.69 is satisfied, substitution into the Fredholm equation of second kind yields

$$\varphi(x) = f(x) + \lambda \sum_{j=1}^{n} M_j(x) \int_a^b N_j(t) \, \varphi(t) \, dt, \qquad (16.71)$$

interchanging integration and summation. Now the integral with respect to t is a constant,

$$\int_a^b N_j(t) \, \varphi(t) \, dt = c_j. \qquad (16.72)$$

Hence Eq. 16.71 becomes

$$\varphi(x) = f(x) + \lambda \sum_{j=1}^{n} c_j \, M_j(x). \qquad (16.73)$$

This gives us $\varphi(x)$, our solution, once the constants c_i have been determined.

We may find c_i by multiplying Eq. 16.73 by $N_i(x)$ and integrating, to eliminate the x-dependence. Use of Eq. 16.72 yields

$$c_i = b_i + \lambda \sum_{j=1}^{n} a_{ij} c_j, \qquad (16.74)$$

where

$$b_i = \int_a^b N_i(x) f(x) \, dx, \tag{16.75}$$

$$a_{ij} = \int_a^b N_i(x) M_j(x) \, dx.$$

It is perhaps helpful to write Eq. 16.74 in matrix form, with $A = (a_{ij})$.

$$\mathbf{c} - \lambda A \mathbf{c} = \mathbf{b}$$
$$= (1 - \lambda A)\mathbf{c},$$

or

$$\mathbf{c} = (1 - \lambda A)^{-1} \mathbf{b}. \tag{16.76}$$

This is equivalent to a set of simultaneous linear algebraic equations

$$(1 - \lambda a_{11})c_1 - \lambda a_{12} c_2 - \lambda a_{13} c_3 - \cdots = b_1,$$
$$-\lambda a_{21} c_1 + (1 - \lambda a_{22})c_2 - \lambda a_{23} c_3 - \cdots = b_2, \tag{16.77}$$
$$-\lambda a_{31} c_1 - \lambda a_{32} c_2 + (1 - \lambda a_{33})c_3 - \cdots = b_3, \qquad \text{etc.}$$

If our integral equation is homogeneous, $[f(x) = 0]$, then $\mathbf{b} = 0$. To get a solution we set the determinant of the coefficients of c_i equal to zero,

$$|1 - \lambda A| = 0, \tag{16.78}$$

exactly as in Section 4.5. The roots of Eq. 16.78 yield our eigenvalues. Substituting into Eq. 16.76, we find the c_i's and then Eq. 16.73 gives our solution.

EXAMPLE 16.3.2

To illustrate this technique for determining eigenvalues and eigenfunctions of the homogeneous Fredholm equation, we consider the simple case

$$\varphi(x) = \lambda \int_{-1}^1 (t + x) \varphi(t) \, dt. \tag{16.79}$$

Here

$$M_1 = 1, \qquad M_2(x) = x,$$
$$N_1(t) = t, \qquad N_2 = 1.$$

Equation 16.75 yields

$$a_{11} = a_{22} = 0,$$
$$a_{12} = \tfrac{2}{3},$$
$$a_{21} = 2.$$

Equation 16.78, our secular equation, becomes

$$\begin{vmatrix} 1 & -\dfrac{2\lambda}{3} \\ -2\lambda & 1 \end{vmatrix} = 0. \tag{16.80}$$

· Expanding, we obtain

$$1 - \frac{4\lambda^2}{3} = 0,$$

$$\lambda = \pm \frac{\sqrt{3}}{2}. \tag{16.81}$$

Substituting the eigenvalues $\lambda = \pm \sqrt{3}/2$ into Eq. 16.76, we have

$$c_1 \mp \frac{c_2}{\sqrt{3}} = 0. \tag{16.82}$$

Finally, with a choice of $c_1 = 1$, Eq. 16.73 gives

$$\varphi_1(x) = \frac{\sqrt{3}}{2}(1 + \sqrt{3}x), \qquad \lambda = \frac{\sqrt{3}}{2}, \tag{16.83}$$

$$\varphi_2(x) = -\frac{\sqrt{3}}{2}(1 - \sqrt{3}x), \qquad \lambda = -\frac{\sqrt{3}}{2}. \tag{16.84}$$

Since our equation is homogeneous, the normalization of $\varphi(x)$ is arbitrary.

EXERCISES

16.3.1   Using the Neumann series, solve

(a) $\varphi(x) = 1 - 2 \int_0^x t\, \varphi(t)\, dt,$ $\varphi(x) = e^{-x^2},$ (b) $\varphi(x) = x + \int_0^x (t - x)\, \varphi(t)\, dt,$

(c) $\varphi(x) = x - \int_0^x (t - x)\, \varphi(t)\, dt.$

16.3.2   Solve the equation

$$\varphi(x) = x + \tfrac{1}{2} \int_{-1}^1 (t + x)\, \varphi(t)\, dt$$

by the separable kernel method. Compare with the Neumann method solution of Section 16.3.

Ans. $\varphi(x) = \tfrac{1}{2}(3x + 1).$

16.3.3   Find the eigenvalues and eigenfunctions of

$$\varphi(x) = \lambda \int_{-1}^1 (t - x)\, \varphi(t)\, dt.$$

16.3.4   Find the eigenvalues and eigenfunctions of

$$\varphi(x) = \lambda \int_0^{2\pi} \cos(x - t)\, \varphi(t)\, dt.$$

Ans. $\lambda_1 = \lambda_2 = \dfrac{1}{\pi},$

$$\varphi(x) = A \cos x + B \sin x.$$

16.3.5   Find the eigenvalues and eigenfunctions of

$$y(x) = \lambda \int_{-1}^1 (x - t)^2\, y(t)\, dt.$$

Hint. This problem may be treated by the separable kernel method or by a Legendre expansion.

16.4 Hilbert-Schmidt Theory

Symmetrization of kernels.   This is the development of the properties of linear integral equations (Fredholm type) with symmetric kernels.

$$K(x, t) = K(t, x). \tag{16.85}$$

Before plunging into the theory, we note that some important nonsymmetric kernels can be symmetrized. If we have the equation

$$\varphi(x) = f(x) + \lambda \int_a^b K(x, t)\, \rho(t)\, \varphi(t)\, dt, \tag{16.86}$$

the total kernel is actually $K(x, t)\, \rho(t)$, clearly not symmetric if $K(x, t)$ alone is symmetric. However, if we multiply Eq. 16.86 by $\sqrt{\rho(x)}$ and substitute

$$\sqrt{\rho(x)}\, \varphi(x) = \psi(x), \tag{16.87}$$

we obtain

$$\psi(x) = \sqrt{\rho(x)}\, f(x) + \lambda \int_a^b \left[K(x, t)\sqrt{\rho(x)\, \rho(t)} \right] \psi(t)\, dt \tag{16.88}$$

with a symmetric total kernel, $K(x, t)\sqrt{\rho(x)\, \rho(t)}$. We shall meet $\rho(x)$ later as a weighting factor in this integral equation Sturm-Liouville theory.

Orthogonal eigenfunctions.   We now focus our attention on the homogeneous Fredholm equation of the second kind:

$$\varphi(x) = \lambda \int_a^b K(x, t)\, \varphi(t)\, dt. \tag{16.89}$$

We shall assume that the kernel $K(x, t)$ is symmetric and real. Perhaps one of the first questions the mathematician might ask about the equation is, "Does it make sense?" or more precisely, "Does an eigenvalue λ satisfying this equation exist?" With the aid of the Schwarz and Bessel inequalities, Courant and Hilbert (Chapter III, Section 4) show that if $K(x, t)$ is continuous there is at least one such eigenvalue and possibly an infinite number of them.

We shall show that the eigenvalues, λ, are real and that the corresponding eigenfunctions, $\varphi_i(x)$, are orthogonal. Let λ_i, λ_j be two *different* eigenvalues and $\varphi_i(x)$, $\varphi_j(x)$, the corresponding eigenfunctions. Equation 16.89 then becomes

$$\varphi_i(x) = \lambda_i \int_a^b K(x, t)\, \varphi_i(t)\, dt, \tag{16.90a}$$

$$\varphi_j(x) = \lambda_j \int_a^b K(x, t)\, \varphi_j(t)\, dt. \tag{16.90b}$$

If we multiply Eq. 16.90a by $\lambda_j \varphi_j(x)$, Eq. 16.90b by $\lambda_i \varphi_i(x)$, and then integrate with respect to x, the two equations become[1]

---

[1] We assume that the necessary integrals exist. For an example of a simple pathological case, see Exercise 16.4.3.

$$\lambda_j \int_a^b \varphi_i(x)\, \varphi_j(x)\, dx = \lambda_i \lambda_j \int_a^b \int_a^b K(x,\, t)\, \varphi_i(t)\, \varphi_j(x)\, dt\, dx, \qquad (16.91a)$$

$$\lambda_i \int_a^b \varphi_i(x)\, \varphi_j(x)\, dx = \lambda_i \lambda_j \int_a^b \int_a^b K(x,\, t)\, \varphi_j(t)\, \varphi_i(x)\, dt\, dx. \qquad (16.91b)$$

Since we have demanded that $K(x, t)$ be symmetric Eq. 16.91b may be rewritten

$$\lambda_i \int_a^b \varphi_i(x)\, \varphi_j(x)\, dx = \lambda_i \lambda_j \int_a^b \int_a^b K(x,\, t)\, \varphi_i(t)\, \varphi_j(x)\, dt\, dx. \qquad (16.92)$$

Subtracting Eq. 16.92 from Eq. 16.91a, we obtain

$$(\lambda_j - \lambda_i) \int_a^b \varphi_i(x)\, \varphi_j(x)\, dx = 0. \qquad (16.93)$$

Since $\lambda_i \neq \lambda_j$,

$$\int_a^b \varphi_i(x)\, \varphi_j(x)\, dx = 0, \qquad i \neq j, \qquad (16.94)$$

proving orthogonality. Note that with a symmetric kernel no complex conjugates are involved in Eq. 16.94. For the self-adjoint or Hermitian kernel see Exercise 16.4.1.

If the eigenvalue λ_i is degenerate,[1] the eigenfunctions for that particular eigenvalue may be orthogonalized by the Schmidt method (Section 9.3). Our orthogonal eigenfunctions may, of course, be normalized, and we will assume that this has been done. The result is

$$\int_a^b \varphi_i(x)\, \varphi_j(x)\, dx = \delta_{ij}. \qquad (16.95)$$

To demonstrate that the λ_i are real it is necessary to get into complex conjugates. Taking the complex conjugate of Eq. 16.90a, we have

$$\varphi_i^*(x) = \lambda_i^* \int_a^b K(x,\, t)\varphi_i^*(t)\, dt, \qquad (16.96)$$

provided the kernel $K(x, t)$ is real. Now, using Eq. 16.96 instead of Eq. 16.90b the analysis leads to

$$(\lambda_i^* - \lambda_i) \int_a^b \varphi_i^*(x)\, \varphi_i(x)\, dx = 0. \qquad (16.97)$$

This time the integral cannot vanish (unless we have the trivial solution, $\varphi_i(x) = 0$) and

$$\lambda_i^* = \lambda_i \qquad (16.98)$$

or λ_i, our eigenvalue, is real.

If the reader feels that somehow this state of affairs is vaguely familiar, he is right. This is the *third* time we have passed this way, first with Hermitian matrices, then with Sturm-Liouville (self-adjoint) equations, and now with Hilbert-Schmidt

---

[1] If more than one distinct eigenfunction corresponds to the same eigenvalue (satisfying Eq. 16.89), that eigenvalue is said to be degenerate.

integral equations. The correspondence between the Hermitian matrices and the self-adjoint differential equations shows up in modern physics as the two out-standing formulations of quantum mechanics—the Heisenberg matrix approach and the Schrödinger differential operator approach. In Section 16.5 we shall explore further the correspondence between the Hilbert-Schmidt symmetric kernel integral equations and the Sturm-Liouville self-adjoint differential equations.

The eigenfunctions of our integral equation form a complete set[1] in the sense that any function $g(x)$ that can be generated by the integral

$$g(x) = \int K(x, t)\, h(t)\, dt, \qquad (16.99)$$

in which $h(t)$ is any piecewise continuous function, can be represented by a series of eigenfunctions,

$$g(x) = \sum_{n=1}^{\infty} a_n\, \varphi_n(x). \qquad (16.100)$$

The series converges uniformly and absolutely.

Let us extend this to the kernel, $K(x, t)$, by asserting that

$$K(x, t) = \sum_{n=1}^{\infty} a_n\, \varphi_n(t), \qquad (16.101)$$

and $a_n = a_n(x)$. Substituting into the original integral equation (Eq. 16.89) and using the orthogonality integral, we obtain

$$\varphi_i(x) = \lambda_i\, a_i(x). \qquad (16.102)$$

Therefore for our homogeneous Fredholm equation of the second kind the kernel may be expressed in terms of the eigenfunctions and eigenvalues by

$$K(x, t) = \sum_{n=1}^{\infty} \frac{\varphi_n(x)\, \varphi_n(t)}{\lambda_n}, \qquad \text{(zero not an eigenvalue)}. \qquad (16.103)$$

It is possible that the expansion given by Eq. 16.101 may not exist. As an illustration of the sort of pathological behavior that may occur, the reader is invited to apply this analysis to

$$\phi(x) = \lambda \int_0^{\infty} e^{-xt}\, \phi(t)\, dt$$

(cf. Exercise 16.4.3).

It should be emphasized that this Hilbert-Schmidt theory is concerned with the establishment of properties of the eigenvalues (real) and eigenfunctions (ortho-gonality, completeness), properties that may be of great interest and value. The Hilbert-Schmidt theory does *not* solve the homogeneous integral equation for us any more than the Sturm-Liouville theory of Chapter 9 solved the differential equations. The solutions of the integral equation come from Sections 16.2 and 16.3 (or from numerical analysis).

---

[1] For a proof of this statement see Courant and Hilbert, Chapter III, Section 5.

Nonhomogeneous integral equation.   We need a solution of the nonhomogeneous equation

$$\varphi(x) = f(x) + \lambda \int_a^b K(x, t)\, \varphi(t)\, dt. \tag{16.104}$$

Let us assume that the solutions of the corresponding homogeneous integral equation are known.

$$\varphi_n(x) = \lambda_n \int_a^b K(x, t)\, \varphi_n(t)\, dt, \tag{16.105}$$

the solution $\varphi_n(x)$ corresponding to the eigenvalue λ_n. We shall expand both $\varphi(x)$ and $f(x)$ in terms of this set of eigenfunctions.

$$\varphi(x) = \sum_{n=1}^{\infty} a_n\, \varphi_n(x), \tag{16.106}$$

$$f(x) = \sum_{n=1}^{\infty} b_n\, \varphi_n(x). \tag{16.107}$$

Substituting into Eq. 16.104, we obtain

$$\sum_{n=1}^{\infty} a_n\, \varphi_n(x) = \sum_{n=1}^{\infty} b_n\, \varphi_n(x) + \lambda \int_a^b K(x, t) \sum_{n=1}^{\infty} a_n\, \varphi_n(t)\, dt. \tag{16.108}$$

By interchanging the order of integration and summation the integral may be evaluated by Eq. 16.105, and we get

$$\sum_{n=1}^{\infty} a_n\, \varphi_n(x) = \sum_{n=1}^{\infty} b_n\, \varphi_n(x) + \lambda \sum_{n=1}^{\infty} \frac{a_n\, \varphi_n(x)}{\lambda_n}. \tag{16.109}$$

If we multiply by $\varphi_i(x)$ and integrate from $x = a$ to $x = b$, the orthogonality of our eigenfunctions leads to

$$a_i = b_i + \lambda \frac{a_i}{\lambda_i}. \tag{16.110}$$

This can be rewritten as

$$a_i = b_i + \frac{\lambda}{\lambda_i - \lambda}\, b_i \tag{16.111}$$

which brings us to our solution

$$\varphi(x) = f(x) + \lambda \sum_{i=1}^{\infty} \frac{\int_a^b f(t)\, \varphi_i(t)\, dt}{\lambda_i - \lambda}\, \varphi_i(x). \tag{16.112}$$

Note that if $f(x) = 0$ there is no solution unless $\lambda = \lambda_i$. This means that our homogeneous equation has no solution (except the trivial $\varphi(x) = 0$) unless λ is an eigenvalue, λ_i.

In the event that λ for the nonhomogeneous equation (16.104) is equal to one of the eigenvalues, λ_p, of the homogeneous equation, our solution (Eq. 16.112) blows up. To repair the damage we return to Eq. 16.110 and give the value

$$a_p = b_p + \lambda_p \frac{a_p}{\lambda_p} = b_p + a_p \qquad (16.113)$$

special attention. Clearly, a_p drops out and is no longer determined by b_p, whereas $b_p = 0$. This implies that $\int f(x)\,\varphi_p(x)\,dx = 0$, that is, that $f(x)$ is orthogonal to the eigenfunction $\varphi_p(x)$. If this is *not* the case, we have no solution.

Equation 16.111 still holds for $i \neq p$, so we multiply by $\varphi_i(x)$ and sum over $i\,(i \neq p)$ to obtain

$$\varphi(x) = f(x) + a_p \varphi_p + \lambda_p \sum_{\substack{i=1 \\ i \neq p}}^{\infty}{}' \frac{\int_a^b f(t)\,\varphi_i(t)\,dt}{\lambda_i - \lambda_p}\,\varphi_i(x); \qquad (16.114)$$

the prime emphasizes that the value $i = p$ is omitted. In this solution the a_p remains as an undetermined constant.[1]

EXERCISES

16.4.1 In the Fredholm equation

$$\varphi(x) = \lambda \int_a^b K(x, t)\,\varphi(t)\,dt$$

the kernel $K(x, t)$ is self-adjoint or Hermitian.

$$K(x, t) = K^*(t, x).$$

Show that
(a) the eigenfunctions are orthogonal in the sense

$$\int_a^b \varphi_m^*(x)\,\varphi_n(x)\,dx = 0, \qquad m \neq n\,(\lambda_m \neq \lambda_n),$$

(b) the eigenvalues are real.

16.4.2 Solve the integral equation

$$\varphi(x) = x + \frac{1}{2} \int_{-1}^{1} (t + x)\,\varphi(t)\,dt$$

(cf. Exercise 16.3.2) by the Hilbert-Schmidt method.
The application of the Hilbert-Schmidt technique here is somewhat like using a shotgun to kill a mosquito, especially when the equation can be solved in about fifteen seconds by expanding in Legendre polynomials.

16.4.3 Solve the Fredholm integral equation

$$\varphi(x) = \lambda \int_0^{\infty} e^{-xt}\,\varphi(t)\,dt.$$

---

[1] This is like the inhomogeneous linear differential equation. To its solution we may add any constant times a solution of the corresponding homogeneous differential equation.

Note. A series expansion of the kernel e^{-xt} would permit a separable kernel-type solution (Section 16.3), except that the series is infinite. This suggests an infinite number of eigenvalues and eigenfunctions. If you stop with

$$\varphi(x) = x^{-1/2},$$
$$\lambda = \pi^{-1/2},$$

you will have missed most of the solutions! Show that the normalization integrals of the eigenfunctions do *not* exist. A basic reason for this anomalous behavior is that the range of integration is infinite, making this a "singular" integral equation.

16.4.4   Given

$$y(x) = x + \lambda \int_0^1 xt \, y(t) \, dt.$$

(a) Determine $y(x)$ as a Neumann series.

(b) Find the range of λ for which your Neumann series solution is convergent. Compare with the value obtained from

$$|\lambda| \, |K_{\max}| < 1.$$

(c) Find the eigenvalue and the eigenfunction of the corresponding homogeneous integral equation.

(d) By the separable kernel method show that the solution is

$$y(x) = \frac{3x}{3 - \lambda}.$$

(e) Find $y(x)$ by the Hilbert-Schmidt method.

16.4.5   In Exercise 16.3.4

$$K(x, t) = \cos(x - t).$$

The (unnormalized) eigenfunctions are $\cos x$ and $\sin x$.

(a) Show that there is a function $h(t)$ such that $K(x, s)$, considered as a function of s alone, may be written

$$K(x, s) = \int_0^{2\pi} K(s, t) \, h(t) \, dt.$$

(b) Show that $K(x, t)$ may be expanded as

$$K(x, t) = \sum_{n=1}^{2} \frac{\varphi_n(x) \, \varphi_n(t)}{\lambda_n}.$$

16.5 Green's Functions

While investigating differential operators we saw in Section 8.6 that Poisson's equation of electrostatics

$$\nabla^2 \varphi(\mathbf{r}) = -\frac{\rho(\mathbf{r})}{\varepsilon_0} \tag{16.115}$$

had a solution

$$\varphi(\mathbf{r}) = \frac{1}{4\pi\varepsilon_0} \int \frac{\rho(\mathbf{r}')}{|\mathbf{r} - \mathbf{r}'|} \, d\mathbf{r}'. \tag{16.116}$$

Here we have the infinite case in which the range of integration covers all space. If desired, the potential $\varphi(\mathbf{r})$ may be developed for a finite case by using appropriate charge and dipole layer distributions on the boundaries.[1]

---

[1] Cf. Stratton, J. A., *Electromagnetic Theory*. New York: McGraw-Hill (1941).

Equation 16.116 may be given two interpretations.

1. If the potential function $\varphi(\mathbf{r})$ is known and we seek the charge distribution $\rho(\mathbf{r}')$, which produces the given potential, Eq. 16.116 is an integral equation for $\rho(\mathbf{r}')$.

2. If the charge distribution $\rho(\mathbf{r}')$ is known, Eq. 16.116 yields the electrostatic potential $\varphi(\mathbf{r})$ as a definite integral.

Following up this second (and more frequently encountered) situation, we may use the physicists' customary cause and effect vocabulary. We might label $\rho(\mathbf{r}')$ the "cause" that gives rise to the "effect" $\varphi(\mathbf{r})$; that is, the charge distribution produces a potential field. However, the *effectiveness* of the charge in producing this potential depends on the distance between the element of charge $\rho(\mathbf{r}') \, d\mathbf{r}'$ and the point of interest given by $\mathbf{r}$. This effectiveness or, let us say, the influence of the element of charge is given by the function $(4\pi|\mathbf{r} - \mathbf{r}'|)^{-1}$.

For this reason $(4\pi|\mathbf{r} - \mathbf{r}'|)^{-1}$ is often called an influence function. Although we shall relabel it a Green's function, the physical basis for the term influence function remains important and may well be helpful in determining the form of other Green's functions.

For the sake of simplicity let us return to one-dimensional cases. We consider first the nonhomogeneous Sturm-Liouville equation (Chapter 9)

$$\mathscr{L} \, y(x) + f(x) = 0, \tag{16.117}$$

in which $\mathscr{L}$ is the self-adjoint differential operator

$$\mathscr{L} = \frac{d}{dx}\left(p(x)\frac{d}{dx}\right) + q(x). \tag{16.118}$$

As in Section 9.1, $y(x)$ is required to satisfy certain boundary conditions at the end points a and b of our interval $[a, b]$. Indeed, the interval may well be chosen so that appropriate boundary conditions can be satisfied. We now proceed to define a rather strange and arbitrary function G over the interval $[a, b]$. At this stage the most that can be said in defense of G is that the defining properties are legitimate, or mathematically acceptable. Later, it is hoped, G may appear reasonable if not obvious.

1. The interval $a \leqslant x \leqslant b$ is divided by a parameter t. We shall label $G(x) = G_1(x)$ for $a \leqslant x < t$ and $G(x) = G_2(x)$ for $t < x \leqslant b$.

2. The functions $G_1(x)$ and $G_2(x)$ each satisfy the homogeneous[1] Sturm-Liouville equation: that is,

$$\mathscr{L} \, G_1(x) = 0, \qquad a \leqslant x < t,$$
$$\mathscr{L} \, G_2(x) = 0, \qquad t < x \leqslant b. \tag{16.119}$$

3. At $x = a$, $G_1(x)$ satisfies the boundary conditions we impose on $y(x)$. At $x = b$, $G_2(x)$ satisfies the boundary conditions imposed on $y(x)$ at this end point of the interval. For convenience in renormalizing the boundary conditions are taken to be homogeneous; that is, at $x = a$

$$y(a) = 0,$$

$$y'(a) = 0,$$

---

[1] Homogeneous with respect to the unknown function. The function $f(x)$ in Eq. 16.117 is set equal to zero.

or
$$\alpha\, y(a) + \beta\, y'(a) = 0$$

and similarly for $x = b$.

4. We demand that $G(x)$ be *continuous*,[1]

$$G_1(t) = G_2(t). \tag{16.120}$$

5. We require that $G'(x)$ be *discontinuous*, specifically that[1]

$$\frac{d}{dx} G_2(x)\bigg|_t - \frac{d}{dx} G_1(x)\bigg|_t = -\frac{1}{p(t)}. \tag{16.121}$$

Note that with the first derivative discontinuous the second derivative does not exist.

These requirements, in effect, make G a function of two variables, $G(x, t)$. Also we note that $G(x, t)$ depends on both the form of the differential operator $\mathcal{L}$ *and* the boundary conditions that $y(x)$ must satisfy.

Now, assuming that we can find a function $G(x, t)$ which has these properties, we shall label it a Green's function and proceed to show that a solution of Eq. 16.117 is

$$y(x) = \int_a^b G(x, t)\, f(t)\, dt. \tag{16.122}$$

To do this we shall first construct the Green's function, $G(x, t)$. Let $u(x)$ be a solution of the homogeneous Sturm-Liouville equation which satisfies the boundary conditions at $x = a$ and $v(x)$ is a solution which satisfies the boundary conditions at $x = b$. Then we may take

$$G(x, t) = \begin{cases} c_1\, u(x), & x < t, \\ c_2\, v(x), & t < x. \end{cases} \tag{16.123}$$

Continuity at $x = t$ (Eq. 16.120) requires

$$c_2\, v(t) - c_1\, u(t) = 0. \tag{16.124}$$

Finally, the discontinuity in the first derivative (Eq. 16.121) becomes

$$c_2\, v'(t) - c_1\, u'(t) = -\frac{1}{p(t)}. \tag{16.125}$$

There will be a unique solution for our unknown coefficients c_1 and c_2 if the Wronskian determinant

$$\begin{vmatrix} u(t) & v(t) \\ u'(t) & v'(t) \end{vmatrix} = u(t)\, v'(t) - v(t)\, u'(t)$$

does not vanish. We have seen in Section 8.5 that the nonvanishing of this determinant is a necessary condition for linear independence. Let us consider $u(x)$ and $v(x)$ to be independent. The contrary, which occurs when $u(x)$ satisfies the boundary

---

[1] Strictly speaking, this is the limit as $x \to t$.

conditions at both end points, requires a generalized Green's function. Strictly speaking, no Green's function exists when $u(x)$ and $v(x)$ are linearly dependent. This is also true when $\lambda = 0$ is an eigenvalue of the homogeneous equation. However, a "generalized Green's function" may be defined. This situation, which occurs with Legendre's equation, is discussed in Courant and Hilbert and other references. For independent $u(x)$ and $v(x)$ we have the Wronskian (again from Section 8.5)

$$u(t)\,v'(t) - v(t)\,u'(t) = \frac{A}{p(t)}, \tag{16.126}$$

in which A is a constant. Equation 16.126 is sometimes called Abel's formula. Numerous examples have appeared in connection with Bessel and Legendre functions. Now, from Eq. 16.125, we identify

$$c_1 = -\frac{v(t)}{A},$$

$$c_2 = -\frac{u(t)}{A}. \tag{16.127}$$

Equation 16.124 is clearly satisfied. Substitution into Eq. 16.123 yields our Green's function.

$$G(x, t) = \begin{cases} -\dfrac{1}{A}\,u(x)\,v(t), & x < t, \\[2mm] -\dfrac{1}{A}\,u(t)\,v(x), & t < x. \end{cases} \tag{16.128}$$

Note carefully that $G(x, t) = G(t, x)$. This is the symmetry property that was proved earlier in Section 8.6. Its physical interpretation is given by the reciprocity principle (via our influence function)—a cause at t yields the same effect at x as a cause at x produces at t. In terms of our electrostatic analogy this is obvious, the influence function depending only on the magnitude of the distance between the two points

$$|\mathbf{r} - \mathbf{r}'| = |\mathbf{r}' - \mathbf{r}|.$$

We have constructed $G(x, t)$, but there still remains the task of showing that the integral (Eq. 16.122) with our new Green's function is indeed a solution of the original differential equation (16.117). This we do by direct substitution. With $G(x, t)$ given by Eq. 16.128,[1] Eq. 16.122 becomes

$$y(x) = -\frac{1}{A}\int_a^x v(x)\,u(t)\,f(t)\,dt - \frac{1}{A}\int_x^b u(x)\,v(t)\,f(t)\,dt. \tag{16.129}$$

Differentiating, we obtain

$$y'(x) = -\frac{1}{A}\int_a^x v'(x)\,u(t)\,f(t)\,dt - \frac{1}{A}\int_x^b u'(x)\,v(t)\,f(t)\,dt, \tag{16.130}$$

[1] In the first integral $a \leqslant t \leqslant x$. Hence $G(x, t) = G_2(x, t) = -(1/A)u(t)\,v(x)$. Similarly, the second integral requires $G = G_1$.

the derivatives of the limits cancelling. A second differentiation yields

$$y''(x) = -\frac{1}{A}\int_a^x v''(x)\, u(t)\, f(t)\, dt - \frac{1}{A}\int_x^b u''(x)\, v(t)\, f(t)\, dt$$

$$-\frac{1}{A}\left[u(x)\, v'(x) - v(x)\, u'(x)\right] f(x). \tag{16.131}$$

By Eqs. 16.125 and 16.127 this may be rewritten

$$y''(x) = -\frac{v''(x)}{A}\int_a^x u(t)\, f(t)\, dt - \frac{u''(x)}{A}\int_x^b v(t)\, f(t)\, dt - \frac{f(x)}{p(x)}. \tag{16.132}$$

Now, by substituting into Eq. 16.118, we have

$$\mathcal{L}\, y(x) = -\frac{[\mathcal{L}\, v(x)]}{A}\int_a^x u(t)\, f(t)\, dt - \frac{[\mathcal{L}\, u(x)]}{A}\int_x^b v(t)\, f(t)\, dt - f(x). \tag{16.133}$$

Since $u(x)$ and $v(x)$ were chosen to satisfy the homogeneous Sturm-Liouville equation, the factors in brackets are zero and the integral terms vanish. Transposing $f(x)$, we see that Eq. 16.117 is satisfied.

We must also check that $y(x)$ satisfies the required boundary conditions. At point $x = a$

$$y(a) = -\frac{u(a)}{A}\int_a^b v(t)\, f(t)\, dt = c\, u(a), \tag{16.134}$$

$$y'(a) = -\frac{u'(a)}{A}\int_a^b v(t)\, f(t)\, dt = c\, u'(a), \tag{16.135}$$

since the definite integral is a constant. We chose $u(x)$ to satisfy

$$\alpha\, u(a) + \beta\, u'(a) = 0. \tag{16.136}$$

Multiplying by the constant c, we verify that $y(x)$ also satisfies Eq. 16.136. This illustrates the utility of the *homogeneous* boundary conditions: the normalization does not matter. In quantum mechanical problems the boundary condition on the wave function is often expressed in terms of the ratio

$$\frac{\psi'(x)}{\psi(x)} = \frac{d}{dx}\ln\psi(x),$$

equivalent to Eq. 16.136. The advantage is that the wave function need not be normalized.

Summarizing, we have Eq. 16.122

$$y(x) = \int_a^b G(x, t)\, f(t)\, dt$$

which satisfies the differential equation (Eq. 16.117)

$$\mathcal{L}\, y(x) + f(x) = 0$$

and the boundary conditions, these boundary conditions having been built into the Green's function $G(x, t)$.

Basically, what we have done is to use the solutions of the homogeneous Sturm-Liouville equation to construct a solution of the nonhomogeneous equation. Again Poisson's equation is an illustration. The solution (Eq. 16.116) represents a weighted $[\rho(\mathbf{r}')]$ combination of solutions of the corresponding homogeneous Laplace's equation.

The preceding analysis placed no special restrictions on our $f(x)$. Let us now assume that $f(x) = \lambda \, \rho(x) \, y(x)$. Then we have

$$y(x) = \lambda \int_a^b G(x, t) \, \rho(t) \, y(t) \, dt \tag{16.137}$$

as a solution of

$$\mathscr{L} \, y(x) + \lambda \, \rho(x) \, y(x) = 0 \tag{16.138}$$

and its boundary conditions. Equation 16.137 is a homogeneous Fredholm equation of the second kind and Eq. 16.138 is the Sturm-Liouville eigenvalue equation of Chapter 9.

To complete the discussion of this differential equation—integral equation equivalence—let us now show that Eq. 16.138 implies Eq. 16.137; that is, a solution of our differential equation (16.138) with its boundary conditions satisfies the integral equation (16.137). We multiply Eq. 16.138 by $G(x, t)$, the appropriate Green's function, and integrate from $x = a$ to $x = b$ to obtain

$$\int_a^b G(x, t)\mathscr{L} \, y(x) \, dx + \lambda \int_a^b G(x, t) \, \rho(x) \, y(x) \, dx = 0. \tag{16.139}$$

The first integral is split in two ($x < t$, $x > t$), according to the construction of our Green's function, giving

$$-\int_a^t G_1(x, t)\mathscr{L} \, y(x) \, dx - \int_t^b G_2(x, t)\mathscr{L} \, y(x) \, dx = \lambda \int_a^b G(x, t) \, \rho(x) \, y(x) \, dx. \tag{16.140}$$

Applying Green's theorem to the left-hand side or, equivalently, integrating by parts, we obtain

$$-\int_a^t G_1(x, t)\left[\frac{d}{dx}\left(p(x)\frac{d}{dx} \, y(x)\right) + q(x) \, y(x)\right] dx$$

$$= -\left|G_1(x, t) \, p(x) \, y'(x)\right|_a^t + \int_a^t G_1'(x, t) \, p(x) \, y'(x) \, dx - \int_a^t G_1(x, t) \, q(x) \, y(x) \, dx, \tag{16.141}$$

with an equivalent expression for the second integral. A second integration by parts yields

$$-\int_a^t G_1(x, t)\mathscr{L} \, y(x) \, dx = -\int_a^t y(x) \, \mathscr{L} \, G_1(x, t) \, dx$$

$$-\left|G_1(x, t) \, p(x) \, y'(x)\right|_a^t + \left|G_1'(x, t) \, p(x) \, y(x)\right|_a^t. \tag{16.142}$$

The integral on the right vanishes because $\mathscr{L}G_1 = 0$. By combining the integrated terms with those from integrating G_2, we have

$$-p(t)[G_1(t, t)\, y'(t) - G_1'(t, t)\, y(t) - G_2(t, t)\, y'(t) + G_2'(t, t)\, y(t)]$$
$$+ p(a)[G_1(a, t)\, y'(a) - G_1'(a, t)\, y(a)]$$
$$- p(b)[G_2(b, t)\, y'(b) - G_2'(b, t)\, y(b)]. \qquad (16.143)$$

Each of the last two expressions vanishes, for $G(x, t)$ and $y(x)$ satisfy the same boundary conditions. The first expression, with the help of Eqs. 16.120 and 16.122, reduces to $y(t)$. Substituting into Eq. 16.140, we have Eq. 16.137, thus completing the demonstration of the equivalence of the integral equation and the differential equation plus boundary conditions.

EXAMPLE 16.5.1.   LINEAR OSCILLATOR

As a simple example, consider the linear oscillator equation (for a vibrating string)

$$y''(x) + \lambda\, y(x) = 0. \qquad (16.144)$$

We impose the conditions $y(0) = y(1) = 0$, which correspond to a string clamped at both ends. Now, to construct our Green's function, we need solutions of the homogeneous Sturm-Liouville equation, $\mathscr{L}y(x) = 0$, which is $y''(x) = 0$. To satisfy the boundary conditions one solution must vanish at $x = 0$, the other at $x = 1$. Such solutions (unnormalized) are

$$u(x) = x, \qquad (16.145)$$
$$v(x) = 1 - x.$$

We find that

$$uv' - vu' = -1 \qquad (16.146)$$

or, by Eq. 16.126 with $p(x) = 1$, $A = -1$. Our Green's function becomes

$$G(x, t) = \begin{cases} x(1 - t), & x < t, \\ t(1 - x), & t < x. \end{cases} \qquad (16.147)$$

Hence by Eq. 16.137 our clamped vibrating string satisfies

$$y(x) = \lambda \int_0^1 G(x, t)\, y(t)\, dt. \qquad (16.148)$$

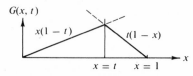

FIG. 16.3   A linear oscillator Green's function

The reader may show that the known solutions of Eq. 16.144.

$$y = \sin n\pi x \qquad (\lambda = n^2\pi^2),$$

do indeed satisfy Eq. 16.148. Note that our eigenvalue λ is *not* the wavelength.

One more approach to the Green's function may shed additional light on our formulation and particularly on its relation to physical problems. Let us refer once more to Poisson's equation, this time for a point charge

$$\nabla^2 \varphi(\mathbf{r}) = -\frac{\rho_{point}}{\varepsilon_0}. \tag{16.149}$$

The Green's function solution of this equation was developed in Section 8.6. This time let us take a one-dimensional analog

$$\mathscr{L} \, y(x) + f(x)_{point} = 0. \tag{16.150}$$

Here $f(x)_{point}$ refers to a unit point "charge" or a point force. We may represent it by a number of forms, but perhaps the most convenient is

$$f(x)_{point} = \begin{cases} \dfrac{1}{2\varepsilon}, & t - \varepsilon < x < t + \varepsilon, \\ 0, & \text{elsewhere}, \end{cases} \tag{16.151}$$

which is essentially the same as Section 8.6. Then, integrating Eq. 16.150, we have

$$\int_{t-\varepsilon}^{t-\varepsilon} \mathscr{L} \, y(x) \, dx = -\int_{t-\varepsilon}^{t+\varepsilon} f(x)_{point} \, dx \tag{16.152}$$

$$= -1$$

from the definition of $f(x)$. Let us examine $\mathscr{L} \, y(\dot{x})$ more closely. We have

$$\int_{t-\varepsilon}^{t+\varepsilon} \frac{d}{dx} [p(x) \, y'(x)] \, dx + \int_{t-\varepsilon}^{t+\varepsilon} q(\dot{x}) \, y(x) \, dx$$

$$= \left| p(x) \, y'(x) \right|_{t-\varepsilon}^{t+\varepsilon} + \int_{t-\varepsilon}^{t+\varepsilon} q(x) \, y(x) \, dx = -1. \tag{16.153}$$

In the limit $\varepsilon \to 0$ we may satisfy this relation by *permitting* $y'(x)$ to have a discontinuity of $-1/p(x)$ at $x = t$, $y(x)$ itself remaining continuous.[1] These, however, are just the properties used to define our Green's function, $G(x, t)$. In addition, we note that in the limit $\varepsilon \to 0$

$$f(x)_{point} = \delta(x - t), \tag{16.154}$$

in which $\delta(x - t)$ is our Dirac delta function, defined in this manner in Section 8.6. Hence Eq. 16.150 has become

$$\mathscr{L} \, G(x, t) = -\delta(x - t). \tag{16.155}$$

It will be recalled that we used this relation in Sections 8.6 and 11.4 to determine our Green's functions.

---

[1] The functions $p(x)$ and $q(x)$ appearing in the operator $\mathscr{L}$ are continuous functions. With $y(x)$ remaining continuous. $\int q(x) \, y(x) \, dx$ is certainly continuous. Hence this integral over an interval 2ε (Eq. 16.153) vanishes as ε vanishes.

Generalizing to n-dimensional space

$$\mathscr{L} \, G(\mathbf{r}_1, \mathbf{r}_2) = -\delta(\mathbf{r}_1 - \mathbf{r}_2), \tag{16.156}$$

with $\mathbf{r}_1$ and $\mathbf{r}_2$ n-component (dimensional) vectors. In multidimensional space our operator $\mathscr{L}$ becomes a partial differential operator. For three dimensions

$$\mathscr{L} = \frac{\partial}{\partial x}\left[p(x, y, z)\frac{\partial}{\partial x}\right] + \frac{\partial}{\partial y}\left[p(x, y, z)\frac{\partial}{\partial y}\right] + \frac{\partial}{\partial z}\left[p(x, y, z)\frac{\partial}{\partial z}\right] + q(x, y, z). \tag{16.157}$$

Summary of (infinite) Green's functions.

1. Poisson's equation.

$$\nabla^2 \varphi(\mathbf{r}) = -\frac{\rho(\mathbf{r})}{\varepsilon_0}, \tag{16.158}$$

$\varphi(r)$ is finite, or, at worst, logarithmically divergent as $r \to \infty$.

(a) One dimension. No Green's function exists for the interval $(-\infty, \infty)$.

(b) Two dimensions. Integrating over a circular *area* centered on the point $\mathbf{r}_1 = \mathbf{r}_2$,

$$\lim_{\mathbf{r}_1 \to \mathbf{r}_2} \iint \nabla^2 G(\mathbf{r}_1, \mathbf{r}_2)\, dA = -1. \tag{16.159}$$

Applying Gauss's theorem (in two dimensions), we go from the area integral of the Laplacian to the line integral of the gradient,

$$\lim_{r_{12} \to 0} \oint \nabla G(\mathbf{r}_1, \mathbf{r}_2) r_{12}\, d\theta = -1. \tag{16.160}$$

Here r_{12} is $|\mathbf{r}_1 - \mathbf{r}_2|$. This integral relation is satisfied by

$$\nabla G = -\frac{1}{2\pi r_{12}} = -\frac{1}{2\pi|\mathbf{r}_1 - \mathbf{r}_2|}, \tag{16.161}$$

and

$$G(\mathbf{r}_1, \mathbf{r}_2) = -\frac{1}{2\pi}\ln|\mathbf{r}_1 - \mathbf{r}_2|. \tag{16.162}$$

The solution of this two-dimensional Poisson equation then becomes

$$\varphi(\mathbf{r}_1) = -\frac{1}{2\pi\varepsilon_0}\int \ln|\mathbf{r}_1 - \mathbf{r}_2|\, \rho(\mathbf{r}_2)\, d\mathbf{r}_2. \tag{16.163}$$

(c) Three dimensions. From Sections 1.14 and 8.6

$$G(\mathbf{r}_1, \mathbf{r}_2) = \frac{1}{4\pi|\mathbf{r}_1 - \mathbf{r}_2|} \tag{16.164}$$

and

$$\varphi(\mathbf{r}_1) = \frac{1}{4\pi\varepsilon_0}\int \frac{\rho(\mathbf{r}_2)}{|\mathbf{r}_1 - \mathbf{r}_2|}\, d\mathbf{r}_2. \tag{16.165}$$

2. Helmholtz equation (space part of the wave equation).

$$(\nabla^2 + k^2)\,\psi(\mathbf{r}) = f(\mathbf{r}), \tag{16.166}$$

$$(\nabla^2 + k^2)\,G(\mathbf{r}_1, \mathbf{r}_2) = -\delta(\mathbf{r}_1 - \mathbf{r}_2). \tag{16.167}$$

For outgoing waves with time-dependence $e^{-i\omega t}$ (remember, the Green's function depends on the boundary conditions imposed).

(a) One dimension.

$$G(r_1, r_2) = \frac{i}{2k}\,e^{ik|r_1 - r_2|}. \tag{16.168}$$

(b) Two dimensions.[1]

$$G(\mathbf{r}_1, \mathbf{r}_2) = \frac{i}{4}\,H_0^{(1)}(k|\mathbf{r}_1 - \mathbf{r}_2|). \tag{16.169}$$

(c) Three dimensions.

$$G(\mathbf{r}_1, \mathbf{r}_2) = \frac{e^{ik|r_1 - r_2|}}{4\pi|\mathbf{r}_1 - \mathbf{r}_2|}. \tag{16.170}$$

In the one-dimensional case we observe that $G(\mathbf{r}_1, \mathbf{r}_2)$ satisfies the homogeneous Helmholtz equation away from $\mathbf{r}_1 = \mathbf{r}_2$ and has the required discontinuity in the first derivative. In the two- and three-dimensional cases the singularities are proportional to $\ln r$ and r^{-1}, respectively, characteristic of $\mathcal{L} = \nabla^2$. In general the two-dimensional Green's function of a linear second-order differential equation will have the form

$$G_2(\mathbf{r}_1, \mathbf{r}_2) = -\frac{1}{2\pi}\ln|\mathbf{r}_1 - \mathbf{r}_2| + H_2(\mathbf{r}_1, \mathbf{r}_2), \tag{16.171}$$

where $H_2(\mathbf{r}_1, \mathbf{r}_2)$ is a regular (nonsingular) function that depends on the form of the differential equation and the boundary conditions. In the corresponding three-dimensional case

$$G_3(\mathbf{r}_1, \mathbf{r}_2) = \frac{1}{4\pi|\mathbf{r}_1 - \mathbf{r}_2|} + H_3(\mathbf{r}_1, \mathbf{r}_2), \tag{16.172}$$

where again $H_3(\mathbf{r}_1, \mathbf{r}_2)$ is regular. To see how H_2 and H_3 vary with the form of the differential equation we list Green's functions for the modified Helmholtz equation.

3. Modified Helmholtz equation.

$$(\nabla^2 - k^2)\,\psi(\mathbf{r}) = f(\mathbf{r}), \tag{16.173}$$

$$(\nabla^2 - k^2)\,G(\mathbf{r}_1, \mathbf{r}_2) = -\delta(\mathbf{r}_1 - \mathbf{r}_2). \tag{16.174}$$

For solutions finite as $r \to \infty$:

(a) One dimension.

$$G(r_1, r_2) = \frac{1}{2k}\,e^{-k|r_1 - r_2|}. \tag{16.175}$$

(b) Two dimensions.

$$G(\mathbf{r}_1, \mathbf{r}_2) = \frac{1}{2\pi}\,K_0(k|\mathbf{r}_1 - \mathbf{r}_2|). \tag{16.176}$$

[1] Cf. Exercise 11.4.10.

(c) Three dimensions.

$$G(\mathbf{r}_1, \mathbf{r}_2) = \frac{e^{-k|\mathbf{r}_1 - \mathbf{r}_2|}}{4\pi|\mathbf{r}_1 - \mathbf{r}_2|}, \tag{16.177}$$

the meson potential. These are the familiar diffusion kernels of Chapter 11, so important in elementary neutron diffusion theory.

It will be noted that here and in the foregoing examples the singularity $\delta(\mathbf{r}_1 - \mathbf{r}_2)$ and the Green's function $G(\mathbf{r}_1, \mathbf{r}_2)$ have been associated with the *radial* part of the separated differential equation. This corresponds to the physical assertion that the interaction (influence function) depends only on the magnitude of the distance, that is, $|\mathbf{r}_1 - \mathbf{r}_2|$ and not on the particular orientation.

Following the analysis leading to Eq. 16.103, if the differential operator is self-adjoint (and therefore has a complete set of eigenfunctions) the Green's function may be expanded in terms of these eigenfunctions. The exception, as seen in Eq. 16.103, is the case in which one of the eigenvalues is zero or zero is a limit point of the eigenvalues. Applications of this eigenvalue expansion appear in Exercises 16.5.8 through 16.5.12.

EXAMPLE 16.5.2.   QUANTUM MECHANICAL SCATTERING

As a concluding example of a Green's function, let us consider a scattering problem in quantum mechanics. A beam of particles, represented by $e^{ik_0 z}$, is partially scattered. The scattered wave (an outgoing wave) has the asymptotic form

$$\Phi(\mathbf{r}) = \frac{1}{r} f(r, \theta) e^{ik_0 r}. \tag{16.178}$$

We shall take our total wave function $\psi(r)$ to be

$$\psi(\mathbf{r}) = e^{ik_0 z} + \Phi(\mathbf{r}). \tag{16.179}$$

Then, assuming that the probability of scattering is much less than one, the Schrödinger wave equation may be *approximated* by

$$(\nabla^2 + k_0^2)\, \Phi(\mathbf{r}) = U(\mathbf{r}) e^{ik_0 z}. \tag{16.180}$$

Here

$$\frac{\hbar^2}{2m}\, U(\mathbf{r}) = V(\mathbf{r}), \qquad \text{scattering (perturbing) potential}, \tag{16.181}$$

$$\frac{\hbar^2}{2m}\, k_0^2 = E, \qquad \text{total energy}. \tag{16.182}$$

We now proceed to solve Eq. 16.180, a nonhomogeneous differential equation The differential operator ∇^2 generates a continuous set of eigenfunctions

$$\nabla^2 \psi_\mathbf{k}(\mathbf{r}) = -k^2\, \psi_\mathbf{k}(\mathbf{r}), \tag{16.183}$$

where

$$\psi_\mathbf{k}(\mathbf{r}) = (2\pi)^{-3/2} e^{i\mathbf{k}\cdot\mathbf{r}}. \tag{16.184}$$

These eigenfunctions form a continuous but orthonormal set in the sense that

$$\int \psi_{\mathbf{k}}^*(\mathbf{r}) \, \psi_{\mathbf{k'}}(\mathbf{r}) \, dr = \delta(\mathbf{k} - \mathbf{k'}) \tag{16.185}$$

(cf. Exercises 15.6.1 and 2). We shall use these eigenfunctions to derive a Green's function.

We expand $\Phi(\mathbf{r})$ in these eigenfunctions,

$$\Phi(\mathbf{r}) = \int A_{\mathbf{k}} \, \psi_{\mathbf{k}}(\mathbf{r}) \, d\mathbf{k}, \tag{16.186}$$

a Fourier integral. Substituting Eq. 16.186 into Eq. 16.180 and using Eq. 16.183, we obtain

$$\int A_{\mathbf{k}}(k_0^2 - k^2) \, \psi_{\mathbf{k}}(\mathbf{r}) \, d\mathbf{k} = U(\mathbf{r})e^{ik_0z}. \tag{16.187}$$

Using the now familiar technique of multiplying by $\psi_{\mathbf{k'}}^*(\mathbf{r})$ and integrating over the space coordinates, we have

$$\int A_{\mathbf{k}}(k_0^2 - k^2) \, d\mathbf{k} \int \psi_{\mathbf{k'}}^*(\mathbf{r}) \, \psi_{\mathbf{k}}(\mathbf{r}) \, dr = A_{\mathbf{k'}}(k_0^2 - k'^2)$$

$$= \int \psi_{\mathbf{k'}}^*(\mathbf{r}) \, U(\mathbf{r})e^{ik_0z} \, dr. \tag{16.188}$$

Solving for $A_{\mathbf{k'}}$ and substituting into Eq. 16.186

$$\Phi(\mathbf{r'}) = \int [(k_0^2 - k'^2)^{-1} \int \psi_{\mathbf{k'}}^*(\mathbf{r}) \, U(\mathbf{r})e^{ik_0z} \, dr] \, \psi_{\mathbf{k'}}(\mathbf{r'}) \, d\mathbf{k'}. \tag{16.189}$$

Hence

$$\Phi(\mathbf{r}) = \int \psi_{\mathbf{k}}(\mathbf{r})(k_0^2 - k^2)^{-1} \, d\mathbf{k} \int \psi_{\mathbf{k}}^*(\mathbf{r'}) \, U(\mathbf{r'})e^{ik_0z'} \, dr', \tag{16.190}$$

replacing $\mathbf{k'}$ by $\mathbf{k}$ and $\mathbf{r}$ by $\mathbf{r'}$ to agree with Eq. 16.186. Reversing the order of integration, we have

$$\Phi(\mathbf{r}) = - \int G_{k_0}(\mathbf{r}, \mathbf{r'}) \, U(\mathbf{r'})e^{ik_0z'} \, dr', \tag{16.191}$$

where $G_{k_0}(\mathbf{r}, \mathbf{r'})$, our Green's function, is given by

$$G_{k_0}(\mathbf{r}, \mathbf{r'}) = \int \frac{\psi_{\mathbf{k}}^*(\mathbf{r'}) \, \psi_{\mathbf{k}}(\mathbf{r})}{k^2 - k_0^2} \, d\mathbf{k}, \tag{16.192}$$

analogous to Eq. 9.75 of Section 9.4 for *discrete* eigenfunctions. Equation 16.191 should be compared with the Green's function solution of Poisson's equation (16.165).

It is perhaps worth evaluating this integral to emphasize once more the vital role played by the boundary conditions. Using the eigenfunctions from Eq. 16.183 and

$$d\mathbf{k} = k^2 \, dk \sin \theta \, d\theta \, d\varphi, \tag{16.193}$$

we obtain

$$G_{k_0}(\mathbf{r}, \mathbf{r'}) = \frac{1}{(2\pi)^3} \int_0^\infty \int_0^\pi \int_0^{2\pi} \frac{e^{ik\rho\cos\theta}}{k^2 - k_0^2} \, d\varphi \sin \theta \, d\theta k^2 \, dk. \tag{16.194}$$

Here, $k\rho \cos \theta$ has replaced $\mathbf{k} \cdot (\mathbf{r} - \mathbf{r}')$ with $\boldsymbol{\rho} = \mathbf{r} - \mathbf{r}'$ indicating the polar axis in k-space. Integrating over φ by inspection, we pick up a 2π. The θ-integration then leads to

$$G_{k_0}(\mathbf{r}, \mathbf{r}') = \frac{1}{2\pi^2 \rho i} \int_0^\infty \frac{\sinh ik\rho}{k^2 - k_0^2} \, k \, dk, \qquad (16.195)$$

and since the integrand is an *even* function of k we may set

$$G_{k_0}(\mathbf{r}, \mathbf{r}') = \frac{1}{4\pi^2 \rho i} \int_{-\infty}^\infty \frac{\kappa \sinh i\kappa}{\kappa^2 - \sigma^2} \, d\kappa; \qquad (16.196)$$

the latter step is taken in anticipation of the evaluation of $G_{k_0}(\mathbf{r}, \mathbf{r}')$ as a contour integral. The symbols κ and σ ($\sigma > 0$) represent $k\rho$ and $k_0\rho$, respectively.

Splitting the integral into two parts so each part may be written as a suitable contour integral gives us

$$G(\mathbf{r}, \mathbf{r}') = \frac{1}{8\pi^2 \rho i} \oint_{C_1} \frac{\kappa e^{i\kappa} \, d\kappa}{\kappa^2 - \sigma^2} + \frac{1}{8\pi^2 \rho i} \oint_{C_2} \frac{\kappa e^{-i\kappa} \, d\kappa}{\kappa^2 - \sigma^2}. \qquad (16.197)$$

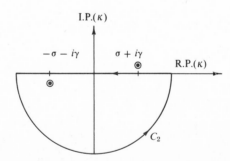

FIG. 16.4   Possible Green's function contours of integration

Contour C_1 is closed by a semicircle in the upper half plane, C_2 by a semicircle in the lower half plane. These integrals were evaluated in Chapter 7 by using appropriately chosen infinitesimal semicircles to go around the singular points $\kappa = \pm\sigma$. As an alternative procedure, let us first displace the singular points from the real axis by replacing σ by $\sigma + i\gamma$ and then, after evaluation, taking the limit as $\gamma \to 0$.

For γ *positive*, contour C_1 encloses the singular point $\kappa = \sigma + i\gamma$ and the first integral contributes

$$2\pi i \cdot \tfrac{1}{2} e^{i(\sigma + i\gamma)}.$$

From the second integral we also obtain

$$2\pi i \cdot \tfrac{1}{2} e^{i(\sigma + i\gamma)},$$

the enclosed singularity being $\kappa = -(\sigma + i\gamma)$. Returning to Eq. 16.197 and letting $\gamma \to 0$, we have

$$G(\mathbf{r}, \mathbf{r}') = \frac{1}{4\pi\rho} e^{i\sigma}$$

$$= \frac{e^{ik_0|\mathbf{r} - \mathbf{r}'|}}{4\pi|\mathbf{r} - \mathbf{r}'|}, \tag{16.198}$$

in full agreement with Eq. 16.165. This result depends on starting with γ positive. Had we chosen γ negative, our Green's function would have included $e^{-i\sigma}$, which corresponds to an *incoming* wave. The choice of positive γ is dictated by the boundary conditions we wish to satisfy.

It should be noted that Eqs. 16.191 and 16.198 constitute an exact solution of Eq. 16.180. However, Eq. 16.180, often referred to as the *Born* approximation, is only a first approximation of the actual physical system.

EXERCISES

16.5.1 Show that $G(x, t) = \begin{cases} x, & x < t, \\ t, & t < x, \end{cases}$

is the Green's function for the operator $\mathscr{L} = d^2/dx^2$ and the boundary conditions

$$y(0) = 0,$$
$$y'(1) = 0.$$

16.5.2 Find the Green's function for

(a) $\mathscr{L} y(x) = \dfrac{d^2 y(x)}{dx^2} + y(x), \qquad \begin{cases} y(0) = 0, \\ y'(1) = 0, \end{cases}$

(b) $\mathscr{L} y(x) = \dfrac{d^2 y(x)}{dx^2} - y(x), \qquad y(x)$ finite for $-\infty < x < \infty$.

16.5.3 Find the Green's function for the Bessel operators

(a) $\mathscr{L} y(x) = \dfrac{d}{dx}\left(x \dfrac{dy(x)}{dx}\right),$ *Ans.* (a) $G(x, t) = \begin{cases} -\ln t, & x < t, \\ -\ln x, & t < x, \end{cases}$

(b) $\mathscr{L} y(x) = \dfrac{d}{dx}\left(x \dfrac{dy(x)}{dx}\right) - \dfrac{n^2}{x} y(x),$ (b) $G(x, t) = \begin{cases} \dfrac{1}{2n}\left[\left(\dfrac{x}{t}\right)^n - (xt)^n\right], & x < t, \\ \dfrac{1}{2n}\left[\left(\dfrac{t}{x}\right)^n - (xt)^n\right], & t < x. \end{cases}$

with $y(0)$ finite and $y(1) = 0$.

16.5.4 Construct the Green's function for

$$x^2 \frac{d^2y}{dx^2} + x \frac{dy}{dx} + (k^2 x^2 - 1)y = 0,$$

subject to the boundary conditions

$$y(0) = 0,$$
$$y(1) = 0.$$

16.5.5 An electrostatic potential (mks units) is

$$\varphi(r) = \frac{Z}{4\pi\varepsilon_0} \cdot \frac{e^{-ar}}{r}.$$

Reconstruct the electrical charge distribution that will produce this potential. Note that $\varphi(r)$ vanishes exponentially for large r, showing that the net charge is zero.

Ans. $\rho(r) = Z\,\delta(r) - \dfrac{Za^2}{4\pi}\dfrac{e^{-ar}}{r}.$

16.5.6 Transform the differential equation

$$\frac{d^2y(r)}{dr^2} - k^2\,y(r) + V_0 \frac{e^{-r}}{r}\,y(r) = 0,$$

and the boundary conditions $y(0) = y(\infty) = 0$ into a Fredholm integral equation of the form

$$y(r) = \lambda \int_0^\infty G(r, t)\,\frac{e^{-t}}{t}\,y(t)\,dt.$$

The quantities V_0 and k^2 are constants. The differential equation is derived from the Schrödinger wave equation with a meson potential.

$$\lambda = V_0$$

$$G(r, t) = \begin{cases} \dfrac{1}{k} e^{-kt} \sinh kr, & r < t, \\[2mm] \dfrac{1}{k} e^{-kr} \sinh kt, & t < r. \end{cases}$$

16.5.7 In the Fredholm equation,

$$f(x) = \lambda^2 \int_a^b G(x, t)\,\varphi(t)\,dt,$$

$G(x, t)$ is a Green's function given by

$$G(x, t) = \sum_{n=1}^\infty \frac{\varphi_n(x)\,\varphi_n(t)}{\lambda_n^2 - \lambda^2}.$$

Show that the solution is

$$\varphi(x) = \sum_{n=1}^\infty \frac{\lambda_n^2 - \lambda^2}{\lambda^2}\,\varphi_n(x) \int_a^b f(t)\,\varphi_n(t)\,dt.$$

16.5.8 The homogeneous Helmholtz equation

$$\nabla^2\varphi + \lambda^2\varphi = 0$$

has eigenvalues λ_i^2 and eigenfunctions φ_i. Show that the corresponding Green's function which satisfies

$$\nabla^2 G(\mathbf{r}_1, \mathbf{r}_2) + \lambda^2\,G(\mathbf{r}_1, \mathbf{r}_2) = -\delta(\mathbf{r}_1 - \mathbf{r}_2)$$

may be written

$$G(\mathbf{r}_1, \mathbf{r}_2) = \sum_{i=1}^\infty \frac{\varphi_i(\mathbf{r}_1)\,\varphi_i(\mathbf{r}_2)}{\lambda_i^2 - \lambda^2}.$$

An expansion of this form is called a bilinear expansion. If the Green's function is available in *closed form*, this provides a means of generating generating functions.

16.5.9 From Exercise 16.5.8 or similar arguments show that the Green's function for Laplace's equation in spherical polar coordinates is

$$\frac{1}{4\pi|\mathbf{r}_1 - \mathbf{r}_2|} = \sum_{n,m} \frac{1}{2n+1} Y_n^{m*}(\theta_1, \varphi_1)\, Y_n^m(\theta_2, \varphi_2) \begin{cases} \dfrac{r_1^n}{r_2^{n+1}}, & r_1 < r_2, \\[2mm] \dfrac{r_2^n}{r_1^{n+1}}, & r_2 < r_1. \end{cases}$$

16.5.10 From the generating function for Legendre polynomials (Section 12.1)

$$\frac{1}{R} = \frac{1}{(r_1^2 + r_2^2 - 2r_1 r_2 \cos \omega)^{1/2}} = \sum_{n=0}^{\infty} P_n(\cos \omega) \begin{cases} \dfrac{r_1^n}{r_2^{n+1}}, & r_1 < r_2, \\[2mm] \dfrac{r_2^n}{r_1^{n+1}}, & r_2 < r_1. \end{cases}$$

Combine this result with the eigenfunction expansion of $1/R$ (Exercise 16.5.9) and derive the Legendre polynomial (or spherical harmonic) addition theorem.

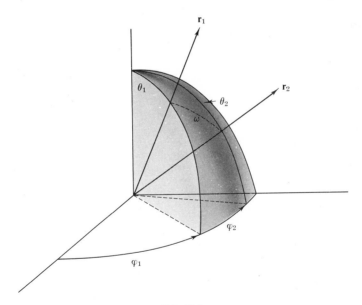

FIG. 16.5

16.5.11 From the eigenfunction expansion of the Green's function show that

(a) $\displaystyle \frac{2}{\pi^2} \sum_{n=1}^{\infty} \frac{\sin n\pi x \sin n\pi t}{n^2} = \begin{cases} x(1-t), & x < t, \\ t(1-x), & t < x. \end{cases}$

(b) $\displaystyle \frac{2}{\pi^2} \sum_{n=0}^{\infty} \frac{\sin(n+\frac{1}{2})\pi x \sin(n+\frac{1}{2})\pi t}{(n+\frac{1}{2})^2} = \begin{cases} x, & x < t, \\ t, & t < x. \end{cases}$

16.5.12 Noting that

$$\psi_k(\mathbf{r}) = \frac{1}{(2\pi)^{3/2}} e^{i\mathbf{k}\cdot\mathbf{r}}$$

is an eigenfunction of

$$(\nabla^2 + k^2)\, \psi_k(\mathbf{r}) = 0$$

(Eqs. 16.183 and 16.184), show that the infinite Green's function of $\mathscr{L} = \nabla^2$ may be expanded as

$$\frac{1}{4\pi \,|\mathbf{r}_1 - \mathbf{r}_2|} = \frac{1}{(2\pi)^3} \int e^{i\mathbf{k}\cdot(\mathbf{r}_1 - \mathbf{r}_2)}\, \frac{dk}{k^2}.$$

REFERENCES

BOCHER, M., *An Introduction to the Study of Integral Equations*. Cambridge Tracts in Mathematics and Mathematical Physics, No. 10. New York: Hafner (1960). A very helpful introduction to integral equations.

COURANT, R., and D. HILBERT, *Methods of Mathematical Physics*, Vol. 1 (English edition). New York: Interscience (1953). This is one of the classic works of mathematical physics. Originally published in German in 1924, the revised English edition is an excellent reference for a rigorous treatment of integral equations, Green's functions and for a wide variety of other topics of mathematical physics.

HILDEBRAND, F. B., *Methods of Applied Mathematics*. Englewood Cliffs, New Jersey: Prentice-Hall (1952). Chapter 4 is a detailed, readable account of integral equations.

LOVITT, W. V., *Linear Integral Equations*. New York: Dover (1950).

MORSE, P. M., and H. FESHBACH, *Methods of Theoretical Physics*. New York: McGraw-Hill (1953). Chapter 7 is a particularly detailed, complete discussion of Green's functions from the point of view of mathematical physics. Note, however, that Morse and Feshbach frequently choose a source of $4\pi\, \delta(\mathbf{r} - \mathbf{r}')$ in place of our $\delta(\mathbf{r} - \mathbf{r}')$. Considerable attention is devoted to bounded regions.

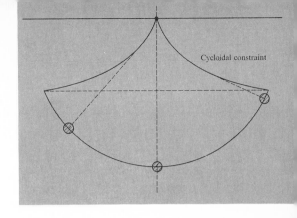
Cycloidal constraint

CHAPTER 17

CALCULUS OF VARIATIONS

17.1 One Dependent and One Independent Variable

Concept of variation.   The calculus of variations involves problems in which the quantity to be minimized (or maximized) appears as an integral. As the simplest case, let

$$J = \int_{x_1}^{x_2} f(y, y_x, x)\, dx. \tag{17.1}$$

Here J is the quantity that takes on an extreme value. Under the integral sign, f is a *known* function of the indicated variables y, $y_x \equiv dy/dx$, and x, but the dependence of y on x is not fixed, that is, $y(x)$ is *unknown*. This means that although the integral is from x_1 to x_2 the exact path of integration is not known (Fig. 17.1).

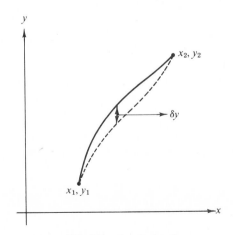

FIG. 17.1   A varied path

615

We are to choose the path of integration through points (x_1, y_1) and (x_2, y_2) to minimize J. Strictly speaking, we shall determine extreme values of J: minima, maxima, or saddle points. In most cases of physical interest the extreme will be a minimum.

This problem is considerably more difficult than the corresponding problem in differential calculus. Indeed there may be no solution. In differential calculus the minimum is determined by comparing $y(x_0)$ with $y(x)$, where x ranges over neighboring points. Here we shall assume the existence of an optimum path, that is, an acceptable path for which J is an extremum, and then compare J for our (unknown) optimum path with that obtained from neighboring paths. In Fig. 17.1 two possible paths are shown. (There are an infinite number of possibilities, of course.) The difference between these two for a given x is called the variation of y, δy, and is conveniently described by introducing a new function $\eta(x)$ to define the arbitrary deformation of the path and a scale factor α to give the magnitude of the variation. The function $\eta(x)$ is arbitrary except for two restrictions. First

$$\eta(x_1) = \eta(x_2) = 0, \tag{17.2}$$

which means that all varied paths must pass through the fixed end points. Second, as will be seen shortly, $\eta(x)$ must be differentiable; that is, we may not use

$$\begin{aligned} \eta(x) &= 1, \qquad x = x_0, \\ &= 0, \qquad x \neq x_0, \end{aligned} \tag{17.3}$$

but we can choose $\eta(x)$ to have a form similar to the functions used to represent the Dirac delta function (Chapters 8 and 16) so that $\eta(x)$ differs from zero only over an infinitesimal region.[1] Then, with the path described with α and $\eta(x)$,

$$y(x, \alpha) = y(x, 0) + \alpha \eta(x), \tag{17.4}$$

and

$$\delta y = y(x, \alpha) - y(x, 0) = \alpha\, \eta(x). \tag{17.5}$$

Let us choose $y(x, \alpha = 0)$ as the unknown path that will minimize J. Then $y(x, \alpha)$ describes a neighboring path, In Eq. 17.1 J is now a function of our new parameter α:

$$J(\alpha) = \int_{x_1}^{x_2} f[y(x, \alpha), y_x(x, \alpha), x]\, dx, \tag{17.6}$$

and our condition for an extreme value is that

$$\left[\frac{\partial J(\alpha)}{\partial \alpha}\right]_{\alpha=0} = 0, \tag{17.7}$$

analogous to the vanishing of the derivative dy/dx in differential calculus.

Now the α-dependence of the integral is contained in $y(x, \alpha)$ and $y_x(x, \alpha) = (\partial/\partial x)y(x, \alpha)$. Therefore

$$\frac{\partial J(\alpha)}{\partial \alpha} = \int_{x_1}^{x_2} \left[\frac{\partial f}{\partial y}\frac{\partial y}{\partial \alpha} + \frac{\partial f}{\partial y_x}\frac{\partial y_x}{\partial \alpha}\right] dx. \tag{17.8}$$

---

[1] Cf. Jeffreys, H., and B. S. Jeffreys, *Methods of Mathematical Physics*. 2nd Ed. Cambridge: Cambridge University Press (1950). Chapter 10, for a more complete discussion of this point.

From Eq. 17.4

$$\frac{\partial y(x, \alpha)}{\partial \alpha} = \eta(x) \tag{17.9}$$

$$\frac{\partial y_x(x, \alpha)}{\partial \alpha} = \frac{d\,\eta(x)}{dx}. \tag{17.10}$$

Equation 17.8 becomes

$$\frac{\partial J(\alpha)}{\partial \alpha} = \int_{x_1}^{x_2} \left(\frac{\partial f}{\partial y} \eta(x) + \frac{\partial f}{\partial y_x} \frac{d\,\eta(x)}{dx} \right) dx. \tag{17.11}$$

Integrating the second term by parts, we obtain

$$\int_{x_1}^{x_2} \frac{d\,\eta(x)}{dx} \frac{\partial f}{\partial y_x} dx = \eta(x) \frac{\partial f}{\partial y_x}\Big|_{x_1}^{x_2} - \int_{x_1}^{x_2} \eta(x) \frac{d}{dx} \frac{\partial f}{\partial y_x} dx. \tag{17.12}$$

The integrated part vanishes by Eq. 17.2 and Eq. 17.11 becomes

$$\int_{x_1}^{x_2} \left[\frac{\partial f}{\partial y} - \frac{d}{dx} \frac{\partial f}{\partial y_x} \right] \eta(x)\, dx = 0. \tag{17.13}$$

In this form α has been set equal to zero and, in effect, is no longer part of the problem.

Occasionally we will see Eq. 17.13 multiplied by α, which gives

$$\int_{x_1}^{x_2} \left(\frac{\partial f}{\partial y} - \frac{d}{dx} \frac{\partial f}{\partial y_x} \right) \delta y\, dx = \alpha \left[\frac{\partial J}{\partial \alpha} \right]_{\alpha = 0}$$

$$= \delta J = 0. \tag{17.14}$$

Since $\eta(x)$ is arbitrary (as already discussed), we may choose it to have the same sign as the bracketed expression whenever the latter differs from zero. Hence the integrand is always non-negative. Equation 17.13, our condition for the existence of an extreme, can then be satisfied only if the bracketed term itself is identically zero. The condition for our extremum is thus a partial differential equation,

$$\frac{\partial f}{\partial y} - \frac{d}{dx} \frac{\partial f}{\partial y_x} = 0, \tag{17.15}$$

known as the Euler equation, which can be expressed in various other forms.

Alternate forms of Euler equations.   One other form (Exercise 17.1.1), often useful is

$$\frac{\partial f}{\partial x} - \frac{d}{dx} \left(f - y_x \frac{\partial f}{\partial y_x} \right) = 0. \tag{17.16}$$

In problems in which $f = f(y, y_x)$ and x does not appear explicitly, Eq. 17.16 reduces to

$$\frac{d}{dx} \left(f - y_x \frac{\partial f}{\partial y_x} \right) = 0 \tag{17.17}$$

or

$$- y_x \frac{\partial f}{\partial y_x} = \text{constant}. \qquad (17.18)$$

It is clear that Eq. 17.15 or 17.16 must be satisfied for J to take on an extreme value, that is, for Eq. 17.14 to be satisfied. Equation 17.15 is necessary, but it is by no means sufficient. Courant and Robbins illustrate this very nicely by considering the distance over a sphere between points on the sphere, A and B. Path (1), a great circle route, is found from Eq. 17.15 as a solution to Exercise 17.1.3. But path (2), the remainder of the great circle through points A and B, also satisfies the Euler equation. Path (2) is a maximum but only if we demand that it be a great circle and then only if we make less than one circuit; that is path (2) + n complete revolutions is also a solution. If the path is not required to be a great circle, any deviation from (2) will increase the length. This is hardly the property of a local maximum, and that is why it is important to check the properties of solution of Eq. 17.15 to see if they satisfy the physical conditions of the given problem.

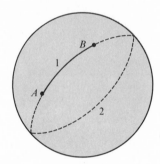

FIG. 17.2   Extreme paths over a sphere

EXERCISES

17.1.1 Show the equivalence of the two forms of Euler's equation:

$$\frac{\partial f}{\partial y} - \frac{d}{dx}\frac{\partial f}{\partial y_x} = 0$$

and

$$\frac{\partial f}{\partial x} - \frac{d}{dx}\left(f - y_x \frac{\partial f}{\partial y_x}\right) = 0.$$

17.1.2   Find the Euler equation corresponding to Eq. 17.15 if $f = f(y_{xx}, y_x, y, x)$.

Ans. $\dfrac{d^2}{dx^2}\left(\dfrac{\partial f}{\partial y_{xx}}\right) - \dfrac{d}{dx}\left(\dfrac{\partial f}{\partial y_x}\right) + \dfrac{\partial f}{\partial y} = 0$

with $\eta(x_0) = \eta(x_2) = 0,$
               $\eta_x(x_1) = \eta_x(x_2) = 0.$

17.1.3 Show that the shortest distance over the surface of a sphere joining two points on the sphere is a great circle. This result is usually concealed or confused by the familiar Mercator projection used for maps.

17.1.4 Derive Euler's equation by expanding the integrand of

$$J(\alpha) = \int_{x_1}^{x_2} f[y(x, \alpha), y_x(x, \alpha), x]\, dx$$

in powers of α, using a Taylor expansion for the two variables (Section 5.6).
Note. You must set $\alpha = 0$ (after differentiating with respect to α). Otherwise there will be terms $2\alpha\eta\eta_x\,(\partial^2 f/\partial y\ \partial y_x)$, etc.

17.2 Applications of the Euler Equation

EXAMPLE 17.2.1. STRAIGHT LINE

Perhaps the simplest application of the Euler equation is in the determination of the shortest distance between two points in the xy-plane. Since the element of distance is

$$ds = [(dx)^2 + (dy)^2]^{1/2} = [1 + y_x^2]^{1/2}\, dx, \tag{17.19}$$

the distance J, may be written

$$J = \int_{x_1,y_1}^{x_2,y_2} ds = \int_{x_1}^{x_2} [1 + y_x^2]^{1/2}\, dx. \tag{17.20}$$

Comparison with Eq. 17.1 shows that

$$f(y, y_x, x) = (1 + y_x^2)^{1/2}. \tag{17.21}$$

Substituting into Eq. 17.16, we obtain

$$-\frac{d}{dx}\left[\frac{1}{(1 + y_x^2)^{1/2}}\right] = 0 \tag{17.22}$$

or

$$\frac{1}{(1 + y_x^2)^{1/2}} = C, \quad \text{a constant.} \tag{17.23}$$

This is satisfied by

$$y_x = a, \quad \text{a second constant} \tag{17.24}$$

and

$$y = ax + b, \tag{17.25}$$

which is the familiar equation for a straight line. The constants a and b, of course, are chosen so that the line passes through the two points (x_1, y_1) and (x_2, y_2). Hence the Euler equation predicts that the shortest[1] distance between two fixed points is a straight line.

EXAMPLE 17.2.2

As a second illustration (Fig. 17.3) consider a surface of revolution generated by

---
[1] Technically, we have an extreme value. By inspection it is identified as a minimum.

revolving a curve $y(x)$ about the x-axis. The curve is required to pass through fixed end points (x_1, y_1) and (x_2, y_2). The variational problem is to choose the curve $y(x)$ so that the area of the resulting surface will be a minimum.

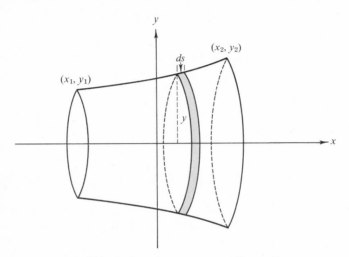

FIG. 17.3   Surface of rotation—soap film problem

For the element of area shown in Fig. 17.3

$$dA = 2\pi y \, ds = 2\pi y (1 + y_x^2)^{1/2} \, dx. \qquad (17.26)$$

The variational equation is then

$$J = \int_{x_1}^{x_2} 2\pi y (1 + y_x^2)^{1/2} \, dx. \qquad (17.27)$$

Neglecting the 2π,

$$f(y, y_x, x) = y(1 + y_x^2)^{1/2}. \qquad (17.28)$$

Since $\partial f / \partial x = 0$, we may apply Eq. 17.16 directly and get

$$y(1 + y_x^2)^{1/2} - y y_x^2 \frac{1}{(1 + y_x^2)^{1/2}} = c_1, \qquad (17.29)$$

or

$$\frac{y}{(1 + y_x^2)^{1/2}} = c_1. \qquad (17.30)$$

Squaring, we get

$$\frac{y^2}{1 + y_x^2} = c_1^2 \qquad \text{with } c_1^2 \leqslant y_{min}^2, \qquad (17.31)$$

and

$$(y_x)^{-1} = \frac{dx}{dy} = \frac{c_1}{\sqrt{y^2 - c_1^2}}. \qquad (17.32)$$

This may be integrated to give

$$x = c_1 \cosh^{-1} \frac{y}{c_1} + c_2.$$ (17.33)

Solving for y, we have

$$y = c_1 \cosh \left(\frac{x - c_2}{c_1} \right)$$ (17.34)

and again c_1 and c_2 are determined by requiring the hyperbolic cosine to pass through the points (x_1, y_1) and (x_2, y_2). Our "minimum" area surface is a catenary of revolution or a catenoid.

Soap film—minimum area.   This calculus of variations contains many pitfalls for the unwary. Perhaps some respect for some of these hazards may be developed by considering a specific physical problem. Consider the minimum area problem with $(x_1, y_1) = (-x_0, 1)$, $(x_2, y_2) = (+x_0, 1)$. The minimum surface is a soap film stretched over the two rings of unit radius at $x = \pm x_0$. The problem is to predict the curve $y(x)$ assumed by the soap film.

By referring to Eq. 17.34, we find that $c_2 = 0$ by the symmetry of the problem. If we take $x_0 = \frac{1}{2}$, we obtain the transcendental equation for c_1,

$$1 = c_1 \cosh \left(\frac{1}{2c_1} \right).$$ (17.35)

We find that this equation has two solutions; $c_1 = 0.2350$, leading to a "deep" curve, and $c_1 = 0.8483$, leading to a "flat" curve. Which is our minimum? Which curve is assumed by the soap film? Before answering these questions, consider the physical situation with the rings moved apart so that $x_0 = 1$. Then Eq. 17.34 becomes

$$1 = c_1 \cosh \left(\frac{1}{c_1} \right),$$ (17.36)

which has *no real solutions*! The physical significance is that as the unit radius rings were moved out from the origin a point was reached at which the soap film could no longer maintain the same horizontal force over each vertical section. Stable equilibrium was no longer possible. The soap film broke (irreversible process) and formed a circular film over each ring (with a total area of $2\pi = 6.2832 \cdots$). This is the Goldschmidt discontinuous solution.

The next question is—how large may x_0 be and still give a real solution for Eq. 17.34? Letting $c_1^{-1} = p$, Eq. 17.34 becomes,

$$p = \cosh p x_0.$$ (17.37)

The requirement that $dx_0/dp = 0$ (for the double root) gives

$$1 = x_0 \sinh p x_0$$ (17.38)

These two equations may be combined to form

$$p x_0 = \coth p x_0$$ (17.39)

with the root

$$p x_0 = 1.200.$$ (17.40)

Substituting into Eqs. 17.37 or 17.38, we obtain

$$p = 1.811 \quad (c_1 = 0.5523) \tag{17.41}$$

and

$$x_{0\,\text{max}} = 0.663. \tag{17.42}$$

Returning to the question of the solution of Eq. 17.35 that describes the soap film, let us calculate the area corresponding to each solution. We have

$$A = 4\pi \int_0^{x_0} y(1 + y_x^2)^{1/2}\, dx = \frac{4\pi}{c_1} \int_0^{x_0} y^2\, dx \quad \text{(by Eq. 17.30)}$$

$$= 4\pi c_1 \int_0^{x_0} \left(\cosh \frac{x}{c_1}\right)^2 dx$$

$$= \pi c_1^2 \left[\sinh\left(\frac{2x_0}{c_1}\right) + \frac{2x_0}{c_1}\right]. \tag{17.43}$$

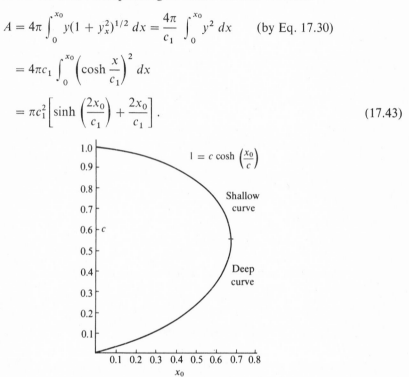

FIG. 17.4   Solutions of Eq. 17.34 for unit radius rings at $x = \pm x_0$

For $x_0 = \frac{1}{2}$, Eq. 17.35 leads to

$$c_1 = 0.2350 \rightarrow A = 6.8456,$$

$$c_1 = 0.8483 \rightarrow A = 5.9917,$$

showing that the former can at most be only a local minimum. A more detailed investigation (cf. Bliss, *Calculus of Variations*, Chapter IV) shows that this surface is not even a local minimum. For $x_0 = \frac{1}{2}$ the soap film will be described by the "flat" curve

$$y = 0.8483 \cosh\left(\frac{x}{0.8483}\right). \tag{17.44}$$

This "flat" or shallow catenoid (catenary of revolution) will be an absolute minimum for $0 \leqslant x_0 < 0.528$. However, for $0.528 < x < 0.663$ its area is greater than that of the Goldschmidt discontinuous solution (6.2832) and it is only a relative minimum.

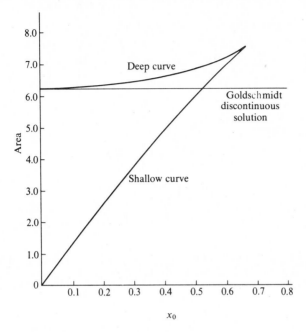

FIG. 17.5 Catenoid area (unit radius rings at $x = \pm x_0$)

For an excellent discussion of both the mathematical problems and experiments with soap films, the reader is referred to Courant and Robbins.

Brachistochrone.   The original physical problem that led to the development of the calculus of variations was the brachistochrone or shortest time problem. A particle is sliding freely along a curve from (x_1, y_1) to the origin under the influence of gravity. The curve is chosen to minimize the time of descent. Here the time of descent, J, is given by

$$J = \int_0^{x_1, y_1} \frac{ds}{v}. \tag{17.45}$$

Since

$$\tfrac{1}{2}mv^2 = mg(y_1 - y) \tag{17.46}$$

by conservation of energy, we obtain

$$v = \sqrt{2g(y_1 - y)} \tag{17.47}$$

and

$$J = \int_0^{x_1} \left[\frac{1 + y_x^2}{2g(y_1 - y)} \right]^{1/2} dx. \tag{17.48}$$

Ignoring the constant $2g$, our function f is now

$$f = \left(\frac{1 + y_x^2}{y_1 - y}\right)^{1/2}.$$ (17.49)

Again $\partial f/\partial x \doteq 0$ and using Eq. 17.16 we have

$$\left(\frac{1 + y_x^2}{y_1 - y}\right)^{1/2} - \frac{y_x^2}{[(y_1 - y)(1 + y_x^2)]^{1/2}} = c$$ (17.50)

or

$$\frac{1}{[(y_1 - y)(1 + y_x^2)]^{1/2}} = c.$$ (17.51)

Solving for y_x, we get

$$y_x = \frac{dy}{dx} = \left(\frac{b + y}{a - y}\right)^{1/2},$$ (17.52)

where

$$a = y_1,$$

$$b = \frac{1}{c^2} - y_1.$$ (17.53)

This differential equation may perhaps best be solved by introducing a new parameter θ by letting

$$y = \frac{a - b}{2} - \frac{a + b}{2} \cos \theta.$$ (17.54)

Then

$$dx = \frac{a + b}{2} \left(\frac{1 + \cos \theta}{1 - \cos \theta}\right)^{1/2} \sin \theta \, d\theta$$

$$= \frac{a + b}{2} (1 + \cos \theta) \, d\theta,^{[1]}$$ (17.55)

from Eq. 17.52, and we obtain

$$x + d = \frac{a + b}{2} (\theta + \sin \theta)$$

$$y + b = \frac{a + b}{2} (1 - \cos \theta).$$ (17.56)

These are the familiar equations of a cycloid. The parameters b and d, both constants of integration, are determined by requiring the cycloid to pass through the point (x_1, y_1) and the origin while the parameter a is fixed by the choice of y_1, an initial condition of the problem. For the very special case $x_1 = (\pi/2)y_1$, the parameters b and d vanish and we have

$$x = \frac{y_1}{2} (\theta + \sin \theta),$$

$$y = \frac{y_1}{2} (1 - \cos \theta),$$ (17.57)

---

[1] The angle-half angle trigonometric identities are helpful in establishing this result.

a cycloid described by the point on the circumference of a circle of radius $y_1/2$ rolling along the line $y = y_1$, upside down.

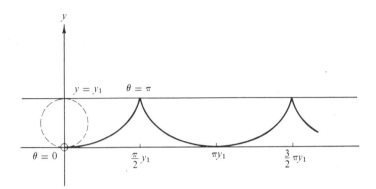

FIG. 17.6 Brachistrochrone—cycloidal path

One interesting extension is the following. The time of descent along the cycloid (Eq. 17.57) from point (x_2, y_2) to the origin is

$$T = \frac{1}{\sqrt{2g}} \int_0^{x_2} \left(\frac{1 + y_x^2}{y_2 - y}\right)^{1/2} dx = \frac{\pi}{2}\left(\frac{y_1}{2g}\right)^{1/2}, \qquad (17.58)$$

independent of the starting point![1] Compare it with a particle sliding on a circular

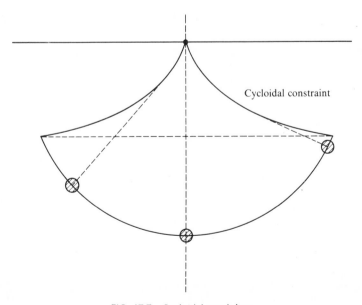

Cycloidal constraint

FIG. 17.7 Cycloidal pendulum

[1] This is the tautachrone problem of Chapter 15 (Laplace transform convolution theorem).

path (or ordinary pendulum). This property of the cycloid can be used to construct a pendulum whose period is independent of the amplitude. We recall that the involute of a cycloid is a cycloid, and if a pendulum is constrained by a cycloidal barrier, as shown in Fig. 17.7, the bob will follow a cycloidal path and behave like a friction-free particle sliding on a cycloid.

EXERCISES

17.2.1   A soap film is stretched across the space between two rings of unit radius centered at $\pm x_0$ on the x-axis and perpendicular to the x-axis. Using the solution developed in Section 17.2, set up the transcendental equations for the condition that x_0 is such that the area of the curved surface of rotation equals the area of the two rings (Goldschmidt discontinuous solution). Solve for x_0 (Fig. 17.8).

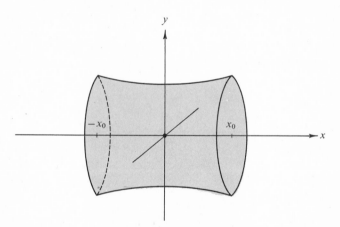

FIG. 17.8   Surface of rotation

17.2.2   Under the influence of gravity a particle slides down a frictionless cycloidal track described by

$$x = c\,(\theta + \sin\theta),$$
$$y = c\,(1 - \cos\theta).$$

Show that the time taken to slide down to the origin is

$$T = \frac{\pi}{2}\sqrt{\frac{c}{g}},$$

independent of the starting point on the curve $(0 < \theta \leqslant \pi)$.

17.2.3   Fermat's principle of optics states that a light ray will follow the path, $y(x)$, for which

$$\int_{x_1, y_1}^{x_2, y_2} n(y, x)\, ds$$

is a minimum when n is the index of refraction. For $y_2 = y_1 = 1$, $-x_1 = x_2 = 1$ find the ray path if

(a) $n = e^y$,   (b) $n = a(y - y_0)$, $y > y_0$.

17.3   Generalizations, Several Dependent Variables

Equation 17.1 may be generalized in several respects. In this section we consider the integrand, f, to be a function of several dependent variables, $y_1(x), y_2(x), y_3(x) \cdots$, all of which depend on x, the independent variable. In Section 17.4 f again will contain only one unknown function y, but y will be a function of several independent variables (over which we integrate). In Section 17.5 these two generalizations are combined. Finally, in Section 17.7 the extreme value is restricted by one or more constraints.

For more than one dependent variable Eq. 17.1 becomes

$$d = \int_{x_1}^{x_2} f[y_1(x), y_2(x), ..., y_n(x), y_{1x}(x), y_{2x}(x), ..., y_{nx}(x), x] \, dx. \quad (17.59)$$

As in Section 17.1, we determine the extreme value of J by comparing neighboring paths. Let

$$y_i(x, \alpha) = y_i(x, 0) + \alpha \eta_i(x), \qquad i = 1, 2, ... n, \quad (17.60)$$

with the η_i independent of one another, but subject to the restrictions discussed in Section 17.1. By differentiating Eq. 17.59 with respect to α and setting $\alpha = 0$, since Eq. 17.7 still applies, we obtain

$$\int_{x_1}^{x_2} \sum_i \left(\frac{\partial f}{\partial y_i} \eta_i + \frac{\partial f}{\partial y_{ix}} \eta_{ix} \right) dx = 0, \quad (17.61)$$

the subscript x denoting differentiations with respect to x, that is, $y_{ix} = dy_i/dx$, etc. Again each of the terms $(\partial f/\partial y_{ix})\eta_{ix}$ is integrated by parts. The integrated part vanishes and Eq. 17.61 becomes

$$\int_{x_1}^{x_L} \sum_i \left(\frac{\partial f}{\partial y_i} - \frac{d}{dx} \frac{\partial f}{\partial y_{ix}} \right) \eta_i \, dx = 0. \quad (17.62)$$

Since the η_i are arbitrary and *independent* of one another,[1] each of the terms in the sum must vanish *independently*. We have

$$\frac{\partial f}{\partial y_i} - \frac{d}{dx} \frac{\partial f}{\partial (dy_i/dx)} = 0, \qquad i = 1, 2, ..., n \quad (17.63)$$

a whole set of Euler equations, each of which must be satisfied for an extreme value.

The most important application of Eq. 17.59 occurs when the integrand f is taken to be the Lagrangian L. The Lagrangian is defined as the *difference* of kinetic

---

[1] For example, we could set $\eta_2 = \eta_3 = \eta_4 \cdots = 0$, eliminating all but one term of the sum, and then treat η_1 exactly as in Section 17.1.

and potential energies of a system,

$$L \equiv T - V. \tag{17.64}$$

Hamilton's principle.   Using time as an independent variable instead of x and $x_i(t)$ as the dependent variables,

$$x \to t,$$

$$y_i \to x_i(t),$$

$$y_{ix} \to \dot{x}_i(t);$$

$x_i(t)$ is the location and $\dot{x}_i = dx_i/dt$, the velocity of particle i as a function of time. The equation $\delta J = 0$ is then a mathematical statement of Hamilton's principle of classical mechanics,

$$\delta \int_{t_1}^{t_2} L(x_1, x_2, \cdots, x_n, \dot{x}_1, \dot{x}_2, \cdots, \dot{x}_n; t) \, dt = 0. \tag{17.65}$$

In words, Hamilton's principle asserts that the motion of the system from time t_1 to t_2 is such that the line integral of the Lagrangian L has a stationary value. The resulting Euler equations are usually called the Lagrangian equations of motion,

$$\frac{d}{dt} \frac{\partial L}{\partial \dot{x}_i} - \frac{\partial L}{\partial x_i} = 0. \tag{17.66}$$

These Lagrangian equations can be derived from Newton's equations of motion and Newton's equations can be derived from Lagrange's. The two sets of equations are equally "fundamental". However, the Lagrangian formulation has certain valuable advantages over the conventional Newtonian laws. Whereas Newton's equations are vector equations, we see that Lagrange's equations involve only scalar quantities. The coordinates $x_1, x_2, \ldots$, need not be any standard set of co-ordinates and need not be lengths. They are selected to match the conditions of the physical problem. Finally, Lagrange's equations, although further removed from "common sense", are much better adapted for treating complex systems and for extension to other branches of physics (such as quantum mechanics).

EXAMPLE 17.3.1.   MOVING PARTICLE—CARTESIAN COORDINATES

Consider Eq. 17.64 which describes one particle with kinetic energy

$$T = \tfrac{1}{2} m \dot{x}^2 \tag{17.67}$$

and potential energy $V(x)$, in which, as usual, the force is given by the negative gradient of the potential,

$$F(x) = -\frac{d V(x)}{dx}. \tag{17.68}$$

From Eq. 17.66

$$\frac{d}{dt}(m\dot{x}) - \frac{\partial(-V)}{\partial x} = m\ddot{x} - F(x) = 0, \tag{17.69}$$

which is simply Newton's second law of motion.

EXAMPLE 17.3.2. MOVING PARTICLE—CIRCULAR CYLINDRICAL COORDINATES

Now let us describe a moving particle in cylindrical coordinates ($z = 0$)-plane. The kinetic energy is

$$T = \tfrac{1}{2}m(\dot{x}^2 + \dot{y}^2) = \tfrac{1}{2}m(\dot{\rho}^2 + \rho^2\dot{\varphi}^2), \qquad (17.70)$$

and we take $V = 0$. The Lagrangian equations yield

$$\frac{d}{dt}(m\dot{\rho}) - m\rho\dot{\varphi}^2 = 0,$$

$$\frac{d}{dt}(m\rho^2\dot{\varphi}) = 0. \qquad (17.71)$$

The second equation is a simple statement of conservation of angular momentum. The first may be interpreted as radial acceleration[1] equated to centrifugal force. In this sense, the centrifugal force is a real force. It is of some interest that this interpretation of centrifugal force as a real force is supported by the general theory of relativity.

EXERCISES

17.3.1 Write out the Lagrangian equations of motion of a particle in spherical coordinates for potential V equal to a constant. Identify the terms corresponding to (a) centrifugal force and (b) Coriolis force.

FIG. 17.9 Spherical pendulum

[1] Here is a second method of attacking Exercise 2.6.3.

17.3.2   The spherical pendulum consists of a mass on a wire of length l, free to move in polar angle θ and azimuth angle φ (Fig. 17.9).
(a) Set up the Lagrangian for this physical system.
(b) Develop the Lagrangian equations of motion.

17.3.3   Show that the Lagrangian

$$L = m_0 c^2 \left(1 - \sqrt{1 - \frac{v^2}{c^2}}\right) - V(\mathbf{r})$$

leads to a relativistic form of Newton's second law of motion,

$$\frac{d}{dt}\left(\frac{m_0 v_i}{\sqrt{1 - v^2/c^2}}\right) = F_i,$$

in which $F_i = -\partial V/\partial x_i$.

17.3.4   The Lagrangian for a particle with charge q in an electromagnetic field described by scalar potential φ and vector potential, $\mathbf{A}$ is

$$L = \tfrac{1}{2}mv^2 - q\varphi + q\mathbf{A} \cdot \mathbf{v}.$$

Find the equation of motion of the charged particle.

Ans. $m\ddot{x}_i = q[\mathbf{E} + \mathbf{v} \times \mathbf{B}]_i$.

Hint. $\dfrac{d}{dt} A_j = \dfrac{\partial A_j}{\partial t} + \sum_i \dfrac{\partial A_j}{\partial x_i} \dot{x}_i$.

17.3.5   The Lagrangian (per unit volume) of an electromagnetic field with a charge density ρ is given by

$$L = \frac{1}{2}\left(\varepsilon_0 E^2 - \frac{B^2}{\mu_0}\right) - \rho\varphi + \rho\mathbf{v} \cdot \mathbf{A}.$$

Show that Lagrange's equations lead to Maxwell's electromagnetic equations.

17.4   Several Independent Variables

Sometimes the integrand f of Eq. 17.1 will contain one unknown function u which is a function of several independent variables, $u = u(x, y, z)$, for the three-dimensional case. Equation 17.1 becomes

$$J = \iiint f[u, u_x, u_y, u_z, x, y, z]\, dx\, dy\, dz, \qquad (17.72)$$

u_x indicating $\partial u/\partial x$, etc. The variational problem is to find the function $u(x, y, z)$ for which J is stationary,

$$\delta J = \alpha \left.\frac{\partial J}{\partial \alpha}\right|_{\alpha=0} = 0. \qquad (17.73)$$

Generalizing Section 17.1, we let

$$u(x, y, z, \alpha) = u(x, y, z, 0) + \alpha\, \eta(x, y, z). \qquad (17.74)$$

$u(x, y, z; \alpha = 0)$ represents the (unknown) function for which Eq. 17.73 is satisfied, whereas again $\eta(x, y, z)$ is the arbitrary deviation which describes the varied function $u(x, y, z, \alpha)$. This deviation, $\eta(x, y, z)$ is required to be differentiable and to vanish at the end points. Then from Eq. 17.74

$$u_x(x, y, z, \alpha) = u_x(x, y, z, 0) + \alpha\eta_x, \qquad (17.75)$$

and similarly for u_y and u_z.

Differentiating the integral (Eq. 17.72) with respect to the parameter α and then setting $\alpha = 0$, we obtain

$$\left.\frac{\partial J}{\partial \alpha}\right|_{\alpha=0} = \iiint \left(\frac{\partial f}{\partial u}\eta + \frac{\partial f}{\partial u_x}\eta_x + \frac{\partial f}{\partial u_y}\eta_y + \frac{\partial f}{\partial u_z}\eta_z\right) dx\,dy\,dz = 0. \quad (17.76)$$

Again we integrate each of the terms $(\partial f/\partial u_i)\eta_i$ by parts. The integrated part vanishes at the end points (because the deviation η is required to go to zero at the end points) and

$$\iiint \left(\frac{\partial f}{\partial u} - \frac{\partial}{\partial x}\frac{\partial f}{\partial u_x} - \frac{\partial}{\partial y}\frac{\partial f}{\partial u_y} - \frac{\partial}{\partial z}\frac{\partial f}{\partial u_z}\right) \eta(x, y, z)\,dx\,dy\,dz = 0. \quad (17.77)$$

Since the variation $\eta(x, y, z)$ is arbitrary, the term in large parenthesis may be set equal to zero. This yields the Euler equation for (three) independent variables,

$$\frac{\partial f}{\partial u} - \frac{\partial}{\partial x}\frac{\partial f}{\partial u_x} - \frac{\partial}{\partial y}\frac{\partial f}{\partial u_y} - \frac{\partial}{\partial z}\frac{\partial f}{\partial u_z} = 0. \quad (17.78)$$

EXAMPLE 17.4.1. LAPLACE'S EQUATION

An example of this sort of variational problem is provided by electrostatics. The energy of an electrostatic field is

$$\text{energy density} = \tfrac{1}{2}\varepsilon E^2, \quad (17.79)$$

in which $\mathbf{E}$ is the usual electrostatic force field. In terms of the static potential φ,

$$\text{energy density} = \tfrac{1}{2}\varepsilon(\nabla\varphi)^2. \quad (17.80)$$

Now let us impose the requirement that the electrostatic energy (associated with the field) in a given volume be a minimum. (Boundary conditions on $\mathbf{E}$ and φ must still be satisfied.) We have the volume integral

$$J = \iiint (\nabla\varphi)^2 \, dx\,dy\,dz$$

$$= \iiint (\varphi_x^2 + \varphi_y^2 + \varphi_z^2)\,dx\,dy\,dz.^1 \quad (17.81)$$

With

$$f(\varphi, \varphi_x, \varphi_y, \varphi_z, x, y, z) = \varphi_x^2 + \varphi_y^2 + \varphi_z^2, \quad (17.82)$$

the function φ replacing the u of Eq. 17.78, Euler's equation (Eq. 17.78) yields

$$-2(\varphi_{xx} + \varphi_{yy} + \varphi_{zz}) = 0 \quad (17.83)$$

or

$$\nabla^2\varphi(x, y, z) = 0, \quad (17.84)$$

which is just Laplace's equation of electrostatics.

Closer investigation shows that this extremum is indeed a minimum. Thus the demand that the field energy be minimized leads to Laplace's equation.

---

[1] Remember that the subscript x indicates the x-partial derivative *not* an x-component.

EXERCISES

17.4.1   The Lagrangian for a vibrating string (small amplitude vibrations) is

$$L = \int (\tfrac{1}{2}\rho u_t^2 - \tfrac{1}{2}\tau u_x^2)\, dx,$$

where ρ is the (constant) linear mass density and τ is the (constant) tension. The x-integration is over the length of the string. Show that application of Hamilton's principle to the Lagrangian density (the integrand), now with *two* independent variables, leads to the classical wave equation

$$\frac{\partial^2 u}{\partial x^2} = \frac{\rho}{\tau}\frac{\partial^2 u}{\partial t^2}.$$

17.5   More than One Dependent, More than One Independent Variable

In some cases our integrand f contains more than one dependent variable *and* more than one independent variable. Consider

$$f = f[p(x, y, z), p_x, p_y, p_z, q(x, y, z), q_x, q_y, q_z, r(x, y, z), r_x, r_y, r_z, x, y, z].$$

$$(17.85)$$

We proceed as before with

$$p(x, y, z, \alpha) = p(x, y, z, 0) + \alpha\, \xi(x, y, z),$$

$$q(x, y, z, \alpha) = q(x, y, z, 0) + \alpha\, \eta(x, y, z)$$

$$r(x, y, z, \alpha) = r(x, y, z, 0) + \alpha\, \zeta(x, y, z), \text{ etc.} \qquad (17.86)$$

Keeping in mind that ξ, η, and ζ are independent of one another, as were the η_i in Section 17.3, the same differentiation and then integration by parts leads to

$$\frac{\partial f}{\partial p} - \frac{\partial}{\partial x}\frac{\partial f}{\partial p_x} - \frac{\partial}{\partial y}\frac{\partial f}{\partial p_y} - \frac{\partial}{\partial z}\frac{\partial f}{\partial p_z} = 0, \qquad (17.87)$$

with similar equations for functions q and r. Replacing $p, q, r, \ldots$ with y_i and $x, y, z, \ldots$ with x_j, we can put Eq. 17.87 in a more compact form:

$$\frac{\partial f}{\partial y_i} - \sum_j \frac{\partial}{\partial x_j}\left(\frac{\partial f}{\partial y_{ij}}\right) = 0, \qquad i = 1, 2, \ldots, \qquad (17.87a)$$

in which

$$y_{ij} \equiv \frac{\partial y_i}{\partial x_j}.$$

An application of Eq. 17.87 appears in Section 17.7.

17.6 Lagrangian Multipliers

In this section the concept of a constraint is introduced. To simplify the treatment, the constraint appears as a simple function and not as an integral. In this section we are not concerned with the calculus of variations, but in Section 17.7 the constraints, with our newly developed Lagrangian multipliers, are incorporated into the calculus of variations.

Consider a function of three independent variables, $f(x, y, z)$. For the function f to be a maximum (or extreme)

$$df = 0. \tag{17.88}$$

The necessary and sufficient condition for this is

$$\frac{\partial f}{\partial x} = \frac{\partial f}{\partial y} = \frac{\partial f}{\partial z} = 0, \tag{17.89}$$

in which

$$df = \frac{\partial f}{\partial x} dx + \frac{\partial f}{\partial y} dy + \frac{\partial f}{\partial z} dz. \tag{17.90}$$

Often in physical problems the variables x, y, z are subjected to constraints so that they are no longer all independent. It is possible, at least in principle, to use each constraint to eliminate one variable and to proceed with a new and smaller set of independent variables.

The use of Lagrangian multipliers is an alternate technique that may be applied when this elimination of variables is inconvenient or undesirable. Let our equation of constraint be

$$\varphi(x, y, z) = 0, \tag{17.91}$$

from which

$$d\varphi = \frac{\partial \varphi}{\partial x} dx + \frac{\partial \varphi}{\partial y} dy + \frac{\partial \varphi}{\partial z} dz = 0. \tag{17.92}$$

Returning to Eq. 17.88, we see that Eq. 17.89 no longer follows because there are now only two independent variables. If we take x and y as these independent variables, dz is no longer arbitrary. However, we may add Eq. 17.90 and a multiple of Eq. 17.92 to obtain

$$df + \lambda \, d\varphi = \left(\frac{\partial f}{\partial x} + \lambda \frac{\partial \varphi}{\partial x}\right) dx + \left(\frac{\partial f}{\partial y} + \lambda \frac{\partial \varphi}{\partial y}\right) dy + \left(\frac{\partial f}{\partial z} + \lambda \frac{\partial \varphi}{\partial z}\right) dz = 0. \tag{17.93}$$

Our Lagrangian multiplier λ is chosen so that

$$\frac{\partial f}{\partial z} + \lambda \frac{\partial \varphi}{\partial z} = 0, \tag{17.94}$$

assuming that $\partial \varphi / \partial z \neq 0$. Equation 17.93 now becomes

$$\left(\frac{\partial f}{\partial x} + \lambda \frac{\partial \varphi}{\partial x}\right) dx + \left(\frac{\partial f}{\partial y} + \lambda \frac{\partial \varphi}{\partial y}\right) dy = 0. \tag{17.95}$$

However, dx and dy are arbitrary and the quantities in parentheses must vanish,

$$\frac{\partial f}{\partial x} + \lambda \frac{\partial \varphi}{\partial x} = 0,$$

$$\frac{\partial f}{\partial \lambda} + \lambda \frac{\partial \varphi}{\partial y} = 0. \qquad (17.96)$$

When Eqs. 17.94 and 17.96 are satisfied, $df = 0$ and f is an extremum. Notice that there are now four unknowns: x, y, z, and λ. The fourth equation is, of course, the constraint (17.91). Actually, we want only x, y, and z; λ need not be determined. For this reason λ is sometimes called Lagrange's undetermined multiplier. This method will fail if all the coefficients of λ vanish at the extremum, $\partial \varphi / \partial x$, $\partial \varphi / \partial y$, $\partial \varphi / \partial z = 0$. It is then impossible to solve for λ.

EXAMPLE 17.6.1.   PARTICLE IN A BOX

As an example of the use of Lagrangian multipliers, consider the quantum mechanical problem of a particle (mass m) in a box. The box is a rectangular parallelepiped with sides a, b, and c. The ground state energy of the particle is given by

$$E = \frac{h^2}{8m}\left(\frac{1}{a^2} + \frac{1}{b^2} + \frac{1}{c^2}\right). \qquad (17.97)$$

We seek the shape of the box that will minimize the energy E, subject to the constraint that the volume is constant,

$$V(a, b, c) = abc = k. \qquad (17.98)$$

With $f(a, b, c) = E(a, b, c)$ and $\varphi(a, b, c) = abc - k = 0$, we obtain

$$\frac{\partial E}{\partial a} + \lambda \frac{\partial V}{\partial a} = -\frac{h^2}{4ma^3} + \lambda bc = 0. \qquad (17.99)$$

Also

$$-\frac{h^2}{4mb^3} + \lambda ac = 0,$$

$$-\frac{h^2}{4mc^3} + \lambda ab = 0.$$

Multiplying the first of these expressions by a, the second by b, and the third by c, we have

$$\lambda abc = \frac{h^2}{4ma^2} = \frac{h^2}{4mb^2} = \frac{h^2}{4mc^2}. \qquad (17.100)$$

Therefore, our solution is

$$a = b = c, \qquad \text{a cube.} \qquad (17.101)$$

Notice that λ has not been determined. It remains an undetermined multiplier.

EXAMPLE 17.6.2. CYLINDRICAL NUCLEAR REACTOR

A further example is provided by the nuclear reactor theory. Suppose a (thermal) nuclear reactor is to have the shape of a right circular cylinder of radius R, height H. Neutron diffusion theory supplies a constraint:

$$\varphi(R, H) = \left(\frac{2.4048}{R}\right)^2 + \left(\frac{\pi}{H}\right)^2 = \text{constant.}[1] \tag{17.102}$$

We wish to minimize the volume of the reactor

$$f(R, H) = \pi R^2 H. \tag{17.103}$$

Application of Eq. 17.96 leads to

$$\frac{\partial f}{\partial R} + \lambda \frac{\partial \varphi}{\partial R} = 2\pi R H - 2\lambda \frac{(2.4048)^2}{R^3} = 0,$$

$$\frac{\partial f}{\partial H} + \lambda \frac{\partial \varphi}{\partial H} = \pi R^2 - 2\lambda \frac{\pi^2}{H^3} = 0. \tag{17.104}$$

By multiplying the first of these equations by $R/2$ and the second by H we obtain

$$\pi R^2 H = \lambda \frac{(2.4048)^2}{R^2} = \lambda \frac{2\pi^2}{H^2} \tag{17.105}$$

or

$$H = \frac{\sqrt{2}\pi R}{2.4048} = 1.847R. \tag{17.106}$$

for the minimum volume right-circular cylindrical reactor.

Strictly speaking, we have found only an extremum. Its identification as a minimum follows from a consideration of the original equations.

EXERCISES

The following problems are to be solved by using Lagrangian multipliers.

17.6.1 The ground state energy of a particle in a pillbox (right-circular cylinder) is given by

$$E = \frac{h^2}{2m}\left(\frac{(2.4048)^2}{R^2} + \frac{\pi^2}{H^2}\right),$$

in which R is the radius and H, the height of the pillbox. Find the ratio of R to H that will minimize the energy for a fixed volume.

Ans. $\dfrac{R}{H} = 0.5414.$

[1] 2.4048 $\cdots$ is the lowest root of Bessel function $J_0(R)$ (cf. Section 11.1).

17.6.2   Find the ratio of R(radius) to H(height) that will minimize the total surface area of a right-circular cylinder of fixed volume.

17.6.3   A rectangular box has no top. Find the ratios of the sides that will maximize the volume for a given total surface area.

17.6.4   A thermal nuclear reactor is subject to the constraint

$$\varphi(a, b, c) = \left(\frac{\pi}{a}\right)^2 + \left(\frac{\pi}{b}\right)^2 + \left(\frac{\pi}{c}\right)^2 = B^2, \text{ a constant.}$$

Find the ratios of the sides of the rectangular parallelepiped reactor of minimum volume.

Ans. $a = b = c$, cube.

17.6.5   A frictionless particle is sliding on the inside of a paraboloid of revolution. Show that the force of constraint (F^c) holding the particle on the surface is proportional to the curvature of the surface. *Hint.* Use parabolic coordinates. Constraint $\varphi = \xi - \xi_0 = 0$.

Ans. $F^{(c)} = \lambda \nabla \varphi|_\xi = \dfrac{\lambda}{(\xi_0^2 + \eta^2)^{1/2}}$

$$K, \text{ curvature} = \frac{c}{(\xi^2 + \eta^2)^{1/2}}.$$

17.6.6   The reduced mass μ is given by $1/\mu = 1/m_1 + 1/m_2$. Maximize μ for fixed $(m_1 + m_2)$.

17.6.7   For a simple lens of focal length f the object distance p and the image distance q are related by $1/p + 1/q = 1/f$.

Find the minimum object-image distance $(p + q)$ for fixed f. Assume real object and image (p and q both positive).

17.6.8   (a) Show that for a fixed-length perimeter the figure with maximum area is a circle.

(b) Show that for a fixed area the curve with minimum perimeter is a circle.

17.6.9   A rectangular parallelepiped is inscribed in an ellipsoid of semiaxes a, b, and c. Maximize the volume of the inscribed rectangular parallelepiped. Show that the ratio of the maximum volume to the volume of the ellipsoid is $2/\pi\sqrt{3} \approx 0.367$.

Note concerning the following exercises:

In a quantum-mechanical system there are g_i distinct quantum states between energy E_i and $E_i + dE_i$. The problem is to describe how n_i particles are distributed among these states subject to two constraints:

(a) Fixed number of particles:

$$\sum_i n_i = n.$$

(b) Fixed total energy:

$$\sum_i n_i E_i = E.$$

17.6.10   For identical particles obeying the Pauli exclusion principle the probability of a given arrangement is

$$W_{FD} = \prod_i \frac{g_i!}{n_i!(g_i - n_i)!}.$$

Show that maximizing W_{FD} subject to a fixed number of particles and fixed total energy leads to

$$n_i = \frac{g_i}{e^{\lambda_1 + \lambda_2 E_i} + 1}.$$

With $\lambda_1 = -E_0/kT$ and $\lambda_2 = 1/kT$, this yields Fermi-Dirac statistics. *Hint.* Try working with $\ln W$ and using Stirling's formula.

17.6.11 For identical particles but no restriction on the number in a given state the probability of a given arrangement is

$$W_{BE} = \prod_i \frac{(n_i + g_i - 1)!}{n_i!\,(g_i - 1)!}.$$

Show that maximizing W_{BE}, subject to a fixed number of particles and fixed total energy, leads to

$$n_i = \frac{g_i}{e^{\lambda_1 + \lambda_2 E_i} - 1}.$$

With $\lambda_2 = 1/kT$, this yields Bose-Einstein statistics. *Note.* Assume that $g_i \gg 1$.

17.6.12 Photons satisfy W_{BE} and the constraint that total energy is constant. They clearly do *not* satisfy the fixed number constraint. Show that eliminating the fixed number constraint leads to the foregoing result but with $\lambda_1 = 0$.

17.7 Variation Subject to Constraints

As in the preceding sections we seek the "path" that will make the integral

$$J = \int f\left(y_i, \frac{\partial y_i}{\partial x_j}, x_j\right) dx_j \tag{17.107}$$

stationary. This is the general case in which x_j represents a set of independent variables and y_i, a set of dependent variables. Again

$$\delta J = 0. \tag{17.108}$$

Now, however, we introduce one or more constraints. The constraint may have the form

$$\varphi_k(y_i, x_j) = 0, \tag{17.109}$$

as in Section 17.6. In this case we may multiply by a function of x_j, say $\lambda_k(x_j)$ and integrate over the same range as in Eq. 17.107 to obtain

$$\int \lambda_k(x_j)\, \varphi_k(y_i, x_j)\, dx_j = 0. \tag{17.110}$$

Then clearly

$$\delta \int \lambda_k(x_j)\, \varphi_k(y_i, x_j)\, dx_j = 0. \tag{17.111}$$

Alternatively, the constraint may appear in the form of an integral

$$\int \varphi_k(y_i, x_j)\, dx_j = \text{constant}. \tag{17.112}$$

We may introduce any *constant* Lagrangian multiplier and again Eq. 17.111 follows—now with λ a constant.

In either case by adding Eqs. 17.108 and 17.111, we obtain

$$\delta \int \left[f\left(y_i, \frac{\partial y_i}{\partial x_j}, x_j\right) + \sum_k \lambda_k\, \varphi_k(y_i, x_j) \right] dx_j = 0. \tag{17.113}$$

The Lagrangian multiplier λ_k may depend on x_j when $\varphi(y_i, x_j)$ is given in the form of Eq. 17.109.

Treating the entire integrand as a new function

$$g\left(y_i, \frac{\partial y_i}{\partial x_j}, x_j\right),$$

that is,

$$g\left(y_i, \frac{\partial y_i}{\partial x_j}, x_j\right) = f + \sum_k \lambda_k \varphi_k, \qquad (17.114)$$

we find that g must satisfy the usual Euler equations

$$\frac{\partial g}{\partial y_i} - \sum_j \frac{\partial}{\partial x_j} \frac{\partial g}{\partial(\partial y_i/\partial x_j)} = 0, \qquad (17.115)$$

there being one such equation for each dependent variable y_i (cf. Eqs. 17.78 and 17.87). These Euler equations and the equations of constraint are then solved simultaneously to find the extremum.

Lagrangian equations. In the absence of constraints Lagrange's equations of motion (Eq. 17.66) were found to be

$$\frac{d}{dt} \frac{\partial L}{\partial \dot{q}_i} - \frac{\partial L}{\partial q_i} = 0,$$

with t (time) the one independent variable and $q_i(t)$ (particle position) a set of dependent variables. Usually the generalized coordinates q_i are chosen to eliminate the forces of constraint, but this is not necessary and not always desirable. In the presence of constraints φ_k Hamilton's principle is

$$\delta \int \left[L(q_i, \dot{q}_i, t) + \sum_k \lambda_k(t)\, \varphi_k(q_i, t) \right] dt = 0. \qquad (17.116)$$

and the constrained Lagrangian equations of motion are

$$\frac{d}{dt} \frac{\partial L}{\partial \dot{q}_i} - \frac{\partial L}{\partial q_i} = \sum_k a_{ik} \lambda_k. \qquad (17.117)$$

Usually $\varphi_k = \varphi_k(q_i, t)$, independent of the generalized velocities $\dot{q}_i$. In this case the coefficient a_{ik} is given by

$$a_{ik} = \frac{\partial \varphi_k}{\partial q_i}. \qquad (17.118)$$

If q_i is a length, then $a_{ik}\lambda_k$ (no summation) represents the force of the kth constraint in the q_i-direction, appearing in Eq. 17.117 in exactly the same way as $-\partial V/\partial q_i$.

EXAMPLE 17.7.1. SIMPLE PENDULUM

To illustrate, consider the simple pendulum, a mass m, constrained by a wire of length l to swing in an arc. In the absence of the one constraint

$$\varphi_1 = r - l = 0 \qquad (17.119)$$

there are two generalized coordinates r and θ (motion in vertical plane). The Lagrangian is

$$L = T - V$$
$$= \tfrac{1}{2}m(\dot{r}^2 + r^2\dot{\theta}^2) + mgr \cos \theta. \tag{17.120}$$

FIG. 17.10   Simple pendulum

By Eq. 17.117 the equations of motion are

$$\frac{d}{dt}\frac{\partial L}{\partial \dot{r}} - \frac{\partial L}{\partial r} = \lambda_1, \qquad (a_{r_1} = 1, a_{\theta_1} = 0),$$
$$\frac{d}{dt}\frac{\partial L}{\partial \dot{\theta}} - \frac{\partial L}{\partial \theta} = 0, \tag{17.121}$$

or

$$\frac{d}{dt}(m\dot{r}) - mr\dot{\theta}^2 - mg \cos \theta = \lambda_1,$$
$$\frac{d}{dt}(mr^2\dot{\theta}) + mgr \sin \theta = 0. \tag{17.122}$$

Substituting in the equation of constraint ($r = l$, $\dot{r} = 0$), we have

$$ml\dot{\theta}^2 + mg \cos \theta = -\lambda_1,$$
$$ml^2\ddot{\theta} + mgl \sin \theta = 0. \tag{17.123}$$

The second equation may be solved for $\theta(t)$ to yield simple harmonic motion if the amplitude is small ($\sin \theta = \theta$), whereas the first equation expresses $-\lambda_1$, the tension in the wire in terms of θ and $\dot{\theta}$.

EXAMPLE 17.7.2.   SLIDING OFF A LOG

Closely related to this is the problem of a particle sliding on a cylindrical surface. The object is to find the critical angle θ_c at which the particle flies off from the surface. This is the point at which the radial force of constraint goes to zero (Fig. 17.11).

FIG. 17.11   A particle sliding on a cylindrical surface

We have

$$L = T - V = \tfrac{1}{2}m(\dot{r}^2 + r^2\dot{\theta}^2) - mgr\cos\theta \tag{17.124}$$

and the one equation of constraint

$$\varphi_1 = r - l = 0. \tag{17.125}$$

Proceeding as in Example 17.7.1 with $a_{r1} = 1$,

$$m\ddot{r} - mr\dot{\theta}^2 + mg\cos\theta = \lambda_1(\theta),$$
$$mr^2\ddot{\theta} + 2mr\dot{r}\dot{\theta} - mgr\sin\theta = 0, \tag{17.126}$$

in which the constraining force $\lambda_1(\theta)$ is a function of the angle θ.[1] Since $r = l$, $\ddot{r} = \dot{r} = 0$, Eqs. 17.126 reduce to

$$-ml\dot{\theta}^2 + mg\cos\theta = \lambda_1(\theta), \tag{17.127a}$$

$$ml^2\ddot{\theta} - mgl\sin\theta = 0. \tag{17.127b}$$

Differentiating Eq. 17.127a with respect to time and remembering that

$$\frac{df(\theta)}{dt} = \frac{df(\theta)}{d\theta}\,\dot{\theta}, \tag{17.128}$$

we obtain

$$-2ml\ddot{\theta} - mg\sin\theta = \frac{d\lambda_1(\theta)}{d\theta}. \tag{17.129}$$

Combining this equation with (17.127b) and integrating, we have

$$\lambda_1(\theta) = 3mg\cos\theta + C. \tag{17.130}$$

Since

$$\lambda_1(0) = mg, \tag{17.131}$$

$$C = -2mg. \tag{17.132}$$

The particle m will stay on the surface as long as the force of constraint is non-negative, that is, as long as the surface has to push outward on the particle

$$\lambda(\theta) = 3mg\cos\theta - 2mg \geqslant 0. \tag{17.133}$$

[1] Note carefully that λ_1 is the *radial* force exerted by the cylinder on the particle. Consideration of the physical problem should show that λ_1 must depend on the angle θ. We permitted $\lambda = \lambda(t)$. Now we are replacing the time-dependence by an (unknown) angular dependence.

The critical angle lies where $\lambda(\theta_c) = 0$, the force of constraint going to zero. From Eq. 17.133

$$\cos \theta_c = \tfrac{2}{3}, \qquad \text{or } \theta_c = 48° \ 11' \tag{17.134}$$

from the vertical. At this angle (neglecting all friction) our particle takes off.

It must be admitted that this result can be obtained more easily by considering a varying centripetal force furnished by the radial component of the gravitational force. The example was chosen to illustrate the use of Lagrange's undetermined multiplier without confusing the reader with a complicated physical system.

As a final illustration of a constrained minimum, let us find the Euler equations for the quantum mechanical problem

$$\delta \iiint \psi^*(x, y, z) H \, \psi(x, y, z) \, dx \, dy \, dz = 0, \tag{17.135}$$

with the constraint

$$\iiint \psi^*\psi \, dx \, dy \, dz = 1. \tag{17.136}$$

Equation 17.135 is a statement that the energy of the system is stationary, H being the quantum mechanical Hamiltonian for a particle of mass m, a differential operator,

$$H = -\frac{\hbar^2}{2m} \nabla^2 + V(x, y, z). \tag{17.137}$$

Equation 17.136, the constraint, is the condition that there will be exactly one particle present; ψ is the usual wave function, a dependent variable, and ψ^*, its complex conjugate, is treated as a *second*[1] dependent variable.

Integrating by parts, we have

$$\int \psi^* \frac{\partial^2 \psi}{\partial x^2} \, dx = \psi^* \frac{\partial \psi}{\partial x}\bigg| - \int \frac{\partial \psi}{\partial x}^* \frac{\partial \psi}{\partial x} \, dx. \tag{17.138}$$

We will assume either periodic boundary conditions (as in the Sturm-Liouville theory, Chapter 9) or that the volume of integration is so large that ψ and ψ^* vanish strongly[2] at the boundary. Then the integrated part vanishes and Eq. 17.135 may be rewritten

$$\delta \iiint \left[\frac{\hbar^2}{2m} \nabla\psi^* \cdot \nabla\psi + V\psi^*\psi \right] dx \, dy \, dz = 0. \tag{17.139}$$

The function g of Eq. 17.114 is

$$g = \frac{\hbar^2}{2m} \nabla\psi^* \cdot \nabla\psi + V\psi^*\psi - \lambda\psi^*\psi$$

$$= \frac{\hbar^2}{2m} (\psi_x^*\psi_x + \psi_y^*\psi_y + \psi_z^*\psi_z) + V\psi^*\psi - \lambda\psi^*\psi, \tag{17.140}$$

---

[1] Cf. Section 6.1.
[2] $\lim_{r \to \infty} r^{1/2}\psi(r) = 0.$

again using the subscript x to denote $\partial/\partial x$. Equation 17.115 now yields

$$-\frac{\hbar^2}{2m}\,\mathbf{\nabla}^2\psi + V\psi = \lambda\psi. \tag{17.141}$$

Reference to Eq. 17.137 enables us to identify λ physically as the energy of the quantum mechanical system. With this interpretation, Eq. 17.141 is the celebrated Schrödinger wave equation. This variational approach is more than just a matter of academic curiosity. It provides a very powerful method of obtaining approximate solutions of the wave equation (Ritz variational method).

EXERCISES

17.7.1 A particle, mass m, is on a frictionless horizontal surface. It is constrained to move so that $\theta = \omega t$ (rotating radial arm, no friction). With the initial conditions

$$t = 0, \qquad r = r_0, \qquad \dot{r} = 0,$$

(a) find the radial positions as a function of time. *Ans.* $r(t) = r_0 \cosh \omega t$.
(b) find the force exerted on the particle by the constraint.
$$\textit{Ans. } F^{(c)} = 2m\dot{r}\omega = 2mr_0\omega^2 \sinh \omega t.$$

17.7.2 A flexible cable is suspended from two fixed points. The length of the cable is fixed. Find the curve that will minimize the total gravitational potential energy of the cable.
Ans. Hyperbolic cosine.

17.7.3 Find the maximum value of the directional derivative of $\varphi(x,y,z)$,

$$\frac{d\varphi}{ds} = \frac{\partial\varphi}{\partial x}\cos\alpha + \frac{\partial\varphi}{\partial y}\cos\beta + \frac{\partial\varphi}{\partial z}\cos\gamma,$$

subject to the constraint
$$\cos^2\alpha + \cos^2\beta + \cos^2\gamma = 1.$$
$$\textit{Ans. } \left(\frac{\partial\varphi}{\partial s}\right) = |\,\mathbf{\nabla}\varphi\,|.$$

17.7.4 Show that requiring J, given by

$$J = \int_a^b (p(x)y_x^2 - q(x)y^2)\,dx,$$

to have a stationary value subject to the normalizing condition

$$\int_a^b y^2\,w(x)\,dx = 1$$

leads to the Sturm-Liouville equation of Chapter 9:

$$\frac{d}{dx}\left(p\frac{dy}{dx}\right) + qy + \lambda wy = 0.$$

Note. It is convenient to require

$$py_xy\,\Big|_a^b = 0$$

as a boundary condition.

17.7.5 A fixed volume of water is rotating in a cylinder with constant angular velocity ω. Find the curve of the water surface that will minimize the total potential energy of the water in the combined gravitational-centrifugal force field.   *Ans.* Parabola.

Note concerning the following exercises:

From the results of 17.7.4 we find that the eigenvalues λ_n of the Sturm-Liouville equation are the stationary values of $F(y(x))$,

$$F(y(x)) = \frac{\displaystyle\int_a^b (p y_x^2 - q y^2)\, dx}{\displaystyle\int_a^b y^2 w\, dx}$$

The absolute minimum of F is the lowest eigenvalue λ_0.

17.7.6 Rayleigh-Ritz variational method. The trial function

$$y = y_0 + \sum_{i=1} c_i y_i$$

is an *approximation* to the ground state eigenfunction y_0. The coefficients c_i are small. Show that $y(x)$ leads to an estimate of λ_0 that differs from λ_0 by *second-order* quantities.

17.7.7 Use the Rayleigh-Ritz approach (17.7.6) to estimate the lowest eigenvalue of

$$\frac{d^2 y}{dx^2} + \lambda y = 0,$$

with $y(0) = y(1) = 0$. *Hint.* With one eye on the boundary conditions, try $y(x) = x(1 - x)$.

Ans. (estimated): $\lambda \leqslant 10$

(exact): $\lambda = \pi^2 = 9.8696\ldots$.

How could you refine your estimate?

REFERENCES

BLISS, G. A., *Calculus of Variations*. The Mathematical Association of America, Open Court Publishing Company. Illinois: LaSalle (1925). One of the older texts but still a valuable reference for details of problems such as minimum area problems.

COURANT, R., and H. ROBBINS, *What Is Mathematics?* 2nd Ed. New York: Oxford University Press (1943). Chapter VII contains a fine discussion of the calculus of variations, including soap film solutions to minimum area problems.

SAGAN, H., *Boundary and Eigenvalue Problems in Mathematical Physics*. New York: Wiley (1961). This delightful text could also be listed as a reference for Sturm-Liouville theory, Legendre and Bessel functions, and Fourier Series. Chapter 1 is an introduction to the calculus of variations with applications to mechanics. Chapter 7 picks up the calculus of variations again and applies it to eigenvalue problems.

WEINSTOCK, R., *Calculus of Variations*. New York: McGraw-Hill (1952). A detailed, systematic development of the calculus of variations, applications to Sturm-Liouville theory and to physical problems in elasticity, electrostatics, and quantum mechanics.

YOURGRAU, W., and S. MANDELSTAM, *Variational Principles in Dynamics and Quantum Theory*. 2nd Ed. New York: Pitman (1962). A comprehensive, authoritative treatment of variational principles. The discussions of the historical development and the many metaphysical pitfalls are of particular interest.

GENERAL REFERENCES

1. E. T. WHITTAKER and G. N. WATSON, *A Course of Modern Analysis,* 4th ec Cambridge: Cambridge University Press (1962) paperback. Although this the oldest (original edition, 1902) of the references, it still is the classi reference. It leans strongly to pure mathematics, as of 1902, with full mathe matical rigor.

2. P. M. MORSE and H. FESHBACK, *Methods of Theoretical Physics* (2 Vols.) New York: McGraw-Hill Book Company (1953). This work presents the mathematics of much of theoretical physics in detail but at a rather advancec level. It is recommended as the outstanding source of information for supple- mentary reading and advanced study.

3. H. S. JEFFREYS and B. S. JEFFREYS, *Methods of Mathematical Physics,* 2nd ed. Cambridge: Cambridge University Press (1950). A scholarly treatment of a wide range of mathematical analysis. Considerable attention is paid to mathematical rigor. Applications are to classical physics and to geophysics.

4. R. COURANT and D. HILBERT, *Methods of Mathematical Physics,* Vol. I. First English edition. New York: John Wiley and Sons (Interscience) (1953). A valuable reference for mathematical physics, particularly for existence theorems and for discussions of areas such as eigenvalue problems, integral equations, and calculus of variations.

5. J. IRVING and N. MULLINEUX, *Mathematics in Physics and Engineering.* New York: Academic Press (1959). The choice of topics and emphasis is some- what different from the present text but the presentation is at a level that the advanced undergraduate can understand.

6. *Handbook of Mathematical Functions with Formulas, Graphs, and Mathe- matical Tables.* Applied Mathematics Series .55 (AMS-55), National Bureau of Standards, U.S. Department of Commerce (1964). This is a tremendous compilation of just what the title says. An extremely useful reference.

Additional more-specialized references are listed at the end of each chapter.

INDEX